PLAN OF UNION AND CONGREGATIONAL CHURCHES OF CHRIST IN THE MIDDLE ATLANTIC STATES

Richard H. Taylor
Providence, Rhode Island
2005

PLAN OF UNION AND CONGREGATIONAL CHURCHES OF CHRIST IN THE MIDDLE ATLANTIC STATES

A directory of Congregational and Plan of Union Churches in the states of New Jersey, New York, and Pennsylvania. Includes post-merger Congregational Christian and United Church of Christ congregations, and Unitarian Churches begun by 1850 in these states, and early churches in the Presbyterian Church, U.S.A. in New York state. A demographic and organizational history of Congregationalism in the area, reviewing its interaction with Presbyterianism and the workings of the Plan of Union, is also included.

[Title page illustration: The second meetinghouse of the First Congregational Church of Paterson, New Jersey.]

Books by the same author: Richard Henry Taylor (1943-)

Historical Directory of the Congregational, Christian, and United Church of Christ Congregations in Berkshire County, Massachusetts, 1979

The Churches of Christ of the Congregational Way in New England, 1989

The Congregational Churches of the West, 1992

Southern Congregational Churches, 1994

Congregations of the German Evangelical Synod of North America and Related Groups, 1998

Providence, Rhode Island
2005

Library of Congress Control Number: 2005906609
ISBN-13: 978-0-962248-64-9
ISBN-10: 0-962248-64-9

Limited Edition

Copyright and Distribution Information:
Richard H. Taylor
70 Oak St., Apt. B
Providence, RI, 02909
pilgrimrht@verizon.net

WRITTEN TO THE

GREATER GLORY OF GOD

AND DEDICATED

TO THE PASTORS AND MEMBERS OF THE

FIRST CONGREGATIONAL CHURCH

OF PATERSON, NEW JERSEY

(1836-1973)

INTRODUCTION

When I was a teenager, in the late 1950's, someone showed me a recent issue of the *Congregational Christian Yearbook*. I remember being totally fascinated. That book listed the various churches in the denomination by geographic location, name, and presented information on their current pastors and statistical data. I knew enough about geography to be filled with questions: Why were there so many churches in one state and hardly any in the next? Even church names seemed to have geographical connotations: why were saint's names and exotic Biblical names popular in some areas, and unknown in others? In those days, when Southern Congregational Christian bodies were segregated by race, I wondered why Congregationalism accepted segregation, and why racially oriented churches were so unevenly distributed across the South?

Thus began a life-long curiosity: reading in history, religion, and demographics to try to understand the origins of these differences. I read, took notes, and kept this unusual interest primarily to myself.

Only in seminary did I begin to appreciate the academic necessity of such questions. I read a book that purported to give an overview of New England worship during a particular period. While the book was copiously researched, I knew enough by that time to realize that the church records footnoted were primarily from those parts of New England that had by then become small cities. The author had described worship in New England's cities, not necessarily worship in rural areas. It then occurred to me that the only effective way to track religious change (or any other for that matter) was to prepare a spread-sheet of population totals and sub-environments, and then determine whether studies were truly representative of the varieties in the whole.

To do that, for New England Puritanism, required a list of dates and locations of Puritan congregations. To do it for the various formative denominations of the United Church of Christ would require similar national lists for each group. So began my quest to formulate such research tools. Only later did I discover that I was not the first person to attempt such a task for a denomination. The Corwin-Vanden Berge (85) tradition had identified congregations in the Dutch Reformed Church in America. Glasgow (32) and others had done the same for the United Presbyterians. Frederick Lewis Weis has compiled a Unitarian list (15). Then I met Russell E. Hall, who was attempting to do the same for the Presbyterian Church, U.S.A. (75H). Many other scholars had prepared similar studies for states or regions within states.

When I realized that many of these studies could be developed in parallel with each other, and combined with the statistical data banks of the various denominations, I understood that the result would be an unexplored tool for tracking religious growth and decline over long historical periods.

Yet, personally, I was also interested in understanding the dramatic shifts of growth and decline in my own denominational tradition with more depth than the simple sloganeering of church fights.

Having grown up in a Finney-ite revivalistic church that made its way from radical Presbyterianism into Congregationalism (First Congregational Church of Paterson, New Jersey), I soon understood that to study Congregationalism you had to study Presbyterianism. I also knew the complaint of some Congregational authors that through the Plan of Union the Presbyterians had been able to "steal" two thousand Congregational Churches. Those complications made me despair of doing all the work of both of these major traditions until, meeting Russell Hall, I realized how much his efforts had simplified my task.

To understand the Congregational/Presbyterian interaction hinged on an understanding of the Middle Atlantic region. Unfortunately (perhaps caused by the difficulty or the embarrassment of the Plan of Union), no extensive history of Congregationalism in any of the three Middle Atlantic States has ever been written. The closest claimant to the title is the government-sponsored Work Projects Administration study of Congregational Christian Churches in New Jersey (24). While it is helpful, it is vastly inadequate.

[For that matter, most treatments of early Middle Atlantic Congregationalism have been submerged in Presbyterian histories. Gaustad (08), for example, shows four Presbyterian churches on Long Island in 1650, and reports twenty-eight in the colonies in 1700, before there even was a presbytery. While some Irish and Scottish congregations existed in Maryland and Virginia by 1700, and some Middle Atlantic congregations had mixed Puritan-Yankee and other ethnic memberships, histories like this blot out much of Congregational history in the Middle Atlantic region.]

A concentrated review of both groups in the Middle Atlantic area - church by church - would finally give us some realistic handles with which to delineate the effect of the Plan of Union.

This book does not claim to be a history of Congregationalism in the Middle Atlantic area. The treatment here is limited to demographic and organizational dynamics, and theology as related to these issues. Nevertheless, I hope to provide the parameters within which a more exhaustive history could be written. Instead, this is an organizational directory that seeks to survey the extent of the Congregational presence in this area, and to document the interaction and overlap of that tradition with Presbyterianism.

INTRODUCTION

As the book that most directly treats the places of my religious origin, and the intellectual questions raised in my youth, I see this book as the keystone, the centerpiece in my documentation of congregations in the United Church of Christ tradition.

For students of Congregational demographics, this is my fourth regional book (in addition to New England, West, and Southern) to be completed. Two more books (Great Lakes, and Plains states) are envisioned to complete a national directory.

Goals as Part of the Continuing Series of Directories:

The purpose of this study is to compile a complete list of the churches of the Congregational Way in the Middle Atlantic States, from the time of the first separatist Puritan congregations down to the ecumenical mergers of the last century.

It is my continued hope that this data will help to provide the framework on which a careful long-term study comparing church membership and population trends can be assembled. It is also my desire to see this information used as a foundation for inventories of church records for genealogical and similar studies; local history studies of states, parts of states and counties and cities; ethnic histories as they relate to Anglo-Saxon Congregationalism; and studies in ecumenism as they relate to both federations and interdenominational local church unions on the one hand, as well as the twentieth century church unions of Congregationalism on the other. These lists should be utilized to determine whether sociological studies of church history are drawn from truly representative samplings in regard to ethnic, geographic and social strata methods of study. The bibliographic sources should help future Congregational historians in the Middle Atlantic region, as well as Presbyterian historians, and also provide a format for setting design parameters for a complete catalog of ministerial biography.

The Middle Atlantic Region:

The scope of territory covered in this book as the Middle Atlantic region coincides with the United States Census area of the same name, Middle Atlantic, and includes the states of New Jersey, New York, and Pennsylvania.

Because of the opposition to Congregationalism in Virginia in colonial days, that state (then including present West Virginia) proved to be a barrier separating religious development in the Middle Atlantic region from that farther south. This continued to be true for the early Presbytery of Philadelphia, as well as for Congregationalism in the nineteenth and twentieth centuries. In both groups churches in Delaware, Maryland, and the District of Columbia, and sometimes parts of northern Virginia and northeastern West Virginia were attached in intra-church bodies to Middle Atlantic churches. Thus our historical religious region would stretch below the Mason-Dixon line.

Nevertheless, because of the divide caused by that line (generally the Maryland - Pennsylvania border) as the historic and symbolic separation between the North and the South and the demarcation of slavery; and because of the ongoing demographic identity of these three states by the Census Bureau; this study has been limited to the three named states.

MIDDLE ATLANTIC CONGREGATIONALISM

Without doubt, New England was the original home of American Congregationalism, and its ethos, theology, and even genealogical heritage have dominated the development of this family of churches. However, New England and its churches evolved in a way that would not survive in the new nation of the United States. New England Congregational churches were - in what are now four of the states of that region - generally the churches that were supported by parishes and societies established by law and funded by the taxes of their towns. This continued in some areas until as late as 1834. They also so dominated the early settlement of New England that for generations the population grew primarily from only this one major ethnic and religious group.

However, when the Yankee Puritans of New England moved into what is now the Middle Atlantic states they encountered two drastic changes that would not only dramatically reshape the history of American Congregationalism, but also significantly impact the religious life of the country. These changes can be reflected in two questions: (1) How does a congregationally-based polity survive without the support of a religious establishment? and (2) How will New England Puritanism be reformed by its first real encounter with a wider religious and ethnic culture - initially Dutch Reformed, Quakers, a large Anglican establishment, Scottish and Irish Presbyterians, and Germans – Lutheran, Calvinist, and the pietistic sects?

INTRODUCTION

While America's first serious religious demographer, Ezra Stiles, predicted that, by the mid-nineteenth century, Congregationalism would be America's largest religious denomination, with many millions of constituents (Stiles, 1761), the realities of the Middle Colonies were what broke his predictions into pieces.

In many ways the Middle Atlantic states were the crucible for forging America's non-established religious pluralism. Certainly this area played the decisive role in shaping modern American Congregationalism. This specific history was also closely intertwined with, and significantly influenced the other leading English-speaking Calvinist population in the area: Scottish and Irish Presbyterianism. Developments here also hedged in and defined those aspects of Puritanism which would empower American culture and which would be stripped away.

The text offered here, in addition to the documented church lists, is meant to document the outlines of this history, and to open some new doors to understanding American Congregationalism, Presbyterianism, and their various Plans of Union.

THE SCOPE OF THE LISTINGS

The lists attempt to show every Middle Atlantic Congregational church, as well as every Presbyterian Church in New York state connected with the Presbyterian Church U.S.A. through 1837, and every New School Presbyterian Church in New York state through 1852. In New Jersey and Pennsylvania all Congregational churches are included, but only those Presbyterian congregations specifically identified as Congregational or Plan of Union at some point in their history by some historical authority, or which were independent and outside Presbytery in the earlier years (and thereby acting in a way considered Congregational at that time). In New Jersey and Pennsylvania, this form of listing probably under- counts the number of Presbyterian churches with New England origins. Indeed, tracking the biographies of New England raised or educated clergy would cover significant parts of the early histories of Presbyterian congregations in New Jersey and Pennsylvania not included here.

In these states in the early colonial period it would have been preferred to have reconstructed Congregational Church lists by the communications of their pastors or ecclesiastical council delegates, or the announced communal recognition admitted by their founders, rather than conjecturing lists based on theological vagaries or genealogical connections. Nevertheless, these latter standards were applied where lack of other information made these standards necessary. Changing local forms are also helpful in discerning group identity even though they do not conform to a consistent definitional boundary. (This is particularly helpful during the nineteenth century periods of transition, when issues such as the existence of a committee rather than a session of ruling elders within a church, the existence of, and relation to a separate religious society outside of a session, and/or long periods of not being part of a Presbytery, when nearby Presbyteries existed.)

Defining Congregational Churches:

An essay on the definition of Congregational and Presbyterian churches is provided later in this book. However, for the new reader, these words of introduction may be helpful:

As indicated in the Cambridge Platform of 1648, which was the first major attempt of a group of congregations of this tradition in America to define their identity, the Congregational Churches are Christian congregations in the Reformed tradition. Indeed many of the early pre-nineteenth century congregations were known by the name "Church of Christ." Inclusion as a Congregational Church in these listings is more narrowly defined than congregations of a particular polity. Here a Congregational Church is Congregational in that it is part of the fellowship deriving from the Pilgrim-Puritan congregations and is mutually recognized by the other congregations of that fellowship as such. This fellowship appeared in its earliest forms through extending the mutual right hand of fellowship at services of covenanting for local churches. In later years churches organized by clearly denominational mission agencies were organized as part of the fellowship.

A congregation is not "Congregational" simply because it uses that name in its title. For example, a congregation of the Evangelical Congregational Church, a denomination headquartered in Pennsylvania and tracing its history to German pietistic Methodism, would not be included in this study. On the other hand a local church with a name such as Union or Community which never had the word "Congregational" in its title could still be a full member of the fellowship.

In the early part of the nineteenth century Unitarian churches also claimed the name Congregational, and they also shared a Puritan origin. References to Unitarian development before 1850 are included.

The definition of fellowship does become confusing between Presbyterian and Congregational churches because of the Plan of Union which existed 1801 to 1852, and continued in some local congregations affiliated to the

Presbyterian judicatories until 1870 or later, as well as because of interaction of these fellowships at earlier dates. These issues are discussed in the text that follows.

Where a question has arisen of whether to include a given congregation because of disagreements in sources, such congregations have uniformly been included. Arguments about their inclusion are noted in the appropriate text.

A Congregational Church is a Church in that it is a group of Christians who have consented together in covenant to submit themselves to worship and the ordinances of the Lord (*Cambridge Platform, IV,* see Walker, 1893/1960, pp.207-209). In early New England most Congregational churches were formed in fellowship with towns, ecclesiastical parishes or societies which were separate organizations that handled their secular affairs. After disestablishment, donors, pew holders or particular trustees could be legally incorporated as societies or parishes to hold property. Originally these were generally composed of only adult male persons. Both town support of pastors and meeting houses, and later separate incorporated bodies existed in this region as well. The Church, on the other hand, was made up of believers, accepted both sexes and people under the legal age, and had Biblical officers: elders and deacons. Many writers confuse these two organizations and often describe the organization of a society as if it were a church. To avoid this error, information that refers to the parish, society, or town has been noted in the text. In most modern situations the societies and churches have merged as one legal entity.

PREFACE

The production of a book of the magnitude of this one must be an engagement in thanksgiving. Were it not for the people who kept churches records, wrote things down, saw to their printing, and carefully preserved these records over the years, and the donors that make and have made these archives and libraries possible, this work would have been impossible. All have contributed to this endeavor. My gratitude extends to each one.

The two libraries whose collections have provided the core of materials to put together this work have been the Congregational Library in Boston and the Presbyterian Historical Society in Philadelphia. The efforts of their staffs over many years have been an ongoing blessing to me.

While the goal of attempting to list all of America's Congregational churches arose some time ago, I was challenged by the confusing movement of Congregational churches in and out of presbyteries as part of the Plan of Union and other cooperative ventures. Figuring out this movement seemed daunting until I encountered the Presbyterian lists of the late Russell E. Hall. This book rests in part on his strong foundation.

Over the last several decades I have traveled to many libraries in the northeast and Midwest. In some libraries I found information on one particular congregation. In others I met gracious attendants, even if their collections yielded no new data. Other libraries whose collections have been particular help in this endeavor include the New York State Library in Albany, the Chicago Theological Seminary Library, and the joint library of the McCormick Theological Seminary and the Lutheran School of Theology in Chicago.

Dr. Harold Worthley, former Librarian of the Congregational Library has actively encouraged this publication, and has graciously read sections of it. My sister-in-law, Dr. Marjorie Royle, former Research Director of the United Church of Christ has perhaps read more of this than she might wish. She and Lester Page Jr. have been major helps in designing computer programs to record the church lists, while Marcia Middleton provided much help during the early stages of New York research. My thanks also to the many correspondents that have responded to inquiries about federated and dual churches and other matters.

In a book of this magnitude errors are bound to appear. Your patience and understanding are appreciated. May I request that corrections be sent to me for record keeping and any future editions.

It is my desire to complete the survey of American Congregational and Plan of Union congregations with publications covering the Great Lakes and Plains states. If energy and time permit, I would also like to draw together some materials on Christian and German Reformed congregations, although divergent bibliographic difficulties make those efforts more challenging. Those desiring information, or having suggestions on this work are encouraged to write.

Richard H. Taylor
Providence, Rhode Island
June, 2005

TABLE OF CONTENTS

TABLE OF CONTENTS

TABLE OF CONTENTS

TABLE OF CONTENTS

TABLE OF CONTENTS

FIGURES IN THE TEXT

DEVELOPMENT OF THE MIDDLE ATLANTIC STATES

English and Welsh Puritan, and Scottish and Irish Presbyterian Churches, the two oldest English-speaking branches of the Reformed tradition in Christianity began to settle in what is now the Middle Atlantic States after the British crown gained hegemony over the area. Because the history of the Churches was also directly impacted by the historical development of the area, an overview of the history of the area is a good starting point.

Furthermore, even though New England is outside the focus area of this study, its development not only provided the first English settlers and settlements in the Middle Atlantic area, but its system of church development framed and impacted the churches here. Therefore, an overview of New England development is important and included as well.

English interest in the New World developed over a long period of time. As early as 1496, John Cabot was commissioned to undertake a voyage of discovery. Attempts to settle colonies in Newfoundland in 1583 and in North Carolina in 1587 proved unsuccessful.

With the accession of the Stuart King, James I., to the throne of England in 1603 all of the British Isles came under one crown. [Later, in 1707, the nations of England and Scotland were formally united with one Parliament.] King James' government showed increased sentiment for settling America, and with the end of hostilities with Spain in 1604, an opportunity for expansion was opened. In 1606 two grants were made to trading companies to settle and do business in America. One company headquartered in London was given the opportunity to settle between thirty-four and forty-one degrees of north latitude. The other company, headquartered at Plymouth, was given the right to settle in the area between thirty-eight and forty-five degrees of north latitude. In the areas in which the two companies charters overlapped, thirty-eight to forty-one degrees of north latitude, the current Middle Atlantic coast, neither company could make a settlement within one-hundred miles of a settlement already made by the other company. These charters were restricted to the areas within fifty miles of the coastline. They theoretically placed the entire American coast north of thirty-four degrees north latitude under British control.

The London Company acted quickly on their charter, and sent out a company in 1607 that selected a place for settlement at Jamestown, Virginia. Its charter was revised in 1609 as the Virginia Company of London, and again in 1612. The revised charters made the proprietors of the Company the government of the colony, and also extended their grant, from "sea to sea" with thirty-four degrees of north latitude as the southern boundary, and a northern boundary beginning where forty degrees of north latitude crosses the Atlantic coast, and extending from that point in a northwest direction. The company was dissolved in 1624, and after temporary control by a special commission, Virginia was made a royal colony directly governed by the King in 1625.

The Plymouth Company was less active, but in 1620 was re-chartered as the Plymouth Council for New England. It also was then given jurisdictional powers, and new boundaries, between forty and forty-eight degrees north latitude, "sea to sea." The chartered lands of the Plymouth Council and the Virginia Company began at the same point on the coast, but increasingly overlapped as the assigned boundaries moved inland. By these charters claims had been set up on behalf of Britain for lands stretching across the North American continent between thirty-four and forty-eight degrees north latitude.

The Plymouth Council for New England acted through assigning patents and grants to others to settle the new area. Religious issues were beginning to split England at this time, and a large number of Puritans wished to leave the country. The Council initially took economic advantage of these willing colonials. A group of Puritan Separatists was given permission by the Virginia Company to settle on their land near the Hudson River. That group, however, settled on land of the Plymouth Company in 1620, organized themselves through the Mayflower Compact, and received a patent (the Pierce Patent) as a company from the Plymouth Council for New England in 1621. The grants of the Plymouth Council for New England also included, among others, those to Gorges and Mason for what is now New Hampshire and Maine in 1622; to a settlement from the Dorchester Company of 1623; to the new New England Company in 1628; the Lygonia grant in Maine of 1630 (Lygonia was a forty mile square of land centered at a trading post on the Kennebec River, granted to the (New) Plymouth Colony); Pemaquid in eastern Maine in 1632; and the Warwick grant in what is now Connecticut, also in 1632. All of these were grants of land, while government was still vested in the Plymouth Council for New England. In 1630 the Council granted the settlement at Plymouth separate existence as the (New) Plymouth Colony, with some governmental authority, though the King never formally acknowledged this. The Mason and Gorges grants were divided in 1629 respectively as New Hampshire and Maine.

The Dorchester Company, which held a 1623 grant, collapsed in 1626. A new New England Company was chartered in 1628, and then received a grant from the Council for much the same land that had previously been given to the Dorchester group. However, the situation of English rule in the northern area became more complicated in 1629, when the New England Company secured a direct charter from the King as the Massachusetts Bay Company. It was given powers to rule, and a grant from three miles north of the Merrimack River, to three miles south of the Charles River, "sea to sea," even though it was within the bounds of the Plymouth Council for New England. Then, in 1630, the

Massachusetts Bay Company took their charter to New England, where it was in less danger of whimsical or rapid infringement from the royal courts.

Both the Plymouth Colony proprietors (particularly from 1626, when the colonists set up a plan to buy out the rights of other financial supporters) and the Massachusetts Bay Company were dominated by Puritan interests. They spurred a massive Puritan migration to New England and the establishment of Puritan churches. Two conflicting charters (that of the Plymouth Council for New England and that of the Massachusetts Bay Company) made it unclear who was ruling in Massachusetts. However, the Massachusetts Bay Company clearly had the support of the Puritan population.

By this time the crown had realized that the rise of large Puritan colonies could be disruptive to the Anglican establishment and church settlement at home. Archbishop William Laud (1573-1645) was appointed as President of a new Commission for Foreign Plantations when it was chartered in 1634. It began to stop the religious migration. In 1635 the Plymouth Council for New England decided to surrender its charter and recommended to the King that he accept their partition of all of their lands among twelve members of their Council, and that also a general governor for all of New England be appointed. The King supported the latter plan, and appointed Sir Ferdinando Gorges as Governor in 1637. The crown also began action to revoke the charter of the Massachusetts Bay Company. Some support was also given to the Council's land claims: including grants of Long Island and the islands near Martha's Vineyard and another in eastern Maine, to William Alexander, Earl of Stirling, both in 1635, a grant to Edmund Ployden of much of New Jersey in 1634 as New Albion, a grant re-confirming Mason's title to New Hampshire in 1635, and one re-confirming Gorges' title to Maine in 1639. (After Stirling's death, the islands near Martha's Vineyard were given to Gorges in 1639 and administered by Thomas Mayhew after 1642.) The Stirling grants, (except Block Island (RI), which was sold in 1661), were purchased by the Duke of York in 1664, while Massachusetts purchased all of Gorges' grants in 1677/1678.

The Puritans in general, and Massachusetts Bay in particular, continued to resist the King. Massachusetts Bay refused to surrender its charter. This proved to be one of many preludes to the full fledged Civil War in England between the Puritan dominated Parliament and the King (1642-1660).

Without royal approval, several independent Puritan and religiously radical towns, following the example of the Mayflower compact, were set up outside of the control of Massachusetts Bay. These began to form alliances, drawing several towns together as new independent colonies. These included Connecticut (first town 1635, drawn together 1639, and purchasing the Warwick Patent in 1644), New Haven (first town 1638, drawn together 1643), and Rhode Island (first town 1639, drawn together 1640). The latter colony joined with two more independent towns on the mainland (including Providence, founded 1636) and procured a charter from the Puritan Parliament in 1644 as Providence Plantations. Both the Connecticut and New Haven Colonies welcomed towns on Long Island in present day New York. Following a War with the Pequot Indians in 1637, Massachusetts claimed the tribe's lands in southeastern Connecticut (later passed on to that colony), and in southern Rhode Island (which later became part of the King's Province).

Puritan settlement also pushed northward into lands that had originally been developed by Mason and Gorges. Puritan towns were settled in what is now New Hampshire in 1638, and soon afterwards in Maine. Unable to get much instruction from England during the Civil War, three Maine towns also set up a colony in 1649.

The New Haven Colony between 1638 and 1642 also tried to launch a community in southern New Jersey also called New Haven, on Salem Creek in what is now Salem County. Later they submitted to the authority of the New Albion grant holder. However, the Dutch destroyed the settlement with Swedish help before 1646.

During the Civil War the New England colonies supported the Puritan Parliament. Massachusetts expanded its authority by taking over several of the areas to the North. By defining their grant of three miles north of the Merrimack River as being three miles north of its source (43° 40' 12"), Massachusetts asserted their titles to the north. They took over all towns in New Hampshire by 1641, claimed Maine in 1651, and took control of the three-town colony in Maine in 1652, and most of the rest of western Maine by 1653. While Lygonia had gained its own government in 1646/1647, it was also taken over by Massachusetts in 1658. The four strongest and most Puritan colonies (Massachusetts Bay, Plymouth, Connecticut, and New Haven) also formed an alliance, the United Colonies of New England in 1643, which lasted until 1684.

Despite all of these English claims, and with the existence of early English colonies on both sides of the Middle Atlantic coast, the Dutch made the first European settlement in the area covered in this book. The Netherlands had been seeking their independence from Spain since 1579. A truce was declared in 1609 that allowed the Dutch some possibility to expand their commercial empire. After an exploratory voyage in 1609, the New Netherlands Company received a trading monopoly for the Hudson and Delaware River valleys in 1614, and a trading post was established on Manhattan Island. The Dutch West Indies Company that intended to make settlements on the coasts of the Americas replaced this company in 1621. This company had the right to govern its territory, and in 1624 organized the colony of

New Netherlands, with settlements at Fort Orange (near Albany), New Amsterdam at the mouth of the Hudson River, a 1632 settlement at the mouth of the Connecticut River (Kievit's Hook, Saybrook), and Fort Nassau (Gloucester, NJ) on the Delaware River. Other settlements included Zwaanendael (Lewes, DE) in 1631, and a settlement further up the Connecticut River called House of Hope (Hartford) begun 1633. English Puritans moving into Connecticut about this time limited Dutch settlements, confining the Dutch efforts to small trading posts.

In 1626 the Swedish King granted a charter to the Swedish South Company, also for settlement in America. Its charter was renewed in 1637, and it began new settlements at Fort Christiana (Wilmington, DE) on the Delaware River in 1638, one at Tinicum Island in Pennsylvania in 1643, and another at Fort New Elfsburg in New Jersey, also in 1643. The company governed the area, including parts of present day New Jersey, Delaware, and Pennsylvania as New Sweden. The Swedes limited their claims to the area between 39° north latitude north to about 40° 15' north latitude. The Dutch protested the Swedish presence, but because they were allies with each other in the Thirty Years' War, no more serious action was taken. When the War ended in 1648, the independence of the Netherlands was written into international treaty, and the need to please Sweden was gone. In 1655 the Dutch forced Sweden to surrender its territory to them. The Dutch then had a clear hold on the land between the two English settlements of New England and Virginia.

As the Dutch presence grew, England responded. In 1632 King Charles I. (1625-1649) gave a grant to Lord Baltimore for a new colony of Maryland to be separated from the royal colony of Virginia. The Maryland grant included both sides of Chesapeake Bay, roughly from thirty-eight degrees north latitude on the Delmarva Peninsula, and north of the Potomac River on the west to forty degrees north latitude. This colony was settled in 1634, and was seen as a limit to Dutch expansion.

The English New Albion grant, in addition to the Puritan settlement at New Haven, NJ, also included Fort Eriwoneck at the mouth of Pennsauken Creek. After the destruction of New Haven, the rest of the New Albion administration faded, particularly after 1648. The 1641 Dutch settlement at Varckenskill (modern Salem, NJ) included many New Englanders.

Proprietary Maryland and royal Virginia supported the King in the English Civil War, which distracted them from issues regarding the Dutch. Puritan and allied forces gained control of Maryland from 1642 to 1646, had it put under Puritan control from Virginia in 1652, and had direct control again from 1654 to 1657 when the colony was returned to the proprietor. The Puritan Parliament took control of Virginia in 1652.

To the north, the period of the English Civil War allowed the English Puritans to move into the Middle Atlantic area for the first time. Four Puritan settlements on Long Island joined the independent colony of Connecticut: Southampton (settled 1640, joined Connecticut 1644); East Hampton (settled 1648/1649, joined 1657); Brookhaven (Setauket, settled 1645/1655, joined 1659); Huntington (settled 1653/1658, joined 1660). Two additional Puritan settlements on Long Island joined the independent colony of New Haven: Southold (settled 1640, joined 1648); Oyster Bay (settled 1653, joined 1655). In 1650 a boundary was negotiated between the Dutch and the United Colonies of New England. In 1660, an English group purchased Rye, in present day Westchester County, New York, and control was transferred to Connecticut.

The Dutch, eager for development, and sometimes friendly to their fellow Calvinists, also accepted English and Puritan settlements in their territory. These included a settlement at Gravesend (Kings County) by 1639, which became predominantly Quaker; and settlements related to the Great Puritan migration at Hempstead (settled 1643/1644); Flushing (settled 1642/1645); Newtown (settled 1651/1656); and Jamaica (settled 1655/1656), all on Long Island. Similar settlements were made on the mainland. Westchester in the present Bronx, settled 1642, included the settlement by Massachusetts dissenter Anne Hutchinson and her followers near Pelham (Westchester County) that year. Its land was purchased by the Dutch from the Indians in 1643, but was claimed by the New Haven Colony as part of Stamford from 1642 to 1656. Stamford also exercised authority for the New Haven Colony in the Bedford area in Westchester County from 1640. Eastchester, in present Westchester and Bronx Counties, was settled between 1649 and 1664, and although owned by people from the Colony of Connecticut, was under Dutch authority.

By 1660 Puritans had direct control of all of present Suffolk County, New York, and parts of present Nassau and Westchester Counties. English settlements in Dutch controlled areas included Queens County, the rest of present day Nassau County, a part of Kings County, and the eastern shores of Westchester and Bronx Counties.

With the collapse of the Puritan Commonwealth in England, and the restoration of the Stuart Dynasty in 1660, Charles II. (1660-1685) became King. Freed from Civil War direct English interest in America was increased. But Puritans, losers in the now concluded Civil War, were in fear for their future. The proprietary colony of Maryland and the royal colony of Virginia resumed their former status. Rhode Island submitted to the new Stuart dynasty in 1660, and Connecticut and Plymouth followed early in 1661. Massachusetts Bay initially resisted, but late in 1661 resubmitted to their charter of 1629. Resistance to the Stuarts in the New Haven Colony was even stronger. New Haven protected two English refugees who had been involved in the orders to kill Charles I.. They also made overtures to the

Dutch about possibly moving their people to New Jersey. Only under pressure from the crown did the New Haven Colony finally submit to the King late in 1661.

While the restored House of Stuart was never friendly to the Puritan colonies, they initially needed to bring order to the confused situation in North America, and not too quickly to upset the new fragile peace. In 1662 the King granted a charter to the Colony of Connecticut, and granted them land running from the southerly line of the Massachusetts Bay colony to the Ocean (including Long Island) and from the Narragansett River (Bay) to the west, "sea to sea." This eliminated the Colony of New Haven, and its towns were expected to conform to Connecticut. There was open opposition to the new charter in New Haven, and the Dutch also rejected the terms of the charter in 1663. Oyster Bay (Long Island), Stamford (including some lands in present day New York), and Guilford soon joined Connecticut (1662). The New Haven Colony continued to resist the Connecticut Charter until 1664, when it gave up its existence, and the towns of Southold (Long Island), Milford, and finally New Haven joined Connecticut in 1664 and 1665. Opposition was so strong in Branford, however, that between 1665 and 1667 most of the population removed to New Jersey, taking a sizable minority of people from other New Haven towns with them.

In 1663 a new charter was also granted to Rhode Island and Providence Plantations which reunited parts of that Colony which had been at odds, and clarified the eastern boundary of Connecticut. However, a disputed area was still claimed by Rhode Island, Connecticut and Massachusetts, and was governed through Rhode Island as the King's Province from 1665 to 1686. Block Island joined Rhode Island in 1664.

Also in 1663, four English towns under Dutch control decided to withdraw from Dutch authority and join the newly chartered Connecticut: Hempstead, Flushing, Jamaica, and Newtown. Then, in 1664, they and Oyster Bay decided to leave Connecticut. However, events happened later that year which changed the future of the Middle Atlantic region forever.

In 1664 King Charles II. gave a land grant to his brother, the Duke of York (later King James II.). This grant included all the lands between the Connecticut and Delaware Rivers, as well as Long Island, also the islands around Martha's Vineyard previously administered by Mayhew (except Block Island), and eastern Maine. Before the year was out the English had taken New Netherlands by force, and the Duke renamed the territory New York.

The Duke also claimed all the lands of New Netherlands, including those in Delaware and Pennsylvania "by conquest" even though they were not part of his brother's grant to him. Maryland also claimed the Delaware area by their charter, and attempted to set up a county there in 1669. Almost immediately the Duke, in 1664, sold New Jersey to Lord Berkeley and Sir George Carteret.

Some Puritans took advantage of English control of this new area. Puritan settlements began at Elizabethtown, New Jersey (now Elizabeth) in 1664, and Milford, New Jersey (later New Ark, then Newark) between 1665 and 1667. These included the people from Branford and other parts of the New Haven Colony. Also, a group of New England Baptists settled in Monmouth County, where they had worship at Middletown from 1664.

But the Duke of York, although English, was no Puritan. Friction between the Puritans and the Duke began immediately. The boundaries of the Duke's grant overlapped much land already granted to Massachusetts, and particularly to Connecticut.

A royal commission was sent to America in 1664 and 1665 that threatened all the Puritan colonies, and called for the revocation of the charter of the Massachusetts Bay Company. In 1667 the boundary dispute between Connecticut and the territory of the Duke of York was settled by granting the Duke all of the islands, while Connecticut was given the mainland as far west as twenty miles east of the Hudson River. Its "sea to sea" grant then theoretically picked up at the Delaware River and ran to the west.

The Connecticut-New York boundary dispute continued to be debated for some time. It was re-surveyed in 1683 and 1684. Connecticut controlled Rye and Bedford in Westchester County from 1665 until 1683, and again exercised authority in both towns from 1696 to 1700.

During another British-Dutch War, in 1673, the Dutch regained control of much of this area. Three towns at the end of Long Island (East Hampton, Southampton, Southold) tried to rejoin Connecticut. At this time Massachusetts also tried to reassert its claim to the Duke's territory in eastern Maine. However, English authority was re-established in 1674 and boundaries fell back to the previous arrangement.

In 1676 New Jersey was divided into two colonies: East Jersey, and West Jersey, the latter under a group including the noted Quaker William Penn. Their boundary was adjusted in 1687.

In 1681 the Duke also granted to Penn a charter for Pennsylvania, to include lands west of the Delaware to five degrees of longitude, and between forty and forty-three degrees of north latitude, except for a circle around the city of New Castle, Delaware. This Pennsylvania grant conflicted with the charters previously given to Massachusetts Bay and Connecticut "sea to sea" grants. Also, in 1682, the Duke leased to Penn the counties of Delaware, which were attached administratively to Pennsylvania in that year. When the Duke received full title in 1683 he immediately transferred it to Penn. Because Penn was a member of the Society of Friends (Quakers), his now significant role introduced a new element in the historical evolution of the religions of the area.

Conflict between the Puritans and the Stuart Kings continued. Between 1664 and 1668 pressure was put on Massachusetts questioning their control of western Maine. Massachusetts, which had won title to eastern Maine in a 1668 court case, lost it back to the Duke of York in 1674. In 1677 an English court redefined the northern boundary of Massachusetts, limiting the claims north and east of the Merrimack River to areas three miles north of the River from its mouth to three miles above the southerly point of the River and from that point due west to the River. Massachusetts still claimed lands to its old northern claim west of the Merrimack to the far sea. Massachusetts purchased the Gorges' Grants in 1677/1678. In 1679/1680 Massachusetts' claim to New Hampshire was revoked and it was made a separate royal colony. In 1683 Charles II. again began a process to revoke the charter of Massachusetts Bay, and it was revoked in 1684.

In 1685 the Duke of York became King James II. (1685-1688), and New York became a royal colony. He immediately confirmed his grants of Delaware and Pennsylvania, and directed a division of the Delmarva Peninsula between Maryland and Pennsylvania (Delaware). A Catholic, and never a friend of the Puritans, James used his new power to force them into submission. Steps to revoke the charter of Connecticut were begun immediately. Actions soon followed to seize the charters of Rhode Island, and the proprietary colonies of East and West Jersey. In 1685 James set up the Dominion of New England to take over the governments of the entire area. In 1686 Edmund Andros, who had previously served James as an unpopular Governor of New York, arrived in Boston as Governor of the new Dominion. He promptly took control of Massachusetts, New Hampshire, western Maine and the King's Province. Later that year New Plymouth, Rhode Island and Providence Plantations and eastern Maine were added to the Dominion, as was Connecticut in 1687. In 1688 the royal colony of New York and the proprietary Colonies of East and West Jersey were also added to the Dominion. The future of Puritanism and Congregationalism in both New England and the Middle Atlantic region was then seriously in doubt.

In England James had antagonized Anglicans as well as Puritans, who joined in his overthrow in 1688 in the "Glorious Revolution." William and Mary ascended to the throne starting the House of Orange. As the War to establish the new regime in Europe continued until 1692, the Americans moved quickly against the Dominion of New England. Dominion leaders in Boston were jailed in 1689 and each of the colonies resumed their independent activity. James' deputy in New York was overthrown in 1689 and the Colony acted independently until 1691.

The new British crown sought to compromise their dealings with America. Massachusetts Bay never regained their surrendered charter. Instead, in 1691, a new charter for Massachusetts made it a royal colony. Plymouth, eastern and western Maine, and the islands around Martha's Vineyard were added to that Colony, but it now had a royal governor. From then on Massachusetts was often a colony with established Puritan preaching and an Anglican governor. New Hampshire also retained its status as a royal colony, but shared its governor with Massachusetts (except for one year) until 1741. Connecticut and Rhode Island, however, were permitted to be re-established under their 1662 and 1663 charters. Rhode Island now had full control of the former King's Province.

Virginia continued as a royal colony, but Maryland had its proprietary charter removed in 1689, not to be restored until 1716. William Penn, considered an ally of the Stuarts, also lost his proprietary rights to Pennsylvania and Delaware in 1692, but regained control in 1694. A 1701 provision allowed for the separation of Delaware from Pennsylvania, which made it a separate colony in 1704, but retaining Penn's proprietorship.

The lands of East and West Jersey were often sold and questions persisted as to whether the proprietors held only land rights or rights to govern as well. After much maneuvering, the two areas were reunited as a royal colony in 1702. It shared a governor with New York until 1738.

In 1691 New York again became a royal colony. In the realignment of the colonies that year it gave up its claims to the islands around Martha's Vineyard and eastern Maine to Massachusetts, although administration in some areas was not transferred until 1695.

From this time on the three governments - New York, New Jersey, Pennsylvania - continued in the Middle Atlantic region until the American Revolution.

Under the restored Stuarts the Middle Atlantic region began to set up local county government. Some of New York had been divided into "Ridings" in 1665. It had also inherited some Dutch counties functioning here by 1674 and established regular counties elsewhere by 1683. East Jersey was divided into four local court areas in 1675, (Bergen and vicinity, Elizabeth and Newark, Woodbridge and Piscataqua, and Middletown and Shrewsbury), that became the full-fledged counties of Bergen, Essex, Middlesex, and Monmouth in 1682/1683. West Jersey established local courts at Burlington and Salem in 1681 and at Cape May in 1685. A local organization was set up in Gloucester in 1686. Cape May was made a full county in 1692, and the others in 1694. When Pennsylvania absorbed Delaware in 1682, that area already had counties dating from as early as 1673. In 1682 Pennsylvania began to set up counties in its territory beyond the old Swedish and Dutch areas.

DEVELOPMENT OF THE MIDDLE ATLANTIC STATES

Despite the imperial claims of the English colonies and their "sea to sea" land claims, reality admitted to an extensive French hegemony in the Saint Lawrence River, Great Lakes, and Mississippi River basins. France had begun settlements along the Saint Lawrence at an early date, including Quebec (1608). They spread into western New York, with a fort at Niagara by 1679, and then moved into western Pennsylvania in 1753, and as far as Fort Duquesne in 1754 (modern Pittsburgh). The French and Indian War (1754-1763) was partly caused by the pressure from the populated English settlements to move west into the French areas. The French lost their lands in this area by 1760, but their Indian allies continued the War until 1763. The Peace of Paris (1763) granted all territory east of the Mississippi to Britain.

After the continuity of three English colonies in this region was established, they still continued to have disputes over boundaries with each other and the colonies near them.

The Connecticut-New York boundary was finally established in 1731.

In 1681 King Charles II had ordered Lord Baltimore and the Penn proprietors to settle the boundary of the Maryland-Pennsylvania border. A 1732 course for that boundary had little effect. Another 1750 agreement, signed in 1760 became the basis for the present line. The Mason-Dixon Line between Pennsylvania and Maryland was surveyed from 1763 to 1767 and moved the boundary line from 40° north latitude south to 39° 44' north latitude.

The western extent of Maryland by charter was a "true meridian" running north from the "first fountain" of the Potomac River. Virginia and Maryland debated whether that meant the northern or southern branch of the Potomac. The so-called Deakins line of 1787 using the north branch of the River eventually became the line.

West of the western boundary of Maryland, Virginia and Pennsylvania still had disputed territory. Because the northern boundary of Virginia by charter ran in a northwesterly direction, Virginia had extensive claims in western Pennsylvania. Virginians began exploration and settlement in that area, pushing to Pittsburgh by 1754, and organizing an administrative district in 1773. Three new Virginia Counties (1776) served in what is now Pennsylvania and West Virginia: Monongalia, Ohio, and Yohogania County. The Mason-Dixon Line was extended to the west in 1779, and settled as the boundary in 1780, and ratified in 1784. Pennsylvania gained control of its present territory in 1780. Monongalia and Ohio remained Virginia Counties, while Yohogania was discontinued in 1786.

Massachusetts had assumed it also had a claim to twenty miles east of the Hudson River and to the west of the Delaware River, similar to the Connecticut/New York boundary settlement. However, that was never clearly written, and even those who agreed with the basic assumption did not know exactly where that line ran. Armed conflict broke out between the two Colonies. The present line was agreed to in 1773 and laid out in 1787. A minor adjustment was made in 1853.

New York always had a claim for land above Massachusetts's northern line east to the Connecticut River from the original 1664 grant to the Duke of York. Because Massachusetts considered its northern boundary to be three miles north of the source of the Merrimack River (43° 40' 12" north latitude), New York's claim was contested by Massachusetts. However, in 1741, a British court treating a boundary dispute between New Hampshire and Massachusetts ruled that the northern boundary of Massachusetts was only three miles north of the southerly point of the River, and continuing west from that point across the River to the far sea. This gave New Hampshire much territory between the Merrimack and Connecticut Rivers. However, it also made New York's claim to the area north of Massachusetts and west of the Connecticut River more valid. However, New Hampshire began to sell land west of the Connecticut in 1741, even though it had no written claim. Massachusetts still claimed the area, but became less active in the struggle. All three colonies put forward claims to this area that eventually became Vermont. New York was given the right to control Vermont in 1764, even though descendants of the Puritan New Englanders were then settling the area.

Connecticut decided to take advantage of its claims west of the Delaware (mostly in Pennsylvania, but a sliver in modern New York as well). It organized a town in northeastern Pennsylvania in 1751 and attached it to Litchfield County. This was divided into five towns and Westmoreland County was set up in 1776. A fierce conflict arose between the Connecticut and Pennsylvania governments, and the Connecticut government withdrew in 1782, but some colonists remained.

The end of the French and Indian War created interest in the colonies' western claims. After the War Britain tried to limit the settlement areas (and thereby the western boundaries) of all Colonies to the summit of the Alleghenies. This became one of the causes of Revolution.

The establishment of the British Province of Quebec in 1763 implied that New York's northern territory extended to 45° north latitude and the Saint Lawrence River, and westward to Niagara. This was confirmed by the Quebec Act of 1774. New York had also expanded its land claims through treaty cessions of all the western lands of the Iroquois nation and their subjects.

DEVELOPMENT OF THE MIDDLE ATLANTIC STATES

The New York-Pennsylvania boundary was settled at 42° north latitude formally in 1774. The western boundary of Pennsylvania was also clarified at Ellicott's line, a line running due south from the point where 42° north latitude (the agreed northern boundary) met the coast of Lake Erie. This was implied by the 1774 Quebec Act.

The New York-New Jersey line had been debated since 1674. A boundary marker was set on the Delaware River in 1719. The line was redrawn in 1769, and confirmed in 1773. The Pennsylvania-New Jersey boundary was clarified in 1783.

When the United States of America declared itself independent on July 4, 1776, legislatures from each of the Middle Atlantic colonies - New York, New Jersey, and Pennsylvania - joined in the move to independence. Although independence was recognized through the Treaty of Paris (1783), Britain continued to hold some forts in the west until 1796. One of the first issues facing the new government was the clarification of the various boundaries and land claims of the new states.

Inspired by the rebellion round about it, Vermont declared itself independent in 1777 from both Britain and New York. It claimed and, to some degree, took control of some lands now in New Hampshire and in NewYork between the Hudson River and the present boundary. This friction continued until 1790 when New York recognized Vermont and the present boundary was set. Vermont became a state in 1791.

New York also gave up its claims to Indian lands in the west (west of the western end of Lake Ontario) in 1780 (confirmed 1782). Also in 1781 New York released to the federal government sovereignty over the extreme western tip of the state. In 1792 this area was sold to Pennsylvania, giving that state a port on Lake Erie.

Claims by the New England states were harder to settle, and had an impact on Congregational church development in the Middle Atlantic area. Connecticut had shut down its county government in Pennsylvania in 1780, and had withdrawn in 1782. It finally gave up its claim to land in New York and Pennsylvania in 1786. Massachusetts still had a claim over much New York territory west of the Delaware River including the corner on Lake Erie that later passed to Pennsylvania. By a 1786 settlement Massachusetts gave up sovereignty to all its western lands, but retained title to a large track of land west of the eighty-second milestone on the New York-Pennsylvania line and also to an area east of that known as the "Boston Ten Towns."

With these land claims settled, the governments of the three states have continued essentially in their present boundaries until the present time.

EXTINCT COUNTIES

These four New York Counties are extinct: Cornwall (claimed 1665 to 1675 and re-established 1683) covered eastern Maine, and its territory was transferred to Massachusetts in 1691. Dukes County (established 1683) including the islands around Martha's Vineyard, had its title transferred to Massachusetts in 1691, and was divided to become two Counties in that Colony in 1695. Cumberland County (established 1766), and Gloucester County (established 1770) were set up to govern territory in present day Vermont. Their territory was transferred to that state in a 1790 agreement.

The Dutch had organized three counties, New Amstel, Upland, and Hoarkill in present day Delaware and southeastern Pennsylvania in 1673. The English continued these Counties from 1674 as part of New York. New Amstel became New Castle in 1674. Hoarkill became Deale in 1681. A new County, Saint Jones was added in Delaware also in 1680. When Pennsylvania was given to Penn in 1681, Upland County (in southeastern Pennsylvania) was discontinued. The other three Counties were annexed to Pennsylvania in 1682. Deale became Sussex in 1682, and Saint Jones became Kent in 1683. All three were transferred to Delaware in 1704.

Two additional New York Counties have changed their names. Charlotte, established 1772, became Washington in 1784. Tryon, established 1772, became Montgomery in 1784.

One Pennsylvania County has changed its name: Ontario established 1810, became Bradford in 1812. Sullivan County Pennsylvania, established 1847, has sometimes been referred to as LaPorte.

Monongalia, Ohio, and Yohogania Counties were organized by Virginia in 1776 on land in present Pennsylvania and West Virginia. Pennsylvania gained control of most of the area in 1780. Yohogania County was abolished in 1786, but the other two continued as Virginia and then West Virginia Counties.

CONTRIBUTIONS TOWARDS A HISTORY

EUROPEAN ROOTS

Protestantism in Europe, following Luther's break with Rome in 1517, early broke into three factions. Lutheranism gained the support of the princes of many German states and in Scandinavia. Many Anabaptist and radical groups, of varied beliefs and practices, eschewing government support, protection, or even contact, came out of the established churches with small numbers and were often persecuted, sometimes obliterated, and usually harassed and restricted. In between these two extremes were the groups that came to be designated by the general word "Reformed." Like the Lutherans, they sought to reform entire states and often pursued alliances with secular power. On the other hand, they generally had a strong sense of discipline, which gave them more active congregations, similar to some Anabaptist communities.

Reformed leaders, such as the Geneva Reformer John Calvin, sought to form a broad Protestant alliance in Europe. Over the first century of the Reformation such a Reformed alliance did form. This alliance tolerated various views of the sacraments from Zwingli's symbolic views through Calvin's sense of the real presence, and also a wide variety of organizational forms that included bishops in Hungary and Tudor England, and refugee congregations which, in their isolation, acted as independent autonomous bodies. Lutheranism, however, resisted the moves towards Protestant unity, insisting on its own more narrow views on the sacraments and other issues.

Reformed churches appeared in much of Western Europe by 1618, from Transylvania to west Scotland, and from the Pyrenees of southern France to East Prussia. In some places the Reformed church became the established church, either as the church exclusively related to the state, or the one church, or one of a group of churches, granted special privileges. Elsewhere they were a church receiving some form of toleration. In other territories they were a severely persecuted church forced to survive only in refugee settlements. Reformed leaders traveled widely among these nations and settlements, and often Reformed emigrants by the thousands would severely depopulate one place seeking refuge elsewhere. This gave the movement much of its international flavor. "Reformed Protestant churches not only flourished, or at least cohabited with other confessions, in several cultures, they exhibited a marked sense of confessional solidarity." (Duke in Pettegree *et al* (1994), p.1)

While these groups had a consensus on a core of beliefs, the various locations and political situations of the Reformed churches led to a variety of forms of organization. "Calvin had taken a rather relaxed view of church government." (*Ibid.* (1994), p.7) "Calvin's... attitude to church order (to a degree) [had been] pragmatic, [and] his influence extended well beyond the synodical-presbyterian churches emerging in the late 1550's." (*Ibid.* (1994), p.3)

Theodore Beza, who aided and succeeded Calvin in Geneva, and who joined him in trying to build up the Huguenot Reformed Church of France, favored a scheme of regional synods where presbyterial representatives reached decisions. In England, however, Thomas Cranmer, John Hooper, and other Reformed-minded clerics accepted bishoprics in the Church of England. The Reformed desire to use discipline to achieve a more saintly and pious identity for the church also varied. While discipline was to some degree obvious and assumed in a refugee congregation, it was often opposed by powerful political figures in lands where the church had a special privilege. Even in a single nation, such as Holland, the churches' ability to impose discipline varied according to the political realities of separate towns. (See, e.g. Pettegree *et al* (1994), pp. 160-180).

Of most relevance to the development of Congregational churches in the Middle Atlantic colonies is the rise of the Reformed churches primarily in England and Wales, and secondarily in Scotland and Ireland.

THE ENGLISH REFORMATION

The Reformation in England formally began on a peculiar and uncertain foundation when King Henry VIII. separated the Church of England from the Papacy in 1534 for political and personal reasons. The unique status of the English Church made the nation a target for both the theologies of the Reformation and the Catholic Counter-Reformation. The short reigns of Protestant Edward VI. (1547-1553), and Catholic Mary Tudor (1553-1558) swung the country in wild directions and engendered persecutions until Elizabeth I. (1558-1603) sought to bring peace to the country with a moderate Anglicanism.

As early as the 1530's, English religious thinkers who had been influenced by the Continental Reformation began to feel uncomfortable with the lack of total reform in the Tudor Church (Bremer, (1995), p.2). Under King Edward strong ties were established with Geneva and moves were made towards an episcopally-governed Reformed church. Under Mary, much of that sympathy went underground. Many Reformed leaders took refuge on the Continent, where they developed their Reformed identity and built theological and personal ties with other European reformers.

The sentiment for a more complete Reformation quickly rose to the fore under Elizabeth. Initially it had strong support in Parliament. More of Calvin's theological works had been translated into English than any other language during the sixteenth century (see Higman in Pettegree *et al*, (1994) particularly pp. 96-99), particularly during the 1570's when the Reformed sought to "forward Protestantism" in the Elizabethan Church.

Reformed exiles who returned at Elizabeth's accession were aggressive in their hopes. Many gained lay patronages outside the diocesan congregations, from which they were able to push for change. But Elizabeth began to look for a middle way to pacify extremes in the realm. In 1565, and again, with the suspension of Archbishop William Grindal in 1576, she sought to confine the Puritan movement, fencing in Parliament's reform efforts and moving to limit reform to an intellectual rather than an organizational phenomenon.

In 1570 Thomas Cartwright, Professor of Divinity at Cambridge University, sought to build on these new theological directions. Influenced by Beza, he advocated a synodical rather than an episcopal form for the church. However, entrenchment had begun and his radicalism led to his removal from his position at the University.

Cartwright's followers had been able to organize classes of clergy for consultation and reform, had tried to seek redress in Parliament, and had held two national synods while still within the Anglican Church. The English classes were not full blown Presbyterianism, serving in a more consultative than authoritative role. But with the death of the friends of the classes in Court, the tide turned against the movement and Cartwright and others were arrested. Some leaders took refuge on the Continent, but in England by 1592 the classis movement was dead.

Nonetheless, Calvinism persisted. The episcopacy continued to endorse Calvin's views of issues such as predestination. Authorized preaching of a Calvinist slant continued in London until the 1630's (Bremer (1995). p.10). Similarly, London served as a chief city of respite for refugee congregations from the Lowlands, France, and the Palatine.

Submerged energies also created a radical Reformed movement, which sought to move to full reform "without tarrying for any." Independent congregations appeared under the reign of Catholic Mary Tudor. Initially, independency fell off under Protestant monarchs. But by 1568 Separatist Protestant congregations, outside the Church of England also began. Suppressed at first, the Separatist movement again resurfaced in the 1580's with such leaders as Robert Browne, John Greenwood, and Henry Barrowe. With an established Church unable to provide even a disciplined clergy, much less a disciplined membership, those separating sought "purified" congregations. Persecution flared up and Greenwood and Barrowe were executed in 1593. Other Separatists fled to exile in Holland.

In the latter Elizabethan period, intellectual Puritanism quietly gained support in the universities, particularly Cambridge, and trained pious and articulate preachers who would attract congregational support when compared to the often poorly educated, sometimes scandalous, usually politically-appointed clergy who were named to the Anglican diocesan parishes. On the other hand, Elizabeth appointed bishops who would keep her firmly in control of the ecclesiastical machinery and suppress any change in organizational tendencies, either presbyterial or separatist.

The English middle road in the Reformation came to a fork when Elizabeth died in 1603 without an heir. Her cousin, King James VI. of Scotland now ascended the English throne and the future of the church seemed malleable.

The first seventy years of the Reformation in England were dominated by the nation's strong government and the decisions of two powerful monarchs, Henry VIII., and Elizabeth I.. While Reformed Calvinism became widely known in England, it was forced into an uncertainty and division both internally over ecclesiology and polity, and externally over discerning the proper relation of church and state. Nonetheless English Puritanism had gained footholds in vernacular printed materials, strong congregations - often in lay patronages, influence within a great university, and many well-trained and pious clergy.

THE CHURCH OF SCOTLAND

Protestantism in Scotland during the same period developed differently. The nominally Catholic royal House of Stuart was weak and plagued by child rulers who were easily manipulated by egotistical advisors. James V., King 1513-1542 became King at the age of one, his daughter, Mary, Queen of Scots 1542-1567 at age one week, and her son James VI., King 1567-1625 at age one. The royal family was also often at odds with the independent Highland clans. The nation's Parliament was weak and unrepresentative.

Although James V. was the son of Henry VIII's sister, the House of Stuart had turned from England and built an alliance with Catholic France, an alliance which dominated Scotland during the early years of Mary's reign.

Protestantism arose for religious sentiments but soon moved into the nation's power vacuum. The Catholic Church of Scotland had been notoriously corrupt, often led by dissolute appointees from powerful families. It also controlled over half the nation's wealth (Maclean, (1993), p.82). English Bibles were smuggled in, and a spontaneous lay-led Reformation began. Persecutions of early Protestants brought attention to the movement. It also sent many young Reformers as refugees to the Continent, where they strengthened their Calvinism and their ties to the international Reformation.

Protestants aligned themselves with an English invasion 1544 to 1549, which was thwarted by King Henry's death and French support for the young Mary.

John Knox was a close ally and friend of one of the key Protestant Martyrs in Scotland. Knox, after years of travel during which he built strong ties with Reformers in England and on the Continent, returned to Scotland in 1559 to attack the corrupt church, the rule of the French regents, and to lead the growing Protestant movement. Several key nobles had adopted a Protestant covenant in 1557. After a brief alliance with England's new Queen Elizabeth, and the death of the French regent, the Protestants gained an upper hand. In 1560 Parliament removed the authority of the Pope and established Protestantism under documents prepared by Knox. An ally of Beza, Knox implemented strong powerful sessions of lay elders in local congregations, regional presbyteries, and a national General Assembly that met once or twice a year. Many key nobles held places in the new Kirk. In a nation with little cohesive political power, the General Assembly often filled that space and was not afraid to venture beyond religious issues into the secular needs of the nation.

When Catholic Mary was overthrown in 1567, her infant son James was assigned a Protestant regent to be raised within the Scottish Kirk. Murders and intrigue led to many changes in the regency, and James, while usually under Protestant tutelage, was wooed by Catholics and friends of his exiled mother.

When James rose to power as the prospective heir to the English throne, he maintained his Protestantism. However, he was troubled by the General Assembly's power. In 1584 he appointed bishops for the Scottish Church, and tried to limit General Assembly meetings to his call. He failed to stop the General Assembly from meeting, but bishops continued. Whereas, in England, the church was a tool of the crown, in Scotland, it existed in spite of the crown (Maclean (1993), p.105).

Scottish and English Calvinism differed culturally, as well as politically and structurally. Jane Dawson (in Pettegree *et al* (1994)) has written informatively about the fact that the early Scottish Reformation served in two differing cultural areas, the Lowland Anglo-Scottish culture, and the Highland Gaelic culture. The latter, often without widely available written texts (as was the case in most other Calvinist areas), depended on "oral transmission and memorization," with the Catechism requiring "learning by rote." This may have contributed to a Scottish tendency towards exact language, different from England whose legal systems, for instance, were constantly evolving. The more thinly populated Highland areas also led to itinerant preaching, open air services, less emphasis on the parish as a primary religious unit, and an allowance for regional clan leaders to play major roles in the church life of their areas. All of these practices arose among Irish and Scottish settlers on the American frontier, and were generally opposed by New England Congregationalists.

In *Holy Fairs* (1989), Leigh Eric Schmidt documents the development of open air weekend communion services among the Covenanter Presbyterian movement in southwest Scotland opposed to Charles I's imposed liturgy. Schmidt documents how this style of worship spread to Ulster, and flourished again during the Stuart Restoration and the time of persecution. Of interest is that this very Scottish development also ran against the worship principles of the Westminster Directory (which was for obvious reasons closer to English Puritanism), and caused a division in Scottish ranks which would later be seen in America. Fischer (1989, p.615) says that these New Light 'field meetings' and 'prayer societies' became the dominant identity of Scottish and borderlands religion and their later migration to America. These were the roots of the frontier camp meetings and revivals, a style that would be well known among many Scottish and Irish migrating to America, but relatively unknown among English Puritans.

BRITISH DELIBERATIONS, DEBATES, DIVISIONS: PROTESTANTISM UNDER JAMES AND CHARLES

In 1603 James VI. of Scotland became James I. of England, and the King packed for London. Two nations with diverse histories and disparate Protestant traditions now shared the same King.

In 1604 English Puritan leaders met James at Hampton Court to urge reforms in the church. James agreed in theory to support upgrading of the quality of the clergy, including ending non-residency. He also indicated some interest in other reforms. One major reform (a new Bible translation - 1611 - that bears his name) was strongly endorsed.

But James would not give any leeway to serious reform of church organization in England. Instead he moved to conform the Scottish Church to the English. The General Assembly was not allowed to meet after 1603, key Kirk leaders were imprisoned in 1606 and he then appointed more bishops for Scotland and increased their powers. He also took steps to require a more Catholic Anglican liturgy in the Scottish Church, and called a special General Assembly in 1618 to impose his desires to do so.

James also instituted a policy to subdue Irish Catholicism. "Early in the seventeenth century, the English government tried to displace the Roman Catholic Irish population of northern Ireland..." Property was seized and given to influential people, who were obligated to settle colonists on their estates. Leasing land on these estates seemed an opportunity for prosperity for many Scots, and "by 1641 100,000 Scots had settled in Ulster." (Olmstead (1960), p.145). Many of these were dedicated Presbyterians. Also moving to Ulster were many from the northern borderlands of England with less denominationally distinct Protestant sympathies. The first Presbyterian congregation in Ulster was begun by 1610, and a Presbytery was organized in 1642.

While James' liturgical systems were a heavy burden in Scotland, to English Puritans they seemed like relief from Elizabeth's formality about vestments and related aspects of worship. James was trying to move to a middle ground liturgically in an episcopally-governed church under the control of the crown. Nevertheless, the lack of a full reformation resulted in another surge of Separatism in England, including the famed Scrooby congregation, mother of the Mayflower Pilgrims.

Under James neither the nation nor the field of philosophy were static. New ideas were arising in Europe and finding a voice in England's great universities. Arminianism, a modification of Calvinist thought which leaned towards good works rather than election took root. New English theologians saw that work flowering in a restored sacramentalism, which resulted in steps to move the liturgy in an even more Catholic direction. These new intellectuals formed a new force which modern scholars have called the "anti-Calvinists."

Despite her liturgical strictness, Elizabeth had retained a foreign policy that supported the Protestant states of Europe. James, however, while wanting control over both the Scottish and English Churches, chose a foreign policy independent of religion. He sought alliances with Catholic nations, and did not support the beleaguered Protestants at the onset of the Thirty Years' War in 1618. At a time of widespread religious persecution, English Puritans were outraged by James' refusal to support their co-religionists, and began to question the King. James responded by turning away from the Puritans and moving the anti-Calvinists into leadership.

In 1625 James' son Charles I. became King. In Scotland, at the start of the Reformation, the lands of the Catholic Church had been seized and distributed among the Scottish lords. Immediately on accession Charles moved to confiscate the lands for the Scottish Episcopal Church, thereby alienating the lords. In 1629 he proclaimed that the Scottish Church should conform to the Anglican; in 1633 he threatened to abolish Presbyteries; and in 1637 he imposed prayer book liturgy on the Scottish Church, thereby alienating the religious leadership.

In England Charles allied himself with the anti-Calvinists, abandoned his father's greater laxity about the liturgy, and imposed rigid adherence to the most high church practices. One result was that the Separatist movement, which had grown under James, now splintered off new congregations.

Puritan and Scottish fears were also inflamed by a growing Catholic circle around Charles' French Catholic Queen (Bremer (1995), p.37). Charles named the leading anti-Calvinist, William Laud, as Bishop of London (and thereby in charge of foreign Anglican congregations) in 1628, and elevated him to Archbishop of Canterbury in 1633. Many key Puritan leaders were removed from their parishes, and some of these took refuge in Holland.

Again fractured by the strong government, English Puritanism turned to the individual action that had allowed it to survive. One result was the Great Migration to New England and the setting up of the Puritan "City on the Hill."

In Scotland, however, where absent monarchs had often caused and allowed the churches and the lords to unite in opposition, a National Covenant was promulgated in 1638 calling for a return to reform and loyalty to the King. Charles allowed the General Assembly to meet again that year, and it promptly removed all the King's bishops and abolished the prayer book. Scotland was on the verge of religious war.

THE GREAT MIGRATION
PURITANISM COMES TO AMERICA
1620-1640

James I. had begun a colonial empire in North America. Migration to the new lands for religious reasons was first undertaken by a small group of Separatists, which had grown from a congregation in the small village of Scrooby and later fled to Holland. In 1620 they purchased a patent from the Virginia Company and made their way to Plymouth. Under James most Puritans stayed at home and sought avenues of survival. In 1625 an organization was formed to purchase church livings (pastoral and lecture positions not under the control of diocesan bishops) for the Puritan clergy. Archbishop Laud took steps to end this movement.

Pressures increased rapidly under Charles I.. In 1626 the King prohibited the teaching of certain Calvinist doctrines at Cambridge University, and extended the ban to Oxford in 1628. In 1629 he dissolved Parliament, and in 1630 began better relations with Catholic Spain.

Amid poor economic conditions in the 1620's some Puritans invested in fishing outposts in the New World, where they also hoped they might begin missions to the Indians. These contacts began to lay seeds for migration as a possible alternative to submission. Convinced that a providential God had a role for them in worldly salvation, and eager to show a godly example of what a purified community could do through God's grace, the planning of the "City on a Hill" in America took root. Many of those Puritan clergy who had been removed from their livings or fled to exile saw a revived role for themselves in a Puritan cause extended to America, and many of their former parishioners and allies followed. The new England in America was designed to inspire others and to potentially reform the old. The contacts already made through the fishing companies were strengthened until a charter for Massachusetts Bay was sealed in 1629. Then, in little more than a decade, about 21,000 Puritans: key leaders, families, supporters, friends, and dependents, made their way to America. They were only part of a larger migration of 80,000 Puritans seeking refuge at the time (Dollarhide, 1997, p.7). By 1640 two congregations were formed on Long Island, and Congregationalism in the future New York was begun.

(The best review history of the early American Puritans currently available is probably Francis J. Bremer's *The Puritan Experiment* (1995).)

THE ENGLISH CIVIL WAR

Most Puritans stayed in England and had to deal with Charles' rising hostility. Charles' plan to rule without calling a Parliament increased opposition from a widening coalition of excluded voices. But it was the Scottish National Covenant that first triggered war. In order to suppress the rebellious Scots, a war between the King and Scotland began in 1639. Needing funds to finance the War, Charles finally called a Parliament. It sought to bargain with the King for a variety of reforms. Charles responded by dissolving the Parliament. The Scots then invaded northern England and won a truce from the King.

Financially strapped, the King called another Parliament in 1640 (the "Long" Parliament) which pressed for more reforms in the church, and had Archbishop Laud arrested. Parliament insisted on regular meetings, and sent grievances to the King.

Trying to ward off Scottish support for the English Parliament, Charles journeyed to Scotland in 1641, agreed to Presbyterianism in the Scottish Church and some independence for the Scottish Parliament.

In 1642 civil war broke out between the King and the English Parliament. With war and the possibility for major change in England, immigration to, and interest in, New England waned. Some New England leaders returned to England to be at the center of the action.

By 1643 the English Parliament needed the support of Scotland in the war. Having been granted concessions by the King, the chief motivation for Scottish entry into the War would be the extension of their Calvinistic faith and Presbyterian polity to England and Ireland as well. The English Parliament then agreed to the Solemn League and Covenant with Scotland which provided that the church government for all three realms would be similar to that in "the best Reformed churches." To fulfill the requirement to reform the English church, they summoned the Westminster Assembly (see below).

In 1645 the Parliament, strengthened with the support of the Scottish Army, had Archbishop Laud executed and established Presbyterianism in the English church. Their Army gained the superior hand, and the King surrendered in 1646.

However, the previous oppression and silencing of English Puritanism and dissent now led, in freedom, to a rise of a vast array of radical voices. The Quaker movement began in 1646. The Levellers. Sectaries and Erastians grew in strength. Baptists grew apace, and, despite the Parliament and Assembly's choice of a Scottish style Presbyterianism, an independent Congregational position spread - particularly through the ranks of the Army under their eventual head, Oliver Cromwell.

In 1648 Charles I. escaped confinement, and the war began again. This time Scotland, dissatisfied with the English Parliament's inability to impose Presbyterian uniformity, sided with the King. But by this time Parliament's New Model Army was much stronger. They moved against the King, won decisively and had the King executed in 1649. The Parliament also purged itself of its members that had supported a Scottish-style Presbyterianism.

Scotland, recently allied to Charles I., was offended by the English execution of their Stuart monarch and named his son King Charles II.. Cromwell sent an army North, which defeated the Scots, and attached Scotland to England in 1651.

In 1653 Cromwell dissolved the now united British Parliament and was made Lord Protector. Cromwell did foster a period of religious toleration that allowed the sects to grow. Free of an established church, and now able to provide better training of pastors, an evangelical wave led to the founding of new local organizations. Congregationalism grew.

In 1658 the Savoy Declaration was written by leading Congregational divines with the view of establishing Congregationalism in England. In theology it was based on the Westminster confession, but veered away on matters of polity.

Cromwell, however, died later in the year. His son Richard, named Lord Protector, brought back the long Parliament, then resigned, creating a constitutional crisis. In 1660 a Convention Parliament called the Stuart heir Charles II. back to the throne and executed those most directly involved in the death of Charles I.. Many Puritans immediately fled to New England.

THE ASSEMBLY AT WESTMINSTER

Before the writing of the Westminster Confession, Puritans had engaged in theoretical and academic debate about the nature of the church. While nearly all hoped for a unified national church with a common confession, its form was unclear. A wide range of ecclesiologies came to the table, including Puritans willing to accept a mild episcopate, those inclined towards synods, either on the rigid strict nationalist Scottish model, or those set up by Beza to serve churches less clearly related to the government or politics. Other people were attracted to the Congregational system evolving in New England, while still others were willing to consider compromise or something new.

Some of the ecclesiological tensions within English Puritanism focused on issues not clearly related to the national organization of the church. For example, those called "Presbyterial" were more interested in the power and respect of the clergy within their local congregations than they were in the power of overarching judicatories. Robert Paul reminds us (1985, p.566) that "the greater number of parliamentary supporters entered the struggle with Charles without any clear ideas on ecclesiastical polity, except for certain features in the existing Establishment that they were determined to avoid."

When the Westminster Assembly opened in 1643, key New England leaders declined their invitations to attend. However, a group of very gifted Scottish delegates were present to see to their interests. Paul tells us (1985, p.195 and *passim*) that debates at the Assembly, while to the core theological, were slowed or stepped up to conform to the need and movement of the Scottish, Parliamentary, and royal armies in the field.

By 1649 the Assembly had prepared various Directories for the work of the church, a Confession of Faith, two Catechisms, and a Psalter. They did their political duty by recommending the adoption of a Scottish-type Presbyterian system, but not without opposition. In 1643/1644 five stalwart Congregationalists issued what amounted to a minority report, *An Apologeticall Narration.* In fact the Westminster debate was the first time the word "presbyterian" came into general use, and its debate and conclusions are often used as the defining standards of the two polities, which were before - and actually after - the Assembly, in continual flux.

New Englanders responded to the Westminster documents by calling together a Synod at Cambridge, which met starting in 1646. In 1648 the Synod issued the Cambridge Platform, which, while endorsing the Westminster Confession of Faith, presented a summary of the alternative church order which had been evolving in the new settlements. While the life of the Westminster church order was brief in England, it quickly became the basic document for Scottish and other Presbyterian churches.

EARLY MIDDLE ATLANTIC PURITANISM: PURITAN COMMONWEALTHS 1640-1660

The first churches covered in this book were organized on Long Island as part of the Puritan settlement of New England. Despite the Dutch settlements in the Middle Atlantic area, the King of England had claimed the entire east coast as English, and specific grants of Long Island were being made from 1635.

On the eve of the English Civil War, Puritans moved onto Long Island as if it was part of New England. As was the case in most of southern New England, independent settlements were set up with Puritan churches, even though they had no specific charters or titles. The first two of these both occurred in 1640 at Southampton, and Southold. By 1660 six independent Puritan colonies (East Hampton, Huntington, Oyster Bay, Setauket-Brookhaven, Southampton, Southold) had been formed on the eastern end of Long Island. By this date also, four had joined the colony of Connecticut and two had joined the colony of New Haven. All of these, except Oyster Bay, had functioning congregations in 1665.

Like the congregations to the north, these first Puritan congregations represented a spectrum within English Puritanism. Some leaders had a preference for a strong pastor and elders, while others relied more heavily on the laity. Their divergent views are reflected in the decision of Southold and the settlement related to the short-lived congregation at Oyster Bay to relate to the strict New Haven colony, while the other four attached themselves to the looser structure of Connecticut.

The United Colonies of New England worked out a boundary between them and the Dutch in 1650. Some Puritans had begun to settle in areas under Dutch control. The Dutch gave Puritans the right to set up communities at Hempstead, Jamaica, and Newtown within their territory on the Island, and also at Westchester on the mainland. Trinterud (36) suggests that these town churches on the western end of the Island were particularly attractive to people with English Presbyterian sentiments, and even suggests that the Jamaica Church was always Presbyterian, although, if so, it was a Presbyterianism without higher church courts.

TERROR AND TRANSITION 1660-1664

In England in 1660 when the Puritan Commonwealth was overthrown, and the Stuart dynasty restored under Charles II., key Puritan clergy were immediately removed from significant roles. In 1662 clergy who would not submit to the Church of England were ejected from their pastorates, affecting literally thousands of pastors. Many conformed, more in favor of one established national church than of its particular form. The ejected clergy: Presbyterian and Congregational now entered a period of great persecution where they were forbidden from preaching, and their meetings were broken up. The persecutions were also extended to the surviving sectarians, mostly Baptists, forcing all the nonconformists into a common camp. Nonconformists in England were now reduced to a small minority.

At the same time Charles set out to destroy Scottish Presbyterianism. He forced submission to episcopal orders, and eliminated local selection of pastors. Most clergy submitted, but a significant portion did not. In Scotland unauthorized congregations were meeting, and an ongoing guerrilla war against Charles' government began.

Presbyterianism had been the majority position among Puritan clergy in England during the Puritan Commonwealth and at the return of the Stuarts. The cataclysm of the ejection, however, put enormous pressures on those willing to attempt clandestine meetings. Isolated underground meetings supported the slow process of moving English Calvinist congregations away from Westminster's faith in synods towards local autonomy. The non-conformist Protestant dissenting congregations in England and Wales often date their birth as congregations outside the Church of England from the excision of 1662.

At the same time, the future of the entire Puritan population in America was in question. The delay of some American colonies to recognize the new King did not win friends in court.

In America the first acts under the restored Stuarts were a clarification of the charters. Connecticut, the first Puritan Colony to recognize the King, got the most advantage. In 1662 Connecticut was given a charter which included the entire New Haven Colony, thereby eliminating a particularly strict Puritan colony. But the new 1662 charter of Connecticut could also be seen as a plan to stabilize British administration before trying to take over the adjoining Dutch territories. It also caused internal factionalism within Connecticut, as many New Haven towns fought their incorporation into the older colony.

The new royal hegemony caused confusion in Puritan settlements and changing concepts of how to respond. In 1663 four Dutch towns on Long Island with Puritan sentiments decided to leave Dutch protection and to join Connecticut under the protection of its new charter. The town of Westchester on the mainland tried to make a similar move, but was held back.

Early in 1664 five of the Connecticut towns on Long Island, the four that had joined the year before plus Oyster Bay, decided to withdraw from the colony. Their goal was never completed.

Later that year the King gave the land between the Connecticut and Delaware Rivers, and the offshore islands to his brother the Duke of York, and before the year was out, the Duke had taken the Dutch New Netherlands by force and also laid claim to Dutch territories beyond his grant. At the time of the English take-over of New York, five Puritan congregations existed on eastern Long Island, three on western Long Island and one in Westchester on the mainland. All of these, except Westchester, had functioned for some of their life as New England town churches, and Westchester had tried to do so.

Because of boundary disputes, two other churches in what is now New York functioned as established Connecticut churches. Connecticut purchased Rye from the Dutch in 1660. A Church there begun probably between 1674 and 1677 was part of Connecticut to 1683 and again from 1697 to 1700. The Bedford Church, founded 1680 or 1681, was also in Connecticut until 1683 and from 1697 to 1700.

UNDER THE DUKE
1664-1688

Under Catholic James, Duke of York (1664-1685), who became King James II. (1685-1688), Puritan growth in New York almost stopped. Between 1664 and 1700 only two more churches on Long Island (Bridgehampton and Smithton), and one more on the mainland (Eastchester) were formed. Thus ten of the fourteen New York churches in 1700 had been New England congregations.

The political changes of 1664 did produce the start of a Puritan movement in New Jersey. In 1664 the Duke of York had granted New Jersey to a group of proprietors who soon began a process of selling and reselling titles and power in the new colony. A few of these purchasers were known dissenters or friendly to dissenter settlement. The confused ownership of New Jersey, and its no longer being under the direct rule of James made it attractive to Puritan expansion. When the 1662 Connecticut charter had incorporated the New Haven Colony into its neighbor to the north, several former New Haven colonists desired more strictly religious communities. They had already considered moving to present day New Jersey when it was still under the Dutch. Richard Nicolls (LeBeau (1997), p.13), the Duke's first Governor of the province, "required [each settlement] to have one corporately supported minister chosen by its freeholders..." This provision, which implied a type of local town establishment, added to the colony's appeal to New Englanders. Many unhappy people in the old New Haven Colony, including most of the town of Branford, moved to New Jersey beginning the towns of Elizabeth and Newark. They had a clear plan to establish new Puritan commonwealths in New Jersey. A compact entered into at Branford in 1666 provided for their planned new town on the Passaic River (Newark) that none shall be made freemen of such town "but such Planters as are members of some or other of the Congregational Churches..." and also that "We shall with Care and Diligence [sic] provide for the maintenance of the purity of Religion professed in the Congregational Churches..." (Moffat) Other Puritan settlements in New Jersey began from similar origins.

Puritans also gained ascendancy in two formerly Dutch Reformed settlements at Norriton, Pennsylvania, and in New Castle, Delaware.

Also during this period James granted Pennsylvania, and then Delaware (1681 and 1682) to his Quaker friend William Penn. The Quakers were dissenters, but at this time had poor relations with the Puritan groups. The grants to Penn rewarded a friend, and did create a religious toleration in the Middle Atlantic area, which also flowed into New Jersey where Quakers became prominent among the proprietors. However, this may have been a move by the Stuarts to move yet another dissenting group off the playing field of Britain to a remote isolated spot where they could - at least theoretically - be dealt with later.

Thus initially the return of the Stuarts allowed for expansion of dissenter populations into this area. But the attacks by the Stuarts on the Reformed faith in both Scotland and England soon put a pall over their sister churches in America, and expansion became frozen in its tracks.

Population movements within the colonies were also slowed by the quick succession of three wars. A war between New Englanders and the Indians, King Philip's War (1675-1678) led to an abandonment of outpost settlements, re-centering the population in coastal towns, and reawakening a fear of moving into new areas. It was closely followed by two European Wars that included combative alliances with Indians, and continued danger on the frontiers (King William's War (1689-1697) and Queen Anne's War (1702-1713)).

Stuart policies in America toward the Puritans were antagonistic but slow. Charles II. was often distracted: facing a plague, the great fire of London, and Parliamentary attempts to exclude James from the succession to the throne. The royalists sought first to gain stability and economic viability in the colonies in an area where they knew the friends of the King were not the majority. Then they directed their energies to taking over direct royal control of the colonies. This was to be done first through the courts, but then by force. These delays gave the New England churches a hiatus in which they continued to operate in much the same ways they had under Cromwell's commonwealth.

Undoubtedly much of the energy directed to America under the restored Stuarts was to take over New Netherlands, and to secure title and resist Dutch attempts to regain control. As discussed in the section on the development of the colonies, Charles and James took all the Dutch lands "by conquest." They then began to move through charters, grants, and in the courts to get control over all the islands from Nantucket to Long Island, eastern Maine, and the western claims of Connecticut and Massachusetts.

The King also took New Hampshire away from Massachusetts in 1679, and began steps to impose the Church of England in the northern colony in 1683. After much haggling in the courts, the charter of Massachusetts was revoked in 1684. Then, under James I, a master plan was revealed to unite all of New England, New York, and New Jersey in one royal colony under the control of the King to be known as the Dominion of New England. The Dominion began with Massachusetts and New Hampshire. Plymouth was taken over by the crown's agent in 1686, and Connecticut in 1687. By 1688 the new dominion included Rhode Island, New York, and New Jersey as well. Governor Andros moved quickly against the Puritans, forbidding towns from collecting funds to support the churches.

James was also making enemies in Britain, and movements began to overthrow the Stuart dynasty. These were quickly followed by revolution in Boston, and on the streets of New York. William and Mary were brought to England from Holland to be the new monarchs, and established the House of Orange. This "Glorious Revolution," was seen as an opportunity for Protestant relief.

AFTER THE GLORIOUS REVOLUTION
1688-1706

Some had hoped that the accession of William and Mary might lead to an established Presbyterian system, similar to the Scottish system, in England. But that was not to be. The Anglican bishopric was retained in England, and new arrangements were sought for the expansive empire. But things did change. Parliament passed an act of toleration (1689), which, while allowing for established tax supported churches in British lands, provided that the major Protestant sects, be they Anglican, Presbyterian, Congregational, Baptist, or Quaker, must be allowed freedom of worship. The Church of Scotland was now established under its Presbyterian plan, but had to tolerate both Anglicans and the Cameronians, the early forerunners of the Reformed Presbyterians.

In America in 1688 the colonies had begun to act as they had before the imposition of the Dominion, but the issue of the revoked Massachusetts charter remained. Delegations from New England, including the Boston pastor Increase Mather, sought to work out a plan. The Puritans could not regain their theocracy. Massachusetts got a new charter in 1691, which made it a royal colony. Plymouth Colony was abolished and attached to Massachusetts. New Hampshire was also continued as a separate royal colony. While town government in New England was retained, religious qualifications for voting were abolished and toleration of Anglican, Baptist, and Quaker worship required. New Hampshire and the enlarged Massachusetts also lost the ability to choose their own governors - now appointed by the King - and the governor had veto power in the choice of the upper houses of their legislatures. The theocracy had come to an end.

A compromise was now in place. Except for the City of Boston (whose churches were supported by free will donations), Massachusetts and New Hampshire colonial laws provided for the support of "an able, learned, orthodox minister of good conversation." The laws did not specify a denominational designation. Nevertheless, since the Congregationalists were the majority in most of the towns at this time, they continued to elect their own, but now had to have their ministerial choices approved by the towns, parishes, or societies where dissenters from Congregationalism could vote. At least implicitly a pastor could come from outside Congregational circles. Four towns in the former Plymouth Colony supported dissenter churches and in 1722 a New Hampshire town approved the pastor of the Scotch-Irish Presbyterian Church as the town pastor. Connecticut retained its old charter, and eventually through the Saybrook Synod formed a more "denominational" establishment. Even there, however, town, parish or society tax-payers who were not members of the church, were given vote at society meetings in matters that affected the town tax, usually interpreted to include the settling of a minister. Eventually the compromise also meant in the royal colonies the end of New England's system of occasional synods to resolve current issues. Though not written into the new system, the royal governors simply would not allow such synods to meet. The ecclesiastical polity of New England was severely distorted. The churches were stripped of their ability to change.

Even before the imposition of the new Massachusetts charter, clergy in New England had realized their precarious situation and had begun to form regional ministerial associations about 1690. They also continued annual election sermon gatherings and conventions and college alumni meetings, which allowed them to explore strategies for further action. (The annual Massachusetts clergy convention met informally at first, and later took on an organizational format. It was a regular factor in the colony by 1690.) Puritans in the Middle Atlantic area were on the edge of these discussions.

Other changes were at work as well. The seventy years of Puritanism in America had produced parish churches. Not all of the children of the emigrants experienced the saving grace of their forebears. Therefore the situation in New England had come close to that of the English Presbyterians: clergy felt they were dealing with less converted and more hostile congregations. Associations provided a means of support from which to assert clerical authority.

If compromise with the crown in New England meant the eradication of church strength, imagine the uncertainty of the few Puritan churches in the Middle Atlantic region. The congregations on Long Island, in Westchester, and in New Jersey up to and during the reign of Governor Andros had acted like New England churches supported by the taxes of their towns. Yet there were no charters, colonial or local, to guarantee the legal continuance of these arrangements, nor of the churches themselves. They were unprotected and exposed to any royal whim.

THE RELIGIOUS SITUATION IN 1700

By 1700 ten Puritan churches were on Long Island, and four were in the Westchester area of New York. At least two predominantly Puritan congregations were in Pennsylvania, although they already had culturally mixed memberships. The number of congregations in New Jersey is less clear. There were surely four strong congregations: Newark, Elizabeth, Woodbridge, and Cohansey. Some sources suggest that Puritan or mixed proto-congregations without clergy also existed in Cape May, Maidenhead, Piscataway, Freehold, Middletown, Shrewsbury, and Pilesgrove. Another source estimates fifteen congregations by 1700, but does not list the other four. Clearly, all the named proto-congregations, except Piscataway, gave birth to congregations early in the eighteenth century. While some of the proto-congregations in New Jersey included Irish and Scottish settlers, and while both Pennsylvania churches were culturally mixed, none of the strong churches in these three colonies in 1700 could be described as Presbyterian. The Puritan migration still left its mark.

In England and Wales, the Toleration acts following the Glorious Revolution allowed Puritan worship but isolated those choosing Puritan beliefs from the political process. The switch from being part of large parish churches which had many marginal members to twenty-seven years of dedicated groups of courageous people carrying on an underground faith had strengthened the will of the leaders, but had moved English dissent into a small minority. Now worship was allowed, but dissenters had to be willing to give up some rights and privileges for their beliefs. These conditions made their churches at the start of the eighteenth century small and activist. You had to choose to be a member of a dissenting congregation. Economic and political restrictions also limited clergy career training and development. Congregations, therefore, became lay centered. In addition, the isolated nature of rural congregations before the Industrial Revolution joined these other changes in encouraging a Congregational polity of called-out believers in autonomous congregations, no matter what the preference for polity had been earlier.

The Toleration Acts also allowed dissenters to begin to form visible methods of relationship. Congregational clergy in London had been meeting on a regular basis since the Commonwealth, and probably underground during the persecution. These meetings became public again after the Glorious Revolution. When the established church in

England under William and Mary became Anglican, Presbyterians and Congregationalists in London consulted together, aided by Increase Mather from New England. In 1690 a General Fund was begun to support feeble churches and to aid in educating clergy. The following year, 1691, the "United Ministers In and about London Formerly called Presbyterian and Congregational" published the "Heads of Agreement," and began to meet regularly. This non-conformist unity influenced the beginnings of associations in America. In England additional joint groups of Presbyterian and Congregational clergy followed. One in Somerset, Wiltshire and Gloucestershire had begun by 1690. Groups were organized in the West Riding of Yorkshire, Cheshire, and Devon and Cornwall in 1691, and a large Lancashire group in 1693. Similar bodies were formed in Hampshire, Norfolk, and Nottinghamshire.

Some disputes led to a break up of the United Ministers in London by 1695, and in that year a separate fund to support Congregational churches and students was also established. However, the country unions persisted. Many rural or country congregations became known as simply "Protestant Dissenter," received aid from either fund, and hired pastors who identified themselves with either ecclesiology.

In London a parallel body, including Baptists, was organized in 1689. This group was designed to speak for non-conformity on political issues. While it was only a London group, it had influence around the nation. It evolved into the General Body of Protestant Dissenting Ministers in and About London, formally organized 1702, disrupted 1719, and reorganized 1727. It later worked in consultation with a lay group, the Protestant Dissenting Deputies begun 1732/1736.

As the century continued a high percentage of what had been Presbyterian dissenter congregations became mixed, then Congregational, and Congregationalism became the chief Calvinist dissenter group in England and Wales.

THE NEW ANGLICAN THREAT

After barely a decade of learning how to live in the new era of compromise and toleration, the succession of James II's daughter Anne as the new Queen of England in 1702 re-ignited fears on both sides of the Atlantic about the continuation of the Reformed Churches. Animosity to the Puritan churches and colonies in America had not died out in England. The new era of "toleration" changed the tactics. No longer did the crown concentrate on getting direct legal control of the Puritan colonies. Instead its chief strategies involved interpreting and imposing the type of establishment allowed by the toleration acts and also financing extensive evangelizing for the Anglican Church in Puritan territory.

The Church of England and their friends in the royal government used two primary tactics to overcome the Puritans: establishment of the Church of England and organization of the Society for the Propagation of the Gospel in Foreign Parts.

Virginia had had an Anglican establishment since 1619, and had supported the Stuart dynasty during the Puritan Revolution. Now this was extended. The Church of England was established in Maryland in 1692. A similar Anglican establishment began in the Carolinas in 1698 and was extended by two strong acts in 1704. After North Carolina separated from South Carolina, it also received an imposed Anglican establishment in 1715. Georgia, only settled in 1733, also received an Anglican establishment in 1758.

The other method was the grant by the King of a royal charter in 1701 to the Society for the Propagation of the Gospel in Foreign Parts, the "**SPG**." Its main purpose was to channel aid to Anglican parishes and pastors in the colonies. While initially it was thought that the Society would oversee Anglican work in the colonies where it was established, its primary function came to be to aid Anglican work in areas where Reformed dissenting congregations were strong. The SPG was no idle threat. Between 1702 and 1776 it supported seventy-six missionaries in New York, forty-four in New Jersey, and forty-seven in Pennsylvania.

Other actions also diluted Puritan hopes. The Puritan colonies on Long Island had continued to act like they were New England towns, taxing their residents for meeting house and clergy support. The Puritan towns in New Jersey limited the vote to church members, and were in many ways more strictly Puritan than ecclesiastical arrangements in Connecticut at the time. In New Jersey the frequent changes in the ownership of the colony, and the economic prosperity these towns provided it, played roles in encouraging the proprietors to pay little attention to local practices about the franchise. However a Quaker resident of the town of Woodbridge brought a civil action because he had been denied the right to vote. In 1700 he won the case (cf. Jamison (84)). The Middle Atlantic churches now realized their isolation from New England and the precariousness of their institutions.

The biggest danger to the Middle Atlantic churches was the threat of an Anglican establishment, which soon became real in New York. In the words of Clifton Olmstead (1960):

> "In 1693, the [New York] Assembly passed a bill entitled 'Act for Settling a Ministry, and raising a Maintenance for them in the City of New York, County of Richmond, Westchester and Queens' county.' The act was later interpreted by the governors as establishing the Anglican Church in the counties named in the legislation. It is highly doubtful, however, if this was the intention of many who voted for the act. The document does not mention the Church of England. It provided only that the six named parishes were each to be served by a 'good sufficient Protestant minister' and were to be supported by an annual tax. In English legal

usage the phrase 'good sufficient Protestant minister' meant a clergyman of the Church of England. This meaning was doubtless not understood by the Dutch members of the Assembly who voted for it, only to find themselves deceived." (p.57)

The same could be said for the Puritans in the colony. In Massachusetts the law provided that each town support "an able, learned, orthodox minister of good conversation," and there that usually meant a Puritan. The Dutch apparently got some wind of what was about to happen, because, after a generous gift to the governor, they were able in 1696 to procure a charter to protect their Collegiate Church in New York, the year before the Anglican parish was set up. However the Puritans out in the country were less able to ward off the effects of the Act.

What the 1693 New York law meant was slow to be seen. The six parishes mentioned in the act were New York, Westchester, Hempstead, Jamaica, Oyster Bay, and Staten Island, and included the present counties of New York, Bronx, Westchester, Richmond, Queens, and Nassau. The act had overlooked strongly Dutch Reformed Kings County, and the strongly Puritan Suffolk County. An Episcopal Parish was established in New York in 1697 (Trinity), and in Westchester in 1702, and the others followed shortly thereafter. The problem was that there were already eight active congregations, seven Puritan and one Huguenot, in these parishes.

St. Paul's Parish, Westchester (1702) took over the Westchester Puritan Church that year. Later it became its own Parish, St. Peter's, and St. Paul's also took control of the Eastchester Puritan congregation in 1708. The Puritans here attempted to reorganize from 1717 to 1720, but failed. That Parish then birthed other Parishes in the area. Christ Parish got control of the Rye Puritan congregation in 1704. However the congregation split into two factions in 1719, and between 1723 and 1728 the Congregationalists reorganized. That Parish also set up St. Matthew's Parish in 1706 and tried unsuccessfully to get control over the Puritan congregation at Bedford. In 1709 a new Trinity Parish took over the majority of the French Huguenot congregation in New Rochelle. A minority reorganized and affiliated with the Dutch Church and later transferred to the Presbyterians.

On Long Island, the Grace Parish of 1702 seized the building of the Puritan congregation in Jamaica in 1703, but agreed to joint use of the building with the Puritan congregation in 1709, and the Anglicans abandoned it in 1728. The same Parish took over the building of the Puritan congregation in Newtown from 1703 to 1708. St. George's Parish of 1704, took over the Puritan congregation in Hempstead in 1705, but allowed some mixed Puritan practices to continue. The congregation split into two factions about 1717, and the Puritans, by then Presbyterians, regained control in 1724. This loss of two congregations, and the severe disruption of six others set a precedent that encouraged an organized Puritan response.

In 1702 the crown took control of New Jersey, uniting it and making it a royal colony. Edward Lord Cornbury, the Governor of New York was appointed Governor of New Jersey as well.

After the visit of the first SPG missionaries to the area in 1702-1704, Governor Cornbury and others began to urge the further establishment of the Anglican Church. A convention of Anglican pastors in Burlington, New Jersey called for restricting public office to those receiving the sacrament according to the Church of England. In the first few years of the eighteenth century, the threat to all the colonial Reformed churches, and particularly to those in the Middle Atlantic area was quite real.

THE ARRIVAL OF THE SCOTCH-IRISH

Before 1700 occasional Scottish or Irish pastors had served in America. Most, however, served Puritan congregations, while a few served short lived or isolated settlements. None made any attempt to form "higher church courts" on any kind of a continuing basis.

By 1680 Maryland and Virginia had received some Scotch-Irish settlement, and they were a long way from any Puritan aid. They appealed to Ulster for help and the Presbytery of Laggan sent William Traill in 1682 and Francis Makemie in 1683 to Maryland. Traill left in 1688, but Makemie remained to make a mark. He served churches along Chesapeake Bay in Maryland and Virginia.

The new Scotch-Irish immigrants shared with the Puritans the experience of religious persecution at the hands of the Church of England. Since the rule of James I. conditions for Protestants in Ulster (Northern Ireland) had deteriorated. Rents had increased dramatically, and England took steps that destroyed the trade and economic potential of the area. In addition, Ireland had an Anglican establishment. Presbyterians there had to pay taxes to the Anglican Church, their clergy were not allowed to perform marriages, and from 1704 they were barred from public office unless they received the sacraments at an Anglican Church. So the great tide of the Scotch-Irish emigration to America began. While these new immigrants descended from mostly Scottish families, they had lived in Ireland for some generations. Most had endured the situation in Ulster, and had had their fill of church establishments.

Makemie began to visit widely scattered settlements in the Carolinas and even Barbados. In 1692 he preached in Philadelphia, where he laid some foundations for the eventual united Puritan and Scotch-Irish congregation there. Makemie met many Puritans on his travels, and in 1684 began a life-long correspondence with the prominent Boston Puritan pastor, Increase Mather. Makemie often visited England seeking support for the new immigrants. In 1691 he met Mather in London, where Mather was serving as a Massachusetts negotiator trying to work out a compromise to protect the New England churches when a new charter would be issued for Massachusetts. In London Mather was also a sponsor of the "Heads of Agreement" adopted in 1691 as an attempt to unify the newly tolerated Congregational and Presbyterian clergy in the city. Makemie's career confirms his support for the Heads of Agreement. London friends often provided financial support for his work. Makemie had experience with both the English and Scottish polities, and from that wide perspective he decided to keep alive the principles of the London union. How he related to the various divided groups in London after their 1695 division is unclear, however. Trinterud (36) reports that in 1704 the "London United Brethren" sent Makemie two helpers in the ministry, John Hampton and George McNish. Which clergy actually joined in sending these helpers is unclear, although clearly they followed Makemie's steps in building strong ties with Puritans in America. Although both Hampton and McNish were educated in Scotland, they obviously had strong English connections, and would have been influenced by the ecclesiology there. Little financial aid was available from Ulster, from which the refugees were streaming. Makemie's close alliance with the London clergy connected aid to the united theology and looser polity of England. It also encouraged keeping New England ties strong.

The Ulster population in America grew, first along the Chesapeake in Maryland and Virginia, then into Pennsylvania and Delaware. Ulster settlements in New Jersey probably began by 1685, and New York followed later. While Makemie and his associates often formed new Presbyterian churches which reflected the Scottish and Irish organizational forms, others joined already existing congregations of Puritan or mixed background in Maryland, Delaware, Pennsylvania, New Jersey, and New York.

Shortly after the start of the new century Welsh Independents also arrived, at the "*Dyffryn Maur*" or *Tre'rdyffryn,* Great Valley in Pennsylvania by 1710 and at Pencader Hundred or Welsh Tract at Glasgow Delaware in 1710.

THE FIRST UNION
1706-1741

The Heads of Agreement in London had brought together Presbyterians and Congregationalists, and in rural England union persisted. Increase Mather had been involved in adopting the Heads of Agreement, and brought union back to America. Francis Makemie also worked closely with union groups in England and kept friendly ties with the Mathers. It was natural that union steps could grow in America.

Related to this move was the need for America's independent congregations to organize for protection from the ongoing British threats.

The new New England associations, instead of being the final solution to the quest for a new polity, became a forum to explore a polity that could resist the new Anglican incursions.

In 1700, Massachusetts pastor Solomon Stoddard published *The Doctrine of the Instituted Churches*. He "sought to have the instituted church organized on a national basis. It would be governed by a synod consisting of elders representing the constituent churches and responsible for maintaining sound doctrine and for training and placing ministers. Regional synods would act as administrative agents of the national body." (Bremer (1995) p.214).

Also in 1700 the annual Massachusetts ministerial convention, following the lead of Cotton Mather, passed a resolution encouraging the reconsideration of Consociations of Churches, which had been previously approved at the Synod of 1662.

In 1702 Cotton Mather published *Proposals for the Preservation of Religion in the Churches, by a Due Trial of Them that Stand Candidates for the Ministry.* Ostensibly directed at increasing the piety and learning of the clergy, Mather's ideas called for stronger ministerial bodies, which could begin to act with some degree of unity and definition. In particular, Mather called on the associations to be the place where candidates for the ministry were first examined and approved, a policy similar to one enacted in the Heads of Agreement.

In 1704 the convention sent a circular to the churches which, among other initiatives to increase piety, encouraged the strengthening of ministerial associations and their communication with each other. Another circular followed this later in the year from the Cambridge (and Boston) ministers' association calling for the organizing of associations where they did not exist, and again for contact among them.

The next year, 1705, representatives from five Massachusetts ministerial associations (one of which included part of New Hampshire) met in Boston and agreed to adopt the "***Proposals of 1705***." They proposed, among other things, that all the ministers of the country form themselves into associations, that the associations' powers be extended to include examination and approval of ministerial candidates, that an annual meeting be held of the associations together, that pastors in each association form with delegates from their churches standing or stated councils in consociation. Consociations also would have the right to withdraw fellowship from churches with "gross disorders."

These proposals were then approved by an association later that year (probably Cambridge-Boston) and by the entire Massachusetts convention in 1706.

The proposals had the support of a wide range of clergy, both theologically and geographically. But Cotton Mather reported that they were opposed in Massachusetts by "some very considerable Persons among the *Ministers*, as well as of the *Brethren...*" One of the "considerable persons" opposing the plan was probably Cotton's own father, Increase Mather. Youngs (1976, p.72) says that an answer to the proposals, supporting more lay participation in church affairs, appears in Increase's personal papers probably from this date. However, he did not publish these ideas until 1716. And Increase, in 1706, was only a few years past a controversy that had forced him out of the Presidency of Harvard; an episode, which Cotton believed, had ended his father's public life. (Silverman (1985), p.179). Later, in 1713, John Wise would publish a pamphlet agreeing with Increase in justifying the loose knit ecclesiology that had evolved in Massachusetts. Thus these religious opponents to the plan belatedly called for more lay control in the churches.

Yet in 1706, the proposals, as both Walker (1960/1893, pp.493-494) and Youngs (1976,p.72) agree, fell dead in their tracks because the royal Governor of Massachusetts, Joseph Dudley, refused to allow a synod to meet, which was the historically accepted forum for changing interconnections between and among the churches under the former Puritan charter. The proposals, however, had been adopted by both the annual minister's convention, and the five existing ministerial associations at the time, and were therefore clearly endorsed by an overwhelming majority of the religious leadership. Furthermore, the desire for a synod was an attempt to bring lay representatives to the planning table. Consociations, a goal of the proposals, also increased lay power. The squashing of the synod limited the power of the laity to sit at synods, and also denied the province's churches the right and power to consult about their future.

Some of the ecclesiological ideas of the proposals did take effect. More ministerial associations were organized in various parts of the colony, and they did take over the role of examining and approving candidates for the ministry through the process of licensure by association. These religious changes gave more power to the clergy, but the full acceptance of the proposals would have balanced clergy strength with a lay role in the consociations.

In 1715 some clergy in Massachusetts again encouraged the Colony's General Court (legislature) to call a synod. This time Increase Mather came forward to testify against calling a synod saying the clergy were "more in fear than there was any need of." (Alliman, (1971) pp.34-35) This time, though, fears of Anglican encroachments and known conflicts with the government over the synod, were the contested issues in calling a synod, not ecclesiology. In this regard, Increase undoubtedly wanted to protect the delicate balance of the 1691 Massachusetts charter that he had helped to engineer. Since 1702 two Massachusetts towns with strong Quaker constituencies had a case in court seeking relief from having to settle and support congregational ministers in their towns. Now the New England Yearly Meeting of Friends threatened to petition their allies in London if a synod were held. Again the government kept the churches from meeting.

The final colonial attempt of Massachusetts Congregationalism to determine its own ecclesiology took place in 1725 when the Convention of Ministers petitioned the Lieutenant Governor for a synod. Before the General Court could act, two Anglican pastors in Boston (one of whom was Timothy Cutler, who had led the Anglican schism at Yale in 1722) appealed to their superiors in England protesting a move to strengthen Congregationalism. They were able to get a ruling from the Lords Justices that reprimanded the Lieutenant Governor for not telling them of the ministers petition, declaring there was no national or provincial church in Massachusetts, and that, therefore, it was illegal "for the clergy to assemble in a synod without [the King's] authority." (Alliman, (1971), pp.36-37; Walker, 1960/1893, p.525) This ruling crippled Massachusetts Congregationalism (and by implication New Hampshire - which shared the same royal Governor and similar charters) for the rest of the colonial period, and has had incredible ecclesiological implications ever since. Alliman (1971, p.34) reports that "In addition to a growing sense among the standing ministers of a declining religious fervor, most Congregationalists were alarmed by the expanding influence of the Church of England. Consequently many came to believe that only a semi-Presbyterian system could consolidate enough authority to halt the decline of piety while simultaneously enabling Congregationalists to demonstrate that they were still the predominant religious force in the province."

The ideas of the proposals did take root elsewhere. More formal union among the Calvinist churches did not die. In 1703 the trustees of the new Yale College in Connecticut sent a circular calling for "addressing our Religious Government." Connecticut still had its own charter, and in 1707 elected a minister, Gurdon Saltonstall, as Governor of the colony. In 1708 the Connecticut legislature called for a Synod for that state, which met later in that year at Saybrook. The Saybrook Synod lifted up the ideas of the Proposals of 1705, and adopted them in a revised form as the Saybrook Platform. The Saybrook system was approved by the Connecticut legislature later in that year, and in 1709 a new ecclesiastical polity was established in Connecticut, including regional ministerial associations, a colony wide general association of representatives of the regional associations, and standing consociations of churches (which included laity) in each of the association areas.

In western Massachusetts, distant from the watch of the royal Governor in Boston, Solomon Stoddard took the lead in creating the Hampshire Association in 1714. While it was a ministerial association, it was chartered and approved by votes of the churches that the pastors served. These votes granted the Association certain powers.

THE FIRST PRESBYTERY

As the Proposals of 1705 circulated, and the threat of an Anglican establishment was stirring, Middle Atlantic clergy also had to decide what to do. Because they did not have the protection of some type of establishment as did the New England churches, a more formal organization was all the more urgent. They were aware of the ferment of this decade in the issues of church polity. Cotton Mather, a key player in the Proposals of 1705 was in correspondence with Makemie and John Wilson, among others in the Middle Atlantic region. Benjamin Colman, pastor of Boston's Brattle Square Church, also carried on regular correspondence with Philadelphia pastor Jedediah Andrews. Because most Middle Atlantic churches were not tied to their colonial governments, like Connecticut and Massachusetts, their options were different. Assuming they did not need governmental approval for a Synod, they were free to act. The response of Cotton Mather and Colman's friends was the organization of a Presbytery in 1706.

Makemie took the lead in gathering a group of seven clergy together in 1706, which became the Presbytery of Philadelphia. The seven were Francis Makemie, Samuel Davis, Jedediah Andrews, John Wilson, Nathaniel Taylor, John Hampton, and George McNish. Makemie was chosen as the first Moderator.

This was the first union of Puritan, Scottish, and Irish clergy in America. Because the Presbytery is the organizational root of the modern Presbyterian Church, U.S.A., this organization is the beginning of organized American Presbyterianism. However, in addition, it was also a union of Puritans and Scotch-Irish.

Trinterud (36) reminds us that history has often debated the origins and sentiments of these founders. Some Presbyterians have claimed that "if it could be shown that a majority of these seven ministers came from a certain country, then the original charter of American Presbyterianism could readily be constructed by studying the Presbyterian Church of that land as it then was." Trinterud calls this "fallacious reasoning." Indeed the origins and service of the seven are in doubt. What, however, is abundantly clear, is that they represented a mixed group of people with mixed origins. Makemie came from Ulster, and most agree that Davis came from Ireland. Andrews was a New Englander and a Harvard graduate. Hampton was from Scotland, and McNish was educated in Scotland, but Makemie's friends in London sent both to America, and therefore they had both English and Scottish mixed credentials. The biggest debate about origins is over Wilson and Taylor. Weis (1978/1957) and LeBeau (1997) contend that both were Scottish. However Trinterud (36), Nichols (49), and Olmstead (1960), all say they were New Englanders. Trinterud says that Wilson was sent to Delaware by Increase and Cotton Mather to serve many New Englanders who had settled on land there purchased by Connecticut. Initially the new Presbytery was serving primarily below the Mason-Dixon Line and outside the Middle Atlantic area. Andrews was the only exception, serving the predominantly Puritan congregation in Philadelphia. Wilson was serving a very mixed congregation in New Castle, Delaware, and Taylor a congregation with Puritan roots in Patuxent, Maryland. The rest were serving congregations that were predominantly Scotch-Irish: Makemie in Maryland and Virginia, Davis in Lewes, Delaware, and Hampton in Maryland. McNish was at this point serving as an itinerant evangelist, but would soon settle in Virginia. The Presbytery's interest in the northern settlements, however, was clear, for they soon ordained the young Scottish immigrant John Boyd to serve a mixed congregation in Monmouth County, New Jersey.

The actual polity and assumptions of the new Presbytery can not be equated with the Presbyterian polity that evolved over time. The first meeting of the Presbytery had been called "to consult the most proper measures for advancing religion and propagating Christianity..." (Armstrong *et al* (1956), p.11), not exactly a call for establishing a denominational hierarchy. The first minute book of the new Presbytery has its first page missing, which leaves some questions in doubt. Makemie did not attribute much judicial authority to the new body. In a letter he said that those at the first meeting had set a "design... to meet yearly, and oftener, if necessary, to consult the most proper measures, for advancing religion, and propagating Christianity, in our Various Stations, and to maintain Such a Correspondence as may conduce the improvement of our Ministeriall ability by prescribing Texts to be preached on by two of our number at every meeting, which performance is Subjected to the censure of our Brethren..." (Note, p.1 of the 1976 printing of the Minutes). The group did choose the name Presbytery, and followed some procedures common in Ulster and Scotland "in respect to lay representation, excuses, absences, calls, and overtures..." (Armstrong *et al*, (1956) *ob.cit.*) However, "Neither questions of doctrinal uniformity nor matters of organization occupied the minds of the presbyters at the first meetings. The result was that no constitution was drawn up and many details were left to be worked out later" (Olmstead (1960), p.148).

Unlike many immigrant Protestant churches in America (including Dutch and German Reformed and the Seceder Associate Presbyterian Church), the new Presbytery was not set up under any European judicatory, and was autonomous. Loetscher (34, p.61) also points out that it "was organized 'from the ground up,' not 'from the top down,'" as was the Presbyterianism of Scotland which had been adopted by Parliament and implemented by the General

Assembly. In America, on the contrary," the higher judicatories were created by the lower..." Most historians agree the new Presbytery had an organizational style deliberately designed to welcome several ecclesiologies and cultures, and not designed to impose an existing European system on America.

Almost immediately the new Presbytery began to move north of the Mason-Dixon Line. While some Scotch-Irish population continued to flow into Maryland and Virginia, the few isolated clergy found it more and more difficult to function opposed to the Anglican establishment in those colonies. Only later, when a strong flank of clergy could be sent there, did churches to serve the new immigrants really gain a foothold. However, new Scottish and Irish congregations in tolerant Pennsylvania and Delaware were able to sink strong roots. By 1750 "one fourth of the inhabitants of Pennsylvania were Scotch-Irish."(Olmstead (1960), p.146) Also, the common agenda shared with the Puritan Churches led one after another of the Middle Atlantic Puritan clergy and their congregations to join in this union by joining the Presbytery.

One of the most important spurs to Presbytery growth came almost immediately. In 1707, Francis Makemie and John Hampton made a missionary journey to the Puritan and Scotch-Irish residents of the established Anglican town of New York. They also visited the Newtown church, then ousted from their building by the Anglicans, and were planning to proceed on to New England to solidify ties there. Lord Cornbury, the Governor, had them both arrested on charges of preaching without a license. After several months of being detained, Hampton was released, but Makemie was held for trial. In the trial Makemie directly challenged the Governor, saying that the act of toleration should mean that preachers in tolerated dissenting groups would be allowed to preach. Makemie defended the license that he had to preach in Barbados, Maryland, and Virginia. The Governor claimed that the act of toleration did not extend to any of the colonies. Makemie also cited the Puritan pastors preaching on Long Island, and the Governor then threatened their independence. The court, however, acquitted Makemie. The Governor retaliated by levying heavy court costs on Makemie. Yet Cornbury did not realize the rising sentiments against him. Some allies of the Calvinists sat in the colonial assembly, ready to limit his establishment plans. The next year the assembly declared the Governor's actions illegal. The rising opposition to Cornbury then led to his recall as Governor. The Moderator of the Presbytery had stood against the opposition and won.

Soon Puritan congregations began to join the Presbytery and the union grew. In 1716 a new united Puritan and Scotch-Irish church was organized in New York City, the scene of the trial. By 1716 the new Presbytery was serving at least forty churches.

The presence of Churches of New England origin in the Presbytery, however, did not mean they gave up their New England traditions. As late as 1727 the New York City and Cohansey, New Jersey congregations ordained new pastors through congregational vicinage councils without formal Presbytery participation.

Tensions within the new Presbytery, though, came not only from the variant cultures and practices within. Activities in Europe kept alive the threat of an Anglican imposition. In 1713 the British Parliament broke a promise and again imposed lay patronage on the Church of Scotland, Presbyterian resolve against the crown and governmental control of the churches was also enhanced.

Yankee New England fears of Anglican growth were also fired up in 1722 when Timothy Cutler, the rector of Yale College, joined by some additional Connecticut clergy, announced at the College commencement their defection to the Anglican faith. Encouragements for the Calvinist churches to defend themselves were vivid and clear. The thwarting of the Massachusetts attempts to hold a synod in 1706, 1715, and 1725 added fuel to the fire.

The letters and pleadings of Cotton Mather, Makemie and others to organize against the Anglican threat also had an affect on one additional set of Calvinist friends. Baptists in the Middle Atlantic colonies were closely aligned to the other dissenter congregations. Baptist and Presbyterian congregations in Philadelphia grew from the same root. The first Pennsylvania Baptist Church at Cold Spring (1684) was a colony from New England, and several early settlements in New Jersey, such as Middletown (1668), Piscataway, and Cohansey included both Baptists and Puritans of New England origin. In 1707 the Middle Atlantic Baptists followed the other Calvinist dissenters in forming a united body, the Philadelphia Baptist Association, the first continuing Baptist Association in America. It was something of a new form of polity, an Association that included churches. Olmstead (1960, pp.108-109), says it "had no power as a judicatory over its member churches." Nonetheless, as time went on, C.C. Goen (10, p.273) described this Association as "well structured denominationally," and carrying on "all the missionary and disciplinary functions of an actual denomination." This Association and its allies became an important voice in opposing both the Anglican religious establishment, and in time, that of New England. It also offered the contending forces within the pedobaptist Reformed tradition a new alternative polity.

OPPOSING A RELIGIOUS ESTABLISHMENT

One aspect about the inter-church Reformed unity forming in the Middle Atlantic region, indeed one of its chief attributes, was a firm conviction against the religious establishment and state church. This may seem odd. Presbyterianism in Scotland sought to be independent of the crown, but was still the national church. Congregational churches had the advantage of local establishments in Massachusetts, Connecticut, and New Hampshire. An understanding of the historic context makes the change in positions more understandable: (1) Many of the key leaders in the Middle Atlantic region, as well as some of the new immigrants, had close ties to English and Welsh dissenters who had suffered terribly under the cross from the ejections of 1662 until the toleration act of 1689. Friends in England continued to be excluded from participation in democratic institutions. (2) Most of the Presbyterians in America had come from Ulster, rather than directly from Scotland. In Ulster the Anglican establishment had been not only a religious threat, but also a social threat, with the same powerful leaders condemning Scotch-Irish workers to poverty. Those from Ulster had had their fill of establishment. (3) Presbyterians from Scotland had experienced the imposition of the crown through the ejection and the imposition of lay patronage. (4) New England immigrants were well aware of how the British government had confined and threatened the New England churches. British decisions restricting church polity, such as the polity without synods that had been imposed on Massachusetts and New Hampshire, were not welcome. (5) Early attempts to recreate Puritan establishments in towns in New York and New Jersey had been squashed by a loss of control of the franchise. Even the right of their churches to exist had been challenged by Governor Cornbury. The Yankee churches found that minority status no longer made the precarious New England establishment an attractive alternative. (6) The New York establishment in some counties through extension of 1693 law was a direct threat to every congregation in the region. (7) The decision to make New Jersey a royal colony in 1702 emphasized the ongoing power of the crown. (8) Makemie and Hampton's arrests in 1707, were threats to every Puritan minister in the colonies. Their temporary victory over Cornbury brought prestige to the Presbytery and united Reformed resistance. (9) The continued Anglican threats exercised through support of SPG missionaries and the impact of the Yale defections of 1722, brought up a strong guarding action. (10) As time passed, perhaps the most important reason the view of establishment changed was that the churches learned they could live without it. During the eighteenth century other faiths grew: Quakers, Dutch and German immigrant churches and sects, and Anglicans with or without establishment privileges. Because of their use of the dominant language and their founding role in many Middle Atlantic communities, Presbyterian and Congregational Churches had prestigious positions, which won them voluntary support. The denominations of Burr, Witherspoon, and Green forged a *de facto* establishment even if not a *de jure* one. Puritans and the Scotch-Irish in the Middle Atlantic region gave up on the idea of official establishment. This molded American Presbyterianism. It also strongly influenced the minority Congregational communities that grew up here. Eventually the small anti-establishment Congregational groups in the Middle Atlantic region impacted and changed New England itself, finally calling on American Congregationalism to free itself from establishment corruptions.

The new anti-establishment position was best articulated by Jonathan Dickinson, who developed a supportive theological rationale. Dickinson defended the ordination of dissenter clergy in the Middle Atlantic Colonies (including himself) as well as in Britain in a 1724 pamphlet, *A Defense of Presbyterian Ordination, In Answer to a Pamphlet, Entitled, A Modest Proof of the Order and Government Settled by Christ in the Church.* Dickinson directed this pamphlet at Anglican attempts to impose apostolic succession in America. The pamphlet (published in Boston) was also very popular in New England, where ordination by other teaching elders ("presbyterian ordination") was already the rule. Dickinson, though, praised moves towards "the liberalization of the Puritan establishment in New England," and, considering the reality of his own New Jersey parish, advanced the cause of religious toleration. (See LeBeau (1997), pp.70,83).

Another point of union was a common missionary aspiration. Early New England Puritans had often seen their migration in part as a mission to the Indians. Leading clergy in Scotland had a similar desire. English and Scottish missionary societies had begun to directly support Indian missions through commissions in New England from 1730, and in New York from 1741. These alliances of British supporters with those of similar interests in the Colonies, and particularly that of the Scottish Society with the New York clergy and their related Presbyteries gave their local cooperation and united work an international endorsement.

The first union in the Middle Atlantic region was not a unanimous situation. After the arrest of Presbytery leaders in New York, the churches nearest to the City joined the Presbytery, but not everyone followed. Some members of the Newark Church formed the Orange, New Jersey Church (1719), at least in part because they did not wish to follow that congregation into the Presbytery. In southern New Jersey the churches at Cape May and Pilesgrove had joined the Presbytery in 1715 and 1720, but they and the Presbyterian Church at Blackwood Timber Creek, near Gloucester were outside the Presbytery again during most of the 1720's and 1730's.

The largest number of Congregational churches not participating in the first union was on Long Island. In 1700 Long Island had ten Congregational churches. The three on the western end of the Island (Hempstead, Jamaica, and Newtown in present Queens and Nassau Counties) were all harassed with potential Anglican takeovers. Those loyal to the Reformed heritage sought the protection of the Presbytery. The seven churches in Suffolk County were not as challenged by the Anglicans, and seemed a long way from a Presbytery or Synod in Philadelphia. Most also had some type of tax support, which encouraged an independent protection of their privileges. However both the Setauket-Brookhaven Church and the ancient Church at Southampton joined with Jamaica and Newtown when the new Long Island Presbytery was set up in 1717. They were soon joined by the Hempstead church and a newer church at Mattituck. The rest of the churches remained Congregational. However, during pastoral vacancies, some of the Long Island Presbytery churches returned to Congregational forms and vicinage councils when new pastors were needed. Southampton left the Presbytery in 1727, Mattituck in 1735, and Hempstead in 1736. By 1738 the Presbyterian Synod had to attach their three remaining churches on the Island to the new New York Presbytery. Meanwhile, new Congregational churches continued to be formed in Suffolk County. The Presbyterians tried to strengthen their connections on the Island. Mattituck rejoined the Presbyterians in 1740, missions to the Indians were strengthened in 1741, and the newer churches in Cutchogue and Orient were briefly in the regular Presbytery from 1740 to 1747, when they transferred to the new independent Suffolk Presbytery.

In the period from 1706 to 1745 new Congregational and Presbyterian churches were formed in the Middle Atlantic area. Some would be formed under a Congregational pattern (a vicinage council or local covenanting) then rather quickly join the nearest Presbytery. Others remained unaffiliated for varying lengths of time. Other new churches were formed under the auspices and care of a Presbytery.

However, the number, style, and background of congregations began to shift markedly after the end of the Indian Wars in 1713. With the threat of Indian invasion lessened, New Englanders had the opportunity to move into much of their own territory in greater numbers. Inland Connecticut, central Massachusetts, and coastal Maine and New Hampshire opened. Locations on the east side of the mountains were also protected from the now farther removed Indian threat and the French. The end of the War also solidified English claims to the coastal regions. The continued tax support of churches in three New England colonies made them most attractive to newly trained clergy and strongly religious Yankees.

In the Middle Atlantic region, areas already populated by descendants of New Englanders kept up ties with their eastern Yankee relatives. As the population grew in the second generation, new churches were founded in the Puritan areas of Long Island, the east side of the Hudson River, and Essex and Union Counties in New Jersey. These settlements also spread into adjacent territory such as Morris County, New Jersey and Orange County, New York. However, few really new Yankee outposts were undertaken.

However changes in Europe stood ready to make a difference in America. In Ulster the initial one hundred-year leases given to the Scotch-Irish and borderland settlers were running out. Landlords raised rents and removed the poor. Attempts by the Anglican Church to limit political participation by Calvinists created a sentiment for emigration. In 1717 a mass migration began to America from Ulster including native Irish, and descendants of Scottish Presbyterian and English borderland peoples who had moved earlier to Ireland. From 1717 to 1775 "historians estimate that at least 150,000 people came to America directly from the Ulster counties of northern Ireland..." (Dollarhide (1997), p.33, see also pp. 38-39). This migration was seven times larger than the great Puritan migration of a century earlier. (Fischer (1989), p.787) sees this as part of a broader British borderlands migration which totaled as much as 250,000 people.) This new wave made significant settlements in central Pennsylvania. Immigrants also intermingled with earlier Puritan settlements in areas such as Monmouth and Mercer Counties and southern New Jersey, and the Philadelphia area.

As the first union moved along, the demographic growth in the Middle Atlantic region shifted from Yankees towards the new Scotch-Irish wave. The origin and distribution of the congregations began to shift radically.

THEOLOGICAL DISPUTES

Not only did cultural patterns change in the region at this time, but two significant theological disputes occurred.

The first of these began in Britain, and was related to the different traditions and practices of the Scottish and English churches. At the time of its re-establishment under a Presbyterian plan in 1690, the Church of Scotland accepted the Westminster Confession as its legal confession. Thereafter judicatories could require candidates for ordination to subscribe to the doctrines of the Confession (literally sign ("subscribe") the Confession vowing complete unqualified acceptance.) In 1696 the Scottish General Assembly forbade clergy and laity from publicly disagreeing with any position in the Confession. By 1717 some Presbyteries were even attempting to force candidates to subscribe to particular interpretations of the Confession.

Similarly in 1698 the Presbyterian General Synod in Ulster required that candidates for licensure must subscribe to the confession of faith. In 1705 subscription was required to the "worship, discipline, and government" of the Synod. Tensions continued in Ireland. A "New Light" faction was against compulsory creedal subscription. A new push for subscription began in 1719, but was temporarily abated by the "Pacific Act" of 1720 which, while calling for loyalty to the Westminster Confession, allowed ministerial candidates who were otherwise sound in faith, to publicly scruple any phrase or phrases with which they disagreed. Nonetheless controversy went on.

These confessional approaches to orthodoxy were very different than the personal testimonies of the work of God in one's life, which were the more common form of both church membership and ordination councils among Congregationalists.

In England neither the Congregationalists nor the English Presbyterians had ever had a General Assembly or Synod to impose subscription. None of the English factions had ever been particularly interested in the synodical polity system, and they emerged from the great persecution under the Toleration Act with no energy to create the Scottish system.

Within the independent structure of the English dissenters new theological movements could easily take root. However, some pastors and congregations were still loyal to the traditional Calvinism of their forbears. Forces in Parliament sought to suppress new theological innovations among the dissenters. These issues erupted into a great theological divide in 1719. English dissenters did not want to appear too tolerant of unorthodox ideas because they might keep the Parliament from granting them political privileges. A paper of "Advices" was presented to the General Body of Dissenting Clergy in London in 1719. The text offered contended that the dissenting ministers would withdraw communion from ministers holding errors in doctrine, and that issues about the Divinity of the Son of God should rest on the common foundation of the Scriptures. However some clergy felt that the document should include a specific reference of loyalty to the doctrine of the Trinity. When the majority did not include the specific trinitarian reference, a minority seceded and subscribed to a statement specifically avowing the Trinity. Although most of the majority would probably have assented personal loyalty to the Trinity, they favored the primary affirmation of personal commitment to the scriptures rather than confessional details.

Roger Thomas (in Bolam *et al.* (1968), p.163) suggests that the signers of the adopted Advices (the Non-Subscribers) included 48 English Presbyterians and only 8 Independents (Tudor Jones (1962), gives the number as 10), while the Subscribers (those insisting on Trinitarian language) statement included 3 Scottish Presbyterians, 27 English Presbyterians, and 28 Independents. (Baptists and six people whose background is not clear made the total number of non-subscribers 73, subscribers 78. The larger number for the minority reflects signatures gained after the first divisive meeting.) Clearly the English Presbyterians were interested in a wider theological toleration, and parted company with the Scottish and Irish Presbyterians on subscription. Congregationalists were generally still committed to traditional Calvinism. Some English Presbyterians who had subscribed later disowned their subscription, but others, or their successors, eventually amalgamated with the evangelical Congregationalists.

The English division of 1719 pointed out both ancient and evolving distinctions and disputes among the descendants of the British Reformed heritage. It also established new party labels, "subscribers," and "non-subscribers." However, the English division was not a permanent demarcation. In England people were being asked to sign two versions of a particular document at one moment in time. The question was which language best reflected their concept of orthodoxy in the presentation of advices to the Parliament. In Scotland and Ireland subscription was meant to be a lifelong adherence to particular confessional language required of all in the church, and particularly candidates for the ministry.

Subscription did not become the doctrine of English Congregationalists. There were no Congregational synods; no future subscription would be required. Evangelical Congregationalists could influence recruitment of pastors and question the orthodoxy of candidates at ordination councils, but this event put no rigid straight jacket on the English denomination. Subscription in England was not a permanent fissure and demarcation between the parties in dissent. It had little effect on polity. Both English Presbyterians and Congregationalists continued to have independent nonconforming congregations. Ministerial cooperation in rural areas continued for nearly a century. Also small mixed rural congregations often asked both funds for support of their clergy. It was still true that congregations with strong pastoral authority tended towards the Presbyterian definition, while those with greater lay participation were labeled Congregational. However, the memory of the subscription controversy in England did point to the slowly emerging separation between evangelical Calvinists on the one hand, and Arminians tending towards Unitarianism on the other hand. Clergy with the more liberal views now tended to look to the Presbyterian Fund for support, while evangelicals turned to the Congregational Fund.

SUBSCRIPTION IN AMERICA

In America these definitions and divisions began to appear in the new emerging congregations in the Middle Atlantic region. English Presbyterians making their way to America were organizationally and sometimes theologically far from the Scottish and Scotch-Irish immigrants. In 1722 the First Church in New York City, which had been founded only in 1716, divided. A new schismatic congregation called itself the "English Presbiterians for the Public Worship of God," and called the young Jonathan Edwards from New England as their pastor. Edwards encouraged the reunification of the two congregations a year later. By 1756 when another Second Presbyterian Church was formed in New York, it was popularly known as the Scotch Church and affiliated with the Associate Church and not the New Side Synod. In the meantime the reunited First Presbyterian Church was often popularly known as the English

Presbyterian Church. Churches in Staten Island and Rockland County, New York, and Passaic County, New Jersey, at Richmond, New Hempstead, Haverstraw, and West Milford also clearly distinguished themselves as English Presbyterian and English Protestant. When the Caldwell, New Jersey church joined a Congregational fellowship as part of the second schism it also called itself English Presbyterian. These names have not only ethnic, but also organizational and theological significance.

In New England, while the majority of congregations were then, as in England, still evangelical, they, like the English Independents, had no documents which ordinands were expected to subscribe. (An exception was the Hampshire Association in western Massachusetts. In 1732 it voted to require subscription to the Westminster Confession or "an equivalent." (Marsden, 2003, p.177) They still reflected the Presbyterianism of their former leader Solomon Stoddard. Yet the allowance of "an equivalent" still indicates a characteristically New England breadth in their theological parameters.) Most New England Congregationalists developed an inclusive way, as was the case with the majority of non-conformists in England.

However the increasingly large number of new clergy in America from Scotland and Ulster were aghast at the lack of clear procedures, policies, and subscription in the young American Presbyterian Synod (the 1717 expansion of the 1706 Presbytery). In 1721 George Gillespie, a New Castle Presbytery member who had come to America from Scotland in 1712 after graduating from the University of Glasgow, introduced a motion at the Synod to the effect that, "As we have been for many years in the exercise of Presbyterian government and church discipline, as exercised by the Presbyterians in the best reformed Churches, as far as the nature and constitution of this country will allow, our opinion is, that if any brother have any overture to offer to be formed into an act by the Synod, for the better carrying on in matters of our government and discipline, that he may bring it against next Synod." Although the motion passed by a majority, six ministers - four New Englanders and two Welshmen - entered a written protest.

Trinterud (36, p.39) interprets this motion as follows: "...since for many years these Presbyterians have been using the general forms and procedures of the European Presbyterian Churches, there would be nothing against carrying European Presbyterian usage farther by allowing any member who wished to present overtures looking forward to the passage of such acts as would improve the government and discipline of the Church. The wording of the overture indicates that previous to that time no such acts or laws had been made, and that some agreement was necessary before such acts or laws could be of any binding authority. Whatever constitution they then had did not allow such measures." Up to this time the Presbytery/Synod had acted according to English common law, where previous practice set the normative standards. They had not acted according to the written constitutional confessional methods of the Scottish Church.

Ashbel Green later saw this move as the first skirmish of the subscription controversy in America. Jedediah Andrews, the New Englander pastoring First Church in Philadelphia wrote to Boston pastor Benjamin Colman and traced the new developments in the American Synod to the Irish subscription controversy.

When the 1722 Synod met, the opening sermon was given by Jonathan Dickinson, the Massachusetts born and Yale educated pastor in the Yankee Church at Elizabeth, New Jersey, which had only joined a presbytery in 1716/1717. In that sermon Dickinson propounded the position of the English non-subscribers, that the Bible alone is all sufficient for doctrine and rules. In response to Dickinson's sermon, the actual acts determined by the Synod were rather moderate. The presbyteries and synod had executive power in "mere circumstantials of church discipline, such as time, place, and mode of carrying on in the government of the church" conforming to scripture, that these acts may not be imposed on those with conscientious objections, synods may write outlines for church government but only "recommend" them to others, and appeals may be made. As Trinterud points out (36, p.44), this compromise was certainly similar to the Massachusetts Proposals of 1705 or the Saybrook Platform.

At this early date tensions were apparent between the Puritans of English dissent and the Scotch-Irish and Scottish members of the new united judicatory. These same issues would rise again and again for over a century.

Despite the Synodical compromise the New Castle Presbytery began to practice formal subscription in 1724.

Controversy in Europe continued and was closely followed in America. In 1726 the subscription party in Ireland threw the non-subscribers out of the Synod. This model of excision would be copied in America in 1741, and again in 1837. In Scotland, the subscription party's iron hold onto the reins of church government, the reimposition of lay patronage and other issues led in 1733 to the "Secession," and the organization of an Associate Church outside the established order.

In 1727 a resolution calling for adoption of and subscription to the Westminster Confession was proposed at the American Synod. It was referred to the Presbyteries, and then delayed in 1728. Jonathan Dickinson published a paper in response. Dickinson realized both the theological heat around the issue and the growing Scotch-Irish majority in the Synod, yet he held to his earlier position. Andrews wrote another letter to Colman in which he contended that the "Scotch-Irish group would just as soon be rid of all but their own party." (Trinterud, 36, p.47) The Synod responded with a new compromise, the Adopting Act. This 1729 vote adopted the Confession as a standard explanation of the

Synod's position, but indicated that some of the Confession was essential and necessary, but not all of it. New England's Cambridge Platform (1648) had also picked and chosen among the sections of the Westminster acts. But the Adopting Act did not specify which sections of Westminster were essential and necessary and which were not, other than excluding some sections about the civil magistrate. However both current and future members were allowed to present any scruple about portions of the Confession, and these could be accepted by the Synod or Presbytery if not essential points. Here again the American Synod enlisted a compromise that had been proposed in Ireland in 1720. At the 1729 meeting members of the American Synod presented scruples which were found capable of solution, and the Synod adopted the Confession for their own use and recommended it to the Presbyteries.

But political pressures began to push against the compromises. In 1730 the New Castle Presbytery demanded unqualified subscription, and the Donegal Presbytery concurred in 1732. In 1734 an action was sought at the Synod to review Presbytery records as to their insistence on subscription. An assistant minister to Andrews at Philadelphia began to preach Arian views and was found to have engaged in dishonesty. When he had been admitted to the Synod he had not noted any scruples against the Confession. Now he called for a wide interpretation. His disruption of Andrews' congregation led the senior pastor into the hard-nosed subscription camp. Issues about moral latitude and the emotional beginnings of the revival led the Synod into a more confrontational spirit, ordering solutions to difficult situations.

In 1736 attendance at the Synod was very low, with few New Englanders present. The subscriptionist majority reaffirmed the Adopting Act of 1729, but removed the sections allowing for scruples being presented by candidates. This move, in effect, now made the American Synod, at least on paper, a Presbyterian body, similar to those in Scotland and Ireland.

But what was to be done about the many New Englanders on the roll of the Synod, most of whom were not present at this vote? Were they by their absence turned into subscriptionist Presbyterians?

When the Presbyterian Synod approved subscription, Scottish Presbyterianism could be said to exist in America. However, at this point no clear alternative Congregational polity existed. Churches not desiring the Scottish system had not yet designed a clear substitute.

The theological dispute over subscription tested the organizational possibility of English and Scotch-Irish cooperation. But before it could be resolved, a second and even more powerful theological controversy swept through the region and impacted all denominations. While this new issue had some roots in divisions in Scottish and other European churches, it was far wider in its swath than the subscription controversy, and cut across the grain of the previous divisions.

THE GREAT AWAKENING

The new issue was a sudden and dramatic revival of religious piety and sentiment known as the Great Awakening. Piety and religious enthusiasm were not sentiments dependent on church polity nor limited by national boundaries. Nevertheless American Calvinism had been positioned around these issues.

English Puritanism had developed in opposition to a corrupted English clergy and church. Outside the center of the power structures, the Puritan case stressed piety, and their chief form of presentation was the sermon. Unlike many other European Protestant movements, Puritanism - not in control of a state church - was still able to continue as a movement with influence inside and outside the national establishment.

Puritanism began to influence German Protestantism, where evangelical forces had been divided into warring Lutheran and Reformed confessions. The German churches, tied to a view of religion based on uniform adherence to specific theological formulations, had become moribund. An opposition to this confessionalism arose partially under the influence of Puritan writings. Pietism stressed a personal relationship with God, prayer, devotional practices, and Bible study. It led to a rise in missionary concerns and social responsibility.

New England Puritanism, as the first generation died, had become intertwined in the issues of power, war, and politics, and fell away from the piety and devotion of the original settlers.

Cotton Mather came into contact with German pietists, brought their literature to America, and began to spread their ideas. His drive to strengthen inter-church relationships in both New England and the Middle Atlantic States was always couched in a desire to spread piety, faith, and devotion. Meanwhile, Scottish Covenanters cast out of the Scottish Kirk during the Stuart Restoration, had developed their own stress on devotional life, expressed in open air extended worship ("holy fairs", see Schmidt,1989) held in defiance of the authorities.

Yet these impulses, while part of the culture, remained only marginally effective until a sudden rise of religious sentiment beginning about 1735. In America the incredible revival of religious interest developed in two related but different ways.

One type followed the example of Jonathan Edwards, the pastor in Northampton, Massachusetts. Edwards' sermons led to excitement and emotion within his congregation, which he reported in a number of publications. Other pastors imitated Edwards, and he and his disciples were invited by other settled pastors to visit their parishes.

CONTRIBUTIONS TOWARDS A HISTORY

With the arrival in 1739 of the English preacher George Whitefield, a new style of itinerant evangelism began, with general preaching tours, often with or without the approval of local pastors. His enormous emotional open-air meetings challenged more conservative views of proper decorum. People imitating Whitefield's style, often became more and more emotional, disrupting the lives of many ordered parishes.

Both of these manifestations of a new spirit met with opposition. Some pious and evangelical pastors objected to itinerancy and invasions of their parishes. Other opposition was alarmed at the extreme emotionalism of some of the leaders and followers in the movement. Still others maintained strong intellectual and theological opposition to even moderate forms of the Awakening.

In New England, established congregations and their parishes could choose pro-revival, anti-revival, or moderate pastors and still remain Congregational and established. However, some revivalists joined their theology to opposition to the tax-supported establishment system and "hireling ministers," and sometimes also a class rejection of elitist well-educated clergy.

These radical forces formed Separate or Strict Congregational Churches outside the established parishes. Many of these congregations chose pastors from the laboring classes, bypassing the educated centers of New England. Some of the leaders of these churches were imprisoned. Non-established Congregational or Presbyterian worship was forbidden in Connecticut. Many churches found a loophole in the law. Since the Parliament's Act of Toleration allowed for unmolested worship for Baptists, entire congregations were immersed, taking the name Baptist and thereby achieving toleration. That movement forever changed the Baptist denomination in America by moving it from an Arminian and quietist majority to a clearly Calvinist and revivalist stance.

In the Middle Atlantic colonies, the subscription controversy had produced a conformity very close to that of German confessionalism. Unsupported by established parishes, Middle Atlantic clergy were also more vulnerable to sudden shifts in financial support caused by visiting itinerants. Therefore the subscription party in the Synod formed a strong flank against the revival, and sought to enforce a confessional and cultic conformity.

Yet the Synod had a Scotch-Irish element not shackled to uniformity, which was led by William Tennent Sr., who had come to America in 1718. A graduate of the University of Edinburgh, he was probably better educated than most of the Scotch-Irish clergy, whose educations are often obscure. He had secured Episcopal ordination while in Ulster, thereby placing himself outside the Presbyterian mainstream. When he came to America he promptly joined the Presbytery of Philadelphia. His first American pastorates were in the old Yankee settlements of Eastchester (1718-1720) and Bedford (1720-1726), New York, where he was put in close touch with both New England culture and New England clergy. These congregations had played a major role in fighting the attempt by the Episcopal establishment to suppress Puritanism in Westchester County. Tennent's ties with New England became so strong that he was considered for the Presidency of Yale in 1725, and he sent his eldest son Gilbert there for a graduate degree. [LeBeau (1997, p.106) and others contend that this close relationship with New England connected some members of the Tennent family and those whom they educated and influenced closer to New England than to their Scotch-Irish origins.]

In 1726 Tennent moved to Bucks County, Pennsylvania, near the heart of the Presbyterian Synod. There he continued to educate his children, four of whom became pastors. He then expanded his clergy training, building what came to be known as the "Log College." Almost all of Tennent's students eventually became pro-revival pastors.

Tennent's previous Episcopal ties, his close relations to New England, and his psychological and theological influence over a growing number of Synod clergy probably threatened other centers of power in the Synod. Tensions initially erupted against Tennent's son Gilbert, when he took a pastorate at New Brunswick, New Jersey in 1726, after originally accepting a call to Delaware. The Synod was not pleased. In 1737, on his way to a Synod meeting, Gilbert had preached to a vacant church in Maidenhead, New Jersey. The latter Church's Presbytery, which was not Gilbert's, had already appointed two nearby pastors of New England background (David Cowell, and Eleazar Wales) to occasionally supply the Church. Tennent had not sought their permission or that of their Presbytery to preach, and Cowell and Wales, like most New England pastors at the time, detested "invasions" by itinerants. While the Synod, at that time, had no rules against itinerancy, this made it an issue, and afterwards the Synod tried to limit the practice.

The next year five clergy, three of whom were Log College alumni, convinced the Synod to set them off as a new New Brunswick Presbytery in central New Jersey. Members of Tennent's family later admitted that the plan to establish this Presbytery with a pro-revival majority was meant to ease Log College graduates and supporters of the Awakening into the ministry (Coalter (1986), p.48). The Synod responded by finding ways to take under their control some aspects of ordination, and refusing to recognize some New Brunswick candidates.

In the meantime a similar revival had begun in Britain, both Arminian and Calvinist. It included the English revivalist George Whitefield, the Wesley brothers, John and Charles, and the Scottish reformer Ebenezer Erskine. Whitefield and John Wesley were among British religious figures of the time who came to America.

Gilbert Tennent, now rising to leadership in the family, became enamored with Whitefield, imitated and followed him in itinerancy. He began general attacks on many unnamed clergy in addresses like his sermon "The Danger of An Unconverted Ministry."

The revival had now become the key issue of schism, not only in the Synod, but also in most American churches. Just as Separate churches appeared in New England, new pro-revival churches also began in the Middle Atlantic area. Some of these were New England congregations that migrated to the Middle Atlantic area seeking freedom from the establishment. Others were new congregations begun here. Some of these were or became Baptist congregations. Others, however, began on Congregational principles, outside and independent of the Synod.

In the Synod, the Awakening complicated the traditional factions. The Scotch-Irish were divided into two factions: subscriptionists and revivalists. Many New Englanders yearned for a growth in piety and devotion but could not abide the disorder of itinerancy. A wide variety of clergy were uncomfortable with wild emotional excesses and general unspecific attacks on clergy. Serious issues about polity complicated these feelings: the role and power of synods; and theological issues of deep comport on the nature of ministry, worship, evangelization, and other issues. At a time when intelligent assessment would have helped, personal relationships were now strained to the breaking point.

THE FIRST SCHISM
1741-1758

Tensions finally reached a climax at the 1741 meeting of the Synod. None of the New England-dominated New York Presbytery were present. At this meeting the opponents of the revival narrowly voted a Protestation where they cast the Tennent faction out of the Synod. The Irish example of 1726 had been taken up. As soon as the minority was gone, the Old Side majority unanimously reaffirmed subscription to the Confession and Directory.

The minority, which contained the entire New Brunswick Presbytery and scattered members of the other southern Presbyteries, met and formed two "conjunct" Presbyteries to act in place of the Synod. The boundaries of the New Brunswick Presbytery were enlarged, and a new Londonderry Presbytery (later known as New Castle (New Side)), served in areas farther south and west. The original New Castle Presbytery was fractured, and the Lewes Presbytery was diminished. In 1742 the Old Side Synod united these remnants as the New Castle Presbytery (Old Side).

One interesting aspect of this schism is the appearance of what may be called the "Constitutional" position. George Gillespie had long been the strongest adherent to a proper Presbyterial order within the new American body. While many revivalists had attacked what they called "an unconverted ministry," those in the Synod had seldom named specific clergy. That had caused the Old Side to ask that specific charges be brought and examined, or that the scurrilous slander be stopped. However, when the Old Side now excised a large body of clergy without any specific charges or trial the "champions of order" had, in Gillespie's words, committed an "act of supreme disorder." (Coalter (1986), p.82) Gillespie joined the Tennent group.

[Coalter says (1986, p.187), that eleven clergy were cast out, but lists a "John Henry," there being no such clergy person on the Synod role. The ten who clearly were excised (including Gillespie), were soon joined by Richard Treat, and David Alexander. John Rowland, who had been ordained by the New Brunswick Presbytery, but never recognized by the Synod, also became a full participant in the conjunct Presbyteries.]

Immediately at the 1742 Synod Dickinson and his allies in the New York Presbytery began to work for a process of reconciliation and reunion. However, parties were now intransigent. Six of the seven New York Presbytery members at the 1742 Synod (led by Dickinson), and one Philadelphia Presbytery member entered into the Old Side Synod minutes a protest to the exclusion of ministers without charges and trial, and also supporting the Awakening.

Meanwhile, the conjunct Presbyteries were facing new difficulties. Alexander Craighead proposed to the new group that they adopt the Scottish National Covenant of 1638 and the Solemn League and Covenant of 1643. These covenants would magnify the Scottish identity of the churches. The conjunct Presbyteries rejected Craighead's proposal. He then seceded and initiated the Covenanters or Reformed Presbyterian movement in America.

Also, in 1744, the orderly George Gillespie, disturbed by continuing excesses by revival preachers in the colonies, gave up on his association with the conjunct Presbyteries and returned in contrition to the Old Side.

Gilbert Tennent, who had emerged as the successor to his father as the leader of the New Side, knew that much of the future of English-speaking Reformed churches in the Middle Atlantic area depended upon the direction of the absent New York Presbytery. In early 1742, even before the first Synod where Dickinson attempted reconciliation, Tennent took a conciliatory view, confessing his own extremes in the revival, and wrote to Dickinson hoping for reunion.

In 1743 the Dickinson party met with the conjunct Presbyteries, and attempted another move for reconciliation at the Old Side Synod. This again failed. The New York Presbytery was absent from the 1744 Synod. In 1745

Dickinson's party again sought reconciliation, but failing that proposed the withdrawal of the New York Presbytery, and the setting up of a separate New York Synod, which would be in correspondence with the Philadelphia Synod. This was reluctantly granted, and later in 1745 a New York Synod was created, which included not only the New York Presbytery, but also both of the conjunct Presbyteries. The new Synod, while adopting the Westminster Confession, "supported the individual's right to follow his or her conscience in nonessential matters", and was "guided by the looser conditions of the 1729 Adopting Act." (Coalter (1986), p.127).

This first schism reflects difficulties inherit in an attempt to unify English Puritan with Scottish and Irish Calvinists in America. While many would classify this break as merely a schism within Presbyterianism, it was clearly effected by the cultural fault lines revealed in a more autonomous polity within the Synod.

Dickinson and his allies were not supra-organizational submissive Presbyterians. The early Synod (1717-1758) required full attendance by all clergy and representative lay elders from each session at a lengthy national meeting in Philadelphia. Later writers have pointed out that this was an ineffective structure. It simply did not work. Trinterud (36) says, "the entire theory on which the synod was supposedly based had been false." The New Englanders, particularly those in the distant northern New York Presbytery, were often absent, many times without submitting excuses. Some of their absenteeism was undoubtedly due to weather, health, pastoral emergencies, length of journey, etc.. None of Dickinson's Presbytery attended the 1736 Synod, when the more stringent version of the Adopting Act was passed, nor the 1741 Synod, when the Tennent party was thrown out, nor the 1744 Synod. Coalter (1986, pp.37-38) contends that the first case was due to passive cooperation in the planned act (hardly likely in view of Dickinson's later actions), and, in 1741 (p.82), to try to keep the Synod from acrimonious debate. Even if these were the clear and only reasons for absence, which is debatable, a strategy of absence could hardly be considered the highest form of respect for the synodical system. Their learned preference for autonomy was creeping into their actions. The decisions by the majority of the Synod during the absences of 1736 and 1741 were clearly anathema to those not present, and show far different concepts of the role of synods.

To what extent was the division a reflection of the differing backgrounds in ethnicity and polity? A look at the origin and leanings of those participating in the schism is helpful. While the immediate cause of the schism of the Synod into Old Side and New Side was primarily Awakening issues, these deeper roots need to be assessed.

The original Presbytery had clearly been a union body encompassing many polities and English, Scottish, Irish, and other ethnicities. Its move towards Scottish rigidity and constitutional requirements created and agitated tension. The subscription controversy also chafed at the unity. Unlike the Synod of Philadelphia, the new New York Synod returned to a union scheme, allowing a wider range of views.

Cultural origin can be seen geographically. In 1741 the Presbyterian Synod had six Presbyteries. The members of two of these, New York and New Brunswick, became entirely supportive of the New Side. The New Castle Presbytery was almost evenly divided, but had an Old Side majority. The other three Presbyteries, Philadelphia, Lewes, and Donegal, had clear Old Side majorities, but each had at least one member supportive of the New Side. Geographically those congregations closest to New England, and most affected by New England immigration were those most strongly in favor of the New Side.

This division can also be investigated by studying the pastors involved. Both the origin of Old and New Side clergy, and the places of their education were examined by matching the names on the pastoral rolls of the Synods with the pastoral biographies found in Weis' books (14, 1978/1957, and 1977/1936).

Forty-nine clergy were identified with the Synod in 1741. [Because he initially went to the New Side, but soon returned to the Old Side, George Gillespie was included with both the Old Side and the conjunct Presbyteries, making fifty entries for 1741 in Figures 1 and 2.] Twenty-five stayed with the Old Side, thirteen were exscinded or moved to the conjunct Presbyteries, while twelve were part of the New York Presbytery. By 1745 the conjunct Presbyteries had added eleven more clergy, the New York Presbytery, five, while the Old Side had added seven.

Figure No. 1 identifies each of these clergy by their birthplace, divided into three major categories. The first includes those who were born in areas where New England settlement clearly dominated: New England itself, Long Island, or New Jersey. (Both of the New Jersey born pastors came from the old Yankee Church at Newark, one the son of the first President of Yale.) The second category is people who came from areas where New England Puritan and Irish and Scottish sentiments would have been muted: England, Wales, and the Welsh colony in Pennsylvania. The third category is those born in the areas with the most traditional Presbyterian sentiments: Ireland and Scotland.

As Figure No. 1 clearly shows, while both the conjunct Presbyteries and the Old Side had clear Scottish and Irish majorities, the New York Presbytery was dominated by descendants of the Puritans. Their actions towards a looser fellowship and a more tolerant acceptance of views reflected both their English and New England forebears. The one non-Yankee clergy person who joined the New York Presbytery by 1745, was Robert Sturgeon, who had served pastorates in New England from 1721 to 1732 before entering the Middle Atlantic region.

FIGURE NO. 1
BIRTH ORIGINS OF PRESBYTERIAN CLERGY 1741-1745

Group	New York Presbytery				Conjunct Presbyteries				Old Side Synod			
Years	1741		Added by 1745		1741		Added by 1745		1741		Added by 1745	
Birthplace:	#	%	#	%	#	%	#	%	#	%	#	%
Group 1:												
New England	8	66%	1	20%	2	15%	1	9%	4	16%	-	-
Long Island	2	17%	3	60%	-	-	1	9%	-	-	-	-
New Jersey	2	17%	-	-	-	-	-	-	-	-	-	-
Group 2:												
England	-	-	-	-	-	-	1	9%	1	4%	-	-
Wales	-	-	-	-	1	8%	-	-	2	8%	-	-
Pennsylvania (Welsh)	-	-	-	-	-	-	-	-	-	-	2	29%
Group 3:												
Scotland	-	-	.5	10%	3	23%	1	9%	3	12%	1	14%
Ireland	-	-	.5	10%	7	54%	7	64%	12	48%	2	29%
Group 4:												
Unknown	-	-	-	-	-	-	-	-	3	12%	2	29%
TOTAL	12	100	5	100	13	100	11	100	25	100	7	100

[Percentages are rounded. Weis describes one pastor as born in Scotland or Ireland which explains the assignment of one half to each nation as a birth place.]

FIGURE NO. 2
EDUCATION OF PRESBYTERIAN CLERGY 1741-1745

Group	New York Presbytery				Conjunct Presbyteries				Old Side Synod			
Years	1741		Added by 1745		1741		Added by 1745		1741		Added by 1745	
Education:	#	%	#	%	#	%	#	%	#	%	#	%
Group 1:												
Yale	11	92%	3	60%	2	15%	1	9%	2.5	10%	2	29%
Harvard	1	8%	1	20%	-	-	-	-	3	12%	-	-
Group 2:												
Log College	-	-	-	-	6	46%	8	73%	-	-	1	14%
Group 3:												
Edinburgh or Glasgow	-	-	-	-	2	15%	-	-	3.5	13%	-	-
Group 4:												
Unknown	-	-	1	20%	3	23%	2	18%	16	64%	4	57%
TOTAL	12	100	5	100	13	100	11	100	25	100	7	100

[Percentages are rounded. One pastor educated at both Glasgow and Yale is shown as one half at each institution.]

Figure No. 2 shows the educational training of each of the clergy shown in Figure No. 1, and was developed using the same sources. Yale and Harvard are clearly New England institutions. The Log College was the name given to William Tennent Sr.'s efforts to train clergy, beginning about 1727 and more formally from 1735. Tennent's three surviving sons, tutored by their father, have been included with the Log College group. Eighteen clergy were educated here, and fifteen had entered the Presbyterian fold by 1745. [Gillespie is listed twice.]

Weis, who had access to Harvard and Yale class lists, has not identified where most Old Side, and many Scottish and Irish pastors were educated. Those shown as unknown were more likely educated in Ireland or Scotland. Nevertheless, New England degrees, particularly from Yale, are predominant in the New York Presbytery, while Tennent's Log College is the center of conjunct Presbytery education. Note, though, that the educational chart is not quite as suggestive as the birthplace chart, showing the tendency of a few Irish or Scottish immigrants to get their education in New England.

In 1746, the year of William Tennent Sr.'s death, several of the leaders of the New Side secured a charter for the College of New Jersey, which eventually became Princeton University. In its earliest years it was closely connected to the New England-raised and educated leaders, such as Dickinson. The New Side thus insured its ability to continue educating clergy, and far outstripped the Old Side in this endeavor. The New Side had a minority of clergy on the scene in 1741. As soon as 1745 it had developed a clear majority. This had varied effects upon the development of the Calvinistic churches in this region. On the one hand, Princeton and the New Side could extend New England hegemony and educational practices. However, many of their new students were Irish and Scottish immigrants who were commissioned to serve in new Irish and Scottish American settlements. Soon the changes in settlement patterns and cultural origins of the congregations in the area overwhelmed the power of the New Englanders in the Presbyterian Church.

The Old Side floundered after the division. By 1747, five of their clergy had defected to the Episcopalians. They also suffered more clergy deaths in the first decade of the split. They were not able to duplicate clergy growth among younger men as the New Side had at the Log College and later Princeton. While the Old Side remained nearly static in some areas or shrunk in others, the New Side grew at a fast pace. Francis Alison, an Irish-born pastor, student at Glasgow, and graduate of Yale, stayed with the Old Side, and tried valiantly to help them gain clergy by opening a school in 1743, but he could not keep pace with the New Side's gains.

On the one hand, the New Side was able to solidify its alliances with the New Englanders in New York by welcoming the new Suffolk Presbytery on Long Island into its Synod in 1749. This Presbytery had been founded two years earlier by six pastors of Congregational churches on the Island, two of which had formerly been part of the Presbyterian Church. By 1752 the Presbyterian Church had also transferred their Mattituck and Setauket-Brookhaven congregations to this Presbytery. This new Presbytery included most of the oldest and strongest churches on the Island. (Among the oldest churches, only the ancient church at Southold stayed Congregational at this time, along with some of the smaller and newer churches.) The new Presbytery was obviously more at home in the strongly New England-oriented New Side Synod than in the older Synod, and was naturally pleased with the initiatives towards an educated clergy and the new College of New Jersey. This new Presbytery strengthened the New England and Congregational elements within the New Side, and also permanently established the Presbyterian Church on the eastern end of the Island. From then on, some churches would switch back and forth, but Presbyterianism would include the stronger Island churches. However, the New Side grew even faster by providing clergy for Irish and Scottish immigrant communities and even for some congregations formerly served by Old Side pastors.

This first schism, however, did not break entirely along ethnic, birthplace or educational lines. Four New Englanders remained in the Old Side. The persistent pattern of unity and schism among the English speaking Reformed congregations always cut unevenly. People from either background had made friends with people from the other background, they served churches primarily from the other tradition or significantly split internally, or they may have married into families from different backgrounds. Thus, once the merge - withdraw pattern was begun, a long-term pattern of cross-fertilization became entrenched.

The esteemed long-term pastor of First Church Philadelphia, Jedediah Andrews, joined by Daniel Elmer, David Cowell, and John Guild, were the four New Englanders staying in the Old Side. Three of them (all but Cowell) were also the three Harvard graduates in the Old Side. Those with New England backgrounds had tended to be opposed to itinerancy, and Cowell had early had a disagreement with Gilbert Tennent over that issue. Andrews had joined the subscriptionists after his unfortunate experience with an Arian associate. After a painful schism in his congregation, he had accepted a subscriptionist and anti-revival leader as his new associate in 1738. Also inclined to peace, Andrews had gone along with the excision of 1741 as a way to end confusion and rancor (Coalter (1986), p.84). His congregation had also suffered from the founding of a new pro-revival congregation in Philadelphia, which Gilbert Tennent came to pastor, and which later became the Second Presbyterian Church. The Harvard alumni seemed less sympathetic to the revival in general (as was the case in New England), than their Yale counterparts, although alma mater was not the decisive issue. Even though one New Englander (Richard Treat) had left the Philadelphia Presbytery with William Tennent Sr. to go to the New Side, the others also may have stayed partially out of loyalty to Andrews, or in an attempt to subdue the controversy at the main port of entry for new Scotch-Irish immigrants. Elmer served the formerly Congregational Church at Cohansey, New Jersey, whose congregation had also experienced a New Side split in 1744. Cowell and Guild served the mixed churches in Mercer County, New Jersey. Cowell had also been one of the targets of the radical New Brunswick revivalist John Rowland. Later Cowell maintained close relations with the New Side, and was elected a Trustee of Princeton in 1748, and acting President in 1757, being a source leading to the reunification of the two Synods.

This period of the first schism was more disruptive of the Congregational and Presbyterian relationships in the Middle Atlantic area than is shown in simply the division of the Synod. In New England the Awakening had caused a schism called the Separate or Strict Congregationalists. These churches were revivalistic, independent of the tax supported establishment, and often chose pastors without a formal education.

This movement also affected the development of Congregationalism and Presbyterianism in the Middle Atlantic area. New congregations sprang up, particularly on Long Island and east of the Hudson River, that took a revivalist stance and called pastors from Separate circles. Other existing churches moved into this camp. Elisha Paine and James Davenport, two of the most prominent Separate pastors served on Long Island. In addition a few New England Separate congregations, or groups of their members, decided to beat the establishment by picking up lock, stock, and barrel, and moving to New Jersey or New York. A few of these groups had already become Baptists, or did so quickly after their settlement. Some congregations established on Separate Congregational lines continued.

The flamboyance of the Separates probably had an effect on some of the more established churches with educated pastors (such as Orange, New Jersey, and those on Long Island), by encouraging them to join ranks with the other churches with better educated clergy in the New Side Presbyterian Synod.

Divisions came from still another source. In Scotland, two earlier schisms had divided the established Church of Scotland. Supporters of Richard Cameron left the Church of Scotland in 1680 in opposition to the Stuarts and reorganized in 1706. In 1712 the British Parliament imposed itself upon the Scottish Church, allowing lay patronage, a system under which the peerage or other wealthy landholders could impose pastors onto congregations without the consent of the people. In 1733 Ebenezer Erskine led a secession from the Church of Scotland in opposition to lay patronage and other issues. In 1743 these two groups realigned, and most of Cameron's followers came to be known as the Reformed Presbyterians, or the Covenanters, while most of Erskine's followers came to be known as the Associate Church, or the Seceders. In 1742 an Associate congregation was formed in Pennsylvania, followed by a Presbytery in 1753, directly subordinate to the Associate Synod in Scotland. In 1743, when Craighead left the New Side, his congregation in Pennsylvania became a Reformed Presbyterian congregation. A Presbytery was formed in 1774. So two groups of Presbyterian churches outside of the union also arose beginning during this period of the first schism. Both of these groups demonstrated a strong ethnic uniformity and maintained a conservative stance in psalm singing and other issues. As a result they were very distant from the New England Yankees and did not participate in unions with them. (Covenanter or Seceder churches are not listed in this book unless they entered the Presbyterian Church, U.S.A. within the parameters included for publication.) In the nineteenth century, however, this group began its slow movement into union with the mainstream Presbyterians, and thereby contributed to pulling them away from the New England descendants.

At the height of the first union there had been a unity of most of the churches in these traditions in the Synod of Philadelphia, and a few independent Congregational churches (some relating to Connecticut consociations). In this schism the churches became five bodies: the Old Side Synod of Philadelphia, the New Side Synod of New York, independent Congregational Churches of several stripes (some related to Connecticut consociations, others clearly defined as Separate, and some autonomous others); and two conservative Presbyterian immigrant groups: the Seceders and the Covenanters.

THE SECOND UNION
1758-1780

The move towards a second union was empowered by the growth and energy of the New Side, a rising supply of pastors, and especially by significant growth in the Scotch-Irish immigrant population. The New Side had the method to educate pastors and evangelists, and recruited ministerial candidates among the new Scotch-Irish immigrants and their children. The rising fortunes of their new College of New Jersey, and its attractiveness to some Old Side clergy such as David Cowell, gave them a respectable and energetic source for clergy. By organizing a Presbytery of Hanover in Virginia (1755), and also another in Pennsylvania (Abington, 1751), they had surrounded the Old Side churches, and had become the most effective evangelists to the new Irish and Scottish immigrants. As time went on, some of the excesses of the revival faded, and cooperation became easier. Political issues also favored reunion. Both the Old Side and the new New Side Abington and Hanover Presbyteries pushed towards the western mountain frontiers by 1758. New Scottish and Scotch-Irish immigrants hoped to move into still newer lands farther west. Both had common cause in trying to ward off Indian raids on the frontier settlements. As the French and Indian War broke out (1758), many church members were already cooperating in common political cause. Furthermore, leaders such as Dickinson had always advocated the reunion of the two Synods, seeing the first schism as an unfortunate temporary setback.

The New Side's effective missionary endeavors to new Scotch-Irish settlements, had restored that ethnic group's hegemony in the New York Synod. Growth spread south through Virginia to the Carolinas.

The New Side's receipt of a strong Presbytery on Long Island also gave them active well-to-do congregations able to provide leaders and finances. However, neither the Suffolk Presbytery, nor the later Dutchess Presbytery, took a key role in the Synod. At the same time the old New England voices for toleration and inclusion were fading in the key New York Presbytery. Jonathan Dickinson died in 1747. Ebenezer Pemberton, the pastor at First Church in New York City left for Boston in 1753. Aaron Burr, the long time Newark pastor, after a brief stint as President of Princeton, died in 1757. Jonathan Edwards, brought from New England that year to lead the school, died early in 1758.

Issues deeper than the rising Scotch-Irish hegemony on the Piedmont also motivated the cause of unity in this period. The elevation of a noted foe of American Calvinism, Thomas Secker, to the post of Archbishop of Canterbury re-emphasized long held fears. Secker tried to create uniform Anglican establishments in the colonies. (Fischer (1989), p.825) Rhode Island pastor and later Yale President Ezra Stiles, feared the power of the Anglican Church to move against the colonial churches, and saw the plans to set up a bishop in America as a threat (see Heimert & Miller (1967), pp.593 ff.). In 1760 he published a call for an alliance of non-Anglican colonial churches.

Both Synods saw a similar need. In addition, Scotch-Irish majorities in both sides supported those who had leaned towards reunion. In 1758 the two synods reunited as the Synod of New York and Philadelphia, on principles that reflected a Scotch-Irish consensus. The united Synod would henceforth center their meetings in Philadelphia.

The new united Synod grew in its early years. On its northern frontier it added another group of former Congregational churches by receiving the Dutchess County Presbytery in New York into membership. Most of these churches had previously related to Connecticut consociations. This was followed in 1766 by the initiation of annual meetings of delegates from the Presbyterian Synod and the Connecticut General Association. They formed a "Plan of Union," (Walker (1960/1893), p.526 note) but disclaimed any jurisdiction over the churches. They described themselves as "Pastors of the Congregational, Consociated, and Presbyterian Churches in North America." The group also conducted a correspondence with the Congregational ministers of Massachusetts, New Hampshire, and Rhode Island, although clergy in these states did not send delegates to the meetings. The meetings continued until 1775. They promoted unity as a barrier to Anglican advances.

These new impulses reinforced many of the issues that had led to the Proposals of 1705, the Saybrook Synod, and the first Presbytery. They also attracted the interest of a wide theological base - Old Light and New - thereby minimizing the importance of the Awakening divisions.

The churches were also united in the growing patriot cause leading to the American Revolution. Anglican and Tory supporters of the King were inclined to see American Presbyterians and Congregationalists all of one stripe, and as the primary harbingers of revolt.

But change was coming in the Synod. The agreement for the merger had approved and received the Westminster Confession of Faith and its catechisms as their confession. It also provided that candidates for the ministry declare their acceptance of the confession and "promise Subjection to the Presbyterian Plan of Government in the Westminster Directory." It also provided that while people have a right of conscience before God to state their protestations against acts of the judicatories, that in general they would be expected to "actively concur with or passively submit to" the actions of these groups. This language reflected that of the Scottish and Irish Churches, and created a church with a clear Presbyterian polity, imposing what could be considered a form of subscription. This move seems natural, since both sides of the merger had become predominantly Scottish or Irish in background, and most clergy were from families that had conformed to this methodology in Scotland or Ireland.

A question remains, though, of how well this was understood or enforced. Unfortunately those in the Synod of Congregational background, like their New England cousins, were not particularly adept at attending to the work of judicatories, and often lost issues of interpretation or process, merely by not attending or joining the debate. Both the Suffolk and Dutchess Presbyteries acted in semi-autonomous ways, almost disregarding the Synod altogether. After the merger, many New Englanders in the New York Presbytery simply stopped attending Synod meetings. Their voices were not heard as the Presbyterian structure sank deeper roots. As mentioned above, the Synod structure, which required the attendance of all clergy, and elders from all sessions, simply did not work, and became even more unwieldy as the Synod grew in numbers and geographic extension.

Perhaps the most crucial issue in the development of the reunited Synod was what happened at Princeton. The new college was the pride and joy of the New Side, and was originally served by several New England Presidents (Jonathan Dickinson, Aaron Burr, David Cowell(acting), and Jonathan Edwards). Unfortunately for New England interests, Dickinson, Burr, and Edwards all died soon after selection. The school then moved to a more centrist position with three Presidents from the Log College (Samuel Davies, Samuel Finley, John Blair(acting)). But in 1768 the Trustees invited a Scottish pastor and scholar to take over the twenty-two year old institution. John Witherspoon served for twenty-six years as the President, and made his mark on the institution. He was also the first Moderator of the Presbyterian General Assembly in 1789. While Witherspoon claimed to keep the school free from denominational indoctrination, his Presidency put the Scottish governmental model clearly in the fore among graduates of the College. Indeed, one of Witherspoon's "first actions as President of the College of New Jersey was to exorcise the ghost of... Jonathan Edwards... Witherspoon... saw the New Divinity of Edwards and [Joseph] Bellamy as simply a variation of... dangerous idealism, and [he] moved rapidly to squelch that point of view, even to the extent of putting [Edwards' disciple] Bellamy's works on an unofficial kind of index." (Noll, (1980), p. 214) Even students coming from congregations with Yankee New England backgrounds now were being cut off from their roots.

During this period only a few Congregational churches were not part of the united Synod, and most of these few either identified themselves as Separate churches or leaned in the direction of the Separates. Once the Dutchess County Presbytery had become part of the united Synod, few congregations were part of or served by consociations or associations in New England. At the end of 1779 the only clearly Congregational churches included Separate churches in Morris and Sussex Counties, New Jersey, the feeble outpost congregation in Wilkes-Barre, Pennsylvania, and scattered Separate and border congregations in Suffolk, Putnam, Dutchess, Columbia, and Saratoga Counties, New York. In addition some congregations listed by the Presbyteries in this period were really Congregational churches served by members of Presbytery, or churches that considered themselves part of the Presbytery, but maintained internal structures not fully consistent with Scottish expectations of sessional formats. Internal congregational structure during the second union had not proved to be a defining issue.

Only on the Presbyterian side, with the continued isolation of the Covenanters and the Seceders, did large numbers of churches remain outside the cooperative union. On paper, the union was as strong as it would ever be.

Coalescing to finally end the royal threat to Calvinism in America had much to do with the second union and its success in the Middle Atlantic states at the outbreak of the Revolution. This union was fleeting and full of inconsistencies however.

Nonetheless, the significant passage to nationhood in 1776 has focused the attention of many historians on that date. Those interested in religion have used that date to point out Congregationalism's inability to move outside New England and Presbyterianism's commanding position for eventual western expansion.(See, e.g., Newman and Halvorsen (2000), p.18) There is some truth in this analysis, but it fails to appreciate the Congregational sentiment hiding within the Presbyterian Synod, nor New England's great potential soon to be realized in New York.

However, data analysis for this period is often contradictory. Paullin (1932; followed by Newman and Halvorsen, 2000) reports that in 1775/1776 there were 668 Congregational and 31 Separate and independent Congregational churches in the new nation, only eight outside New England, and 588 Presbyterian churches in the country. Gaustad (1976), however, reporting for five years later (1780) finds 749 Congregational churches, and only 495 Presbyterian.

THE SECOND SCHISM
1780-1801

Although the Synod had welcomed most of the Middle Atlantic churches of Puritan origin into its ranks, presbyteries and congregations that simply did not conform challenged the paper unity of the Synod.

While common struggles against the establishment of an Anglican episcopacy and through it an Anglican hegemony in America engaged the energy of both traditions, and while both united in support of the Revolution, after the war these ties no longer were binding. The casual relationship of the Dutchess and Suffolk Presbyteries and many in the New York Presbytery to the Presbyterian Synod would be tested.

Opponents of the Scottish church polity, though, still had no clear alternative polity, nor was a clear language to discriminate polities yet available. Both the Massachusetts polity and the Connecticut Saybrook polity were intertwined with privileges and obligations to the government. The polity of the Separate churches, and that of independent Presbyteries in New England further confused the situation, with little agreement about which of these polities were "Congregational" and which were "Presbyterian."

The choice of a religious life outside of the political realm, as had been forced onto dissenters in England, held no attraction to politically revolutionary Americans.

Intellectual pressure and ferment pushed the theoretical boundaries of the Synod and confused the New England alternatives. But all of these issues were about to be stretched by a new reality: a radical demographic shift in the area. The end of the Revolutionary War opened areas west of the Allegheny mountain region for settlement. A flood of New Englanders poured into upstate New York and into the northeastern corner of Pennsylvania. The War had also slowed and almost stopped immigration from the Presbyterian strong holds of Ireland and Scotland. The balance of power was about to change in the Middle Atlantic states, and the churches would respond.

The second schism formed from two directions. New Englanders, who were not committed to the second union, moved west seeking a new identity. At the same time, a real schism occurred among those forces in the Synod most committed to the New England theology. In addition, these new schismatics developed a new polity to serve the non-established Yankees.

Meanwhile in England, clear lines of demarcation between Presbyterians and Congregationalists were forming at about the same time. The united regional ministerial groups were declining, due to the subscription controversy, the evangelical revival, and theological differences. [Two that remained (the 1764 union of the Cheshire and Lancashire groups, and the Devon and Cornwall group) slowly came into the hands of English Presbyterians with rising Arminian and Unitarian sympathies.] The majority of rural congregations now emerged as Congregational. Congregationalists then began to form their own ministerial associations, societies or unions. The old association in London had long continued, and a group serving Norfolk and Suffolk had begun in 1751. Between 1781 and 1815 twenty-one new groups were organized, bringing the total number of Congregational bodies in England to twenty-three. The most prolific decade was the 1790's. Going (in Bolam *et al* (1968)) says that half of the formerly English Presbyterian Churches surviving in 1968 had become Congregational. The union and division pattern in England eventually moved to strengthen Congregationalism and to help seal the decline of the old English Presbyterians.

At the same time, Presbyterians moving to England from Scotland began to realize the great gulf between them and the English Presbyterians. The new immigrants and a few orthodox remnants of the old Presbyterian group began to form new Presbyterian groupings closer to the Scottish plan, the first being the Presbytery of Northumberland established in 1783. On the other hand, some remnants of the old English Presbyterians organized a Unitarian Fund in 1800.

By the end of the century schism had come to England, with three factions, the non-subscribing liberal remnants of English Presbyterianism, an evangelical Congregationalism in the process of strengthening its organizational identity, and an organized immigrant Scottish Presbyterianism.

Similarly in Scotland in 1795 a Congregational schism came out of the Kirk, beginning a continuing Congregationalism there for the first time.

The missionary zeal about to spread through America was also reflected in England, where Calvinist groups began the London Missionary Society in 1795.

Population shifts leading to change in America began before the Revolution. The desire of New Englanders for territory in the west was promoted by Connecticut's exercise of her claim through her 1662 charter to lands west of the Delaware River in present day northeastern Pennsylvania, and also by land purchases made by Connecticut companies from the Indians in 1754. Settlements from Connecticut begun as early as 1757, were stepped up after the end of the French and Indian War. The New York - Pennsylvania border in this area was also unclear at this time. Connecticut made settlements in what are now Pike, Wayne, Lackawanna, Wyoming, Lycoming, and particularly Luzerne Counties, beginning as outposts, taking on the more formal structure of plantations, and finally being organized as full fledged towns as early as 1769. Connecticut set up Westmoreland County in northeastern Pennsylvania in 1774/1776, with five towns. At this time the Saybrook Platform was still established in Connecticut and new towns were expected to sponsor Congregational churches. The strongest church emerging at this time was the Wyoming Church in Wilkes-Barre. However, many of the new Connecticut towns and settlements never got their churches organized, because of the outbreak of the Revolutionary War which directed the energies of the settlers and their financial backers to other issues. The Revolution also overlapped a local "War" when Pennsylvania sent troops north to expel the Yankee interlopers in what became known as the Pennamite War. By 1780, when Westmoreland County was discontinued, all the settlements had lost population, and only the Wilkes-Barre Church had sunk deep enough roots to survive.

The second schism really began in 1780 in New Jersey, when the energetic Jacob Green, pastor in Hanover, joined with three other clergy (Ebenezer Bradford, Joseph Grover, and Amzi Lewis) in leaving the New York Presbytery. A Massachusetts native and Harvard graduate, Green was a friend of the Awakening. He had been encouraged to enter the ministry by Jonathan Dickinson, was a supporter of Jonathan Edwards, and had been a trustee of Princeton for sixteen years. After the 1758 reunion of the Presbyterian Synod, Green had become one of the absentees at Synod meetings, yet a high respect for him was maintained in his Presbytery.

Green's energy was legion, pastoring sometimes at more than one congregation, "serving as physician, legal advisor, and schoolmaster; he built and ran a grist mill, a brick kiln, and a distillery; and he bought and sold real estate." (Noll, (1976), p.220). In 1776 Green was elected to the New Jersey Provisional Legislature, where he chaired the committee that wrote the new revolutionary Constitution for the State. Soon back home serving his congregation, he aided Washington's Army and busied himself with becoming a controversial, and perhaps New Jersey's most important, anti-slavery leader.

Precisely at this time, with the Revolution still in progress, and with Green's anti-slavery activities leading to demonstrations against him, Green set out to create a new polity. The result was the Morris County Presbytery, in a form described by Green as an "Associated Presbytery."

Committed to the evangelical views of the revival, friendly to the Separates, and anxious for a ministerial supply for new settlements, Green had outlined a simplified training course for ministerial candidates as early as 1775 (Noll, 1980). In 1779 Green resigned from the New York Presbytery for reasons centered in autonomy, but revealing his eagerness for less restraint on new initiates for the ministry. He objected to the Presbyterian Synod's method of "ordering, appointing, and requiring, instead of recommending and desiring." (Alexander (c.1888), pp.22-24) He objected to their assumption of legislative powers, and restraints placed upon ministerial candidates. He concluded by objecting to "the reception of the Westminster Confession of Faith, Catechisms, and Directory, without the liberty to make exception or explanation, and the injunction to teach and preach according to them."

In 1780 Green and his younger allies formed the new Morris County Presbytery, and a year later published a pamphlet, probably written by Green, to explain their views (*A View of the Christian Church and Church Government...*). Even in schism, Green's words point to a higher unity, and seek to be consistent with "that love and unity that ought to prevail among Christians." (p.vii.) Green begins the treatise with a definition, "The word *church* properly signifies a collection of people, a congregation or assembly..." (p.1) Living in the new religious freedom of America, and the non-establishment state of New Jersey, Green attacks the idea of an established church: "The absurdity of supposing an oecumenical [*sic*], national, or provincial, church, i.e. a church united under one form of government, extended through a province, nation, and the world, will easily appear to anyone that considers the nature of church government, according to the directions of the New Testament." (p.5) Green sees local churches as covenanted communities formed by baptized believers who have professed their faith. A congregation may exist without officers, and, while having many elders has some advantages, a congregation can exist with only one teaching elder. In the style of English Presbyterians, Green holds the role of pastor of high regard within the congregation. Yet he also supports the autonomy of congregations, noting that, "No one church, or number of churches, have any power over any other particular church or churches;" (p.24) yet, churches may withdraw communion from a congregation that "maintains damnable or pernicious doctrines or is scandalous in practice..." While holding against a presbytery "being a judicature, and having a constitutional power to receive and determine appeals..." (p.26), the Morris County Presbytery pamphlet asserts that "a number of elders or pastors, from several neighbouring churches, associated and met together, may, without impropriety, be called a *presbytery*, as they are a number of presbyters, or associated and acting together. Such a number of elders may associate, and agree to meet from time to time, to stir up, assist, and quicken one another; consult and agree upon measures to promote religion; may help, and, occasionally, afford some supplies to vacant congregations; may hear and advise in cases that may be left or referred to them, at the desire of particular churches; may ordain a pastor for a particular church when desired... But such an associated presbytery, as a body, has no power over the churches any other way than their advice, or determination of particular cases may be requested by particular churches." (p.27) "A number of associated presbyteries may, occasionally or statedly, meet to consult and advise together about the most proper measures to promote the kingdom of Christ; and by their joint consultations, and endeavours, may encourage, strengthen, and edify one another. And such a society may properly be called a synod... But they have no warrant or right to intermeddle, in any authoritative way, with the affairs of particular churches." (p.29)

Although the new body formed in 1780 was called the Presbytery of Morris County, it is clear that by 1781 they described themselves as an "Associated" Presbytery. In starting the new Presbytery the founders also provided "to invite each church to send an elder or delegate to attend this presbytery, at each session, and join with us in our endeavours to promote the Redeemer's kingdom." (p.51) They also provided that the Presbytery "shall never assume, or claim, any jurisdiction over the churches, or authoritatively intermeddle with their affairs..." (p.52) They also offered to reunite with the Presbyterian Synod if the Synod would meet with them only in the capacity of a "voluntary society."

This pamphlet was a landmark document because, in effect, it created a new polity. Unlike the established churches of Europe, it clearly eschewed an establishment and relocated the church within its membership. While affirming the autonomy of congregations, it called for mutual edification and promotion of the "Redeemer's kingdom."

It thus rejected an absolute independence. Within its first decade it extended this role by creating a chartered society for the promotion of learning and religion. Also, unlike Massachusetts where the only bodies were exclusively ministerial, and unlike Connecticut, with a double system of ministerial associations, and ministerial and lay consociations, Morris County provided for one body, with lay representatives of the congregations sitting with the pastors. Morris County, also in the spirit of local church autonomy, did not set up a form of organization for local churches that required sessions of ruling elders. Instead churches may or may not have ruling elders, and churches may send elders or delegates as their lay representatives to the Presbytery. In all these ways a new polity had been created.

MISSIONARY ZEAL

The period from the end of the Revolution to 1800 is usually seen as a period of religious declension, particularly among the old mainline colonial churches such as the Presbyterians and Congregationalists. Certainly the new political realities, economic pressures brought on by the War, and the opening of vast territories in the west put stresses and strains onto the denominational fellowships.

There was actually, however, a surprisingly consistent rise in missionary activity during this period, particularly among those who had been influenced by the Great Awakening. As the frontier opened, the General Association of Connecticut (Congregational - the only state wide body of Congregationalists before 1795) began in 1774 and 1788, and particularly from 1793, to appoint annually missionaries to tour new settlements in the west. Presbyterian presbyteries, synods, and the General Assembly often did the same. However, these bodies had no legal status and no easy way to finance these endeavors. The impetus then arose to charter incorporated missionary societies to provide a legal means to finance missionary work.

Earlier Indian mission work had been done through a 1649 English Puritan missionary society, and then through a reduced version of the same chartered in 1661 after the Restoration. Then British support increased through the support of the 1709 Society in Scotland for Propagating Christian Knowledge. However the Revolution led the Scottish Society to abandon its American work in 1787.

New England forces had long hoped to have their own missionary societies, but the King thwarted a 1762 attempt. After the War the newly independent state legislatures were more open to missionary organization. A Massachusetts Congregational Charitable Society to serve widows and orphans of clergy got a charter in 1786. A Society for Propagating the Gospel among Indians and Others in North America also got a Massachusetts charter in 1787.

Shortly afterward, many state-wide missionary societies were begun. In New England the first was the Connecticut Missionary Society (1798), set up by the General Association of Connecticut to continue the work they had already begun. This was followed by state societies in Massachusetts (1799), New Hampshire (1801), Rhode Island (1802), Vermont (1807) and Maine (1807). Local societies such as Massachusetts' Hampshire Missionary Society (1802), were also formed.

A key part of the new missionary zeal took place in the Middle Atlantic area, begun by Jacob Green and the Morris County Presbytery. The Presbytery obtained a charter for the Society Instituted in Morris County for the Promotion of Learning and Religion in 1787. Green had long been a supporter of training programs to move ministers into needy areas, and this new society focused on the education and training of pastors.

The New York Missionary Society was begun in 1796 with a wide foundation of support. Nichols (49) contends that the support included Presbyterian, Associate Reformed, Dutch Reformed and Baptist groups, but does not mention Congregationalists. Yet its decision to support Congregational missions to the Indians belies a more New England base than Nichols reports. The Northern Missionary Society of the State of New York was begun in 1797 in the Albany area, with its organization completed in 1800. The Berkshire and Columbia Missionary Society along the Massachusetts and New York border was planned in 1797 and organized in 1798 serving Congregational churches in both states. The first two of these groups concentrated on Indian work, while the third worked with the later statewide bodies in supporting missionaries to new settlements in the west.

GROWTH DURING THE SECOND SCHISM

During this period, schisms from the Presbyterian Church continued, and organizations with polities similar to that outlined by Green were put in place to serve autonomous congregations. The new schisms and immigration reinvigorated Congregationalism in the Hudson valley and northern New Jersey. A treaty with the Six Nations of the Iroquois in 1794 also encouraged the filling of western New York by new settlers.

At the end of 1779 specifically Congregational churches outside presbytery had been limited to Sussex and Morris Counties New Jersey, Luzerne County Pennsylvania, and Suffolk, Putnam, Dutchess, Columbia, and Saratoga Counties New York.

In 1787 the Suffolk Presbytery sought to withdraw from the Presbyterian General Assembly. While an Assembly committee reconciled the majority of the Presbytery temporarily, it had to disband the Presbytery in 1790, and reorganize its churches on the Island. In 1789 the Strict Congregational Convention of Connecticut began to receive New York congregations into membership, and by 1791 a Strict Congregational Convention of Long Island was begun. Similar to Morris County, both of the Strict Conventions valued autonomy and seated both delegates and pastors.

The Morris County Presbytery spread up the Hudson valley and organized the Westchester Associated Presbytery in 1792. It, in turn, with the Berkshire (ministers) Association in Massachusetts cooperated in founding the Northern Associated Presbytery in 1793, a large inter-church body that ran from the Massachusetts border across the Hudson River and through the Catskills to the Pennsylvania border. Weakened by these developments, the Presbyterian Synod disbanded their Dutchess Presbytery in 1795, and was forced to reorganize their valley congregations. These changes had added modern Westchester, Rockland, Orange, and Ulster Counties, New York, and Essex County, New Jersey, to the list of counties with Congregational churches.

A rapid spread of Congregational churches into the Middle Atlantic area followed the new tide of New England migration. Not including Indian missions, counties added by 1790 included Rensselaer, Washington, Greene, Delaware, Fulton, and Oneida in New York, Susquehanna in Pennsylvania, and Warren in New Jersey. By 1800 Bradford, and Cambria, Pennsylvania, and Sullivan, Albany, Otsego, Herkimer, Broome, Chenango, Madison, Onondaga, Cayuga, Wayne, Ontario, Livingston, and Jefferson Counties, New York were added. In a final spurt of growth, by 1810 Congregationalism had returned to the cities of New York and Philadelphia, and had spread into Passaic County, New Jersey, Wayne, Wyoming, and Lycoming Counties, Pennsylvania, and Cortland, Schoharie, Warren, Essex, Clinton, Franklin, Saint Lawrence, Lewis, Oswego, Tioga, Tompkins, Chemung, Seneca, Yates, Steuben, Allegany, Monroe, Orleans, Genesee, Wyoming, Cattaraugus, Chautauqua, Erie, and Niagara Counties in New York.

During this time the arrival of new Welsh immigrants, forming congregations in Pennsylvania in 1797 and New York in 1800, increasing denominational differences and complexity.

The new Green polity was ready to meet and organize these new congregations. The Green bodies evolved in name, moving from "Presbytery," to "Associated Presbytery," and finally to "Association," a more New England word that stressed the free association of the members. However, all these groups included churches as well as ministers in membership. Morris County Presbytery was a direct parent of the Westchester, and through it of the Northern and Saratoga Associated Presbyteries. In addition, people well acquainted with the Green polity were in key positions to help forge these and similar organizations. Joseph Grover, one of the founders of the Morris County Presbytery, moved to Bristol, New York, in 1798. In 1800 he was one of five founders of the Ontario Association which organized under principles similar to that of Morris County. Beriah Hotchkin, a founding member of the Northern Associated Presbytery, founded numerous congregations throughout New York state. Seth Williston, another prominent member of the Northern Associated Presbytery, was also a member of the Susquehanna Association, a missionary of the Connecticut Missionary Society, and the founder of many churches. David Harrower, a member of both the Westchester Associated Presbytery and the Northern Associated Presbytery, as well as the Susquehanna Association, worked with the Berkshire and Columbia Missionary Society, and played a significant role in church organization in Delaware County. Daniel W. Eastman, licensed by the Morris County Presbytery, was ordained in 1802 by the young Ontario Association as a missionary to Canada. One of the most successful missionaries was John Spencer, who was ordained by the Northern Associated Presbytery in 1801, and who became a pastor in Oneida County in 1804, joining the Oneida Association. Supported by the Connecticut Missionary Society, he became the founder of at least twelve Congregational churches and at least one Baptist Church, and also was the first minister to preach in at least ten other towns in Cattaraugus, Chautauqua, Erie, Genesee, and Wyoming Counties between 1808 and 1817. Spencer founded such later prominent churches as the first churches in Buffalo, Batavia, and Jamestown.

The first four inter-church groups (Morris County, Long Island Strict, Westchester Associated, and Northern Associated) all existed by 1793. Nine others followed in quick succession: Oneida Association (1800), Ontario Association (1800), Susquehanna Association (1802 or 1803), Middle Association (1803/1804), Saratoga Associated Presbytery (1806/1807), Black River Association (1807/1808), Union Association (1808), Strict Convention of New Jersey (1809), and the Luzerne Association (1810). During this period three other Congregational bodies were also organized outside of New England, the Congregational Association of South Carolina (1801) and two bodies in Ohio, the Ecclesiastical Convention of New Connecticut (1805) and the Southeast Ohio (or Muskingum) Association (1809).

The desire to follow relatives to new settlements in New York and farther west meant that during this period young New England clergy moving west followed the wagons. This, however, eventually meant that older congregations in the lower Hudson valley and in New Jersey, that had previously looked to New England for clergy supply could no longer do so. Most of these then turned to Presbyterian sources of clergy supply, and this, through ministerial preferences in both theology and polity, began to separate these congregations from those in the newer areas.

Whereas revivals played a role in emotional tensions in both traditions, they were not the cause of this second schism. Rather, the second schism sprang from the cultural and polity differences between the Yankee New Englanders and the descendants of the Scotch-Irish immigrants. For example, Green's strong advocacy about the anti-slavery position, also endorsed by such key New England Edwardseans as Samuel Hopkins, was suspect in many parts of the growing Appalachian and Southern Presbyterian Church.

Initially, running counter to the schism of this period, was a decision of the Scottish Seceder Associate Church and the Covenanter Reformed Presbyterian Church to unite in 1782 as the Associate Reformed Presbyterian Church. These small ethnic groups realized that their European identities lost some meaning in the new American republic. However, the stresses of this period such as the opening of the west, and economic strains, pulled at the merger. Parts of both groups opposed the merger and became continuing bodies, so what had been two groups now became three.

THE RELIGIOUS SITUATION IN 1800

The second schism and the New England emigration into upstate New York had, in just twenty years, vastly changed the religious complexion of the Empire State. Because of the importance of the Plan of Union, particularly in upstate New York, it is helpful to document the conditions before the Plan began in 1801.

An exact picture of 1800 is not possible because the records of the first Oneida Association are not available and the General Assembly of the Presbyterian Church did not publish church lists between the 1798 and 1803 minutes. For this discussion Delaware, Otsego, Herkimer, and Saint Lawrence Counties are defined as the eastern end of the western part of New York state.

In the eastern part of the state, the Presbyterians and Congregationalists had an equal number of overlapping inter-church bodies: i.e., the Strict Congregational Convention of Long Island (1791) and the Long Island Presbytery (1790); Morris County Presbytery (1780) and the New York Presbytery (1738); the Westchester Associated Presbytery (1792) and the Hudson Presbytery (1795); and the Northern Associated Presbytery (1793), and the Albany Presbytery (1790).

In western New York, however, the Congregationalists already had two bodies in place, the Oneida and the Ontario Associations. This move to inter-church organization in the Green model is all the more phenomenal considering that immigrants from Massachusetts and some other parts of New England came from areas where there with no inter-church Congregational bodies. By 1805 the Congregationalists had organized two more Associations serving the area: Susquehanna and Middle.

A Presbyterian Church in far west Niagara had been admitted to the Albany Presbytery in 1790. Other Presbyterian mission work helped to start churches throughout the 1790's. However, no western Presbytery was begun until 1802/1803 in Oneida, and none farther west until Geneva in 1805, the latter including no churches that claimed to have joined a Presbytery before 1802. For that matter only seven Presbyterian Churches in all of western New York were reported in the General Assembly 1803 minute church lists. These were all in Oneida, Herkimer, and Otsego Counties, and one had been Congregational until 1802. For a denomination that holds its identity in a succession of higher judicatories, this lack of presbyterial organization was a severe handicap.

The status of 1800 is revealed more clearly in church data, than in associations and presbyteries. In the City of New York and Long Island the Presbyterians listed all three branches of the First Presbyterian Church of New York as distinct congregations, as well as nineteen churches on Long Island. Two of the nineteen were Congregational Churches being served by Presbytery members, and eleven were previously Congregational. Twelve other Congregational churches existed on the Island, including two Indian congregations. Both Indian congregations and four of the other Congregational churches had been listed some time earlier as part of the regular Presbytery.

In the rest of the eastern part of the state forty congregations were listed in regular Presbyteries, including one Congregational Church being served by a member of Presbytery, two churches in Presbytery being served about this time by pastors who were members of Congregational bodies, one church in the process of leaving the Presbytery, and seven additional congregations that were formerly Congregational. Also, some churches that appear to have been always Presbyterian (such as Goshen in Orange County and Cambridge in Washington County) had clearly New England influences on their histories. There were the same number of additional Congregational churches – forty. Fifteen of these had been listed earlier by regular Presbyteries. The eastern part of the state, which had been so united in the second union, was now divided into almost equally sized church families.

But the scale was tipped by the realities of the western part of the state, that had fifty-three Congregational churches by the end of 1800. Perhaps five had earlier appeared in regular Presbytery lists or had Presbyterian forms. On the other hand, only fifteen Presbyterian churches existed, seven of which were independent of Presbyteries. Perhaps three of the fifteen had been Congregational sometime before 1800, and another three would become Congregational shortly after 1800. Three apparently unaffiliated Indian missions supported by both traditions, were also present. Congregationalism had clearly become the larger group in New York in 1800, particularly in the west. New York Presbyterianism also still showed the profile of its New England origins.

The second schism had not been nearly as significant in the other states in this region. In 1800 New Jersey had only six Congregational churches, and Pennsylvania had only four, three in the northeastern corner of the state, and one Welsh church.

This division and the ethnic origin of the upstate New York churches also supports the position that New England influence lay behind the emerging missionary societies in New York and other regional religious institutions.

THE HISTORIANS' BLANK PAGES

Amazingly most Congregational historians have ignored the churches in the Associated Presbyteries. For example, the Work Project Administration's Inventory of New Jersey Congregationalism (24) jumps right over this group of churches. Presbyterian historians are inclined to treat them as a modified Presbyterian group. This was obviously partly because of the name Presbytery. Those who believed that that word could only be understood from its Scottish meaning quickly pigeon-holed these groups into the Presbyterian fold. Over time the word "Associated," based on the looser "Associations" of New England became a more and more important word - limiting Presbyterial power - among Green's followers. Some sources treat a church that was part of an Associated Presbytery as having been Presbyterian during that period and not Congregational. That reveals a lack of understanding of the word Presbyterian in its English context, and a lack of reading the records of these Presbyteries.

Were the Associated Presbyteries Congregational bodies? Unquestionably yes, as can be seen clearly in the Morris County principles opposing actions that would "intermeddle" with the conduct of particular churches. While the Associated Presbyteries allowed for all types of local forms, and some congregations did have ruling elders, that was considered the more unusual local form. (See, for example, the minutes of the Westchester Associated Presbytery for 1817, in which it is reported that a discussion found it acceptable for local congregations to have ruling elders. This implies both autonomy and the normal lack of the office.) Furthermore, the existence of ruling elders in a church did not guarantee a formal session. Congregations, also continued to send delegates to Presbytery meetings, not necessarily elders. When Associated Presbytery congregations existed next to churches in the regular Presbyteries (such as in Yorktown, New York), the Associated Presbytery Church was widely known as Congregational. Additional evidence can be ascertained by following the origin, training, and support of Associated Presbytery clergy and congregations. Almost all had New England roots. The Northern Associated Presbytery, for instance, in an 1824 circular commented that "most of the congregations, out of which this Presbytery is formed, having emigrated from New England..." Also, the Associated Presbyteries related to bodies named Congregational as their equals. In 1793 the Westchester Associated Presbytery joined with the Congregational Berkshire Association of Massachusetts to form the Northern Associated Presbytery. In both 1801 and 1822 some of the Associated Presbyteries explored union with the Congregational General Association of Connecticut. They were also the main impetus behind the 1806 Harpersfield and 1811 Clinton meetings to explore a general Congregational body for New York. And when twelve of the original thirteen Congregational inter-church bodies gave way to the Accommodation Plan in the early nineteenth century, the last two to disband were both Associated Presbyteries, Northern and Westchester, both in 1830.

Even though temporarily eclipsed by the Accommodation Plan and the Plan of Union, the ecclesiology and polity worked out by Jacob Green and his friends became the basis of later American Congregationalism and the United Church of Christ. Why then did their history disappear? Presbyterian historians have not generally stressed the reality of Congregational history in their midst. But perhaps the most telling reason is Jacob Green's conservative prodigal son, Ashbel. While Jacob was the instigator of all causes liberal, his son Ashbel became one of the most important conservative leaders in American religion. In 1790, the year that Jacob died, Ashbel Green became the Stated Clerk of the new Presbyterian General Assembly, a post he held until 1803. Ashbel also later served as President of Princeton from 1813 to 1823. In his age he sided with the Old School. A historian in his own right, Ashbel heralded the rise of Presbyterian organization. He wrote a biography of his father (1831-1832) which celebrated Jacob's piety and hard work, but which admits yet limits references to his father's Congregationalism.

STEPS TOWARDS REUNION

The growth of upstate New York put the Congregationalists and Presbyterians back into contact. The Irish and Scottish settlements in places like Washington County and Cherry Valley in Otsego County, spread out and soon encountered the waves of New England settlers.

Missionary activity also initiated interaction. Both groups had a common history in serving the same American Indian communities. The Connecticut General Association, and then its Missionary Society, as well as the Associated Presbyteries, were sending missionaries to the new settlements. The Presbyterian General Assembly did the same, but Presbyterian Churches founded in the 1790's were so isolated that they did not join presbyteries.

Contact also took more formal channels. For generations, Presbyterian and Congregational ministers had been seated as guests when attending each other's ministerial and inter-church bodies. The Connecticut General Association and the old Synod of New York and Philadelphia had had regular contact before the Revolutionary War. The new General Assembly sought to renew these contacts in 1790. In 1792 the two groups planned a regular exchange of delegate visitors, and in 1793 a Connecticut delegation of three, including Jonathan Edwards, Jr., sat at the General Assembly. In 1794 this friendly exchange began to slowly compromise rigid polity differences. The delegates between the General Assembly and the Connecticut General Association were given votes at each other's meetings. This relationship became so strong that the Assembly, when referring items to Presbytery votes, also referred them to the Connecticut General Association (Walker (1960/1893), p.528). This exchange continued to grow as other general bodies were formed in New England, with votes at the General Assembly being extended to delegates from Vermont (1803), New Hampshire (1810), and Massachusetts (1811). The New England state bodies also began to exchange voting delegates with each other and thereby formalize some communications that led towards a national Congregational denomination. However, the votes of the New Englanders (who had never subscribed to Presbyterian polity) at the General Assembly sent a signal that rigid denominationalism might be at an end.

Local cooperation also grew in this period. Some Congregational pastors served churches in regular Presbyteries, and some Presbytery members had been called to serve Congregational churches. Local inter-church bodies also began formal contacts, for example, when the Albany Presbytery and the Northern Associated Presbytery adopted a plan of social intercourse in 1801.

In the Mohawk Valley, on the pathway of the New Englanders into central and western New York, a new college was begun in Schenectady in 1794/1795. Absorbing an older Dutch Reformed academy, the college chose the name "Union College," "for the cooperation and union of several religious denominations" in the endeavor (French, 90). The first President of the College was John Blair Smith, a Pennsylvania Presbyterian, and advocate of cooperation. Soon after starting the College, Smith encountered Eliphalet Nott, a young Congregational missionary on his way west. Nott was a member of a family with several Congregational ministers and a 1795 licentiate of the New London Association. Smith convinced Nott of the value of union in the west, and encouraged him to settle locally, where he became pastor of the First Presbyterian Church in Albany, and joined in convincing other New Englanders on their way west to follow in his steps (Sweet, *Presbyterians* (1964/1936), p.41). The Rev. Jonathan Edwards, Jr. was called from a Connecticut pastorate in 1799 to serve as the second President of Union College. The college, in name, leadership, and contacts, led in the popular rise of the idea of union.

Various sources have pointed out that some leaders in New England encouraged unity in the new west. Many recommended that missionaries and pastors going west seek the strong relationship of a presbytery. (Sweet, *Congregationalists* (1964/1939), pp.16-17; Sweet, *Presbyterians* (1964/1936), p.46). It must be remembered, however, that New England Congregational polity at this time was part of the establishment, was tax supported, and had a dual structure that included separate parish or society entities related to each congregation. Tax supported salaries would not be possible in the west. In 1790, as well, only one of the eventual six New England states had enough internal organization to have an inter-church body. The Massachusetts government had thwarted the desire for inter-church fellowship, seen in the proposals of 1705. Some congregations continued to hold to this total independency, in fear that closer denominational connection would put their tax support in jeopardy. With no such fear in the west, tiny new isolated congregations could benefit from inter-church relations. Fully independent congregations in the west would face massive financial, ministerial recruitment, and fellowship needs. A. Hastings Ross understood this, (See, e.g. Ross (1892), and Ross (1890)), although many writers, both before and after him have not. Other authors in defending what they perceived to be congregational polity, have thrown scorn on the New England leaders who encouraged union and accused them of not standing in support of congregational polity. However, the writers' inability to see the difference between establishment Congregational polity, and the different realities of the west is a common error.

THE THIRD UNION
THE PLAN OF UNION
1801-1837

As indicated in the title of this book, the Plan of Union is crucial to our discussion. To try to understand Congregationalism in the Middle Atlantic region, and for that matter in the rest of non-New England America, it is necessary to study the Plan of Union. What happened to the Puritans' heirs after they left the protection of the New England environment?

Unfortunately most approaches to studying the Plan of Union seem to describe two free standing denominations - Presbyterian and Congregational, from two different cultures - Scotland and Puritan England, and located in two parts of America - Middle Atlantic and New England, who now, for the first time, tried to cooperate. The earlier interaction has often been subsumed under Presbyterian denominational history. The polities, which came to the table in 1801, are often pictured as rock-hewn versions of clear ecclesiologies, rigid throughout history and with known differences and sharp boundaries.

The reality, however, emphasized by calling this the third union, was a long interaction, with continual intermingling, as well as an evolution of dogma, and changing definitions that were now attempting to take on new form.

What was taking place during this period was a repeat of issues that had been struggled with earlier. Changing demographics brought forward new populations to grapple with the same questions earlier immigrants had thought they resolved. The first union could be characterized as an attempt to unite two ethnic groups spreading in the Middle Atlantic area. The first schism is similarly a failure of those groups to make that first union work. The second union was prompted by the ever-increasing Scotch-Irish immigration, which overwhelmed all factions in the area. The second schism was a secession of a small ethnic minority that held allegiance to their culture, and then was strengthened by new immigration. Scotch-Irish immigration had slowed to a trickle, while upstate New York and northern Pennsylvania were being overrun with a large Yankee New England population.

However, the vast mission challenges of the new expanse of lands beyond the mountains in New York and farther west, the desire of the new Yankee immigrants, just like their ancestors some generations earlier, to move towards a general Reformed consensus and unity built on wide foundations, and the apparent willingness of the Presbyterian Church to abandon the confessional and organizational uniformity which had been driven by the earlier Scotch-Irish immigration, now seemed to make a new attempt at unification possible.

THE PLAN OF UNION

In 1800 Jonathan Edwards, Jr., now the President of Union College, and Jonathan Freeman, a Presbyterian pastor in diverse and ethnically mixed Orange County, New York, were appointed by the Presbyterian General Assembly as delegates to the Connecticut General Association. There they were appointed to a committee with two Connecticut pastors who were also trustees of the young Connecticut Missionary Society, to prepare a report on the relation of the two polities on missionary ground. They requested that a committee be appointed to approach the General Assembly to propose a "uniform system of Church government... [for] the new settlements." (Walker (1960/1893), pp.529-530).

At the 1801 General Assembly one of the Connecticut representatives was appointed to a committee of five including Edwards, Presbyterian pastors from New York and New Jersey, and a lay associate of Edwards which proposed the ***Plan of Union***, which was thereupon adopted by the Assembly and later that year by the Connecticut General Association. (The text of the Plan can be found in Walker (1960/1893), pp.530-531; Armstrong *et al* (1956), pp.102-104; Sweet, *Congregationalists* (1964/1939), p.15).

Although the Plan was adopted by the entire General Assembly, the key people involved were all from areas with significant Yankee populations, and the key Presbyterian author seems to have been Edwards, who had spent his ministerial life as a Connecticut Congregationalist until just two years earlier.

Other Congregational general bodies in New England later adopted the Plan: Vermont in 1801, New Hampshire in 1810, Massachusetts in 1811, and Maine in 1828.

Written primarily by ministers, the Plan reflected more on issues pertaining to ministers rather than those focused on congregations. Also, because of the strong Calvinist and Edwardsean interest in discipline and the difference between the polities' methods of discipline, discipline was given a central role in the Plan. (Discipline cases in Congregational churches were handled by the entire congregation, while discipline cases in Presbyterian churches were handled initially by the congregation's session, and then could be appealed to presbytery, and then to the synod, and General Assembly.)

The first section of the Plan enjoined missionaries to endeavor to seek forbearance and accommodation among each other and with the settlers in the new west.

The second and third sections deal with how discipline cases were to be handled if a congregation chooses a pastor from the other tradition. They provide that Congregational churches with Presbyterian pastors could handle discipline within the congregation, or by an ecclesiastical council, except that, if a case involved the pastor, it could be appealed to the pastor's presbytery, or a council made up equally of Presbyterians and Congregationalists. A Presbyterian church with a Congregational pastor could handle discipline issues according to Presbyterian forms, except that if a case involved the pastor, it may be appealed to his association, or a council made up equally of Presbyterians and Congregationalists.

These three sections assume that the two denominations would continue to exist side by side. Because some pastors had already served congregations of the other polity, these provisions also offered advice for existing realities and difficulties.

The fourth section broke new ground. It provided for congregations made up jointly of both Presbyterians and Congregationalists. It provided that their local organization shall include a standing committee, not a session of ruling elders. Ever concerned about discipline, this provision allowed Presbyterian members of the congregation to appeal cases to presbytery, but Congregational member discipline issues would be handled within the congregation. It further provided that these mixed churches could be represented at presbytery meetings by a committee member rather than a ruling elder.

Unlike many of the myths that have risen about the Plan, it did not provide that the denominations would not exist side by side, nor did it provide for the eventual death of Congregationalism in the west.

It did create the possibility of a new kind of mixed church. Like most Congregational churches, these mixed churches would not have ruling elders. The Plan did not require a particular type of inter-church relationship. However, the need for a presbytery to which Presbyterian members of mixed churches could appeal discipline cases implies that mixed churches would belong to a presbytery. However, some members of these mixed congregations would have no obligations to the presbytery. The provision to send committee members as delegates to presbytery also implies a relation between such churches and a presbytery. Because, at this time, upstate New York had more Congregational inter-church bodies than presbyteries, these implications contradicted the realities of 1801.

While some churches were formed that were mixed, they seem to have been few in number (Nichols, 1936). When they existed, they often were unique local creations, mixing the two polities in ways that included or excluded the fourth provision of the Plan. No evidence has been found of any mixed congregations distinguishing between their Presbyterian and Congregational members.

The Plan did change the polity of the Presbyterian Church, and it was approved by the General Assembly. Presbyteries could now receive churches without classic Scottish forms, and seat non-elder delegates at presbytery meetings. This action of the General Assembly could be seen as moving back to the polity neutrality of the 1706 Presbytery.

Despite the adoption of the Plan, the two groups continued to grow separately in upstate New York. In the first few years new churches and Congregational inter-church bodies were formed, while the Presbyterians became more vigorous in setting up a presbyterial structure for the area.

However, the Plan had created a climate where other aspects of union could be explored, such as the plan of intercourse between the Albany Presbytery and the Northern Associated Presbytery. In 1803 the Oneida Presbytery allowed that a minister belonging to an association could join the Presbytery without giving up their association membership (Sweet, *Presbyterians* (1964/1936), p.43). The Geneva Presbytery followed suit in 1805 (Nichols, 1936). Thus isolated pastors on the new frontier could keep their denominational affiliation while finding fellowship. But this action also brought down the denominational barriers. In 1806 the Oneida Presbytery suggested a yoking or merger of two feeble nearby congregations, one a Presbytery member, and one Congregational (Fowler, 44).

THE ACCOMMODATION PLAN

The nature of the union took a dramatic turn in 1807 when the Congregational Middle Association sent a delegation to the Albany Synod to explore further ways of cooperation. The delegation sought "some intimate bond of union and correspondence."

The Synod responded in October 1807 (Sweet, *Presbyterians* (1964/1936), pp.468 ff.) in proper Presbyterian fashion, that they stood "ready, with the approbation of the General Assembly, to form as intimate a connection with your Association as the Constitution of the Church will admit." They invited the Association to join the Synod "By assuming the characteristics & scriptural name of Presbytery; adopt our standard of doctrine & government, & sit & vote with us..." However, they then went on to say the "name... [is] of less importance than the thing" and that "we also extend it to delegates from your Churches, whom we are willing to receive as substantially the same with our ruling elders," and that if these churches "prefer transacting their internal concerns in their present mode of Congregational government, we assure them of the utmost cheerfulness in leaving them undisturbed in the administration of that government; unless they shall choose to alter it themselves."

This went far beyond the original Plan, because it only allowed for mixed churches and their delegates to sit in presbytery. This new letter allowed for presbyteries to be called associations and allowed local congregations to be fully Congregational within presbytery and retain their local forms without disturbance. This really did change the polity of the Presbyterian Church.

The Middle Association seized on the offer of autonomy and voted in June 1808 to "acceed to the plan of union with the Presbyterian Church in the United States, on the condition proposed by the Synod of Albany... retaining our present name and mode of Congregational government." They then elected delegates and became part of the Synod.

While this action uses the words "plan of union," and the 1801 Plan includes the word "accommodation," the first act is generally called the Plan of Union, and is so referred to here, and the 1807/1808 decisions are called the Accommodation Plan, and are so referred to here.

Once the Synod of Albany (then the only Presbyterian Synod in upstate New York) had given up on strict Presbyterian polity, the possibilities of union in upstate New York changed radically. Hotchkin reports that by 1810 the

Accommodation Plan was also being used for the admission of churches in other upstate Presbyteries, such as Albany and Columbia Presbyteries, and also in New Jersey's Newark Presbytery.

In 1813 the Ontario Association in western New York disbanded so that its churches and ministers could join Presbyteries. In 1815 the Champlain Presbytery, which had held its first meeting in 1814, sent letters to all the Congregational churches in Essex, Clinton, Franklin, and Saint Lawrence Counties asking them to join the Presbytery under the "Plan of Union." Many responded and this plan became known as the "Essex Union."

In 1810, the Middle Association finally changed its name to Middle Presbytery. The Synod then merged it to Geneva Presbytery, and then divided their total territory into three new Presbyteries named Onondaga, Cayuga, and Geneva. The First Church in Pompey took its seat in the new Onondaga Presbytery by reminding the Presbytery of the freedom of its members (Fowler, 44). Nichols (1936) reports that in 1811 two of these new Presbyteries (Onondaga and Cayuga) had only one church each with Presbyterian forms.

Once the Accommodation Plan was in place Congregational inter-church bodies outside New England began to disappear. The Susquehanna Association had died out because of an internal constitutional problem after 1807. The Middle Association joined the Albany Synod in 1808, the majority of the Black River Association appears to have merged with a Presbytery in 1817, and the Luzerne Association/Susquehanna Presbytery joined a Presbyterian Synod in 1821. Majorities of the Oneida and Union Associations disbanded to join presbyteries, both in 1822. A rump of the Union Association continued to about 1830, when it also disbanded. The Saratoga Associated Presbytery disbanded in 1818, with some members joining Presbyteries, and Vermont members joining Congregational bodies there. The Morris County Presbytery disbanded in 1820, with many members being absorbed by the Westchester Associated Presbytery. It, in turn, disbanded in 1830. The Northern Associated Presbytery probably also disbanded in 1830. Both of these Associated Presbyteries had member churches join regular Presbyteries thereafter. Only the Strict Congregational Convention of New Jersey, which transferred its remaining members to a new Congregational body in New York in 1828, and the Strict Congregational Convention of Long Island, which continued, kept alive a remnant of Congregational organization outside New England. Ohio's Ecclesiastical Convention of New Connecticut also ended its life in 1808 so that its members could join Presbytery, and by 1816 leaders of the Southeast Ohio Association had also given up its existence and joined a Presbytery. The Congregational Association of South Carolina merged with a regular Presbytery in 1822. So this "Era of Good Feeling" swept through non-New England Congregationalism, bringing to an end almost all of its organized manifestations.

In 1800 Congregationalism had been by far the larger of the two denominations in upstate New York. By the end of 1830 a free-standing Congregational denomination had dwindled to a small rump, with only seven inter-church bodies in the entire Middle Atlantic area, several of which were formed by minorities after majorities of earlier bodies had gone into the presbyteries through the Accommodation Plan. On the other hand, while Presbyterianism seemed to rule the day, many New York, and at least one Pennsylvania Presbytery were made up almost entirely of congregations considering themselves internally Congregational.

MISSIONARY SOCIETIES

The missionary emphasis, which had played a role in the developing the Third Union, continued apace through the organization and expansion of freestanding missionary societies. It moved from being a cause of union to something changed as a result of union and the era of good feeling. New societies continued to be organized, such as the New York Domestic Missionary Society (1816) and the Western Domestic Missionary Society of the State of New York (1826).

The independent societies eventually amalgamated extensive resources and influence. With the support of New England dollars and college graduates from Yankee colleges, the independent Societies and Boards played a significant role in church extension, particularly in New York state. Some of the Congregational bodies were meant to be connected to, and thereby controlled by inter-church or clergy groups, as had been the case with Green's Society in Morris County. For example, the Missionary Society of Connecticut was an arm of the General Association of Connecticut. The original plan for the American Board of Commissioners for Foreign Missions (1810) also saw the new Board as an agency jointly under the control of the General Associations of Massachusetts and Connecticut. The Presbyterians also tried to conduct missionary work under church control, through the General Assembly's Standing Committee on Missions (from 1802), and the Western Missionary Society of the Pittsburgh Synod (also 1802).

However, the freestanding missionary societies initially held the ground and began to build up what became known as the Benevolent Empire.

The new societies under Presbyterian judicatories had difficulty sinking strong foundations. Some Presbyteries were able to do missionary work within their bounds. It was only in the areas already impacted by New England settlement that Presbyterians became major supporters of the freestanding missionary societies. Ashbel Green (1893/1837, p.30) points out that "it was only in the northern section of the Presbyterian Church that societies [not formally related to the church]... were at that time patronized."

The freestanding societies soon united their strategies and work. In the area of "Foreign" Missions, which included missions to the Indians, the work of the New York Missionary Society and the Northern Missionary Society were united in the United Foreign Missionary Society (**UFMS**) in 1816/1818. In 1825 it also picked up some remnants of the work of the Western Missionary Society of the Presbyterian Pittsburgh Synod. The Western (Foreign) Missionary Society of New Jersey, which had begun in 1800, died out in a few years. Ashbel Green (1893/1837) and Nichols (49) both identify the new United Foreign body as a Presbyterian, Associate Reformed, and Dutch Reformed body. The support of the New York Missionary Society, for example, of Strict Congregational Indian work on Long Island suggests that the forming bodies were also less fully Presbyterian than claimed. The Board was not Church controlled and was actually a membership association.

Meanwhile in New England the American Board of Commissioners for Foreign Missions (**ABCFM**) had begun in 1810. Its founders, in 1811, encouraged the Presbyterian General Assembly to form a similar board. The Assembly, however, (Loetscher (34), p.87; Ross (1890)) decided to support the American Board, and it responded by abandoning the idea of control by New England General Associations, and instead adding some Presbyterian members to the Board, and becoming a membership association. (See also Tracy (69).)

The United Foreign Missionary Society had overextended itself and gotten into debt, which led, in 1826, to the transfer of all its work to the American Board. In 1828 the American Board also absorbed the work of the Chickasaw Missionary Society which had been under the control of the Presbyterian Synod of South Carolina and Georgia. Thus all the Indian work in the states documented here had come under one united Board with offices in Boston.

Two trends can be seen in the area of domestic missions, supporting pastors and churches for new immigrants west of the mountains. The first was a proliferation of new regional missionary societies. These include the Genesee Missionary Society (Presbyterian and Congregational) 1810, the Young People's Missionary Society of Western New York c.1814, the Young Men's Missionary Society of New York 1815, the New York Evangelical Missionary Society 1816, the Philadelphia Missionary Society 1818, the Female Missionary Society of the Western District 1819, and the Pennsylvania Missionary Society 1826 (the latter incorporating the Philadelphia and three or four other independent Pennsylvania groups).

The other trend was the amalgamation of the work of these various societies. The Presbyterian General Assembly began to take some of this work under their umbrella. They recreated a Board of Missions of the General Assembly in 1816, and reorganized it in 1828, taking over the amalgamated work of the formerly independent Pennsylvania Missionary Society.

In 1822/1823 the Young Men's Missionary Society of New York and the New York Evangelical Missionary Society united as the United Domestic Missionary Society (**UDMS**), which Nichols (49) describes as a Presbyterian, Associate Reformed, and Dutch Reformed body, while Sweet (*Congregationalists* (1964/1939), p.49) sees the UDMS as largely Presbyterian.

In 1825 the various state missionary societies of New England met together in Boston and recommended a consolidation of missionary work in the west. This resulted in 1826 in the formation of the American Home Missionary Society (**AHMS**), which that year absorbed the work of the United Domestic Society. Sweet (*Congregationalists* (1964/1939), pp.48-49) follows other sources in claiming that the new body was dominated by New York Presbyterians until 1833. These conclusions have to be taken with a grain of salt. The Synods of New York in 1826 had too many accommodation and mixed congregations to be considered a fully "Presbyterian" bodies. In 1828 the AHMS began a plan which allowed state societies to become auxiliaries to the national society. The Societies in Massachusetts, Vermont, and New Hampshire did so in 1828, Rhode Island and Maine followed in 1829, and the two Societies in Connecticut followed in 1830/1831 and 1832. Some of these New England bodies were already related to General Associations in their respective states, and the others had all begun close associations which eventually led to the connection of the societies to the Congregational churches in these states. Thus the AHMS became the primary domestic missionary arm of the Congregational churches.

The new system of the AHMS distinguished between auxiliaries (which sent supporting dollars, but did not receive aid), and Agencies (where dollars were collected, but aid also received). Many local auxiliaries began in New York from the start, as well as two large Agencies: Geneva/Western in 1826, and Central in 1828. A Philadelphia body founded in 1834 was twice reorganized until it became extinct in 1861. The Agencies were powerful missionary forces until the removal of Presbyterian support changed the nature of the AHMS. Farther west an 1822 Indiana body related to the AHMS in 1826, but died in 1840. A Society from before 1826 in the Western Reserve of Ohio affiliated in 1831 and died in 1863. There were also Agencies in Marietta Ohio (1840-1863), Cincinnati/Columbus Ohio (1830-after 1854), Canada (1835-1845), and later in Missouri (1842-1859), and Kentucky (1854-before 1861). While headquartered in New York City, the AHMS was clearly driven by its New England financial base.

A third area of mission work involved educational work to train pastors and provide schools, colleges, and seminaries. The American Education Society was begun in 1815 and incorporated in Massachusetts in 1816. It was closely related to the New England churches and often promoted its work by publishing valuable historical biographies of New England Congregational clergy. A Presbyterian Education Society was begun in the New York City area in 1818 and a Western Education Society began in 1819. These two were joined in 1822 and affiliated with the American Education Society in 1827. A separate Presbyterian Education Board related to the General Assembly began in 1819.

One result of the growing strength of the missionary societies was the wide geographic range of pastoral movement. Previously pastors had followed closely on the heels of migration of groups regionally, culturally, and theologically close to their own origins. Now the societies might receive an appeal and respond by sending a young missionary from New Hampshire into central Illinois or eastern Tennessee. The societies also, true to their ecumenical origins, sent Congregationalists into Presbyterian areas and visa versa. To read the biographies of clergy during the height of the Plan of Union, or to read presbytery records or New England Association minutes during the same period, is to marvel at the movements of clergy back and forth between both groups. While extant records of local congregations can be analyzed for signs of Congregational or Presbyterian polity (elders, sessions, submission to presbytery rules, separate societies, financial support for denominational or ecumenical mission groups, etc.), records for clergy can not. Theoretically all clergy members of a presbytery were Presbyterians. Yet, if a pastor could belong to both a presbytery and an association at the same time, they were both. Many clergy called Presbyterian were born, bred, and educated in New England, served congregations with local Congregational forms, and may have ended their careers in clearly Congregational settings. This fact that clergy moved back and forth from associations to presbyteries, often without changing their views on polity is one of the most striking aspects of the life of the Plan.

ADDITIONAL UNITY

The Era of Good Feeling also spread in other directions in a general move towards the Presbyterian Church U.S.A.. The Associate Reformed Church, which was itself a 1782 merger of Associate and Covenanter groups had a movement which began to seek union with the Presbyterian Church U.S.A.. Their General Synod forged a union in 1822, but with much opposition. Two Pennsylvania Presbyteries and one in New York united to the Presbyterian Church, the latter becoming the New York Second Presbytery. The New York Associate Reformed Synod continued on its own. In New York state this merger brought four congregations in New York City, and possibly as many as five other congregations into the Presbyterian Church.

Dutch Reformed congregations in upstate New York had early moved towards the English language, particularly those in areas distant from other Dutch congregations. They also began to receive into membership Calvinists from other traditions. Before 1800 two Dutch churches in New York had transferred into the Presbyterian Church. Between 1803 and 1837 nineteen more made the move. These included three that were jointly transferred in 1824 from the Reformed Montgomery Classis to the Oneida Presbytery. During this period at least two Pennsylvania and two New Jersey churches also made similar moves. These two union movements had the effect of solidifying the judicatory system, by adding churches with no experience of Congregational polity to the Presbyterian Church during the Plan of Union period.

This broader Presbyterian Church was also able in urban areas to begin congregations that represented various ethnicities. In Albany, for instance, a Second Presbyterian Church was formed in 1813, becoming a center of New England influence in the City. In 1829 they called William B. Sprague, a Connecticut native, Yale graduate, and Massachusetts pastor as their pastor. Sprague was a prominent church historian, considered one of the nation's leading preachers, and pastored the Church for forty years. When the Associate Reformed Church there joined the regular Presbyterians, it became the Third Presbyterian Church, and served the more distinctly Scottish community. The old First Presbyterian Church was left to serve the more middle-of-the-road Presbyterian constituency.

This last massive attempt at a Presbyterian and Congregational union in America was not paralleled by a similar movement in Europe. Instead the clearer lines of division there, which had been underscored by the rise of local Congregational ministerial bodies and local Unions of Churches in England from 1781 to 1815, the rise of a Congregational movement in Scotland from 1795, and the appearance of a Scottish style Presbytery in England in 1783, were now only strengthened. Scottish Congregationalists organized a Union in 1812, those in Ireland one in 1829, and a Congregational Union of England and Wales (advocated since 1809) began in 1833. Similarly a Presbyterian Church in England, with an order similar to that of Scotland, was organized in 1836. The remnants of the English Presbyterians were also amalgamated into a British and Foreign Unitarian Association in 1825. (The Welsh speaking Union of Welsh Independents did not organize until 1871, the same year a national Congregational body finally appeared in the United States.)

THE WORKINGS OF THE PLAN

When a presbytery or local church record (and the histories based thereon) says a church was received by Presbytery "under the Plan of Union," or "according to the Plan of Union," it is unclear whether it was truly a mixed church as described in the Plan, or really a Congregational church joining under the accommodation procedures. This distinction is not carefully explained in most records, and the phrases above seem to refer to either possibility. Because most Congregational churches eventually moved towards some kind of standing or prudential committee, and moved away from all business being done at congregational meetings, the distinction also is further blurred through time. Because later Presbyterian rulings insisted that sessions and ruling elders defined Presbyterian churches, one possible conclusion is that all mixed and standing committee churches were - by modern definitions - Congregational.

Also, neither the Plan of Union, nor the Accommodation Plan make any reference to the ownership of property, the ability of a church to connect itself to an independent religious society, or the direct ownership by a church of its own property. Many churches with sessions still were affiliated to independent societies, which held the property. Some churches called "Congregational," had their property held by a society called "Presbyterian" and visa-versa. Some churches got charters with names that tried to include all options: "First Congregational and Presbyterian Church and Society," or some similar form. It is not clear when the theory of presbytery ownership of the property of local congregations became common practice in former Plan of Union territory. Nevertheless, separate societies, names which personify the difference between churches and societies, and local congregational insistence on local ownership of their property are all polity concerns that reveal New England roots or influence.

THE DECLINE OF GOOD FEELINGS: RUMBLINGS IN THE CHURCHES

While good feeling seemed to be growing in New York, the ability to maintain unity was strained by the fact that both traditions seeking unity in the new west were connected to traditions that were unable to maintain very much internal unity within their own circles.

NEW ENGLAND CONGREGATIONALISM IN TRANSITION

New England Congregationalism was pulling apart from a variety of issues: the search for a new polity, the movement towards disestablishment, and growing theological debate. The complex set of issues being faced in New England impacted what went on in the west. In addition, those in New England interested in missions and church extension were also spreading into other places such as northern New England, particularly Maine. This drained resources and clergy candidates away from the western union areas. In northern New England Yankee population movements overwhelmed some small Scotch-Irish outposts, and many Presbyterian churches became Congregational.

With the threat of a royal imposition gone, New England churches finally had the freedom to adopt revised polities such as the Proposals of 1705, as Connecticut had done through the Saybrook Synod. A century of Massachusetts' unique brand of autonomy had actually developed supporters from John Wise to Nathaniel Emmons. In 1800 only Connecticut and Vermont had formal statewide bodies, and inter-church Congregational bodies were few and far between.

While not a major issue of dispute, questions of internal polity still arose within churches. A small minority of Congregational churches still retained the office of ruling elder within their congregations. Worthley (1970) lists seven such Congregational churches in Massachusetts proper in 1800.

In addition, New England at the turn of the century had two independent Presbyteries that included churches with Congregational forms. Other churches called themselves Presbyterian, yet did not belong to presbyteries, sometimes availed themselves of establishment privileges, and had pastors who belonged to Congregational ministerial associations. The new Vermont (1795) general body was designed to include presbyteries, and the New Hampshire general body, when formed (1809), would include Presbyterian pastors, and eventually Presbyterian churches which were also full members of regular presbyteries. In other words, New England had no clear polity.

The period was also impacted by the rise of many newer religious groups such as many varieties of Baptists, Methodists, Universalists, Christians, etc.. Often these groups drew from lower income people who had been forced for generations to pay taxes to the established churches, but had generally been kept out of the ruling educated elite in the parishes and congregations. Also, since the Anglican establishments in New York and the South had been wiped out by the Revolution, the retention of the establishment in New England seemed like an archaic anachronism in a nation that had adopted the First Amendment. These trends made the establishment and its relation to polity issues a major point of contention.

Theological strains and debates were also appearing within New England Congregationalism. Liberal congregations and clergy opposed to the Edwardsean mission movement and Presbyterian cooperation on theological grounds could employ the polity issues to disrupt effective united responses from New England to the west.

Much of the polity fight occurred in Massachusetts. Between 1800 and 1804, Massachusetts proper had about twenty-three regional ministerial associations. In 1802 eight associations met to consider forming a general association. Some shied away from the idea of a state-wide organization. Only five associations joined the new General Association. In 1805 all the state's associations were asked to consider joining the new body. Some voted "no" and many others did not even bother to consider the issue. By 1810 the General Association still had only ten associations, mostly in the west, where the stronger polities of Connecticut, Vermont, and the Grafton Presbytery had influence, and in Essex County, close to the center of New England's Scotch-Irish settlements and Presbyterian influence. Not until the Dedham case (1819) and the formation of the American Unitarian Association (1825) did a flood of associations join the General Association. One older Association waited until 1840 to join. Except for the Mountain Presbytery in western Massachusetts, inter-church bodies did not begin to appear in the state until 1821.

Similar delays occurred in statewide and inter-church organization in other parts of New England. These tasks and tensions consumed the energy of the churches and leaders trying to develop a new polity, and sent westward-bound settlers out without a clear posture on polity.

Societal pressure was also mounting against what was left of the New England tax-supported establishment. It had been fading since the Toleration Act (1692) had allowed dissenting congregations. Many of them had received tax relief after the King's Rule of 1726. The arrival of the SPG missionaries and the Yale defections of 1722 had created more Anglican churches, while the Great Awakening had led to both Separate Congregationalists and Baptists.

Strong minorities outside established churches increased pressures on pastoral salaries, taxes, and peace in town after town. The new west had also caused leading clergy to adopt an inconsistent worldview which enjoyed and protected their tax support privileges at home, but encouraging young clergy moving west to devise something new. The establishment now collapsed.

Vermont never had a formal establishment. Early in its history many towns had followed the example of their New England neighbors and subsidized town meeting houses and places of worship. This was forbidden in 1807, creating for the first time a non-established state with Congregationalism as the largest religion.

Rhode Island had always had religious liberty, but before boundary changes in 1746 and 1862 only a handful of Congregational churches survived there without the benefit of an establishment. Early in the new century Samuel Hopkins took the lead in organizing a Rhode Island Missionary Society. It was aided by the similar society in Connecticut, and more Congregational churches were organized in that state on free standing non-establishment foundations.

The establishment came to an end in New Hampshire in 1817, Connecticut in 1818, Maine in 1820 (separated from Massachusetts), and finally in Massachusetts in 1834. New Englanders finally began to imagine a Congregationalism separate from and not propped up by state privilege. If it could be done in New England, it could perhaps be done elsewhere. New expectations for a non-established Congregationalism began to grow.

Disestablishment had a variety of effects on Congregationalism. Obviously it forced churches which had relied on tax support to pay their pastors and maintain their buildings to develop independent means of raising money to survive. It also forced both clergy and congregations to live in a reality where they were no longer automatically to be considered the spiritual, academic, and cultural leaders of their communities.

Disestablishment also caused its own challenge to the internal polity of Congregational churches. Establishment had produced a dual system of geographic parishes, societies, or towns that were tax collecting entities that controlled meetinghouse expenses and pastoral salaries. Within each parish was a church made up of believers, with scriptural officers: elders and deacons. Since the Great Awakening many churches had strained relationships with their parishes, when they would not concur on the choice of a minister, pay for building repairs, or tax sufficiently for a strong pastoral salary. Some churches had built endowments to cover the tax short-falls.

In the City of Boston, the colony of Rhode Island and other non-established areas before the Revolution, informal unincorporated societies of males interested in supporting given churches were formed to raise money to support their churches, generally through donations, or options like selling and assessing meeting house pews. As non-conformist churches arose in establishment towns, they often had this type of parallel organization, and sometimes received the church tax for people certified as members of the tolerated church with which they were connected.

After the Revolution, when the State legislatures gained the power to set up corporate charters, many of these informal societies procured charters. Faced with disestablishment, most Congregational churches also chartered parallel bodies which, in most cases, eventually took over the assets of the former established parishes.

The new structure, though, still retained the dual system, with a consistent pattern of two different organizations. While women and minors might join the church, some secular men who contributed to the society but never professed belief, were still members there.

This dual status bore no resemblance to Presbyterian organization, where organized sessions appointed trustees to hold property for them. Eventually, the property was considered to be held on behalf of the presbytery.

Not until the late nineteenth century did New England state law allow for the incorporation of churches. Slowly most churches began the process of being united with their societies.

As A. Hastings Ross has noted, these disparate approaches to organization and property caused many frictions in the west. Presbyterians, in whose polity property was controlled by church bodies, claimed to be more democratic than Congregationalists, whose church property was often controlled by societies which seemed to be private clubs.

Theology also hindered early New England Congregationalism's advance west. Massachusetts was particularly burdened. Unlike smaller Connecticut, it was on the verge of schism, facing the greatest theological controversy it ever experienced.

Despite their previous religious and polity differences, the Congregational churches of New England had been historically able to claim a common cultural unity and a broad theologically inclusive base. The Unitarian departure broke down the unity of the Massachusetts churches. Arminianism and the formal dissent against the excesses of the Awakening had grown through the eighteenth century, particularly in Boston and the other larger east coast cities. The rise of the Enlightenment in Europe had often led to a stress on works righteousness, Deism, Rationalism, and Arianism. The formerly Anglican Kings Chapel in Boston had been taken over by a group of proprietors during the Revolution. In 1785 the congregation declared themselves to be under the Cambridge Platform, thereby becoming Congregational, but at the same time they declared themselves to be Unitarian in theology, denying the Trinity. In 1805 Unitarian Henry Ware was named as Hollis Professor of Divinity at Harvard, and a full-scale division began. Many churches and parishes hired or retained pastors of Unitarian sentiments. In 1825 an American Unitarian Association was formed and two denominations existed.

This Unitarian departure was also the last straw in breaking the back of the establishment. Many churches preferred to choose orthodox Trinitarian pastors, while their parishes selected Unitarians. In 1819 the Massachusetts courts ruled in the famed Dedham decision that where there were parishes or towns supporting religious services, they were the recognized legal body, and they owned land, buildings, endowments, communion ware, Bibles, and even church records. Churches held no legal status, and if they did not conform to their parish, they did not exist. This cut the religious life of many of Massachusetts' oldest towns into two factions, which soon had buildings facing each other, both claiming to descend from the original congregation. The Dedham case caused most churches to seek chartered societies to hold their property for a particular denominational name and those trying to maintain the establishment became too few to defend it in the legislature. In Massachusetts many Unitarian churches continued to call themselves Congregational. Those holding opposite theological perspectives often added words like "Trinitarian," "Evangelical," or "Orthodox" to their names. By the time evangelical Congregationalism in Massachusetts had come out of this battle it had a conscious denominational identity, and a fierce fire for extending its worldview.

Unitarianism had already entered the Middle Atlantic area in the 1790's, when Joseph Priestly founded Unitarian congregations in Pennsylvania. The schism also impacted the area as Unitarians moved west, often still calling themselves Congregational. Some congregations called Congregational were clearly Unitarian (see Appendix I.), while other congregations had mixed memberships that were divided on theological issues. This use of the Congregational name fueled Presbyterian suspicions about newly arrived New England settlers.

Only in the late 1820's did most New England Congregationalists begin to see their future clearly outside an establishment, have state-wide bodies in each New England state, see themselves clearly as Trinitarians, and unite around the benevolent empire mission agencies. Inter-church bodies also began to grow at that time, but did not become relatively uniform in New England until the 1860's.

PRESBYTERIAN DIVISIONS

Similarly, issues of denominational identity were aflame in the Scotch-Irish sections of the Presbyterian Church. The impact of the Union on the Presbyterian Church can not be minimized. Because many New England churches were large, compact, and financially well off, they had clergy to spare to move to new mission frontiers. These Yankee clergy moving west were usually well-educated graduates of the New England colleges. On the other hand, the Scotch-Irish population was spread over a much wider area, churches, even in the older Presbyterian areas, were smaller, poorer, and did not have the advantage of a well-established college system. Many pastors had to serve circuits or charges of several congregations. Many pulpits were often vacant. This created two cultures within the Church. New York congregations not only had New England roots, but were more likely to have resident pastors. Nichols (49) reports that by 1824 nearly one-half of the Presbyterian clergy in the entire country were in New York state. Other parts of the Presbyterian Church felt under siege, fearing a take-over by the many New England clergy.

Even though the American Home Missionary Society had not yet been formed, many of the most important new city locations throughout the west also had churches which had been founded by missionaries from the Connecticut Missionary Society, or other New England sources. Resentments arose over these new clergy, the strange theologies they brought with them (such as Hopkinsinianism), and their different cultural and polity views. The farmer-preacher and itinerant models of clergy, which had become classic in many other southern churches, were always a possible alternative within Presbyterianism. The wide spread presence of New England missionaries often gave a sense that Scotch-Irish and Southern cultures were threatened.

In addition, frontier Scotch-Irish Presbyterianism was racked by continuous debates over revivals, a dilution of ministerial educational standards, and a drift away from Calvinism towards a more Arminian pietism. While New England Congregationalism's concurrent battle with Unitarianism, and Scotch-Irish Presbyterian schisms on the frontier both broke with Calvinism and tended towards Arminianism, there the similarities ended. Unitarianism was anti-revival, and held fast with other New Englanders for an educated clergy. The Scotch-Irish schisms were more pro-revival than their parent church, and were inclined to ordain people with little formal education.

The great Cane Ridge Revival in Kentucky in 1801 led to a schism in 1803 when Barton W. Stone and others began an independent Springfield Presbytery, whose churches a year later became the key factor in the beginning of unitive Christian Churches in the west. Thomas and Alexander Campbell, two Seceder Associate Presbyterian pastors in western Pennsylvania, left that group in 1809, and after a flirtation with the Baptists, separated as the Disciples of Christ and Churches of Christ about 1830. Another series of revivals led people from the Cumberland Presbytery in Tennessee to withdraw and in 1810 form the Cumberland Presbyterian Church.

Both Congregationalists and Presbyterians were under attack as to their theology, polity, sense of qualifications for the ministry, and cultural identity. Like the political "Era of Good Feeling," which occurred at much the same time, beneath a surface unity, the radical changes caused by the growth of the new west fermented, until suddenly exploding into deep emotional fissures.

By studying the differences between the issues raised by the schismatic groups coming off the edges of New England Congregationalism and Scotch-Irish Presbyterianism we can identify the ferment of the times. These conflicts illuminate the theological, educational, and worship style views that also divided the two primary groups.

THE RESISTANCE OF THE CONGREGATIONAL RUMP

A small Congregational rump group in New York and New Jersey consistently opposed the third union. It was strongest among the former Separatist churches. The Strict Congregational Convention of Long Island never participated in the Accommodation Plan, and its New Jersey counterpart lasted long enough to join a new radical New York group in 1828. Congregational inter-church bodies, generally adopting the Green polity, began in Essex in 1817, Genesee in 1818, reorganized a group in the Black River area in 1822, and formed minority rumps from previously disbanded groups in Union in 1822 and Oneida in 1825. Bodies began in Saint Lawrence and in the New York City area in 1825. However, farther west, the more isolated Congregational clergy consistently led Union or accommodation congregations, or simply joined and served fully Presbyterian congregations. Outside New England, only in New York and New Jersey did an organized Congregational denomination continue. No other Congregational bodies appeared outside New England until 1834. Also in that year most of these New York bodies combined their destiny by finally coming together to form a General Association of New York.

One difference between the continuing Congregational rump and those moving towards Accommodation Plan unity was actually a social issue reflecting the move from a rural to an urban culture in America. Churches retaining their Congregational preferences often appreciated the intimate way that all members could be involved in church decisions and consultations over discipline. They felt that referring of major issues to small committees or sessions broke down the relational nature of the church. Similarly they appreciated the smaller Congregational associations, where every small country church could be a sometime host and where delegates and pastors came to know each other well. The large, more formal and distant presbyteries that were evolving seemed to lack the personal. These issues, not noticed by most historians, stand out in the minutes of the reorganized Oneida Association from 1825.

These rural/urban issues are at least partially demonstrated by the rapid growth of Presbyterianism in the urban areas of New York City, Rochester, and Buffalo, and the concentration of continuing Congregationalism in rural areas around the Adirondack Mountains. This also helps to explain why Presbyterianism moved more quickly than Congregationalism in serving some new ethnic groups settling in the cities.

However this Congregational rural preference proved to be a problem when combined with Congregationalism's desire for an educated clergy. Congregational churches had to maintain a certain core size to support their trained pastors. Eventually county seat towns and smaller cities - rather than the open country - became the demographic base of non-New England Congregationalism, while Presbyterians grew much more rapidly in large cities.

The New York rump, those inter-church bodies that resisted absorption into the accommodation Presbyteries, was in a way the pioneer in non-established Congregationalism. The new polity (Green's) is plain in this note in the minutes of their General Association 1835 meeting at Paris: "The appellations of *Association* and *Consociation* used in this state, both denote the same *class* of ecclesiastical bodies, viz., those composed of ministers and lay delegates." (*Italics* original.)

UNRAVELING OF MISSIONARY UNITY

Presbyterians began to oppose the New England control of missionary strategy and support, free from direction of Synods and Presbyteries. Ashbel Green writing in 1837 said of the AHMS "it became notorious, that the unhappy and reproachful distractions of the Church, threatening not only its peace but its very existence, were attributable in great measure to the influence of this institution." As the 1830's progressed the Presbyterians strengthened the work of their General Assembly Board of Missions. On the foreign agenda the Pittsburgh Synod set up a Western Foreign Missionary Society in 1831. Its work was transferred to the General Assembly in 1835, and in 1837 the General Assembly created a Board of Foreign Missions to conduct this work.

OPPOSITION TO THE UNION WITHIN THE PRESBYTERIES, SYNODS, AND GENERAL ASSEMBLY

Except for New England and the small New York rump, the Presbyterians and all of the unionist western Congregationalists were living together within the Presbyterian Church in 1830. It was in that setting that the conflict would finally explode. Since New England was thereby removed from the debate, the eventual Scotch-Irish majority in the General Assembly is not surprising.

Many growing urban congregations, already in presbyteries, felt encumbered by the necessity of doing all business and discipline within congregational meetings. The move towards sessions and a committee structure seemed natural, particularly when encouraged by pastors who had graduated from Presbyterian seminaries, or pressured from other nearby congregations. Slowly many churches, beginning with those in urban areas, or whose Congregationalism was isolated and unusual, adopted internal Presbyterian forms.

Presbyteries that included truly union churches consistent with the 1801 Plan, or the more common Congregational churches living under the Accommodation Plan had to figure out how to deal with these differences. Initially they began with modest methods, such as requests that churches submit reports and minutes for review to regular presbytery meetings. Vicinage councils and ministerial standing and installation were regularized through the presbytery. The requirements, initially allowing freedoms but requiring records and reports were adopted by the Oneida Presbytery in 1814, the Saint Lawrence Presbytery in 1818, and others following.

Many churches actually created new and rather unique structures and polities. One congregation in northeastern Pennsylvania described itself as "Halfway Covenant Presbyterian," combining an historical oddity from earlier New England Congregationalism with the name Presbyterian. Some congregations had elders but let a separate society hold their property. Some societies and/or churches sought charters with legal names such as "Presbyterian or Congregational," or "Presbyterian and Congregational." Some churches never elected elders but always used the name Presbyterian. Some churches fought with their presbytery, and withdrew, but kept the office of ruling elder.

One aspect of the growing controversy was that the "cheerfulness" in leaving Congregational churches "undisturbed" in their polity, as the Accommodation Plan had provided, began to fall away as time passed. Particularly galling to traditional Presbyterians was the receipt of new clergy coming west: graduates of New England seminaries, licentiates from New England associations, missionaries from the independent benevolent societies, and fully ordained pastors, who were merely received by transfer and never had to subscribe to the Westminster standards. The old issue of subscription was rising again.

When opposition to the Union began to be expressed in General Assembly, some of the procedures most in violation of traditional Scottish polity were removed. Granting votes at the General Assembly to delegates from Congregational state bodies was opposed, and a plan to drop the votes arose in the late 1820's and was finalized in 1830. Similarly, the practice of sending delegates rather than ruling elders to presbytery meetings was part of both the original Plan and the accommodation plan. At times, the majority of the congregations of many presbyteries did not have ruling elders, so they also began to send delegates who were not ruling elders on to synod meetings, and then on to the General Assembly meetings. For a long time such delegates had been accepted in both places. In 1831 the General Assembly decided it would no longer receive and seat such "committee men." Both of these decisions limited the power of the Yankee forces within the General Assembly. Some presbyteries could now only send lay delegates from a small minority of congregations with full Presbyterian forms to the General Assembly. These decisions also made Congregational churches within presbyteries aware that they were second class citizens.

Initially much of the tension within the Presbyterian Church was theological and intellectual. Some of the theological issues were widespread, and did not initially push the General Assembly to division. Unionists of both backgrounds rejected Unitarianism. A new revivalism spurred by a sense of perfectionism and leaning towards Arminianism spread across "burned over" districts in upstate New York and Ohio. The chief leader of this movement, Presbyterian Charles G. Finney, ran revivals in churches of all stripes. However, most union presbyteries were cool to Finney's practices, and many of his followers were excluded from fellowship. Related to the Finney-ite revivals was the founding of churches taking the name "Free" church, and advocating against slavery and for ending pew rents and the control of congregations by elite and wealthy classes. Finney eventually became a Congregationalist.

Other theological issues impacted even more parts of the Church. Disciples of the New England theologians Samuel Hopkins and Nathaniel W. Taylor agitated Presbyterian stalwarts. Their followers were widely ordained in Congregational circles and began to transfer into union presbyteries, where rifts began to appear. Congregational pastors or missionaries far distant from the Plan of Union areas were the first to be targeted. Albert Barnes left the Presbyterian Church in Morristown, New Jersey in 1830 to become pastor of the First Church in Philadelphia. In 1831 he was charged with error, Ashbel Green being among those leading the charge against him. By 1835 the charges had been raised to heresy. After the prominent former Long Island, Connecticut, and Massachusetts pastor Lyman Beecher went west in 1832 to take charge of a Seminary in Cincinnati, conservative forces brought charges against him in 1834. Meanwhile, in 1833, Beecher's son Edward, and two other Professors at Illinois College were also arraigned before presbytery on theological grounds. In addition to these prominent cases, isolated AHMS and other clergy of New England background were often targets in western presbyteries.

These cases about clergy were really a reworking of the old subscription controversy. A cultural root may be detected here. In England common law could allow for the growth over time of several variations and interpretations of principles. The same worldview that pushed the Scotch-Irish party towards subscription and specific adherence to particular verbal forms of doctrine eventually began to find problems with the fluid view of local church structure.

These and other issues were widely debated. Polemical articles and pamphlets appeared. In 1824 Ashbel Green coined the words "Old School," and "New School" to describe the two factions in the Presbyterian Assembly. The New School was supportive of the Plan of Union, worked in cooperation with the independent missionary societies, was influenced by new currents in New England theology, and generally was more strongly opposed to slavery. The Old School was more rigid in their theology - endorsing subscription to Westminster, sought a uniform polity on the Scottish model - which would have direct control of missionary emphases, and - since it encompassed most of the South where New England influence was at a minimum - tolerated slavery.

By 1830 some congregations began to split.

In 1831 and 1832 Ashbel Green published an autobiography written by his father Jacob. In his notes to his father's work, Ashbel describes his father as "an Independent, or Congregationalist, in the essential principles of church government." He says of his father "when he thought he was called in duty to speak and act in a manner that was not Presbyterian, he... left the Presbytery." Ashbel then goes on to plead, "Why will not those who are now members of the Presbyterian church, and whose doctrinal sentiments and congregational notions differ more widely from our standards,... why will they not take the same honest, frank and consistent course, that was taken by these worthy men? Our controversy with them would cease at once, if they would place themselves where they ought to stand - by themselves." (Ashbel Green (1831-1832), p.146) Ashbel's plea that the opposition get up and leave was not taken up by Yankees with standing and office in the Presbyterian Church.

The split also extended to the schools. Union Theological Seminary was begun in 1836 as a New School institution, but independent of the control of synods or General Assembly.

Yet the controversy did stir up some growth in the dormant non-New England Congregational rump. The New York bodies finally formed a General Association in 1834, and new bodies appeared in a Finney-ite group in Central New York by 1834, and bodies in Western New York in 1835, Long Island in 1836, and a Welsh *Gymanfa* in New York in 1837. Farther west Congregational churches outside presbyteries also began to appear from 1830. New free standing Congregational inter-church bodies also began to appear. These included an Independent Union on the Western Reserve and in Ohio and Pennsylvania (1834), a General Association of the Western Reserve (in Ohio) 1836, which included other sub-groups by 1837, a First Congregational Association in Indiana in 1837, an Illinois Association in 1834/1835, a Fox River Union (also in Illinois) in 1835, and a Michigan Association in 1837.

Figures Nos. 3, 4, and **5** show the extent of Congregationalism and the Plan of Union in this area at the end of 1836. The small Congregational rump in New York already shows a movement out of the Plan of Union. While only one affiliated Congregational Church in the state had previously had Presbyterian forms, 42.3% had been or were still listed in presbytery reports. 47.1% of the independent Congregational churches had also been on presbytery lists. Of the churches in New York on the presbytery lists, 27.9% had Congregational local forms, 3.2% had unclear forms, and 26.8% were formerly Congregational churches that had adopted Presbyterian forms. Only 42.1% of the churches in presbytery had always had Presbyterian forms. Figures 4 and 5 reveal where pockets of Congregational background existed in New Jersey and Pennsylvania, although, except for Welsh congregations, most of these had already made their way into Presbyterianism. Thus, it is clear that New York state Presbyterian churches rose primarily from Congregational roots. There were also significant pockets of Congregational ancestry in other parts of the Middle Atlantic area, such as Bradford and Susquehanna Counties in Pennsylvania.

THE THIRD SCHISM BEGINS WHILE UNION LINGERS 1837-1852

But the center of the controversy was still within the Presbyterian General Assembly. The annual meetings of the Assembly became battlegrounds for appeals in the heresy cases and a host of other issues. Because the Assembly met every year, with different delegates, majorities changed and policies and directions were reversed and rescinded.

FIGURE NO. 3
LIVING PRESBYTERIAN AND CONGREGATIONAL CHURCHES
NEW YORK STATE – END OF 1836

COUNTY	Indep. Pres.	In Presbytery					Affiliated Congregational		Indep. Cong.	Total
		PR Form		P or C	CG Form					
		PR	f. CG		CG	f. PR	CG	f. PR		
Albany		8	1	1				1		11
Allegany		3	2	1	5	1			1	13
Bronx		1								1
Broome	1	3	2		5				3	14
Cattaraugus		2	3	1	6				1	13
Cayuga		6	7	1	3	1			1	19
Chautauqua		3	4		9		5			20 [21]
Chemung		3	2							5
Chenango		1	3	1	9		5		2	21
Clinton		3			5		2			9 [10]
Columbia		5	2		1	1	1		1	11
Cortland		3	1		7	1				12
Delaware		4	2	1	11				2	20
Dutchess		7	5	1			1		1	15
Erie	1	5	3		10		4			23
Essex			2		1		12			15
Franklin			1		5					6
Fulton		5	1		1					7
Genesee		2	5		4		3			14
Greene		3	7		1				1	12
Hamilton										0
Herkimer		3	3	1	3		2		2	14
Jefferson		10	3		2		10		1	26
Kings		3								3
Lewis		1	5				3		1	10
Livingston		10	6	1	3	1				21
Madison		2	1		6	1	7		1	18
Monroe		7	10		4		7		1	28 [29]
Montgomery		2								2
Nassau			1							1
New York		34	1				4			39
Niagara		9					1		2	12
Oneida	1	16	12		4		7		6	45 [46]
Onondaga	1	6	5		10				4	26
Ontario		5	6		5		1		5	22
Orange		14	6				2		1	23
Orleans		2	2		5					9
Oswego		4	1	3	10	2			1	21
Otsego		3	3		10		3			19
Putnam		1	4							5
Queens			2							2
Rensselaer	1	11	3		2				1	18
Richmond										0
Rockland		1	2							3
St. Lawrence		4	2	2	3		18		3	32
Saratoga		4	4		4	1	1		1	14 [15]
Schenectady		2								2

Schoharie		2	3							5
Schuyler		7			1					8
Seneca		7	1							8
Steuben	1	14	4	2	1		2			24
Suffolk		6	13		4		12			35
Sullivan		2	2	1			2			7
Tioga			2		4	1			2	9
Tompkins		4	1	3	4				1	13
Ulster		3	2							5
Warren		3	2							5
Washington		5	3				3		2	13
Wayne		8	2	1	3		3		1	17 [18]
Westchester		4	9				1			14
Wyoming	1		3	2	9	1			2	18
Yates		5	3		1					9
TOTAL	7	291	185	23	181	11	122	1	51	866 [872]
	7	691					123		51	866

NOTES FOR FIGURE NO. 3

[NOTES: (1) The actual 1837 General Assembly report does not include any data for Onondaga Presbytery. Nearby reports and information on the Presbytery's churches have been compared, and 22 churches inserted for that Presbytery. The Tioga Presbytery is reported as having 18 congregations, but only 17 are actually listed. One congregation in Cattaraugus County (Ellicottville) appeared on the lists of two Presbyteries (Angelica and Buffalo), but is shown only once here. One congregation in Chenango Presbytery is listed as if two congregations (South New Berlin, Chenango County), which lowers their total. Included in the presbytery totals, and here, are two Suffolk County churches which appear on the presbytery lists, as served by Presbyterian ministers, but are actually Congregational churches, not members of presbytery. This brings the total number of New York congregations in presbyteries to 691. (2) One congregation in St. Lawrence Presbytery (Depo) is un-located, but because all other congregations in that Presbytery are in St. Lawrence County, that Church is listed in that County here. (3) Of 123 affiliated Congregational Churches, 106 are in the New York General Association; 9 in the Long Island Strict Convention; 3 in the Long Island Association; 3 in Vermont Consociations; 1 in a Connecticut Consociation; and 1 listed with a Massachusetts Ministerial Association. (4) Six congregations are listed both as in a presbytery, and as affiliated to a Congregational body. Four of these are in transition from one group to the other (three Presbyterian to Congregational (Oneida County: Bridgewater; Saratoga Co.: Maltaville; Wayne Co.: Williamson), and one Congregational to Presbyterian (Monroe Co.: Ogden)), while two are double listed for unclear reasons (Chautauqua Co.: Sheridan; Clinton Co.: Peru). While totaling churches in Presbyteries, affiliated Congregational, and independent would total 872 congregations, dropping those in both groups, brings the total to 866. (5) Of the 123 affiliated Congregational churches, 52 (42.3%) are or were formerly listed or mentioned in presbytery reports, and of the 51 independent Congregational churches, 24 (47.1%) were formerly listed or mentioned in presbytery. (6) Six of the independent Congregational churches are Welsh.]

NOTES FOR FIGURE NO. 4

[NOTES: (1) All affiliated Congregational churches are related to the New York General Association. (2) One congregation is listed as both in a presbytery, and as affiliated to a Congregational body. (Essex County: Newark (First Free)). While totaling churches in Presbyteries, affiliated Congregational and independent would total 36 congregations, dropping the one in both groups brings the total to 35. (3) Of seven affiliated or independent Congregational churches, two were or had been in regular presbyteries.]

NOTES FOR FIGURE NO. 5

[NOTES: (1) Of 4 affiliated Congregational churches, three are presumed to be related to the Independent Union of the Western Reserve, and one to a local body of the General Association of the Western Reserve. (2) Of twenty-two affiliated or independent Congregational churches, three, and possibly a fourth, had been in regular presbyteries. (3) One of the four affiliated Congregational churches, and eleven of the eighteen independent Congregational churches are Welsh.]

FIGURE NO. 4
LIVING CHURCHES WITH CONGREGATIONAL BACKGROUND
NEW JERSEY – END OF 1836

COUNTY	In Presbytery			Affiliated Cong.		Indep.	TOTAL
	PR, f. CG	P or C	CG	CG	CG, f. PR	Cong.	
Cape May	1						1
Cumberland	1						1
Essex	4	1	1	1			6 [7]
Middlesex	1			1			2
Monmouth	1						1
Morris	8				1	1	10
Passaic	2			1			3
Salem	1						1
Sussex	1			1		1	3
Union	6						6
Warren	1						1
TOTAL	27	1	1	4	1	2	35 [36]
	29			5		2	35 [36]

FIGURE NO. 5
LIVING CHURCHES WITH CONGREGATIONAL BACKGROUND
PENNSYLVANIA – END OF 1836

COUNTY	In Presbytery			Affiliated	Indep.	TOTAL
	PR, f. CG	CG	CG, f. PR	Cong.	Cong.	
Allegeheny				1	1	2
Bradford	7		1		3	11
Cambria	1			1	1	3
Carbon					1	1
Chester	1					1
Crawford		2			1	3
Erie	1			1		2
Lackawanna					3	3
Luzerne	2				1	3
Mercer				1		1
Montgomery	1					1
Montour					1	1
Philadelphia	2				2	4
Schuylkill					3	3
Susquehanna	5	9				14
Tioga	2					2
Warren	2	1			1	4
Wayne	4					4
Wyoming	1					1
TOTAL	29	12	1	4	18	64
	42			4	18	64

THE EXCISION

Politically motivated caucuses began to be held to strategize as to what would happen on the Assembly floor. The 1836 Assembly had a New School majority, so the Old School planned energetically for the next year.

At the 1837 meeting it became clear that the Old School held a slim majority. They then used that majority to return to the old tactic of 1741: excision. The Assembly voted to remove four Synods from the role of the Church: Utica, Geneva, and Genesee in upstate New York, and Western Reserve in Ohio. The Third Presbytery of Philadelphia was abolished, and the Synods of Albany, New Jersey, Michigan, Cincinnati and Illinois were instructed to set their houses in order. The Plan of Union was abrogated, and cooperation with the interdenominational missionary societies was ended. Local churches were expected to have Presbyterian forms.

The reason given for the excision of the four Synods was that they had been organized under the Plan of Union, and that the Plan was unconstitutional, since it amended Presbyterian law, and had never been submitted by the Assembly to the lower judicatories for approval. The Plan and its adoption probably were not fully in accord with Presbyterian law. However, the fact that it had not been noticed for thirty-six years tests credulity. But the issue of synods and presbyteries being organized under the Plan had little evidence to support it. No acts organizing any synod or presbytery made any reference to the Plan, and all had proceeded in normal Presbyterian form. Only the admission of previously independent bodies, the Middle Association, and later the Susquehanna Presbytery, could be challenged on these grounds, and both of these bodies had been later divided by Synods quite properly.

The Albany Synod, the Synod that had adopted the Accommodation Plan without General Assembly approval was not excised. The New York Synod, containing old Yankee congregations on Long Island and in the Hudson valley was not even challenged.

Later in 1837 New School forces met and planned to rejoin the Assembly in 1838. They were not admitted, and therefore, later in 1838 set up their own General Assembly on New School grounds.

Many other synods and presbyteries, particularly those with strong New England roots, such as the Champlain Presbytery in New York, and the Michigan Synod, joined the New School General Assembly. Other synods and presbyteries split. A host of congregations were pulled apart as well.

Theoretically all Plan of Union or Accommodation Plan churches were now excluded from Old School presbyteries. These had to find affiliations and allies. A few Old School presbyteries were slow to enforce the new rules.

One unusual aspect of this division was the rise of what was called the "Constitutional" position within the New School. Many students of Presbyterian law and practice had noticed that none of the excised Synods were organized under the Plan, as had been charged. More to the point, though, Presbyterian law and its system of judicatories required that before anyone could be removed from the church, formal trials with the right of appeal had to occur. Throwing thousands of members out of the church with no case-by-case hearing was a violation of orthodox Presbyterianism. This posture brought a group of articulate Scotch-Irish leaders into the New School, and set the New School, which included certainly hundreds of accommodation, or loosely organized congregations, on a road to prove that it was truly Presbyterian. This duality of definition eventually made the New School position untenable.

Many of the "Constitutional" Presbyterians who affiliated with the New School were from the South. One of the tensions in the 1830's had been the growing anti-slavery sentiment in many northern Presbyteries, and the refusal of the General Assembly, in order to protect its southern membership, to move in that direction. The New School General Assembly was now faced with the same dilemma, justifying or soft-pedaling slavery to hold onto southern support.

One result of the Presbyterian schism was an encouragement of the growth of Congregationalism outside New England. Between 1837 and 1840 a host of new Congregational bodies appeared in all the Great Lakes states and in Iowa. In the Middle Atlantic region new groups included a Welsh *Gymanfa* in Pennsylvania, a Whitesboro group in New York, a Susquehanna body on the New York-Pennsylvania border, and an association in western Pennsylvania.

If a line were drawn on a map to indicate the extent of settlement on the frontier in 1830, the Plan of Union included almost all Congregational churches or New England settlements founded in that territory. The majority, but not all, of Yankee settlements between 1830 and 1837, would still be included in the Plan (but not all). After 1837 a dramatic change occurred, and new western Yankee settlements almost always formed Congregational churches outside the Plan of Union. This change was caused not only by the schism in the General Assembly, but also by the establishment and polity changes in New England, which now sent Congregationalists to the west knowing how to organize Congregational churches without establishment support.

YANKEES IN THE OLD SCHOOL

One of the most interesting aspects of the split was the large number of people and churches with New England roots that ended up in the Old School. One reason was the nationalization of clergy placement and recruitment. In more localized times, congregations on Long Island, in the Hudson valley, New Jersey or northeastern Pennsylvania had turned to New England and Yale for their clergy. In the new hegemony the colleges and seminaries saw entire classes recruited by the missionary societies for western service. In the 1830's a group from Yale went to Illinois as the "Yale Band," while a group from Andover Seminary went to Iowa in 1843 as the "Iowa Band." Those pastors who did not heed the wanderlust of the missionary call generally settled more closely to home in New England. The lower New York and New Jersey churches, therefore, turned more and more to Princeton, and had pastors who were well indoctrinated in Presbyterian orthodoxy.

On Long Island the ancient church at Southold had finally given way to the spirit of union and reorganized as a Presbyterian Church in 1832. The same year the Long Island Presbytery was divided into two presbyteries. These were reorganized at the time of the excision. The smaller group, more recently Congregational, including Southold, affiliated with the New School, while the larger group, including most of the other older congregations joined the Old School.

A similar split happened in New Jersey. Most of the old Yankee churches had been in the 1809 Jersey Presbytery. It divided into two Presbyteries in 1825 - Newark and Elizabeth. Many of the churches most influenced by the work of Jacob Green, such as Hanover, Parsippany, Bloomfield, and Caldwell, were in the Newark Presbytery, which became part of the New School. The Elizabeth Presbytery, however, including Albert Barnes' former congregation in Morristown, closer to Princeton geographically and philosophically, ended up in the Old School.

One of the more startling aspects of the division, which demonstrates how rapidly things can change occurred in northeastern Pennsylvania. The Congregational Luzerne Association had changed its name to Susquehanna Presbytery in 1817. In 1821 it joined a Presbyterian Synod, but at that time all of its congregations had internal Congregational forms. After joining the Presbyterian Church and hiring Presbyterian-trained pastors, some congregations began to reorganize as Presbyterian. In 1832 it was divided into two Presbyteries, the new Montrose Presbytery taking the more easterly and higher lands of Susquehanna County, with the Susquehanna Presbytery taking the lower Susquehanna valley in Bradford, and Luzerne Counties. Because this was a rural area with small congregations, the number of its pastors often dwindled very low, and candidates were often sought from Presbyterian sources. Immediately after the Presbyteries split (1832), Susquehanna ordered all of its churches with internal Congregational forms to adopt Presbyterian forms. Some did, others withdrew, several split. It is not surprising that this Presbytery went to the Old School. Montrose, however, went into the New School, and kept most of its churches intact.

Despite the headquarters of the AHMS in New York City, and the settlement of Union Theological Seminary in the same place, most of the larger more influential churches in the City went with the Old School. This may have been partially in reaction to the ministry of Charles G. Finney in the City, whose radical perfectionist revivalism not only repulsed many orthodox Presbyterians, but traditional Congregationalists as well.

The churches in the Hudson valley were a mixed bag. Surprisingly, many churches in Westchester County, and all of those in Putnam County, with Congregational roots - many of which had also been part of the Westchester Associated Presbytery - now turned to the Old School. As was the case in Susquehanna Presbytery, many of these churches had had Congregational forms only a few years earlier.

Perhaps the most surprising focus of Old School strength was in the seat of the Albany Synod, the Synod that had created the Accommodation Plan. True, many Scotch and Irish settlements in Washington and Saratoga Counties pulled the Albany Presbytery towards the Old School. But in Albany City both the First and the Second Churches, the latter with a New England membership and the well-known New England born pastor, W. B. Sprague, both went with the Old School. The venerable old New Englander Eliphalet Nott, also went with the Old School. Nott was President of Union College, the largest college in the state at the time, and a school named for the principle of church unity!

In these cases theology and the influence of leaders such as Ashbel Green played a role. However, the years of intermingling had now led many people and churches with Congregational roots into the center of the Presbyterian traditional circles.

"When the separation was complete, the New School had about four-ninths of the ministry and membership of the church, almost all in the Northern States. The line between the New School and the Old School coincided almost exactly with the line between the New England and the Scotch-Irish settlements." (Comin (1950), pp.91-92).

The revival of a radical Congregationalism outside of the Plan of Union also followed the Presbyterian split. The second-class status of many Congregational churches even in New School presbyteries, the renewed New England denominational consciousness forged by the end of the establishment, the gradual clarification of their external polity, and the theological focus brought about by the Unitarian departure, all supported the Congregational revival.

ASSESSING THE INTER-MINGLING OF THE TWO HISTORIC STREAMS

The newly denominationally-aware Congregationalists began to attack the Plan of Union for having "stolen" many Congregational churches. They charged that the "New England's Congregational cows had been milked to produce Presbyterian cheese."

In 1846 the Congregational publication *New England Puritan*, an article by Edward Parsons Cooke charged that 2,000 Congregational churches had become Presbyterian through the Plan. This number became a polemical tool used in denominational debates well into the present. (see, e.g. Starkey (1966), p.183) Frederick Kuhns (1948) has probably been the most helpful person in questioning this number. As Kuhns states, the total number of churches literally changing their polity has to be lower than 2,000. Kuhns, who researched and studied churches in the Old Northwest, is very knowledgeable about congregations there, and notes that the number of churches actually changing polity there, while many hundred, does not justify the 2,000 figure. Kuhns and Nichols (49) point out that at this time the entire New School had fewer than 2,000 churches, which makes the number an incredible exaggeration. However, as discussed, many churches which were Congregational in their early years had made their way into the Old School by the 1840's.

However, Kuhns, following Nichols, underestimates the number of formerly Congregational churches which were in Presbyteries, or had adopted Presbyterian forms in New York State. Kuhns admits that Nichols' figures are too low, but accepts their general premise. Nichols points to a study by William Tower Thayer who concluded that by 1850 not more than 145 Congregational Churches in New York had become Presbyterian. Although Thayer's study has not been found, it appears to be based on the Questionnaires (46A), collected by the older Nichols in 1932. While those questionnaires have a wealth of information, they were only collected from living Presbyterian churches at the time. No rural churches which closed by that date, or churches in presbyteries in the 1840's which returned to the Congregationalists are included. Also, the data collected reflects a hodgepodge of accuracy coming from several local historians with divergent skills. The questionnaires do not even ask congregations what their organizational forms were in the past, when they first elected a session, or if they were ever connected to an ecclesiastical society. They do ask former names, and first date of organization. Information based on names only does not acknowledge the different meanings of the names in Scottish or English contexts. Some church reports give the date as the date of the first session, and merely eliminate earlier Congregational periods. Other reports seem to have decided that congregations which were part of Associated Presbyteries were Presbyterian during those periods. The idea that a congregation could have a local session and still reject the authority of presbyteries within the General Assembly is not even imagined. Because of these problems, it seems fair to conclude that this study is erroneous, and that many more churches in New York presbyteries in the 1840's had been or were Congregational. (See Figure No. 3)

Another study, including only the excluded synods by the Old School writer James Woods (1837) is also tentative. Woods visited a few presbyteries, and corresponded with friends to make estimates of how many churches in the presbyteries actually had Congregational forms at that time. As he himself admits, much of his "data" is pure estimation. For the three New York Synods he concludes that their 477 churches include between 134 and 203 with Congregational forms, and between 274 and 343 with Presbyterian forms. The actual three synod reports count 459 churches in New York state, and 6 elsewhere, for a total of 465.

The growth of the two traditions in New York state from 1800 to 1836 is phenomenal, and points to the size of the migration and the success of the missionary societies. It is clear from the numbers that New York is still primarily rural, and at this point the real test of the Plan of Union is in the vast expanse of upstate New York.

Those congregations in the presbyteries, which had always had Presbyterian local forms (see Figure 3), include all of the former Associate Reformed churches, and all but four of the Dutch Reformed churches transferring into presbyteries by this time. Thirty-eight of the thirty-nine congregations in presbyteries in three future New York City counties (New York, Kings, and the Bronx) had only had Presbyterian forms. Only three congregations had been listed in these counties in 1800. These numbers demonstrate the beginning of urbanization and the preference for Presbyterian forms in the City.

In addition to the City, other New York areas where a significant portion of the churches in presbyteries had always had Presbyterian forms include the Hudson valley (Columbia, Dutchess, Orange, Ulster and possibly Sullivan Counties), and the area around Albany (Albany, Fulton, Montgomery, Rensselaer, Schenectady, Warren, and Washington Counties). Both of these areas received early New England settlement. Their oldest churches had had close identification with presbyteries during both the first and second unions, as well as with the colonial New York New Side Presbytery. These areas also had significant pockets of Irish and Scottish settlements. They had turned increasingly to Presbyterian sources of pastoral supply in the early nineteenth century. Overlooked by New England missionary efforts that were focused on new western settlements, second growth in these areas was under the auspices of the presbyteries.

Another significant Presbyterian area was a territory rising from the Pennsylvania border into central New York (including Chemung, Schuyler, Seneca, Steuben, Wayne, Yates, and possibly Livingston, and part of Tompkins Counties). This area had more settlement from Pennsylvania. Presbyterianism was also strong in the late settled Niagara County.

Congregational and Plan of Union churches dominated the rest of upstate New York. Interestingly, despite Presbyterian dominance in upstate cities such as Rochester, Buffalo, and Syracuse, Congregationalism still was the root of the majority of churches in Monroe, Erie, and Onondaga Counties.

The New England presence in New Jersey and Pennsylvania was rooted in the old colonial churches near the coast. After the Revolution New Englanders played a major role in settling the mountainous northern tier of Pennsylvania counties that had been part of the old Connecticut claim.

The Presbyterian Church reflected the importance of immigration with New England roots in their Synod boundaries. The Synod of New Jersey included the colonial territory in northern New Jersey with old Yankee roots, as well as northeastern Pennsylvania. Another part of the northern tier of counties in central Pennsylvania had their churches attached to New York Synods. The Philadelphia Synod had a much smaller New England colonial base. It included southern New Jersey, Delaware, most of Maryland, and areas in the mountains of southeast and central Pennsylvania with large and early Scottish and Irish settlements. This Synod may have included a few more churches with Yankee origins that have not been uncovered.

Western Pennsylvania, in and beyond the mountains, was coveted territory to Scottish and Irish settlers before and during the Revolution. Southwest Pennsylvania was settled first, and a Redstone Presbytery existed in 1781. However, when Synods were set up in the new General Assembly, Redstone was attached to the Synod of Virginia, reflecting Virginia's political interest in the area. From this beginning the eventual Pittsburgh Synod (1802) was more attached to southern ways than Philadelphia, and became the champion of the ideas and positions of its almost exclusively Scottish and Irish heritage. As northwestern Pennsylvania was settled, Yankees coming due west from Connecticut and down Lake Erie from New York drifted into the Northwest corner of the state, whose Erie Presbytery, as well as the early churches in Ohio's Western Reserve, were under the jurisdiction of the Pittsburgh Synod. (An 1884 history of Erie County says of the early settlers that "most of the colonists were Presbyterians from New England and the valley of the Susquehanna River.") Other than in Erie Presbytery, hardly any Yankee churches were in western Pennsylvania, although some may have existed in that Presbytery and elsewhere. No place in the country became as strong in Irish and Scottish settlements, and Presbyterian churches as western Pennsylvania.

Several factors need to be considered in interpreting the 1836/1837 data (Figures 3, 4, and 5). One is that after the 2,000 church claim was made in 1846, many churches continued to move back and forth between the various denominations. In the Western Reserve of Ohio the majority of Plan of Union churches left the presbyteries and went back to a rejuvenated Congregationalism.

Issues beyond the specific counts also need to be considered. As the New York chart above indicates, in some areas in New York state, nearly every early church in a county or a presbytery had Congregational origins. When these stayed within the New School and later the Presbyterian Church, U.S.A., the eventual effect of such origins on later Presbyterian congregations organized within their areas may have created "grandchild churches" of the Plan of Union. Even if technically organized as Presbyterian from the start, areas where most Presbyterian churches have New England cultural roots and theological and ethnic connections, could be considered to be grandchildren of New England Congregationalism which could or perhaps would have been Congregational if history had proceeded in a different way.

THE NEW ALIGNMENT DOES NOT LAST

The New School started with four-ninths of the divided Presbyterian Church. It also began with a middle-of-the-road position on polity that could be very attractive to local Congregational churches. It needed to clearly state its position. Instead, the New School then made a strategic mistake. Pulled, as it was, between presbyteries with mostly Congregational churches and its desire to prove itself as true "Constitutional" Presbyterianism, and also as the home of many fiercely anti-slavery congregations, and its desire to push that issue away so that it could retain its southern churches, it decided to avoid these issues by not having its General Assembly meet. After three consecutive meetings in 1838, 1839, and 1840, the New School General Assembly decided to meet only every three years, meeting in 1843, 1846, and 1849, after which annual meetings were resumed. This decade of the 1840's proved to be crucial. Congregationalism began to grow rapidly in the west, by claiming new congregations in new settlements, receiving independent congregations into the now more denominationally-distinct associated Congregationalism, and one by one, slowly siphoning off Plan of Union congregations from New School presbyteries. In Wisconsin, northern Illinois, and Oregon, union bodies were created where New School Presbyterian and Congregational churches belonged to inter-church bodies which were not part of the New School General Assembly. These arrangements retarded the growth of the united New School, and created a climate where Presbyterian churches often turned Congregational. New School leaders grew angry with the Congregational groups and leaders seen to be guilty of draining off their churches.

New Englanders moving west now felt no need to join a judicatory trying to prove it was constitutionally Presbyterian, and unable to speak out against slavery.

Attempts were made to heal the growing rift between the New School and the Congregationalists. Joint meetings were held in western cities in years that the New School General Assembly did not meet. But these could not stem the tide of debate and growing distrust.

Disunity also spread into the relationships of churches with their presbyteries. Issues about interpreting the meaning of the Plan had arisen even in presbyteries claiming to be loyal to it. Both the Plan and the Accommodation Plan had provided for mixed churches, and the latter had also provided that Congregational churches could join presbyteries. But once a church adopted internal Presbyterian forms, could it return to Congregational forms? If Congregational churches joined a presbytery, could they leave? Some presbyteries began to forbid churches from adopting Congregational forms once they had Presbyterian forms. When congregations decided to leave a presbytery, even if they always had Congregational local forms, presbyteries would sometimes vote that a tiny minority loyal to the presbytery was the true Congregational church of the community! Many presbyteries tried to claim as members congregations that had long since gone off in other directions.

With three competing large organized English-speaking Reformed bodies: the Old School, the New School, and a reinvigorated Congregationalism, polity could be used as a mask for almost any type of church debate. Congregations in conflict with their pastors, pastors in conflict with their presbyteries, and all manner of internal disputes within congregations could have their issues labeled as a polity debate among the three types of denomination. Factions, minorities, and rumps could suddenly find people rushing to their aid. Undoubtedly many church divisions and changes of relationship and status had a much wider origin than merely the denominational battles.

Middle Atlantic Congregationalism also had some initial conflicts before finding its new identity. Some new inter-church bodies, like the Finney-ite Central Evangelical Association, stood outside the General Association. Many of these remained small but proved to be disruptive.

Within the General Association a critical early crisis came to a head in 1843 when two of the original inter-church bodies, the Genesee Consociation, and the New York City Association, were suspended from membership because of theological and discipline issues centered around perfectionism. In the New York City area, most of the clergy then abandoned the Green polity and formed a ministerial body (the Manhattan Association) which belonged to the General Association. In 1846/1847 the New York and Brooklyn Association restored an inter-church body to the City area. The Genesee body continued independently for a few years. No lasting inter-church body served in its area until a new Ontario Association was begun in 1849.

On the other hand, the new Congregational identity began to be shaped by urban growth centered in a steady progress in the expanding City of Brooklyn. Leading the upward curve was the pastorate of Henry Ward Beecher (son of Lyman, and brother of Harriet Beecher Stowe) at Plymouth Church. Staunchly anti-slavery, Plymouth stood out from churches intertwined with the cautious General Assemblies. On the Heights, overlooking Manhattan, Plymouth also became a model of the new suburban church, serving a relatively compact social class.

Growing disunity in the missionary field impacted identity issues. On the radical side, new missionary bodies opposed to slavery began to siphon off support from the larger bodies which could not separate themselves cleanly from that institution. The Amistad Committee (c.1839) and the Union Missionary Society (c.1841) were united in 1846 as the American Missionary Association (**AMA**, incorporated in New York in 1849). It was willing to undertake both foreign and domestic work. The Committee for the West Indies Mission (1843, taking over work begun 1837) became part of the AMA in 1847, and the Western Evangelical Missionary Society (in the Western Reserve of Ohio, 1843) followed in 1848. A Western Free Missionary Society also existed in Ohio from 1849.

On the other hand, the continued drain off of Congregational churches from the New School, and the control of the independent boards from New England, led the New School General Assembly in 1847 to establish a standing committee on Home Missions. In 1850 the New School established a plan to encourage presbyteries to begin their own local mission support. Finally, in 1861, the New School General Assembly severed all ties with the AHMS.

In 1846 a Convention of western Congregationalists (with some eastern visitors) was held in Michigan City, Indiana. They recommended the end of the Plan of Union, and a renewal of Congregationalism.

Some of the same issues that were eating at the New School and the Congregationalists also had some effect on the Old School. In 1847 a radically anti-slavery group of churches left the Old School in western Pennsylvania. They then joined with a similar schism, which had left the New School in Ohio, to form the Free Presbyterian Church.

THE THIRD SCHISM IS DECISIVE
1852-1870

In 1852, for the first time since the 1600's, all the Congregationalists in America were invited to send delegates to a Convention. It was called to meet in Albany, New York. The location was not only convenient to New England, but also outside enough to suggest that Congregationalism really wanted to become a national denomination. Its site was also symbolic, in the capital of the state most involved in the Plan of Union, and in the Synod where the Accommodation Plan had been devised. The Convention declared the Plan of Union at an end. It also created a mission strategy for the now revived denomination.

However, the decision of the delegates in Albany did not change the status of local congregations, and many congregations with local Congregational forms, and even the name Congregational continued to be part of New School presbyteries. But this union of New England with the New York rump and the new Congregational forces in the west eventually doomed the identity of the churches still operating under the Plan. Eventually they would have to choose their polity.

Congregationalism developed its new national identity following the Albany Convention. The battles of these years had raised polity rather than Reformed theology to be the chief boundary of the new fellowship.

Building construction aid through the American Congregational Union began to put a denominational stamp on mission work. Other new agencies promoted specifically Congregational publishing, library, and archival work.

Accepting Charles Finney's ideas and the wide theological spectrum that had grown in New England also opened doors for inclusion.

In 1820 a group had broken off from the Methodist Episcopal Church in New York in opposition to episcopal government and denominational control of congregational property. They were formally known as Congregational Methodists, and popularly as Stilwellites, because of the leadership of Samuel and William M. Stillwell in the movement. Their congregations were large and visible, but few in number. In 1860 and 1861 the majority of their churches joined Congregational inter-church bodies. While statistically tiny, this was a groundbreaking decision as it brought statedly Arminian congregations into the Congregational fellowship and became a first step towards a wider ecumenism.

In 1865 another national Congregational Convention was held in Boston. It adopted a statement of faith and determined strategies for missions after the end of the Civil War.

INDEPENDENT CONGREGATIONAL CHURCHES

While a new Congregational polity gradually developed, the associating of churches using Green's polity, opposite trends occurred as well.

People who came from churches used to the autonomy of Massachusetts and New Hampshire founded many early Congregational churches in the Middle Atlantic area. Churches influenced by these backgrounds were reluctant to associate. However, unlike New England, no strong ministerial bodies bound their leaders to area congregations, nor was there the advantage of the New England establishment. People found their new churches were far more isolated than their old New England congregations.

Some isolated congregations did not last long, and some may have been so weak that they left no traces. As time passed, most that survived decided to join inter-church bodies or presbyteries.

In 1854 the New York General Association conducted a study (01T) to find all the independent Congregational churches in New York (as well as those in presbyteries under the Plan of Union). The *Congregational Yearbook* continued to list these congregations in the 1855 through 1859 issues. No similar studies or lists exist for New Jersey or Pennsylvania. Beginning in 1860 the *Congregational Quarterly* abandoned this listing, and literally dozens of independent churches disappeared into the mists of history. Most of these were quite small and probably died thereafter.

With the organization of the National Council of Congregational Churches in 1871, the denomination defined itself as a fellowship of associated churches. Therefore, from a denominational perspective, it could be said that the remaining independent congregations were no longer Congregational.

As time passed, many congregations that had survived eventually associated, most by the mid-1870's. A few New York churches maintained long periods of independence outside the associations. Among the most notable of the churches with either longer or later periods of independence, and their unassociated dates are: Blooming Grove (1833-1875), Cincinnatus (1874-1912), Cutchogue (1872-1916), East Bloomfield (1832-1873, 1884-1889, 1892-1915), Elmira (Park Church, 1897-1919), Farmingville (1877-1890), New Lebanon (1848-1884), South Granville (1849-1876), South Hartford (1849-1876), Washingtonville (1847-1889).

While records for the other two states are less complete, some lengthy independent periods occurred there as well, such as Pennsylvania's East Smithfield (1837-1867), and Harford (1870-1886/1887).

UNION ENDS IN DOMESTIC MISSION WORK

At the Albany Convention of 1852 the Congregational denomination began to define its own missionary bodies. The Convention identified two types of bodies, "Congregational," and "Cooperative Societies." The American Education Society was already considered Congregational, as were a group of newer bodies including the American Congregational Union, the American Congregational Association, and the Congregational Board of Publication. However the American Board of Commissioners for Foreign Missions, the American Home Missionary Society, the American Missionary Association, the Society for the Promotion of Collegiate and Theological Education at the West, as well as a long list of institutions part of the Benevolent Empire, were listed as "Cooperative Societies." The 1865 Convention approved a group of agencies for support, both Congregational and ecumenical. However, at the formation of the National Council of Congregational Churches in 1871, a clear list of Congregational agencies was approved, which now included the four Congregational bodies of 1852, and the ABCFM, the AHMS, and the AMA, now all considered Congregational. Indeed, the AHMS became the Congregational Home Missionary Society in 1893.

Even though the New School had given up on the AHMS and had never formally endorsed the AMA, foreign work, and most work with American Indians, continued to be done on a cooperative basis with the Congregationalists through the ABCFM until the 1869/1870 reorganization.

Near the end of the years between 1852 and 1871 a major reorganization of missionary fields was undertaken. Much of the work of the ABCFM was transferred to the merged Presbyterian Board in 1870. With slavery overcome, the previous competition between the AHMS and the AMA was now a moot point. They responded after the Civil War by establishing different goals for each and both seeking the aid of the Congregational churches.

PRESBYTERIANISM DRIFTS AWAY FROM UNION

During its entire life New School Presbyterianism saw a slow drain from its presbyteries to the newly reviving Congregationalism. In addition, the tensions in its General Assembly over slavery finally led to a schism and the withdrawal of most of the southern New School churches in 1857 to form the United Synod of the South.

The Old School was never able to face up to the issue of slavery. Only after the outbreak of the Civil War and the secession of several states, did most of the southern Old School separate out to form the Presbyterian Church in the Confederate States of America in 1861. What had been one General Assembly in 1837 had become four. In addition hundreds more churches had moved over to Congregationalism.

Once the northern Presbyterian bodies supported the anti-slavery cause, the Free Presbyterian Church fell apart, and its congregations merged with or joined regular Presbyterian bodies.

The isolation and emotion of the War led the southern bodies to unite in 1864 in what eventually came to be known as the Presbyterian Church in the United States. In the years immediately following the War, congregations, presbyteries, and synods along the border areas reorganized and shifted loyalties between what would be continuing northern and southern denominations. This included a Maryland Presbytery, Kentucky and Missouri Synods and the movement of some newer African-American congregations as well.

The northern New School, drained on all sides, sat down to union negotiations with the northern Old School. Because by this time, the New School was operating its own domestic missions, free-standing mission boards were no longer an issue. The New School agreed to give up the Accommodation Plan and conform to the rigid definition of Presbyterian polity. The merger was planned in 1869 and completed in 1870. The new northern church (Presbyterian Church, U.S.A.) had already begun mission work in the south, particularly among African-American congregations, and slowly became a national church, while the southern church remained a regional denomination.

The northern merger agreement required that presbyteries were to counsel congregations without proper local forms and see that they conformed to Presbyterian usage within five years. Thus the Plan of Union and Accommodation Plan came to an end in the New School as well. The rules of the merger caused a new wave of adjustments in the early 1870's. Many congregations finally conformed to Presbyterian order, while others left the presbyteries and associated Congregationalism had its last significant spurt of growth in the Middle Atlantic region.

Nevertheless, most Plan of Union area presbyteries still had trouble enforcing the five-year rule. As the lists in this book demonstrate, some churches held onto various Congregational forms, such as relating to an ecclesiastical society or claiming to own their own property, for decades after 1870, yet remained affiliated to presbyteries. The Champlain Presbytery in the northeast corner of New York was particularly tolerant in not enforcing uniformity.

The last known case of change is the Church in Malone, New York, the oldest and largest of the churches of either tradition in Franklin County. It stayed in presbytery for decades, still using the word Congregational in its name, until 1962, when it transferred to the United Church of Christ.

Changes in the Presbyterian bodies descended from the Covenanters and the Seceders were seeking unity when others were dividing. The majorities of the Associate Reformed Church (which had lost its southern churches in 1822) and the Associate Presbyterian Church (which had also lost its southern churches in 1840) united in 1858 as the United Presbyterian Church of North America. Some churches in New York opposed the merger and continued as a Synod until after 1869, when they found other homes. Some other congregations also used this occasion to move into the Old School.

PRESBYTERIANISM AFTER THE BREAK

Major unions in 1858, 1864, and 1869 encouraged other Presbyterian bodies to seek unity along confessional and Scottish lines. Groups from the Covenanter and Seceder traditions sought to join larger Presbyterian groups. Part of a Presbytery of the Associate Reformed Church in the South moved in 1870 to the larger Presbyterian Church in the U.S., while three presbyteries left the Reformed Presbyterian Church, General Synod, two to the Presbyterian Church, U.S.A., and one to the United Presbyterian Church in North America. In 1889 a United Presbyterian Church of North America presbytery moved to the Presbyterian Church, U.S.A..

More significant were larger mergers that extended the national nature of the Presbyterian Church, U.S.A.. It merged with about two-thirds of the Cumberland Presbyterian Church in 1906, and united with the Welsh Calvinistic Methodist Church in 1920. Then, in 1958, the Presbyterian Church, U.S.A. united with the United Presbyterian Church of North America as the United Presbyterian Church, U.S.A.. Union of the expanded northern church with the southern church, however, was often considered and frustrated. Only in 1983, after both groups had suffered conservative schisms, and the merger agreement included a provision to allow local congregations to withdraw over a specified period of time, that the two finally united under the old name, Presbyterian Church, U.S.A..

The steps towards unity were thwarted in the Twentieth Century by schism. In 1936 a small group of key leaders left the northern church to form what became known as the Orthodox Presbyterian Church. It split two years later, when the Bible Presbyterian Church broke off, the latter group continuing to splinter into more sub-groups.

The most significant division came in 1973 when what became known as the Presbyterian Church in America left the southern church. Other schisms left the northern church, including an independent presbytery in 1980 (Siouxland) and the charismatic Evangelical Presbyterian Church in 1981.

A realignment of some of the schismatic groups followed. The remainder of the old Covenanter Reformed Presbyterian Church General Synod and one of the splinters from the Bible Presbyterian Church united in 1965 as the Reformed Presbyterian Church, Evangelical Synod. It, in turn, united with the Presbyterian Church in America in 1982, which had also received the Siouxland Presbytery in 1981.

Particularly in the years just before and after the national merger of 1983, many local presbyteries allowed congregations to transfer (or disband, and take their property) to either the Presbyterian Church in America or the Evangelical Presbyterian Church. Some in the Middle Atlantic region left at this time.

A NEW NATIONAL CONGREGATIONALISM
1870-1931

After the death of the Plan of Union, and the movement of the Congregational churches in presbyteries either to re-organize as Presbyterian, or leave the presbytery and return to Congregationalism, the line of demarcation between the two historic bodies became rigid. The post-1870 lines of definition can still be seen in the current denominational divisions.

Later development followed trends responding to and strengthening ministries among new immigrant groups, additions in growing urban areas, and the later growth of suburbs, and the parallel decline of many small town and rural communities and congregations.

A national meeting in celebration of the two hundred and fiftieth anniversary of the landing of the Pilgrims (1870) called for a formal national fellowship. Another convention a year later (1871) formed the National Council of Congregational Churches. Congregationalism became a denomination.

After the death of the Plan, New York Congregationalism was much smaller than its Presbyterian counterpart. New York was then the nation's most populous state, but only a small proportion of its population was in the Congregational fold. The boundary between New England (where Congregationalism was still the dominant Protestant Church), and New York was clear and vivid. Nonetheless, the role of New York Congregationalism within the denomination was still very powerful. A small proportion of the people in the most populous state is still a lot of people, and New York had much larger delegations at national meetings than many traditionally Congregational states. Also, New York City, with the headquarters of the American Home Missionary Society (Congregational Home Missionary Society from 1893), the American Missionary Association, and the American Congregational Union (Congregational Church Building Society) became the place of real power in homeland missions. By the early 1920's the National Council of Congregational Churches moved their offices to New York City, which became the headquarters of the denomination. One effect was that most denominational officers held their local church membership and ministerial standing in New York area churches, making these the dominant and potentially domineering churches in the fellowship.

New York City, particularly Brooklyn, also became a place of significant Congregational strength. Henry Ward Beecher had created a model for suburban church at Plymouth Church. Its prominence, and the movement of New Englanders into the growing businesses of the City, built many powerful and significant congregations.

In 1900 only fourteen Congregational churches in the entire nation had reached the incredible size of 1,000 members. Seven of the fourteen were in Brooklyn, including the only two over 1,500 members (Tompkins Avenue, and Plymouth. The other five were Church of the Pilgrims, Clinton Avenue, South, Central, and Lewis Avenue.)

In 1930, a few months after the Stock Market crash, and the year before the Congregational Christian merger, only five congregations in the entire denomination had over 2,000 members. Three of them were in Brooklyn: Central, Tompkins Avenue, and Flatbush.

S. Parkes Cadman the long-term pastor of Central in Brooklyn became the first real pioneer in national radio preaching. He broke ground later imitated by many. Frederick K. Stamm at Clinton Avenue Church in Brooklyn, followed suit, with an early widespread radio ministry.

While Congregationalism may not have been a major force in New York, New York Congregationalism was probably the dominant force in the denomination.

Most of modern New Jersey Congregationalism also arose after the Civil War, primarily as suburban congregations were developed around Newark and New York City.

Pennsylvania became (except for Hawaii) the most ethnically diverse of Congregational states. It was also among the last northern states (1886) to have a statewide inter-church body. The northern tier of Pennsylvania counties continued to have remnants of Yankee churches from the early New England settlement in the old Connecticut western claim territory. An English-speaking Congregationalism also gained something of a foothold in Philadelphia after the Civil War. However, most churches in the center of the state came out of the Welsh heritage. Pennsylvania became a center for many of the country's Slavic Congregational Churches, and scattered Scandinavian congregations were also present. After the Evangelical Protestant merger, Pittsburgh was a center of German congregations. The majority of Congregational Churches in most Pennsylvania counties outside Philadelphia and the northern tier came from non-English ethnic groups.

LATE BATTLES IN FORMATTING A POLITY

The Green polity had become the normative form of Congregational organization in the Middle Atlantic area by the 1830's, and became the general model as Congregationalism grew farther west. New England during the latter nineteenth century moved towards a system of parallel ministerial and inter-church bodies. There, consociations, which had sometimes exercised presbyterial powers, gave way to new inter-church conferences that constitutionally articulated the value of autonomy. However, local ministerial associations continued in New England until early in the twentieth century, when even New England church and ministerial bodies merged following the Green model. (A few ministerial associations continued their independence until the 1960's.)

After the New Jersey inter-church body became independent, it followed the New England plan. Separate ministerial bodies functioned in the Newark area until 1880/1882, in Pennsylvania until 1905, and in the Washington, DC area until 1912. Parallel ministerial and inter-church bodies served there until the 1930's. A few places in upstate New York also experimented with the New England model in the late nineteenth century.

However, the National Council of Congregational Churches defined the new fellowship as a covenant of associated churches, after 1871 all churches were expected to belong to either joint ministerial and inter-church bodies in the Green model, or inter-church bodies in the New England model.

One of the last major organizational battles occurred in the Middle Atlantic area. Because of a scandal surrounding Henry Ward Beecher and Brooklyn's Plymouth Church, several ministers and their churches left the New York and Brooklyn Association in 1877 to form the Manhattan Association, which was outside the New York general body until 1891. However, unwilling to lose powerful New York congregations, the state body continued to list the churches served by these pastors, and the Manhattan Association was seated directly at the National Council in 1886. Even after admission to the state general body, it continued to geographically overlap the other group until an 1896 reorganization. Thereafter some clergy continued the New England pattern of a separate ministerial body until the 1920's.

Unfortunately the loose affiliation and overlapping bodies in New York during this period became the legal precedent for segregated inter-church bodies to be recognized in the south following the Congregational Methodist merger.

After states gave church bodies the right to incorporate, steps were taken in the early twentieth century to unite the general state bodies with their parallel missionary societies.

THE RELIGIOUS SITUATION IN 1900

By 1900 clear denominational demarcations were visible. New York reported 287 Congregational churches with 49,184 members; New Jersey 37 churches with 6,894 members; and Pennsylvania 106 churches with 11,102 members. The Presbyterian Church, U.S.A. reported 811 churches with 169,396 members in New York; 329 churches with 68,984 members in New Jersey; and 1,022 churches with 211,658 members in Pennsylvania.

ECUMENICAL MERGERS

Between 1888 and 1892 the national church welcomed into membership many Conferences and parts of Conferences of the Congregational Methodist Church, a southern body dating from 1850/1852. No churches were involved in this area, although the merger introduced the scourge of southern segregation into the denomination.

In 1924 the Evangelical Protestant Church of North America, a German rationalist denomination voted to merge with the Congregationalists, and was received in 1925. This body had been formed in 1911/1912, replacing earlier ministerial fellowships, and was evolving from a German-speaking to an English-speaking body. It was very strong in western Pennsylvania, including the oldest church in the City of Pittsburgh (Smithfield), adding a new center of Congregational strength to that state.

Many other national merger attempts during this period failed, although a few local congregations from other backgrounds became Congregational.

Another growing trend was local ecumenical congregations. In the early nineteenth century, congregations in divergent denominations often built, met in, or shared space in the same building. Sometimes these buildings were owned by independent non-denominational societies, sometimes they were jointly owned by the congregations using them, and occasionally they were owned by some secular group or person. These were often called "Union" arrangements. Most congregations of British heritage sought to leave such situations as soon as possible.

Some union buildings were built by non-denominational religious societies before any denominational churches were formed in their area. These were used to attract preachers to serve the area. Some of these "Union Chapels," or Sunday Schools, or (later) "Community Churches," later attracted a denominational clergy person, and followed their pastors into the pastor's denomination. Some such churches became Congregational.

As rural and small town communities and congregations declined, the federation movement was another form of ecumenism. Local churches of different denominations would call the same pastor and regularly have joint worship, while still maintaining their distinct denominational affiliations, legal identity and membership lists. Sometimes federated churches would also combine into one building. The first of these in this area began in Parishville, New York in 1891, when two congregations (Congregational and Methodist Episcopal) that had been sharing a Union building, finally decided to worship together under the same pastor, while still affiliated to both denominations, and still called a Union Church. The second was in Schroon Lake, New York from 1907. This movement suddenly gained in popularity during the First World War, when some fuels were rationed, and when some clergy were serving as military chaplains. While some federations ended promptly after the War, others continued. This format was particularly popular in New York state, among both Congregational and Presbyterian churches. However, because of the effects of the Plan of Union, only rarely did Congregational and Presbyterian churches federate to each other. Because they had been one fellowship, few smaller communities had both types of congregations. Instead, the vast majority of Congregational and Presbyterian federations in the Middle Atlantic region were with Methodist or Baptist congregations.

Following the history of federated churches is often very difficult. Where one part of the federation was much larger than the other, the small group often slowly ended their affiliation with their denomination, and eventually became absorbed by the larger local church, which might still call itself "Federated Church." In other cases, often if a building burned or was condemned, the group might decide to merge, using the building of one denomination and affiliating to the denomination of the other group. Again the Federated name, or some other union designation might be maintained. Dating is also confusing. Often informal federations ("trial" periods) would last for some years before the federation was formally adopted. [Where two or more federation dates are separated by a slash, the early date is an informal joining, and the latter date a formal federation.]

Some federated churches began local memberships that were reported to neither of the denominational bodies, so that two churches federating would end up with three separate membership rolls. Sometimes a federated church of two or more congregations united as one church and transferred to a totally new denomination.

Another change was the move towards dual alignment. In order to end the organizational confusion often present in federated churches, some congregations would merge outright, becoming one congregation, with one legal identity, and one membership list, but still affiliating to all of the original denominations. This could also lead to a confusing situation, where after dual alignment, one denomination became primary, and the other slowly faded away.

THE CONGREGATIONAL CHRISTIAN MERGER 1931-1957

The first major merger for the tradition was finalized in 1931 when the National Council united with the General Convention of the Christian Church as the General Council of Congregational (and) Christian Churches. The Christian body was a fellowship of congregations growing out of movements on the American frontier in the early federal period. The majority of churches in this area grew out of the New England branch of the Christians, which had separated from the Baptists in 1801, led by Abner Jones and Elias Smith. Some churches in southern Pennsylvania grew out of the southern branch of the connection, begun by James O'Kelly in 1794. Their local churches were autonomous and usually revivalistic, but they had a wide variety of theological positions, eschewing creeds, often having a Quaker attitude towards the sacraments, and sometimes being accused of Unitarian sentiments.

The Congregationalists and the Christians began to publish their statistics together in 1929. However, churches were distinguished as Christian or Congregational through 1933. Beginning in 1934 new congregations appear as Congregational Christian. [Thus, churches first listed as Congregational through 1933 are shown here as

Congregational. Congregational Christian Churches appear in Appendix II. (Christian congregations founded through 1933 are not included in this book.)]

New York had been a major center for the Christian Churches. More of their national meetings were in New York state than any other place. They often maintained their national publishing house somewhere in New York, and the state was often therefore seen as their national headquarters. At least two ministerial training schools existed in the state, at Starkey and Stanfordville.

Three of the six regional conventions of the Christian Churches served in the Middle Atlantic area, with the Central Convention (centered in Ohio, Indiana, and Illinois) including a few churches in Pennsylvania and New York, and the segregated Afro-Christian Convention serving in New York and New Jersey.

The Metropolitan Christian Convention was centered in this area. It had ten local bodies called Conferences. Opposition to the merger with the Congregationalists was strong in this area. Four of the ten Conferences totally opposed the merger and withdrew. One of these, (Tioga River Christian Conference), has maintained some national visibility as an independent denomination. The New York Western Conference delayed a year before approving the merger. It and the New York Central Conference affiliated to the Congregational bodies in their areas, but remained as separate districts until 1947 and 1952. Two bodies joined their local Congregational inter-state bodies (Rays Hill and Southern Pennsylvania joined Pennsylvania, while the Ontario Conference in Canada affiliated with New York). Two other Conferences (New York Eastern and New Jersey) merged with the local Congregational bodies in their areas. However, a large proportion of the Rays Hill and Southern Pennsylvania body split off to form an independent local Conference, while individual churches from the New Jersey and various New York Conferences withdrew, some joining the Tioga River body, and others remaining independent.

No visible opposition occurred among Congregational churches to this merger in this area, probably because most of the Christian Churches were merely added to existing Congregational structures.

During the period of the Great Depression and the Second World War, few new congregations were organized. The great Brooklyn churches diminished due to changing demographics. While some suburban congregations grew and became key leaders within the denomination (such as Garden City and Manhasset on Long Island), they never compensated for the losses in Brooklyn. The Brooklyn decline also meant that key denominational officials in the national and mission offices in New York City now joined congregations in New Jersey, Westchester County, and on Long Island, while Brooklyn's influence waned.

LOCAL ECUMENISM

The Middle Atlantic area hosted two creative local ecumenical endeavors. In 1943 the Western New York Council of Community Churches merged with the local Congregational Christian Association. This body was racially integrated, and included some churches which had begun independently and others which had grown out of federated congregations. This brought some significant growth to the denomination in western New York, setting the stage for further suburban growth there, and also brought in a group of churches with a tolerant theological posture.

In 1952 two of Manhattan's most important liberal Baptist churches: the Riverside Church, and the Judson Memorial Church in Greenwich Village dually aligned with the Congregational Christians. Riverside saw itself extending the ecumenical outlook of its former long-term liberal Senior Pastor, Harry Emerson Fosdick. The lead of these two congregations encouraged several other liberal Baptist congregations in the area to join the Congregational Christians or the United Church of Christ, including Hollis Woods in Queens, and churches in Summit, Middletown, Holmdel, Princeton, and Margate, in New Jersey.

The New Jersey Association was also particularly successful in attracting independent and community churches into its ranks. These included some former Dutch Reformed Churches, and, later, the dual alignment of a Black Disciples of Christ Christian Church. The oldest Disciples Church in Philadelphia also joined the Congregational Christians.

As Congregational Christians moved towards the United Church of Christ, a few other unusual ecumenical endeavors prospered in this area.

The Schwenkfelder Church, an ethnically German denomination settled in eastern Pennsylvania as early as 1735. It culturally and historically overlapped the German Reformed settlements in the same area. However, the more independent Schwenkfelders conducted their foreign missionary work jointly with the Congregationalists through the ABCFM. In 1959 one of their congregations dually aligned with an Evangelical and Reformed Synod following the early stages of the United Church of Christ merger. Eventually four of their five congregations spent some time in the United Church. Schwenkfelder churches and meetinghouses are summarized in Appendix V..

As more and more Black clergy gained the benefits of a seminary education, the United Church also welcomed Black Baptist congregations into membership in New York and Pennsylvania.

CONTRIBUTIONS TOWARDS A HISTORY

THE UNITED CHURCH OF CHRIST
1957-to the present

In 1957 the General Council of Congregational Christian Churches united with the Evangelical and Reformed Church to form the United Church of Christ.

Congregational Christian Churches had to vote on whether or not to be part of the new United Church. Most did that through a vote on the proposed Constitution of the United Church in late 1960 and early 1961. The statistical reports for 1961 are the first to distinguish between Congregational Christian Churches within or outside the United Church. These reports were also the first time that Congregational Christian and Evangelical and Reformed statistics were published in the same book. [Therefore churches listed through 1960 are shown as Congregational Christian (Appendix II.) and those listed from 1961 on as United Church of Christ congregations (Appendix III.). (Two exceptions to this rule are two new church starts in New Jersey sponsored jointly by the Congregational Christians and the Evangelical and Reformed Church, listed 1959, which are in Appendix III., rather than Appendix II.). (Note also that before the end of 1960 three churches in this book were already mergers of Congregational Christian and Evangelical and Reformed congregations. One Evangelical and Reformed Church in New York dually aligned with the Congregational Christians in 1958, and is listed in Appendix II..) Evangelical and Reformed Churches begun by 1960 are not reported in this book, unless special circumstances warrant their mention.]

The United Church of Christ Constitution provided that local Associations and Conferences of the United Church might continue to include Congregational Christian Churches which were not part of the United Church. These have been reported in two groups: Schedule I Churches (Schedule II in the *1962 Yearbook*) includes churches which have not voted or have voted to abstain from making a decision; Schedule II Churches (Schedule III in the *1962 Yearbook*) includes churches which have voted not to be part of the United Church.

Opposition led to the formation of two "continuing" denominations that are active in these states: The National Association of Congregational Christian Churches was formed in 1955, and began to act as a denomination in 1961 when it declared itself to be the successor of the General Council. The Conservative Congregational Christian Conference was formed in 1948. [New congregations first appearing with either of these groups, or as Schedule I. or Schedule II. congregations are shown in Appendix IV.. This list includes some formerly Evangelical and Reformed congregations that have affiliated with continuing Congregational Christian denominations.]

In 1960 the Evangelical and Reformed Church was active in all states in this area. Pennsylvania had more Evangelical and Reformed congregations than any other state. Two synods were centered in New York, and nine in Pennsylvania. A Maryland-centered synod served a small section of Pennsylvania, while the ethnically Hungarian Magyar Synod served in all three states.

CADMAN vs. KENYON

Conversations towards completion of this merger began in the early 1940's. A Basis of Union for the merger was reviewed by local congregations. Because the Evangelical and Reformed Church had a modified presbyterian polity, fears of the loss of autonomy arose in the Congregational Christian community. An exploratory vote of local congregations was initiated. It was indicated that the Basis needed to receive the support of seventy-five percent or more of the Congregational Christian Churches. The votes reported at a critical meeting of the General Council showed over two-thirds of voting congregations favoring the merger, but not three-quarters. The General Council decided to move ahead, and local congregations were encouraged to vote again, and many did, changing to supportive votes. A set of "Interpretations" was also adopted which were meant to support the continuation of local church autonomy.

Fierce opposition continued. New York, with the denominational headquarters and the corporate structures of the homeland boards, became the center of the whirlwind. Churches opposing the merger claimed they were entitled to the endowments and assets of the denomination and missionary societies (since the gifts were given for Congregational work), or, failing that, at least the proportion of assets that belonged to the non-merging congregations. The Minister and Secretary of the General Council (1938-1956) was Douglas Horton, who had grown up at Central Church in Brooklyn under the ministry of S. Parkes Cadman. The Cadman Memorial Church of Brooklyn, a merged church which included the former Central Church, brought the court case against the denomination. Since Ms. Helen Kenyon of the Poughkeepsie, New York Church was the Moderator of the General Council at the time, the case became known as Cadman vs. Kenyon.

The leadership of the Cadman Church in the anti-merger camp, and the call to their side of the remainders of many of the great Brooklyn churches is grist for a potential study on demographics, decline, resentment, and the movements of power.

The court case dragged on for years. Finally the pro-merger forces were able to win approval to move ahead, and the new church was formed in 1957, with details to be developed out later. A proposed Constitution for the United Church of Christ was released in 1960. Then all Congregational Christian Churches were again asked to vote on the proposed Constitution and, by implication, their membership in the new United Church. Most voting was completed by July of 1961, when the new Constitution was declared in force.

ANTI-UNION GROUPS

The Brooklyn Churches opposing the merger moved into the National Association of Congregational Christian Churches. Their opposition probably also influenced some congregations on Long Island to stay out of or delay joining the United Church. But the National Association did not gain much of a foothold in the rest of New York state. As the Brooklyn churches continued to decline, so did its position in the state.

The National Association also attracted a few congregations among the Yankee remnants in Pennsylvania, and a few in New Jersey. Opposition to the merger was very strong in Pennsylvania, possibly because of fear of being swallowed by the enormous Evangelical and Reformed presence in the state. The National Association attracted many Pennsylvania churches of Welsh and German Evangelical Protestant descent. Many of the Welsh churches later closed or became independent.

The Conservative Congregational Christian Conference began as a very small group in this area. Early it had attracted a few old Congregational Churches in the western end of New York state and community churches there and in the Albany area. Through time it has added many Hudson valley churches and additional churches in western New York and the northwest corner of Pennsylvania, from both the Congregational Christian and independent church circles, and has become the largest continuing Congregational Christian group in New York state. Lately it has also added some formerly Evangelical and Reformed congregations in Pennsylvania, and its membership has surpassed the size of the National Association in this state as well.

Many formerly Christian Churches opposed the merger, including the entire Conference in Ontario Canada, that had been affiliated to the New York Conference. It joined the Conservative Conference. A few Christian Churches have joined the Tioga River Conference, while others have become independent or moved towards other groups.

In upstate New York, and the northern tier of Pennsylvania counties, some congregations have kept their Schedule I or Schedule II status. Initially two large upstate New York churches (Park Church in Elmira, and First Church in Ithaca) opposed the merger, but both have since joined the United Church of Christ.

Church affiliations are not static, and some churches joining the merger later withdrew.

THE RELIGIOUS SITUATION IN 2000

By 2000 unions and schisms have increased and decreased the data for the old Plan of Union partners. Both the United Church of Christ and the Presbyterian Church, U.S.A., now include churches from other merging groups, while many of their earlier congregations are now in schismatic groups. Their totals are shown in Figure No. 6. (This data is from: Jones, Dale, *et al,* Religious Congregations and Membership in the United States: 2000 (Glenmary Research Center, Nashville, 2002) It is slightly modified to include inactive Schedule I. and Schedule II. churches.)

FIGURE NO. 6
CHURCHES AND MEMBERS - 2000

STATE	New Jersey		New York		Pennsylvania	
	Chs.	Mmbrs.	Chs.	Mmbrs.	Chs.	Mmbrs.
United Church of Christ	57	11,461	291	47,957	735	197,496
National Association Congregational Christian Churches	5	643	13	1,448	15	790
Conservative Congregational Christian Conference			27	2,596	15	2,472
Schedule I & II Congregational Christian (not above)			14	694	7	877
Presbyterian Church, U.S.A.	373	95,976	717	131,046	1,083	265,158
Presbyterian Church in America	26	1,673	26	3,287	94	16,367
Evangelical Presbyterian Church	1	304	2	467	4	879
Associate Reformed Presbyterian, General Synod			5	257	2	118
Cumberland Presbyterian Church					1	122
Orthodox Presbyterian Church	20	1,443	11	643	35	2,646

Chs. = Churches. Mmbrs. = Members

INTERNATIONAL PARALLELS: RE-AWAKENING COMMON GROUND

As the nineteenth century progressed the two branches of the Reformed faith, Congregationalism and Presbyterianism in both Britain and the United States drew farther and farther apart. The Plan of Union in America failed. Presbyterianism and Congregationalism in England and Scotland were clearly distinct bodies. The same divisions could be seen in other parts of the English-speaking world. Near the end of the century denominations world-wide began to organize international structures for cooperation, fellowship, mission strategy, etc.. The World Alliance of Reformed Churches Holding to the Presbyterian Order was begun in 1875. An International Congregational Council began in 1891. Polity had come to rule over theology, and the schisms seemed to be entrenched internationally.

However, less apparent forces were moving in the opposite direction. The vast size of the missionary frontier called for cooperative planning. Slowly an ever-widening circle of groups met to strategize about missions. Sometimes missionary areas were divided according to "comity" agreements. Small missions of one body were transferred to those of a group stronger or better able to serve in a particular area. Contacts and cooperation made some of the divisions of the past seem insignificant. Most major Protestant traditions came into conversation in Missionary, Faith and Order, and Life and Work councils and programs.

But more dramatic were actual unions of churches. While often discussed, these unions were slow in coming. At first the unions were often re-unions of groups in the same denominational families, such as the merger of most of the Cumberland Presbyterian Church with the Presbyterian Church, U.S.A. in 1906; or the adding of very tiny groups to much larger bodies, such as the Congregational Methodists joining the Congregationalists in 1888/1892. Similar mergers occurred on the mission fields, where missions of various Reformed, Presbyterian, and Congregational bodies, often from differing nations, were united.

Union took a more startling direction in 1925 when the Methodist Church, Congregational Churches, most of the Presbyterian Church, and an organization of community churches in Canada united as the United Church of Canada. Had the sentiment towards reunion been reborn?

In the United States the Presbyterian Church, U.S.A., busied itself with continued mergers of groups with Presbyterian doctrines and forms (1920, 1958, 1983). But the Congregationalists, already united, moved towards union with groups of different character: first a group coming out of frontier Restorationism (1931), and then with a German denomination, of mixed Reformed and Lutheran theology, and a presbyterian polity (1957). After the passage of so many years, American Congregationalists were willing to again seek union with a group with presbyterian polity, but not with their old on-again, off-again partner, but instead an ethnically German group.

Perhaps all the more surprising is that only a few years later the two international fellowships coming out of the Reformed tradition united in 1970 as the World Alliance of Reformed Churches (Presbyterian and Congregational).

Two years later (1972), in Britain, the Congregational Church in England and Wales (the successor to the old Congregational Union) and the Presbyterian Church of England united as the United Reformed Church. The Presbyterian Church in this partnership, while including a few old English Presbyterian Churches, is primarily made up of congregations in England and Wales of Scottish origin. In 1980 this united body also merged with Britain's primary Restorationist body, the Reformed Association of Churches of Christ.

Similar unions of churches with Congregational or Presbyterian polity have followed in Australia, New Zealand, and most mission territories where groups from both traditions existed. However, separations continue in countries where one or the other body is the established church (such as Scotland, and the Netherlands), as well as South Africa, the United States, and a few other places.

Nevertheless, just as the ecumenical movement has been growing, international churches have seen a splintering similar to those in the United States. Conservative Presbyterian denominations have begun in many parts of the world similar to the Presbyterian Church in America, the Evangelical Presbyterian Church, the Orthodox Presbyterian Church, and splinter groups from the Bible Presbyterian Church. Some of these participate in international Presbyterian and Reformed fellowships outside the World Alliance.

Congregationalism has also been splintered. The Congregational Federation in England and Wales (1972) was organized by congregations staying out of the United Reformed Church over polity issues, and is closely related to the National Association. The Evangelical Fellowship of Congregational Churches (1967) another English schism, stresses both polity and theological concerns, and is closely related to the Conservative Conference. Similar three-way divisions have occurred among Congregational Churches in other lands. The International Congregational Fellowship (1975/1977) is an organization of individuals drawn from groups such as the National Association. The World Evangelical Congregational Fellowship (1984/1986) includes the Conservative Conference.

In the United States, the two largest successors of the historic bodies (United Church of Christ and Presbyterian Church, U.S.A.) continue to relate through the National Council of the Churches of Christ, and through statewide and local concilliar groups. In 1962 the United Church of Christ and the United Presbyterian Church in the U.S.A., were two of four denominations that began to explore union through the Consultation on Church Union. That body has expanded to nine denominations, but has evolved more into an agency of cooperation than a body expecting union in the near future. It is now known as the Churches of Christ, Uniting.

Following its formation in 1957 the United Church of Christ became a member of both the World Alliance of Reformed Churches as well as the International Congregational Council. Theoretically this activity brought the

Congregational churches in the United Church into full communion with churches in the World Alliance, including the American Presbyterians, as part of the same international communions. After the Second Vatican Council various Christian confessional communities began dialogues with each other about faith and order. The American discussion group between Reformed and Lutheran denominations led, in 1998, to a public declaration of full communion among the United Church of Christ, the Presbyterian Church, U.S.A., the Reformed Church in America, and the Evangelical Lutheran Church in America.

The United Church of Christ in 1979 also formed a covenant that eventually led to full communion with the most mainline of America's remaining Restorationist denominations, the Christian Church, Disciples of Christ.

This story began with the roots of the Reformed Churches in the Reformation, and the international inter-connections of early Reformed leaders. The focus then moved to three states in the northeastern United States, the introduction of English Puritanism into this area, and its combinations with and eventual partial separation from congregations with an Irish or Scottish Presbyterian heritage. These two traditions still have a powerful witness in this area, and many additional congregations relate to bodies that have broken away from either group. The two largest groups, the United Church of Christ, and the Presbyterian Church, U.S.A., are in full communion and often cooperate but still stand apart. The future of these two inter-twined families is yet to be seen.

SOME CONSIDERATIONS ABOUT POLITY AND DEFINITIONS

This book intends to list Congregational churches that existed in the Middle Atlantic states. However, because of three unions and three schisms with judicatories that eventually became the Presbyterian Church, U.S.A., we are swept up in a problem of definition. What exactly is a Congregational church? What exactly is a Presbyterian church?

The most basic and plain use of the words "congregational" and "presbyterian" is as the modern denominations that bear these names. However, in this book, they most often refer to the two evolving factions in Middle Atlantic English-speaking Reformed churches as discussed in the introduction under the section "The Scope of the Listings."

Since these are historic groupings moving through time, they do not exhibit clear continuous definitions that divide them. For example, while the Presbyterian Church U.S.A. can claim a direct organizational history from 1706, there are significant periods of its history when many of its congregations did not conform to what may be considered as normative Presbyterian ecclesiology. These include, for example, the initial period before the imposition of absolute subscription (1706-1736), in the New Side (1741-1758), mixed congregations under the Plan of Union (from 1801), and congregations members of Presbytery under the Accommodation Plan (1808-legally 1870). Conversely, the polities of unassociated independent Congregational churches and those accepting the authority of Connecticut consociations are also far apart.

Nevertheless, references to the factional and functional groupings should be generally comprehended. Occasionally these factional definitions will be widened, as when, for example, Presbyterian is meant specifically to include Covenanter and Seceder groups as well as the Presbyterian Church, U.S.A..

However, it should be obvious to most readers that these two words were originally used to describe differences in polity (forms of organization), and ecclesiology (theologies of the nature of the church), differentiating religious groups. As such, the words are often used as a short hand in a wider discussion, which places religious organizations on a spectrum of the loci of power from independency to congregationalism, to presbyterianism, to episcopacy, to papal forms. While this modern instructional tool may prove efficient, it gives an over- emphasis to the inter-connectedness of churches, without discerning their interior dynamics. For example, there are Baptist congregations which, while claiming congregational autonomy, are internally governed by pastors with papal-type authority. On the other hand, the American Episcopal Church, even with bishops, gives their congregations far more democratic autonomy than an untrained observer might realize.

In actual fact any perceived difference in religious polity or ecclesiology could be a tool of definition. That, however, might make conversation so complex as to become chaotic. (Which is often the case in the wide range of congregations possible in a large community.) But that diffuse approach would fail to recognize that both polity and ecclesiology have developed historically, and also, that many common views have tended to cluster together.

When we try to compare classic theories against historic reality, we need to be able to distinguish between theories as put together in the mind of one member of a group, with or without group approval and consent, systems or theories widely consented to by a group through general covenant or consensus, and the actual practice of events. We also need to be aware of how the actual practice may have been influenced or determined by issues outside of the theoretical discussions.

While the words “presbyterian” and “congregational” are used here to describe polity and ecclesiological positions and groupings, they are used with caution. This hesitancy is because of the easy tendency to confine these labels to their most common use in recent historical discussions.

The groups studied here are not the only claimants to these polities. Many Lutheran bodies have claimed Presbyterian polity, while Baptists, Restorationist groups, and others claim Congregational polity. Here we limit our explorations to churches in the Reformed tradition, but these issues might broaden if other groups were brought to the table. Conversely, some have tended to subsume the entire Reformed family under the Presbyterian name. (See Loetscher’s use (34, pp.35-36), where some groups with semi-episcopal organization are referred to as Presbyterians.) Such usage is presumptive and not helpful to polity distinctions.

Historians in the late nineteenth and early twentieth centuries, the longest period when the Presbyterian and Congregational denominations were clearly distinct in America, have tended to say that there are classic definitions of each polity and its supporting theological ecclesiology. The most important issue, they said, was the authority of upper church judicatories: Presbyteries and Synods, which was the most divisive issue at the time they wrote. Thus Trinterud (36, p.19) says "the issue which was the occasion of finally separating British Puritanism into Congregationalists and Presbyterians, was... the province and place of the higher councils of the church..."

That is not the entire story. What is really the case is that the classic models probably have never existed in reality. Also, historic progenitors may not fit into our pre-defined boxes. While a given faction may theorize some systematic connection of one idea to another, the pragmatic experience of living says that at some point in time some issues become paramount, and others are not only little thought of, but often not even perceived.

SOME CONSIDERATIONS ABOUT POLITY AND DEFINITIONS

Two Words in Opposition

The two words "congregational" and "presbyterian" have often been seen as polar opposites, defining each other. This tendency emerged as factional names when the majority of the Westminster Assembly (1643-1652), adopted an ecclesiastical system that became the basis of most modern "Presbyterian" denominations, while a minority report encouraged "Congregational" thinking (*An Apologeticall Narration...).* It would appear that the word "presbyterian" made its first appearance at the Assembly, although the earlier form "presbyterial" had been used to describe some of the same tendencies, but without rigid lines of demarcation. The adjective "congregational" had earlier been used by others, including New England Puritans, who used it to describe their experiment in the New World. These new conflicting senses of the words "presbyterian" and "congregational" were continued in the work of the Cambridge Synod and active debates in New as well as old England.

Both words, obviously, have roots in the New Testament. Congregation (Greek: *ecclesia*) referring often to a particular Christian community (*e.g.*, Acts 8:1b, I Corinthians 1:2), but sometimes to the whole people of God (*e.g.*, Acts 20:28, I Corinthians 15:9, Ephesians 3:10, Colossians 1:24). Presbyterian (Greek: *presbyter*) evolves from the Greek word for elder and emphasizes issues of leadership (*e.g.*, Acts 11:30, 15:2).

Both words, in fact, have had fluid definitions since Westminster. Meanings and emphases have changed through time. Clusters of ideas have caused claimants to either word to overlap aspects of their definitions, rather than perpetuating polar opposites.

It would appear that Presbyterianism – suggesting in its modern use an interconnected system of authority - has had a more consistent center of meaning than Congregationalism. The latter, usually conceived as implying autonomy, would be subject to a wider range of possibilities. While this may generally be true, it is often not specifically the case.

Let us describe some of the evolution of both words to help illustrate the changing controversies that employed these names as banners.

Polity in Pre-Reformation Britain

In pre-Reformation Britain cooperation, tense compromises, or outright conflict between the Pope and local kings and lords interacted in the appointment of bishops. These issues were riddled with politics since the Pope and some bishops were secular lords as well as church leaders. Usually bishops appointed local parish priests. The prestige or significance of parishes and appointments varied over a host of issues, not the least being the wealth of the parish. Some parishes, including some housed on large estates, were sponsored by powerful lords or landowners that underwrote all parish expenses. Other parishes had glebes, land, farms, endowments or other holdings that had been given to the parish at an earlier date, which provided income to meet parish expenses. The bishop, a local lord, or landowner, or a local council chosen by any of a number of means might administer these holdings. Other parishes, particularly in growing commercial towns, had town or parish councils that assessed a tax for parish expenses. Almost all parishes received donations. Many parishes were funded by a combination of several of these methods.

While ordination continued to be a prerogative of the bishops, some local well-heeled gentry who promised to fully finance a parish, were sometimes given an advowson, the power to appoint their local clergy. This was also called "lay patronage."

Bishops had many types of candidates for appointments. Some were pious young men who had grown up in the church and been educated for service in the church. Other pious young men may have had no training at all. Some well-endowed parishes could pay such lucrative salaries that they were attractive to younger sons of the gentry who were not in line to inherit their family estates. Many of the latter, educated or uneducated, were drunken playboys more interested in the income than the church.

Bishops needed to play a certain amount of politics to please both candidates from influential families or to please the powerful people in the wealthy parishes. Some parishes with large glebes and dwindling populations would have absentee priests appointed who took the salary and seldom appeared in the parish. Some such "pastors" would receive multiple appointments, taking the "livings" of several parishes and serving in none.

Since the Catholic Church was the state church of all of western Europe, membership was wide. All citizens were expected to be baptized, and all the baptized were church members.

Origins of Scottish Polity

The continental European Reformed Christian faith, which grew out of the Reformation, and particularly the teachings of Zwingli, Calvin, and others is older than the Presbyterian / Congregational debate. That tradition grew up in a variety of languages, cultural, legal, and national systems, each of which had their strengths and weaknesses, and whose reality shaped the Reformed Churches.

SOME CONSIDERATIONS ABOUT POLITY AND DEFINITIONS

The Reformed faith came separately to Scotland and England, which were separate countries. Even though both shared the English language, they had different compromises with their native Celtic and later immigrant peoples and languages. They had divergent cultures and different political systems. Therefore the Reformed faith took on a national and cultural identity which was distinct from polity.

John Knox, when in exile on the Continent, had learned of Calvin's Geneva consistory and Beza's system of organized synods which brought elders together from various congregations. In France the Huguenot synods for the most part stood outside the government. In Geneva the whole nation was considered Reformed Christian, and the consistory was intertwined with the power structure. In Scotland there was a weak and intermittent Parliament. Knox's new annual Presbyterian General Assembly provided a popular glue for drawing the people together. This strong organization could speak to the powers that be. The Scottish Parliament rejected papal authority and adopted the Scots Confession in 1560. This began an internal struggle between episcopacy (governance through bishops) and a system of church organization through an ascending order of church courts, which we today call "Presbyterianism." Representative democracy, as opposed to royal authority, was a political issue intertwined with the Scottish Reformation.

In 1592 the Scottish Parliament adopted the Presbyterian form, but in 1610 the King had three new bishops consecrated to head the Church of Scotland. The King also tried to impose on the Church a liturgy more like that in England. This led to a revolt, and, in 1638, to the adoption in Scotland of the National Covenant, and a return to the Presbyterian system. However, after the return of the Stuart dynasty to power in 1660, bishops were again imposed upon Scotland, and many clergy were removed from service, and their preaching was suppressed. Only after the Glorious Revolution, in 1690, was the Presbyterian system finally re-adopted in Scotland.

The Church of Scotland eliminated bishops and set up the General Assembly modeled after Beza's synods in continental Europe. However, unlike France where synods operated in a Catholic state, the General Assembly was expected to be ***the*** Church of Scotland. Each parish was now expected to have ruling elders – pious persons chosen to lead the parish. Most non-parish church lands (monasteries, convents, etc.) had been seized by the government and re-distributed among powerful people supporting the revolutionary aspects of the Reformation.

However local parish funding was slower to change. Some parishes would elect their local lord or wealthiest landowner as a ruling elder, and the role of the local gentry in the church was strengthened. Conversely, where there were tensions between the new sessions and local gentry, difficulties erupted.

Two polity issues plagued the new Scottish Church for centuries. First was the Stuart desire to impose bishops on the Church of Scotland in the Anglican model. Whenever they king did appoint bishops, and they appointed pastors, the Presbyterian system was abolished.

The second issue was lay patronage. Gentry who had exercised this power in the past expected to be able to continue. This system was often imposed in Scotland. Local parishes desiring pious pastors conforming to the ideals of the Reformation opposed royal imposition of the continuation of lay patronage. It also led to divisions in the church. Schismatic groups in Scotland often defined themselves as free of lay patronage.

The Presbyterian system honored local gentry who cooperated with their session and presbytery, and often gave them power in the church. But it worked to limit those who undermined the Presbyterian system.

Origins of English Polity

England was a different country and had a different history. While Reformed preachers also came to England, the country was swept along on the tides of political intrigue, when in 1534 King Henry VIII. convinced the English Parliament to pass the Act of Supremacy, making him the head of the Church of England. Henry VIII. also seized church lands and divided them among allies. Henry kept the office of bishop – now appointed by him – and established no parallel of local church sessions, maintaining the earlier complex parish system. The new Anglican Church was reaffirmed in 1558. With bishops and its own unique liturgy, it may not have been a Reformed Church on the European model. The friends of the fully Reformed doctrines had to determine how to survive in such a unique atmosphere. The church was partly reformed, partly not. Should they live with what they have or press farther? And if they are to press farther then where, when, and how? Unlike Scotland, the central question was not setting up a new national church and a popular council. England already had a strong Parliament to provide a forum for public discussion. The central question was the purity of the church.

Many believed that the bishops could come from a pure Reformed faith and thereby purify the church. Others believed that they should slowly give way to a more deliberative form such as that in Scotland or Beza's continental Synods. Others saw the loci of change centered in a reformed clergy and groups organized around them. Still others held that the purification of the laity, from the bottom up, if you will, would change the church.

SOME CONSIDERATIONS ABOUT POLITY AND DEFINITIONS

Puritanism initially worked in consort with the episcopal system. Some bishops were Puritans and gave Puritans key appointments. Other bishops may have had little interest in theology and appointed all kinds of candidates, including Puritans. Thus Puritanism grew in many communities. Bremer (1998) documents how Puritanism prospered in many congregations within the Anglican system. Centered on conversion, Puritan faith could dwell within the Anglican communion. Bremer also stresses the communal aspect of sainthood within the Puritan framework.
A person filled with the love of God, would love others and form close bonds of fellowship and identity. The bonds of close friendship among Puritan clergy and their families, as well as among growing numbers of lay people within many parishes proved to be powerful agents of growth.

Clergy meetings sometimes became more formal. Thomas Cartwright's leadership in the founding of classes and synods from 1570 grew out of this tendency, and has often been seen as the start of Puritan interest in changing the polity of the English Church. The bodies formed in response to the work of Cartwright and others provided fellowship but really did not take on the power of the bishops. Conversely, Cartwright said "no particular church has power over another..." (quoted in Bremer (1998), p.11). He also called for a narrower, purer membership within the church. (See David D. Hall in the introduction to *Jonathan Edwards: Ecclesiastical Writings* (Yale University Press, New Haven), p.21.)

Also arising in this period was the idea of "consociations." Robert Parker, whose son later came to New England as a pastor, suggested these and defined them as "meetings of two or more particular congregations, mutually agreed to consider problems that could not be solved on the local level. Their authority derived from the particular congregations and ultimately stayed with them" (quoted in Bremer (1998), p.11).

Later historians would see in these moves the beginnings of a "Presbyterial" polity in English Puritanism. In one way this is true, in that the leaders around Cartwright had "a strong sense of the power of the congregational presbytery – the minister and elders within the congregation..." More politically decisive, however, was the view of some in the establishment that this group really did want to "replace England's episcopal structure with the Scottish system." (Bremer (1998), p.11) Nevertheless Bremer concludes that there was "no call among mainstream English puritans for governing synods or authoritative assemblies." (p.13)

Hall (*ob.cit.*, p.21) suggests that those labeled Presbyterian in the 1500's sound like the Congregationalists of the 1640's. Students of these polities, already at this early date, find linguistic confusion.

At about the same time (1580's) some Separatist Calvinist congregations outside of the established church were begun. These were usually suppressed. However, scholars have found in the work of some of their leaders some of the origins of later Congregationalism. Dexter (1880/1970) and Walker (1893/1960) distinguish between the works of Robert Browne (who advocated a shared democratic leadership within purified congregations), and Henry Barrowe (who advocated stronger leadership on the part of the elders within the congregation).

These two varied initiatives (the classis-consociation movement and the separatist congregations) in the polity area led to the suppression and persecution of both in the latter decade and a half of Elizabeth's reign.

Puritanism, however, continued in the state church. In the academic halls of the universities, and the ministries of pious pastors it continued to grow and flourish. Some wealthy Puritans purchased "livings" to provide pulpits for Puritan clergy. Those Puritan pastors that served Anglican congregations with broad memberships, not all of whose members could be considered converted, continued to stress Cartwright's emphasis on narrow internal presbyterial leadership. In some other congregations, however, as conversions and piety increased, some Puritan pastors began to share leadership with a wider proportion of the membership.

In the last years of Elizabeth's reign and under the Stuarts there were fewer Puritans appointed as bishops, and fewer parish appointments. Puritans continued to take advantage of lay patronage. Under the Stuarts when political, theological, and philosophical concerns turned against Puritanism, pastors could be harassed, silenced, or excluded. Speaking out became more difficult.

While the national Presbyterial system in Scotland was the best way to assure a Reformed appointment to a parish, in England the independence of a local bishop, a lay patron, or an autonomous local parish council proved most effective in placing Reformed clergy. The two national Reformed movements began to part ways on issues of effective governance.

English parishes also began to find differences in the concepts of local leadership and eventually local church membership. Some refugee Separatist congregations, with called out memberships made up of "visible saints" began to develop local polities that employed the entire membership in leadership and discipline issues.

Defining "Presbyterian"

Drawing from the above, the first thing that needs to be said about "presbyterian" is that it had variant meanings in England and Scotland.

SOME CONSIDERATIONS ABOUT POLITY AND DEFINITIONS

This is a major theme of Bolam *et al's "English Presbyterianism"* (1968). While Presbyterian concepts of how to organize the Church of England can be traced before Westminster, during the Commonwealth, and among persecuted non-conformists during the Restoration, some concluded that "after 1689 'the denomination vanished as suddenly as it had arisen'" (quoted on p.17). Duncan Coomer, among others, they report, said of English churches and clergy called Presbyterian that "their 'Presbyterian' title was a misnomer, because 'they never realized their dream of a land covered by a network of Synods, Presbyteries and Church Sessions'." (Quoted, p.19) The authors contend that "The fact is that they failed to set up such a network because they had no wish to do so. The vast majority of them had no enthusiasm for that carefully articulated network of church courts, which was characteristic of Scottish Presbyterianism and which had been introduced into England as part of the price of Scottish support for Parliament in the Civil War. To the average English Presbyterian of the second half of the seventeenth century Coomer's dream might have seemed more like a nightmare" (pp.19-20).

They further argue that this distinction was true in England before Westminster, as we have seen in the boundaries placed around centers of power by Cartwright and his followers. "Right from the beginning English Presbyterianism exhibited features which distinguished it sharply from the system established north of the Border. In England much greater importance was attached to the individual congregation: thus the 'presbytery' or prime unit of church government was not, as in Scotland, a meeting of delegates from different congregations; it was the governing body of a particular church, or what the Scots would call a 'kirk-session'. Although there were English presbyterians who did at times advocate a hierarchical Presbyterian system with higher courts exercising jurisdiction over churches, they generally insisted that a classis or synod should be purely consultative and should not interfere with the sovereign independence of the individual congregations." (p. 20)

The delegates to the Westminster Assembly were "essentially Puritan" (Walker (1893/1960), p.136) and "predominantly English" (Maclean (1993), p.122). Its results "formulated the beliefs of Scotland and Presbyterian America" (Walker, (1893/1960), p. 136). Its decisions were adopted, and later re-adopted for the Church of Scotland.

In England Westminster brought together a broad spectrum of Puritans, seeking ecclesiastical compromise and a Scottish alliance to win the War against the King. But Scotland's loyalty to the English Parliament had been sporadic, Congregationalism grew under Cromwell, and by the time of the Restoration some Puritans were ready to return to an Anglican Church. Indeed, some probably only voted the way that they did at Westminster with the understanding that the proposal would be a standing state church. With that possibility withdrawn, Anglicanism was the national church. Also the English Presbyterians in the Puritan community, if truly different than their Scottish contemporaries, would feel no obligation to Westminster after the Puritan Commonwealth fell.

Polity Changes Within the Scottish Model

It could be said that the modern Presbyterian Church, U.S.A., with a clear polity that it calls Presbyterian, fulfills the Westminster forms as revised and amended in the Book of Order, and interpreted through a long history of case law. However, even in its Scottish sense "Presbyterianism" has not always been an absolutely rigid polity. Americans, for example, have cut out of the tradition those aspects that suggest an established church. Scottish immigrants to England also became non-conformists. The Church of Scotland remains an established church.

Other issues have distinguished Presbyterian denominations over national boundaries, or in sectarian disputes. That differing churches feel free to amend the Westminster documents indicates that they are not quite as rigid as one would imagine. Established churches often take on cultural or ethnocentric dimensions not part of an essential polity. This can be seen in such items as the Scottish National Covenant. While initially established churches assume a connection to the entire population, toleration and freedom of religion have caused even national churches to move towards a more defined membership. Scottish churches have fought over lay patronage but have still been considered Presbyterian by most writers. Some Presbyterian churches expect women to be serving on each session. Others reject female officers altogether. Other schisms have occurred over hymnody and liturgy. Formal subscription in Europe and America arose long after the Westminster Assembly. In America a presbytery's title to local church properties was not assumed at first, and grew gradually into place. While it was previously considered that lay elders were elected for life, time has moved towards a more congregational form of session members being elected to finite terms of office. In America Presbyterian synods, once important bodies close to presbyteries, moved first to becoming larger state bodies on the order of Congregational general associations or conferences, and later to large regional bodies with few duties outside judicial hearings. Executive presbyters and stated clerks have become salaried employees with some power. Again these changes, though real, have not been considered defining. Much of this book explores other departures from the rigid ways of Westminster in the interaction of Congregational and Presbyterian people in the United States.

Some modern changes even go deeper in challenging the idea of Presbyterian rigidity. In the midst of the fundamentalist-modernist controversy (1927) the Presbyterian Church, U.S.A. adopted a report seeking to determine if there were clear and specific "Essential and Necessary Articles" of belief which were required of candidates for ordination under the Adopting Act of 1729. (See Report of the Special Commission 1925 (Excerpt) in *Journal of Presbyterian History, Volume 79, No.1, Spring 2001,* pp.46-52). This compromise seemed to imply that local presbyteries would hear specific challenges to beliefs from candidates for ordination within the context of their own faith journeys and then determine their fitness for ordination. Some have viewed this as an introduction of a type of local autonomy within the Presbyterian system that opens it to heterodox theology. The Presbyterian Church, U.S.A. also adopted a new Confession in 1967, and further moved away from the centrality of Westminster by adopting a *Book of Confessions* which brings Westminster together with many other historic Reformed Confessions, as well as with the modern Barmen Declaration and the 1967 Confession. While this move may be seen as a widening of the base of the Presbyterian Church, others see it as an over-ruling of the "scruples" provision of the 1729 Adopting Act. They would contend that theological differences may be tolerated within the areas in which the Confessions differ, but where they are in agreement no scruple or dissension is possible. (See Beuttler, Fred W., Making Theology Matter..., in *Journal of Presbyterian History, Volume 79, No.1, Spring, 2001, pp.5-22,* and related articles.)

Polities in Conflict

"Terms like "Congregationalist" or "Presbyterian" provide endless confusion for students of early American history. Most want to give those terms the doctrinal definitions and denominational colorations of the present, forgetting that in the late sixteenth or seventeenth centuries they were imprecise terms with various definitions. Occasionally they were used only as epithets... [T]heir meanings, however imprecise, must be conveyed to the reader." (Lucas (1976), pp.15-16).

Most early settlers of New England came from England, and therefore understood the word "presbyterian" in its English sense.

If we were to put the polities of Westminster and the Cambridge Platform next to each other, it might surprise modern readers where the differences can be found. It is not over the issue of ruling elders within local congregations. Both set up that office. Nor is it over the existence of synods. The Cambridge Platform was, after all, written by a Synod. Both documents also expected that in the best setting the church would be closely aligned with the government or Magistrate. Nor are the differences theological. The Cambridge Platform acknowledges accord with Westminster in issues of faith, and goes to pains to place Congregationalism in the wider Reformed community. These types of agreements lead authors such as Trinterud (36) to conclude, "the Cambridge Platform embodied some Presbyterian ideas." That of course, would imply that the classic Congregationalists were not Congregationalists, or that any overlap between the two polities was Congregationalism stealing from Presbyterianism.

Central to Cambridge and Congregationalism was the desire of a narrower church membership "saints by calling." Within such a membership of visible saints the leadership in the church was extended to the entire membership. This was tempered with a continued regard for congregations in the Church of England and Presbyterian congregations, where saintly members were encouraged to remain in their churches whenever possible in order to move those congregations towards purity. Saints are described as "such, as haue not only attained the knowledge of the principles of Religion, & are free from gros & open scandals, but also do together with the profession of their faith & Repentance, walk in blameless obedience to the word, so as that in charitable discretion they may be accounted Saints by calling,..." (quoted in Walker (1893/1960), pp.205-206). These saints are then to form covenanted congregations in each place. "A Congregational-church, is by the institution of *C*hrist a part of the Militant-visible-church, consisting of a company *of* Saints by calling, united into one body, by a holy covenant, *f*or the publick worship of God, & the mutuall edification one of another, in the Fellowship *of* the Lord Iesus." (quoted in Walker (1893/1960), p.205) Particular churches were to be distinguished by their forms, that form being the "*Visible Covenant,* Agreement, or consent wherby they give up themselves unto the Lord, to the observing of the ordinances of Christ together in the same society..." (*Ibid.,* pp.207-208). Thus each congregation was unique in its own authority.

In the Cambridge Platform the term "Presbytery" (chapter X.) follows the English usage of referring to the presbytery "within" a congregation, that is its pastors, teachers, and ruling elders. But while this may seem like a Scottish session, the Platform puts such internal presbyteries "subject to the power of the church..." (*Ibid.,* p.219). Synods are seen as "many times... necessary to the wel-being of churches..." (*Ibid.,* p.233). They, however, are "Not to exercise Church-censures in way of discipline, nor any other act of church-authority or jurisdiction." (*Ibid.,* p.234)

The debate in early New England

The roots of New England Congregationalism could be seen in Britain. But with its blossoming there were questions. Was it a new separatism? Or was it a more ecumenical church, a claimant of the Reformed name, even if not Presbyterian?

The Pilgrim Church that came to Plymouth in 1620 was of the schismatic Separatist model with a narrow called out membership and wide lay participation in the Church. Lay people managed to hold the congregation together until a pastor arrived in 1629. Nonetheless, the polity of this congregation was not independency. Instead of seizing the sacrament, it held out in some expectation of a greater wholeness. Their Leyden pastor John Robinson, hoped for reconciliation with the wider church. Upon the arrival of the Puritans, this congregation immediately sought to establish fellowship with them.

The Puritans, in turn, recognized Plymouth, and also the Presbyterian and Anglican congregations across the sea, and yet sought for ways to explain their own existence.

While the Puritans "had left England as Non-Conformists rather than Separatists... they had all of them nevertheless organized on the model set by Separatist Plymouth. It was natural that such action should excite a degree of alarm in the minds of the Puritans in England..." (Walker (1893/1960), p.134). Questions from England led to long replies from New England, and eventually to the Cambridge Synod. Even before the writing of the Platform a debate had arisen in New England between the standing order and opponents labeled as "Presbyterian." This task elicited the first American debate between Congregationalists and Presbyterians.

Most English Puritan clergy that had served in Anglican churches "where the saints were usually a minority" maintained "the power of the congregational presbytery (the minister and elders)." (Bremer (1998), p.13) In "Massachusetts, where circumstances were different, new forms of nurturing godly communities were explored. Sharing power with the covenanted saints seemed logical in communities where few could be characterized as ungodly, and sharing power even enhanced the sense of community among the saints... Polity was an expression of spiritual experience." (p.13) Bremer reports that "clergy whose social experiences... drew them into communion... with lay believers... were more likely to move in the direction of congregational polity, while those whose parish experiences were distanced them from the laity and led them to find comfort primarily from other clergy would be more distrustful of lay authority and were in essence proto-presbyterians." (p. 13)

Indeed, while the new participatory Congregational polity grew in New England, there was a vocal minority. Governor Winthrop describes a 1643 clergy meeting as being called "because some of the elders went about to set up some things according to the presbytery, as of Newbury, etc." (quoted in Dexter (1880/1970), Volume I., p. 432). Here the New England debate mirrors the definitions in England. Congregationalists are those who share authority with the laity, while Presbyterians give more authority to the leaders. The polity developed by Thomas Parker and James Noyes, the pastor and teacher of the Newbury Church, though, was even an unusual Presbyterianism. Noyes rejected the office of ruling elder, and limited the "Presbytery within" the Church to the pastors, himself and Parker. They wanted to hold the power themselves. While Dexter and others find in Noyes' writings a holding to "the church... kept in good order by the power of the Presbytery within, and of Synods and Councils without..." (p.432), Noyes and Parker did not call into session synods and councils without. The practical reality was a battle internal to the Newbury church, while their pastor and teacher boycotted New England synods.

Indeed, there was no known move in New England at this time to form standing presbyteries and synods. Cambridge and other New England synods were convention synods that disbanded when their business was completed. At its first session the Cambridge Synod decided that "The judgement of a Synod is in some respect superiour, in some respect inferiour to the judgement of a particular Church; it is superiour in respect to direction; inferiour in respect to jurisdiction, which in hath none." (Walker (1893/1960), p. 192) The Synod did write the Cambridge Platform to explain to the world the emerging participatory Congregationalism of America.

It should also be pointed out that later scholars writing about this period (*e.g.* Dexter and Walker) say that New England Congregationalism of this period was more Barrowist than Brownist. The difference between the two was that the Barrowist churches "gives practically all the power into the hands of the officers of the church." (Walker, p.135). This puts New England's idea of Presbyterianism very close to Barrowist thought. Both Barrowe and Browne wrote at times when they advocated Separatism. Browne also, in particular, refused to recognize the Church of England, and called for separation of church and state, items not esteemed by the New Englanders. But in polity we see at this time a spectrum in the definition of local church leadership from Brownist to Barrowist to Newbury Presbyterianism.

So, despite theoretical implications, to early New Englanders "Presbyterian" usually meant giving power to the pastors within the local church.

The debate in second generation New England

By the rise of the second generation in New England a decline in the proportion of the population becoming full church members had set in. This decline continued to grow before the Great Awakening as fewer and fewer seemed ready to declare themselves visible saints and receive full communion. Some saw this as a general declension. However it is clear that some had a scrupulous fear of public pride or taking the sacrament in an unworthy manner. Yet some probably also had a growing indifference in an increasingly secular environment. Clergy made attempts to broaden the church membership. Some sought to keep the membership pure, but allow shy individuals to make their professions of faith before the pastors rather than the entire congregation. A different attempt, promulgated at a 1662 Synod, produced the Half-Way Covenant (not called that until sometime later), that allowed the baptism of children whose parents were baptized but who had made no public profession.

New refugees arrived in New England following the restoration of the Stuarts (1660). Some brought with them the ideas of English Presbyterians who had abandoned the forms of Westminster, disillusioned after its failure to be established in England. Others arrived with sentiments closer to Westminster and Scotland who looked towards the formal interconnection of the churches. Presbyterians in New England now could include some that held Scottish views.

But the word "Presbyterian" still was generally not used in a Scottish sense. It was used to deride anyone who favored private confessions of faith (Lucas (1976), p.60). It was also used to describe anyone who "upheld the ministerial prerogative in certain areas of doctrine and discipline." (*Ibid.*, p.61). Like in Newbury, the issue at stake did not involve a session, but only the authority of the pastor.

There was also a larger issue of broadening the church membership to include those who might not be "visible saints." Presbyterians rejected the idea of visible saints. Bolam *et al* (1968, p.21) report that "While Congregationals thought in terms of the 'gathered church' of true believers, the Presbyterians thought in terms of the parish and were prepared to admit to Communion not just those who could give a satisfactory account of their religious experience but all those in the neighbourhood who had some understanding of the Christian faith and had not disqualified themselves by evil living. The Presbyterian attitude was not changed by the upheaval of 1662 which drove the ministers from their livings: though they were now without parishes they continued to regard themselves as parish ministers, serving the needs of everyone in their locality who wanted to attend their services."

In the 1660's, particularly in Connecticut, some congregations were divided. Others, including the venerable church in Wethersfield were described as having become Presbyterian. There were really three factions at this time. Rigid Congregationalists held out for smaller purer churches. Moderate Congregationalists were willing to try some type of broadening, such as the Half-Way Covenant. Presbyterians spread the net of membership even wider, by baptizing adopted children or servants. In 1669 the Connecticut legislature tolerated Presbyterians. (*Ibid.*, p.68). But Connecticut's Presbyterians "while reflecting both English and Scottish models, generally followed the English pattern. They embraced a parish-like church organization and rule by elder, but preferred congregational autonomy to the Scottish web of interchurch government." (*Ibid.*, p.61).

So, by this time, broader membership had become a primary definitional issue, along with internal congregational organization.

Definitions in Confusion and Evolution

Parameters that would later be considered clear boundaries between the two polities were often crossed in the early days. Early New England Congregationalism called many synods but allowed congregations to reject their conclusions. When synods and similar meetings included only pastors and teachers, some people charged that "they were participating in the creation of a Presbyterian establishment" (*Ibid.*, p.68) because they excluded the laity. In fact the Scottish system would have included lay elders, so it is clear that Presbyterian as a derisive term was still being used inconsistently.

On the other hand the evolution of ordination was a quiet transformation. Most early New England pastors had been ordained in Europe, many even by bishops in the apostolic succession. The first ordinations in New England honored the leadership of the laity and the autonomy of congregations. Congregations ordained ministers, and ordained status was retained only while serving in the congregation. However it was not very long before most congregations would hesitate to ordain a minister without consultation with other clergy in the area. Regional clergy were invited to sit in "vicinage" councils to advise congregations on ordinations. When candidates were approved, the council members would participate in the laying on of hands. While the initiative for ordination still came from the lay members of a local congregation, the approval of regional clergy took on more and more significance. It came to be said that New England clergy had "presbyterian" ordination, at the hands of other presbyters. But ordination at the hands of presbyters is not the same as ordination by a standing over-arching presbytery.

The debate resurfaces in a transitional generation

The transfer of authority in New Hampshire from Massachusetts to the crown, the revocation of the Massachusetts charter, the wiping out of the Plymouth Colony, and the passage of the Toleration Act were parts of a cluster of events that caused significant change in New England. The franchise was no longer limited to church members, and other sects now operated openly. An Anglican threat to the Colonial Reformed congregations was clear. It was only natural that the New England churches should respond by changing their polity.

An immediate result was the organization of regional consultative ministerial associations. These were copied after earlier forms that had developed in England under the Puritan Commonwealth, such as the Bodmin Association of 1655. These began in New England around 1690. About this time there were also plans to try to unite the Presbyterian and Congregational causes in England. Lucas sees the two groups in New England also coming together behind the new associations (p.144).

Further reforms were sought. Some wished to revive the old English Puritan idea of consociations. They had been endorsed at the 1643 pastoral assembly (although Walker says in a "less technical sense", (1893/1960), p.138), and by the 1662 New England Half-Way Synod, but never instituted. Lucas reports that others in New England favored Scottish forms (p.145).

Calls intensified for the broadening church membership by ending the requirement of a public relation of religious experience, inclusion of all baptized male adults in the election of pastors (not merely those in full communion), and liturgical reforms. (See Walker (1893/1960), pp.473-474). One result was the organization of a new Fourth (or Brattle Church) in Boston in 1699 that would not require a personal testimony nor adopt a specific congregational covenant. Unsure if conservative Congregational pastors in Boston would grant the hand of fellowship to the new congregation, leaders of the new church encouraged their candidate for pastor, Benjamin Colman, a New Englander then in England, to be ordained there. He was ordained by Presbyterians in London, and soon came to be considered the leading advocate for English Presbyterianism in New England. However, by 1700 the congregation was recognized as a Congregational church.

The person considered the chief exponent of Scottish ways in New England was Solomon Stoddard, the pastor in Northampton, Massachusetts. His 1700 pamphlet, *The Doctrine of the Instituted Churches,* called for a broadening of church membership to all who were professing Christians. He saw local congregations as part of a national "instituted" church. Therefore local autonomy was to be limited because all churches should have the same standards of inclusion. He also argued in favor of presbyteries within local congregations including ruling elders and powerful synods without. Stoddard even went beyond traditional Calvinism, which had limited communion to believers, and offered it to non-believers as a converting ordinance. (See the discussion in Lucas, pp.151-157.) While Stoddard was never able to get even his local church to accept all of his ideas, they clearly moved to a far more open membership than most other New England churches.

One of the reasons some clergy, including Stoddard, favored broadening the church membership was that they saw it as a way for the church to be able to discipline and have control over a larger proportion of a town's residents.

Conservative Congregationalists responded by blaming New England's problems on the Presbyterians. A leading example of this view was Cotton Mather's history of early New England, *Magnalia Christi Americana* (1702). (On the Stoddard – Mather debate, see Lucas.)

So, by 1700, there had been generations of debates over polity in America pitting Presbyterians against Congregationalists. The only thing is that at this date, there had been few Scottish or Irish immigrants or ministers in America, and there were neither presbyteries nor standing synods on American soil. The words "Presbyterian" and "Congregational" were widely used and variously understood in America before the Middle Atlantic encounters began.

A seldom-discussed polity difference

Like most Europeans before them, both Puritans and Scottish Presbyterians believed in the rule of God in the nation.

In Scotland church leadership was an elected minority of the church members. The General Assembly derived representatively from that leadership presented a united voice for the church to receive the support of or challenge the activities of the royal government. While the Church of Scotland was a state church, the property and prerogatives of the church, as had been the case with the Catholic Church, were clearly distinct and either cooperative, legal, contractual, or independent with or of the government.

New England, however, imagined a government of visible saints. Massachusetts Bay, originally a company, expanded the franchise to freeholders, and then limited it to church members. Thus the government in each community was made up only of men of legal age *who had been examined by the church and found saintly.*

While the early Puritans had hoped to support their churches through the New Testament model of freewill donations, that proved to be effective only in the large capital town of Boston. The General Court, therefore, authorized tax collections in each community to support a minister.

"...[T]he Congregationalism of the seventeenth century was largely imbued with the feeling that the officers of the civil government were to be considered in all affairs of moment concerning the churches..." (Walker (1893/1960) p.167)

Throughout most of the seventeenth century Massachusetts and New Haven limited the vote to publicly professed church members. Connecticut had a wider franchise, but it limited the upper house of its legislature to church members. While the churches respected the Magistrate, the Magistrate was in some way a creature of the churches. In such a society, aspects of the work of the church could be assigned to the state in manners that might be found elsewhere only in the Papal States or Bishoprics. Churches met in meeting houses that were built and maintained by the towns. Church pastors were considered the moral teachers of the community, and were paid as such from the town tax rolls. Requirements for attendance at worship or sabbath observance were not functions of the church, but laws adopted by the legislatures of the various colonies. The colonies also forbade the formation of schismatic congregations. Therefore, (with the exception of Boston), there was only one legal church in each town, and schismatics within any congregation were suppressed by the government. The churches were still independent and autonomous agencies made up only of visible saints, but they enjoyed many privileges provided them by the Town Magistrates, made up entirely of their members. Models similar to these were in place in the early Puritan congregations on Long Island and in New Jersey.

This was all functional until the King revoked the Puritan colonial charters, extended the franchise to include non-Puritans, and allowed for the toleration of non-Puritan congregations. However, the basic operations within each community were not changed. Instead there continued to be two distinct bodies. The church, made up of believing members, could elect their pastor. But in Massachusetts the town, which included non-Puritans, could vote to confirm the selection of the same person as the town's moral teacher, and set the person's settlement package and salary. In Connecticut there was usually only one election, but churches were required to let those qualified to vote in town affairs vote at church meetings on items which might effect the town, such as the choice of the pastor. They also could vote at town meetings on the salary of the pastor, or meeting house maintenance. Soon thereafter many of the larger New England towns began to divide themselves into geographic parishes, precincts, or societies, each with a separate church. Nevertheless the power of those outside the body of believers was maintained.

These changes in effect turned Puritanism on its ears. Their entire legal system was created so that the visible saints would control not only the church, but also the government and the community. Now people who were not even believers could participate in decisions that directly effected the health of the church, such as the choice of the pastor, and the healthy support of the same. While the legal change was revolutionary, it was often not obvious. In many a small town the visible saints in the church dominated the town. When the changes came along, there were few, if any, powerful non-believers, so the same visible saints in the church continued to dominate the town. Such *de facto* power, even if no longer *de jure,* was important to many lay people. It is probable that most pastors assumed that their settlement packages and salaries would be more substantial with tax support, than if there was a full-scale disestablishment. Therefore the compromise was accepted and became normative.

As time went on, however, economic changes, royal impositions, and Anglican and New Light schisms broke up the churches' power in one community after another. Under this new system clergy had to maintain a precarious political balance between the believers in their church and the economically and politically powerful forces in the town or parish.

This secularized polity, the separation of the church from its finances and property, became classic New England polity. It is really the dominant reason that New England leaders encouraged their people going west into the Middle Atlantic and farther areas to seek a new polity. But it is an issue seldom discussed by most writers.

Later examples of non-Scottish Presbyterianism with New England connections

After 1706 the center of the Congregational – Presbyterian debate moved to the Middle Atlantic stage, and is highlighted in the major historical section of this book. It is necessary to remember, though, that people with New England roots often used the word "Presbyterian" in a context that reflected English controversies or the debates above. We summarize here some of the key later battles to illustrate.

By the mid-eighteenth century many Middle Atlantic congregations held the Scottish or English Presbyterian view of being the parish church, or were influenced by the growing parish ideas of New England. Yet they lived in diverse communities with many congregations. Membership in their congregations actually distinguished their people from the rest of the community, and therefore took on a called out reality more typical of Separatist or sectarian congregations.

A long history of polity controversies now began in the Presbyterian Church, U.S.A.. These were often influenced by New England ideas and debates in such areas as: the consultative, non-authoritative form of the original presbytery; the issue of subscription; the New Side schism; the renewal of autonomy in fence-sitting presbyteries such as Suffolk and Dutchess County; the Plan of Union; the Accommodation Plan; the connection of some congregations to autonomous societies or parishes; the lack of enforcement of local form requirements after 1870; and even the 1927 compromises on ordination.

The first independent Presbytery in the Charleston South Carolina also did not require subscription during its first decade and then split when that policy was made normative.

SOME CONSIDERATIONS ABOUT POLITY AND DEFINITIONS

In the tumultuous period from 1685 to 1710 New England Congregationalism had faced its greatest challenge. Massachusetts and New Hampshire, where synods could no longer gather, developed polities of autonomy. Local congregations were most closely connected to their local parish. Interconnectedness was maintained mostly through clergy who belonged to loose ministerial associations and gathered for vicinage councils. This polity moved in two directions at once. While the political constraints against synods and interchurch bodies were obviously moves towards some type of independency, the strong connection to the parish and the non-believers in the parish moved this polity closer to the English Presbyterian model, of a church for the entire community rather than the visible saint called out model. Despite some advocates, this polity was primarily not planned, but accidental.

Connecticut, still free to call synods, called the Saybrook Synod, and set up both ministerial associations and interchurch consociations in each county, as well as a General Association representative of the various local associations. While the Saybrook Platform placed some theoretical power in the consociations, almost immediately some consociations became rather loose-knit bodies with little judicial backbone. Even though the Platform was ratified by the legislature, congregations that disagreed with their consociations sometimes resisted or rejected the Platform, and usually kept their privileged establishment prerogatives without harassment.

Between the formalized Connecticut and loose Massachusetts polities there was at least one attempt at a moderate position. When the Hampshire Association in western Massachusetts was chartered in 1714 it sought the approval of its members' churches to seek counsel with each other. They also specifically anticipated "some superior council [to be] set up in the province to which they might appeal" (see Hall in *Edwards, ob.cit,* p.110). These stronger associations persisted in western Massachusetts for over a century.

The Great Awakening also impacted these polities. Solomon Stoddard had expanded baptism and membership, allowing participation based on simple faith statements and moral living. His grandson, Jonathan Edwards, and other revivalists moved the Church back towards a narrower dependence on personal testimony and experience. (In the rarefied air of early New England a personal testimony was expected to display both theological and emotional evidence of conversion. While some hearing such testimonies might list and enumerate specific marks of the Spirit or tenets of faith, others would listen with a more subjective ear. Those advocating for the broadening of membership sought to privatize the display or eliminate it entirely. In private such testimonials could move easily to a simple affirmation of a creed or confession. This is similar to non-personal objectivity through creedal subscription in ordination. But for those Congregational churches that tended to cling to personal testimony and faith journey for both ordination and membership, the long-term result has been a subjectivity and personal sensitivity of faith, and therefore allowed for varied theological views.)

Semantic Confusion

Since there were at least two New England polities, it became easy to call the Massachusetts polity Congregational and the Connecticut polity Presbyterian. As late as 1799 the Hartford North Association in Connecticut declared that "This Association gives information to all whom it may concern, that the Constitution of the Churches in the State of Connecticut, founded on the common usage, and the confession of faith, heads of agreement, and articles of church discipline, adopted at the earliest period of the Settlement of this State, is not Congregational, but contains the essentials of the Church of Scotland, or Presbyterian Church in America, particularly as it gives a decisive power to Ecclesiastical Councils; and a Consociation consisting of Ministers and Messengers or a lay representation from the churches is possessed of substantially the same authority as a Presbytery. The judgments, decisions and censures in our Churches and in the Presbyterian are mutually deemed valid..." (Walker (1893/1960) p.514.)

In 1805, when the Connecticut General Association decided to release a new edition of the Saybrook Platform, they voted to "publish a new and elegant edition of the ecclesiastical constitution of the Presbyterian Church in Connecticut." (*Ibid.,* p.526).

The venerable Nathan Strong, pastor of the First Church in Hartford (1774-1816), and successor to Thomas Hooker, generally described himself as the pastor of the North Presbyterian Church in Hartford (*Contributions to the Ecclesiastical History of Connecticut (Volume I.),* (William L. Kingsley, New Haven, 1861, reprinted 1973), pp.63-64). Even outside the mixed Congregational and Presbyterian inter-church groups, the name Presbyterian appeared for local congregations often throughout Connecticut, legally or colloquially. There was also a tendency, popularly or legally, that churches sharing the right-hand of fellowship with Congregational churches but whose pastors were not tax supported were referred to as "Presbyterian" (e.g., New Bedford, MA, Providence and Kingston, RI).

However, this New England tendency to call consociationalism Presbyterian was not the way the Presbyterian Synod saw it. When the Synod set up annual meeting with the General Association of Connecticut in 1766 they refer to them as "the consociated Churches in Connecticut." When they wonder whether the rest of New England will join in the conversations they call them "the associated Brethren."

SOME CONSIDERATIONS ABOUT POLITY AND DEFINITIONS

Confusion in congregational names was not limited to New England. The Charleston, South Carolina church now known as Circular Church voted in 1775 that "This Church has never adopted any distinguishing Name, Platform, or Constitution in a formal manner, nor declared of what denomination it is; but suffered itself to be called either Presbyterian, Congregational, or Independent, sometimes by one of these names, sometimes by two of them, and other times by all three." (Edwards, (1947) p.32). In southern usage Independent was often adopted from England and meant independent of state establishment. A church was Presbyterian in that it honored the leadership of its presbyters (pastors or pastors and elders), and Congregational in that it was autonomous of other congregations in its decision making. C. K. Shipton reports that "The seventeenth century ministers here [in the colonies] would have said that they were ordained in the Presbyterian manner over churches of the congregational polity. They usually called themselves Independents or Congregationalists, but would have laid claim to being Presbyterians... In the southern and middle colonies the Dissenters usually took the name Presbyterian because of the large proportion of the Scotch among them. They differed in no way from the New England churches until they were swamped by the Scotch." (quoted in Edwards (1947), pp.32-33.)

The Morris County Presbytery (1780) and the other associated presbyteries clearly broke from the regular Presbyterian Church on issues of autonomy. When inter-church bodies began to be organized outside of Connecticut in New England some of these also chose the name "Presbytery." The Grafton (or Connecticut Valley) Presbytery (1775) and the Mountain Presbytery in western Massachusetts (1790) both included congregations with varied local forms. Probably both had majorities of churches without ruling elders.

When a Congregational state body was created in Vermont (1795) it made provision for presbyteries to join it. The similar body in New Hampshire (1809) included Presbyterian pastors in its local associations. Later, when the state body began to admit interchurch groups, they included Presbyterian congregations that were also members of the regular Presbyterian Church.

The Definitional Boundary in the Nineteenth Century

Through time the office of ruling elder came to be a measure of definition. Harold Worthley (1970) reports that by 1800 only seven congregations in Massachusetts proper retained the office of elder. In most New England churches the secular concerns which were often Biblically assigned to deacons had been taken over by the trustees and officers of the parishes and societies. Deacons, instead, began to pick up many of the spiritual concerns previously assigned to the ruling elders. However, whereas early New England elders and deacons served for life, there was a related development towards term limits. Deacons were also clearly not part of sessions, and their spiritual leadership did not displace the ultimate authority of the congregation.

These differences again made the internal organization a measure of definition. In the nineteenth century, when many Congregational churches belonged to presbytery, the vote to elect ruling elders and a session was considered "re-organizing as a Presbyterian Church." Eliminating the session and returning the agenda to the congregation was considered "re-organizing as a Congregational Church." In the lists in this book this is the most common definition when referring to the realities in particular congregations.

There were also other interesting anomalies during that century. Missionaries sent out by the American Board of Commissioners for Foreign Missions among Indian tribes or in Hawaii organized "presbyteries" which were not part of the Presbyterian Church and that, because of their missionary nature, often included no ruling elders (formal congregations only coming later.) After the excision of 1837 many Congregational churches remained in New School presbyteries. But in Wisconsin, northern Illinois, and Oregon new interchurch bodies were created which included both Congregational and Presbyterian churches, but were not part of the Presbyterian Church, U.S.A..

The debate in Patriotic claims

With the rise of doctrinaire denominational differences in the mid-nineteenth century and thereafter, historians and leaders of both groups stepped up their claims of cultural leadership, power, and prestige. Both Congregationalism and Presbyterianism claimed to be a primary philosophical root of American democracy. Congregationalism saw in the Mayflower Compact and the local church covenant the idea of government deriving from the consent of the governed expressed in the Declaration of Independence. They saw the value and respect for the participatory role of the individual arising from New England church and town meetings. They saw America's free education arising from the seventeenth century requirements of Puritan towns that everyone be provided schooling so that they could read the Bible. They saw America's responsible commonwealths and benevolent concerns growing out of the social conscience of the Puritans and the Benevolent Empire deriving from New England societies and impulses. Conversely Presbyterianism found the birth of American representative democracy in the value of constitutions and the rule of law. They saw in the American Constitution a reflection on the polity of Westminster, and in American courts, a reflection of Presbyterian judicatories.

While there is truth in both of these claims, it could be said that the tensions of American democracy reflect the spectrum between Presbyterian and Congregational approaches to freedom and order.

The Polity Debate: A Subjective Example

Perhaps a way to interpret the continued debate over polity and definitions is to try to apply them to a single individual. Was the noted theologian Jonathan Edwards (1703-1758) a Presbyterian or a Congregationalist? Edwards grew up the son of a Connecticut pastor, whose church became part of a new Consociation when Edwards was still a young child. He studied at Yale. Other clergy are to be found in his near and distant relatives around New England. He was born of Yankee stock that was theologically of the mid-road Connecticut variety. Yet in 1722 Edwards accepted the pastorate of a small new Presbyterian Church in New York City, that had just broken away from the six-year old First Presbyterian Church. Edwards' Church called themselves "English Presbiterians" [*sic*], giving a clue to their theology as well as their genealogy. Edwards left there after only a year, returning to Connecticut as a pastoral candidate and then to teach at Yale.

In 1727 Edwards became colleague to his grandfather Solomon Stoddard in Northampton, Massachusetts. Two years later, when his grandfather died, he became the pastor. As has been shown, Stoddard was the great champion of wider church memberships and considered the chief advocate of Scottish Presbyterianism in New England. While the Northampton Church had broadened its membership, it was still an autonomous congregation whose pastor and meetinghouse were supported by its town. Edwards also became a member of the Hampshire Association, the ministerial association that had been founded by his grandfather. The Northampton Church had endorsed the Association when it was formally chartered in 1714, the Church voting that in "unspecified areas 'church councils' were superior to individual congregations." (Lucas (1976), p.158). The Association's charter had also provided that "We judge it our duty, to be subject to a Council of the County, until there be some Superior Council set up in the Province unto which we may appeal." (*Ibid.*, p.184; see also Hall in *Edwards, ob.cit.*, pp.109-110). While this may be a sign of Presbyterianism in the Association, it was primarily a plea for a General Association as then existed in Connecticut.

When Edwards was still young (1734-1736) the majority of the Association opposed the ordination of a new pastor in Springfield. However, an *ex parte* council, with a majority of clergy from outside the area was called and the candidate was ordained and settled. William Cooper, of Boston's Brattle Church, a member of the *ex parte* council attacked the Association's "Presbyterianism" and vowed loyalty to Congregational local autonomy as supported in the Cambridge Platform. (See discussion by Hall in *Edwards, ob.cit.*, pp.4-17). Edwards wrote a reply supporting the Association and exposing the opponents as "critics of the Cambridge Platform." He pointed out that the Platform endorsed councils of clergy from "neighbouring churches" but not *ex parte* councils. He contended that the members of the council's support of the Cambridge Platform were inconsistent and opportunistic.

At this time Edwards did see the Cambridge Platform as a provincial constitution, and argued that the churches that had authorized the Hampshire Association had also given it constitutional powers. *(Ibid.*, pp.111-113).

Edwards' writing was often more theological or parochial than ecclesiastical. In *A Treatise on Religious Affections* (published 1746) he specifically attacked subscription (*Ibid.*, p.58). Hall believes that Edwards' concern about such impersonal faith statements played a role in his changing his mind about whom to welcome to the communion table. Edwards was also concerned about the broad membership in Northampton, and the power of non-church society or parish members elsewhere in New England. He spoke against unscriptural "voting in church affairs." (*Ibid.*, p.60)

While pastoring in Northampton a revival began under Edwards, and his preaching and writings gained an international reputation. Yet in his drive to build up the piety of his congregation, he finally broke with his grandfather and took steps to return to a pure called out membership. He limited communion and called for a change. Those in the congregation wishing not to lose prerogatives already won turned on Edwards. A 1750 council called with the approval of the Hampshire Association opposed Edwards by a one-vote margin, and the congregation promptly dismissed him.

Edwards was perhaps his most revealing on polity issues in a letter he sent to his Scottish correspondent John Erskine on July 5, 1750. (Hickman, Edward, Ed., *The Works of Jonathan Edwards*, (The Banner of Truth Trust, Edinburgh, 1834, new edition, 1974, pp. cxviii-cxxi)). This was just after Edwards' dismissal and it is not surprising that this would be a low point in his assessment of New England polity. Erskine knew of Edwards' troubles, and had offered to help him find a position in Scotland. He also asked if Edwards would sign the Westminster standards and "submit to the presbyterian form of church government."

Edwards admits, "I have long been perfectly out of conceit of our unsettled, independent, confused way of church government in this land." Gracious for Erskine's offer, Edwards replies kindly. "As to my subscribing to the substance of the Westminster Confession, there would be no difficulty; and as to the presbyterian government… the presbyterian way has ever appeared to me most agreeable to the word of God, and the reason and nature of things;

though I cannot say that I think, that the presbyterian government of the church of Scotland is so perfect, that it cannot, in some respects be mended." But Edwards declines the invitation. His reply, while kind and friendly, is reserved. By agreeing to the "substance" of Westminster rather than its literal entirety he is maintaining a foot in the anti-subscriptionist camp. Even as he says he is willing to "submit" to the Presbyterian form of government – as he has just submitted to the ecclesiology of the Northampton Church and the local council – he is not willing to see Scottish Presbyterianism as "perfect."

Even at this low point emotionally Edwards continued to wrestle with polity issues. In addition to changing his mind on the inclusiveness of church membership, the process of his dismission from Northampton also caused him to depart from his previous views on *ex parte* councils. He tells Erskine that he "insisted" that the council to consider his dismissal "should not consist wholly of ministers and churches of the neighbourhood, who are almost altogether in opposition to me; but that some should be brought from abroad." Edwards' desire was that the theological issues be discussed by an "impartial council." He wanted to be heard "because in this country we have no such thing as appeals from one council to another, from a lesser to a larger." He was also concerned that, since most of the Hampshire clergy were young, that they needed to be balanced with more elderly experienced voices. His desire for elderly voices in councils was consistent with what he had written earlier. It does, however, need to be said on his behalf that when he opposed *ex parte* councils before it was because of both the inclusion of outsiders as well as the exclusion of neighboring clergy. Now, while he tried to add some delegates from abroad, he did not attempt to exclude his neighbors.

In 1750 and 1751 Edwards, with the urging of some in the Association, accepted a call to be the Indian missionary and pastor of a small mixed European and Indian congregation in Stockbridge in the Berkshires. While this was also a Congregational Church, some of the financial support came from a Scottish missionary society. Edwards continued to be a nominal member of the Hampshire Association.

The Church politics of New England had surely done Edwards in. He was disillusioned. Yet it is questionable whether any Middle Atlantic presbytery would have recommended that he remain in such a divided parish. While living at Stockbridge, Edwards at least twice visited the annual meeting of the New Side Synod of New York, preaching at the session of 1752. He saw the Synod as a union of "English and Scotch." (Letter to John Erskine November 23, 1752, (in Hickman, Ed., *Works.. ob.cit.*, pp. cxlix-cli)). In 1757 he was offered the Presidency of the Synod's College of New Jersey (later Princeton), but died shortly after his arrival.

Was Edwards a Presbyterian or a Congregationalist? Most of his career and upbringing were in New England Congregational Churches. His brief forays into the Middle Atlantic region clearly align him with English Presbyterian polity and the pro-revival, non-subscriptionist New Side Synod. While he accepted some of the Presbyterian reforms of his grandfather, he later turned away from them and became the chief advocate for the return of early New England Puritanism. Both groups claim him. Like many others, he emerges as a restless Congregationalist in search of a better polity. It should not be surprising that his son played a key role in creating the Plan of Union.

The Evolution of Congregational Polity

"Congregationalism" does not now, nor has it ever, had a rigid answer to polity questions. A system of autonomy and personal responsibility, it has been in constant evolution. Its classic form may be the minority report from Westminster, *The Apologeticall Narration...*, or the system of the Cambridge Platform. However, no one can claim that these documents, nor the first Constitution of the National Council of Congregational Churches, nor the Savoy Declaration, nor the Saybrook Platform, nor the Constitution of the United Church of Christ, nor any other document is definitive "Congregationalism." We can merely report tendencies and clusters of ideas.

Because it is a system of autonomy changes in Congregationalism through time were seldom uniform or chronologically consistent.

Ordination continued to evolve after the founding of ministerial associations. The most common form in the eighteenth and the start of the nineteenth centuries was that a sponsor, most often their home pastor or a pastor they were assisting would present a candidate to an association. Generally after completing a college education, the candidate would work under some pastor in a type of apprenticeship. That pastor would present the candidate to the local association that, after a lengthy examination, would grant a license to the candidate. Licentiates were then free to candidate in vacant congregations seeking a settlement. When a congregation was pleased, they would issue a call to the person, get the approval of the parish for a settlement package, and summon ministers in the vicinity to an ordination council, that – more and more – would be made up of the association and guests.

During times of controversy some vicinage councils became *"ex parte"* councils where primarily or only clergy of one point of view were invited. This was particularly common around the time of the Unitarian departure.

Initially the vast majority of clergy were "settled" and stayed for life. With urbanization some rural areas were depopulated while some urban churches grew to previously unknown sizes and wealth. This created wide variations in pastoral remuneration and the growth of career patterns with clergy moving often to more pleasant financial circumstances. Clergy then wished to have their ordination recognized beyond their specific parish. Associations then took on the role of granting "standing" to recognized clergy. With the rise of graduate schools of theology, the apprenticeship practices died out. The widespread use of licensure also declined, and was replaced by recommendations from the seminaries, and sponsorships before associations, usually from home congregations or pastors. Licensure became more of a special or unique status.

Connecticut consociations were the first model of interchurch relations. While they claimed authority they were sometimes rebuffed. Consociations were tried in some other places at the end of the eighteenth and in the early nineteenth century, but with little lasting success. In most areas some churches or clergy would reject consociations because of their claims to authority.

Other models of interchurch contact were explored including two New England presbyteries serving mostly Congregational churches. These also failed. One split, and then died. The other became an association. The pro-revival Strict or Separate Congregational churches organized an interchurch body in New England before the regular Congregational churches had begun them in Massachusetts or much of the north. The Strict Congregational Convention of Connecticut began in 1780, and clarified church membership in 1784/1785.

After several decades of successful interchurch bodies outside of New England that guaranteed autonomy on the Green model, New England finally organized local interchurch bodies called "Conferences" which guaranteed autonomy. The Brookfield Massachusetts Ministerial Association in 1821 sponsored one of these, and others followed in Cumberland and York Counties, Maine by 1823. Soon this movement spread throughout New England. Eventually most of the consociations reorganized or were replaced by conferences. However, the new New England organizational pattern maintained the dual system of Connecticut, with the ministerial associations remaining in place. Through time the northern New England general ministerial associations began to admit interchurch bodies into their membership. Maine's state body began including interchurch bodies. In Massachusetts and Connecticut the local conferences organized General Conferences which eventually merged with the General Associations, the new state wide bodies including both local conferences and associations.

The contrary and older system was that of the Green polity, the associated presbytery form begun by the Morris County Presbytery in 1780 where churches and ministers always sat together. Autonomy of congregations was guaranteed. Most Middle Atlantic and western bodies, as well as the Separatist bodies in Connecticut, Long Island, and New Jersey, followed the Green model. The General Association of New York brought together local bodies, most of which were on the Green plan. They, however, were not uniform in name. For example, some later groups influenced by British terminology were called "Unions."

State boundaries had been prominent in New England because of the polity and establishment law differences between the various states. This preference was maintained as Congregationalism moved west. Most interchurch bodies maintained state boundaries. For decades from 1855 even national *Yearbooks* listed churches by state of location rather than interchurch body of affiliation. Some state bodies, such as New York and Pennsylvania were made up by local groups joining together. Others, such as New Jersey, began as one body that later set up smaller regional bodies within their territory. State bodies had originally been made up of representatives from local associations, and later conferences. Some, however, including New York, seated delegates from local congregations in isolated areas not belonging to local bodies. Eventually all the state bodies began to seat delegates directly from each church (rather than conference representatives) as well as all of their clergy (rather than association representatives).

In the early twentieth century the National Congregational Council recommended a consistent pattern of forms and names around the country. While not all, almost all state bodies were thereafter named "Conferences." Local bodies were to adopt the Green polity with clergy and laity sitting together. These were called "Associations."

National conventions of Congregational churches were held in 1852, 1865, and 1870, as well as regional meetings in other years. The National Council of Congregational Churches was organized in 1871as a representative body made up of delegates from state and local interchurch bodies. From this point on there was a "denomination" defined by church affiliation.

While New England churches had collected alms for the poor, they could not own real property nor set up endowments. These were the functions of the town, society, precinct, or parish. When the desire to fund missionaries grew this dual system proved a barrier. Other than tiny collections, real funding required incorporated missionary societies. Before the Revolution, the royal governments generally opposed chartering such organizations in the colonies. After independence many groups began. Some, such as the Missionary Society of Connecticut, were organized as arms of existing church groups, in this case the General Association of Connecticut. In other cases, such as the New York Missionary Society, and the Northern Missionary Society, these were organized as free-standing bodies by concerned individuals. Eventually there was consolidation among missionary societies and with church groups. State missionary societies became auxiliaries of the American Home Missionary Society. If they were not already closely aligned with the state general body, steps were taken in that direction, such as successive annual meetings in the same place. In frontier areas state missionary societies, auxiliaries, or agencies developed the office of "missionary superintendent" or "general superintendent." These officials represented the missionary societies and advised on aided sites and other issues.

The national conventions and then the National Council recommended missionary bodies to the churches. At the 1913 Kansas City National Council meeting major changes were made in the national structure. The Council took over the election of the boards of the major national missionary societies. While they retained their charters, they now became formal agencies of the denomination. It was also recommended that state general bodies merge with their local missionary societies, becoming legally incorporated church bodies. Through this process the "missionary superintendents" became "conference ministers," and the secular and spiritual-standing concerns were united.

Major changes also occurred to the internal structures of congregations. The colonies of Massachusetts (including later Maine), Connecticut and New Hampshire provided for town or parish teachers of morality, and thereby underwrote Congregational pastors in most towns through the parish system separate from the churches. Initially Congregational congregations outside these colonies tried to recreate that system. The earliest Puritan congregations on Long Island and in New Jersey were supported by their towns. While Vermont did not require subsidized teachers of morality, many towns chose to be supportive. Some New England Separatist Churches were able to gain "poll parishes," where their members were excluded from supporting the geographic parish in order to support a selected parish for their congregation. However property titles elsewhere were suspect.

In the Middle Atlantic area only a few pre-Revolutionary congregations gained a charter from Britain or the colonies. The most common solution was to deed property to individuals to hold in trust for a congregation. Some of these unincorporated societies were self-appointed, or appointed by the donor of the land, while others were chosen by congregations or their leaders. Many of these deeds called the church for which land was given "Presbyterian" (either in its English or Scottish meanings). While such deeds were obviously local in their origin, the use of this word later became grounds for courts to grant title to presbyteries. (Courts have not been sympathetic to the way that word has changed meaning.) If these "trustees" were actually self-selected, or named by the land donor, New Englanders often saw them as a parallel organization similar to a New England parish. Presbyterians, conversely, could assume that the same "trustees" were mere stand-ins until their successors could be selected by the session. There has been little research done on how these discrepancies were resolved.

After the Revolution more and more congregations gained their own charter from their state. Where this was allowed it also proved to be a movement towards Presbyterianism by uniting the secular and spiritual concerns of a congregation, and ending the typical New England division.

In old New England laws requiring town teachers of morality and support of meetinghouses were changed. First they were not required, then, in total disestablishment, they were not allowed. From 1780 Massachusetts allowed incorporation of societies to hold and manage real and personal property for churches. These were made up of donors to a particular church or pew holders. Members of these societies or parish organizations had to be males of legal age. They were not limited to church members. After disestablishment these societies became the norm throughout New England. At disestablishment the states usually gave the meetinghouses to the parish or society donors, along with any building debts. This, though, still maintained a dual system. These societies, that might include pew holders or donors who were not church members, handled secular affairs. The unincorporated churches were different bodies.

New Englanders moving west often tried to maintain this dual system. Some Middle Atlantic charters were obtained for separate societies or parishes which were made up of specific trustees, and their hand picked successors, or which were made up of all donors to a given congregation, or all pew holders. The dual system was often attacked as elitist and non-democratic. It gave much power to the wealthy. Evangelicals who wished to exclude non-believers from power in areas that effected the churches also attacked the dual system.

Only some years after the Civil War did most American states allow women to become full members of corporations. When that became the case the National Council of Congregational Churches voted several times to urge all local churches to unite with their parishes or societies. While eventually most churches united with their societies, this movement was constrained by variations in state laws. After unity Connecticut law still provides that contributors may vote in congregational meetings on items that effect their donations. Many states provide that non-members of churches may still be elected as trustees. Other compromises were effected by details in obtaining merger in specific congregations. Many Congregational churches have had generations of local conflict where all male boards of trustees hold the purse strings and manage the buildings, while often female majorities in diaconates, missionary committees, guilds, Sunday school and other groups fight for different objectives. Church councils, with varying degrees of authority and power have often been designed to compromise the old dual nature still often prevalent in Congregational churches. In some communities the churches and parishes have never merged, and dual bodies exist to this day.

Other changes also occurred in internal organization. The local committee structure authorized by the Plan of Union was already a compromise between Presbyterian sessions and Congregational business conducted at general meetings. Congregationalism had long preferred the intimate fellowship of the small group. The Cambridge Platform suggested that a church might grow to be "too numerous." It said of a church that "in respect of it's *quantity* ought not to be of a greater number then may ordinarily meet together conveniently in one place..." (quoted in Walker (1893/1960), pp. 232, 206). When a rump re-organized the Oneida Association in 1825, a major cause was that the presbyteries were becoming too large. (Note that this is the antithesis of modern independent mega-churches that may describe their polity as Congregational.) However, urbanization and its impact on church size couldn't be entirely curtailed. Eventually most Congregational churches moved membership decisions previously handled at Congregational meetings to prudential committees or their diaconates. Some congregations have even begun boards of elders.

Nevertheless, the mix of final internal authority resting with the entire congregations, autonomy and responsibility of members within each congregation, and congregations with each other, and mutual recognition of congregations have continued to be defining elements of the tradition. Changes in polity have occurred in both of the twentieth century mergers, and in the groups splitting away from the majority. Many of these are explored in the historical sections.

Comments on Independency

In England Congregational churches are often called "Independent." This use most often derives from their long-standing independence from the English Church establishment. It is sometimes applied to all non-conformists.

The same word may be used to describe congregations that have no covenant or fellowship with other congregations.

Some Conclusions

In England, through time about nearly one-half of surviving English Presbyterian Churches became Congregational, another large proportion became Unitarian, while only a small handful made their way into the later Presbyterian Church. These patterns are amazingly parallel to what happened to the ancient churches of New England as well. It seems fair to conclude that American Congregationalism and Unitarianism are both descendants of English Presbyterian as well as English Congregational churches.

Historians are correct in identifying external church relationships, and the judicial powers of wider bodies as an important difference between Congregationalism and Presbyterianism. Other significant issues which need to be explored include: the internal organization of local congregations; the broad or narrow definition of membership; the subjective personal or objective subscriptionist definitions of membership and ordination; the relation of church and state; the division or unity of secular and spiritual functions within the Church. All of these have been of importance. Most have left historical marks in modern structures.

ETHNICITY

The early churches were primarily centered in a British ethnic world, which reflected their colonial subservience.

English Puritan settlers of all polities obviously brought English language and culture with them. Early Scottish and Scotch-Irish immigrants who shared the English language, carried with them different national histories. Both of these groups intermingled in many congregations and also welcomed English speakers willing to join their churches, particularly from Dutch and German backgrounds. A few French Huguenot congregations interacted with other Calvinist Churches in their areas. The first Welsh colonial congregations in Great Valley, Pennsylvania and Pencader Hundred, Delaware, were historically related to Independent and Congregational Puritans in Wales, but soon joined Presbytery as part of the first union.

INDIAN MISSIONS

The first major ethnic encounter was with the Native American tribes of the area. The first Puritan missions to the Indians in the Middle Atlantic area began at the end of Long Island where the Puritans first settled. The ministry that developed here mirrored the parallel work in New England.

One of the goals of the Puritan migration was to become missionaries to the Indians, and the early work in New England was extensive. The Society for Propagating the Gospel in New England was formed in England during the Puritan Commonwealth in 1649. It supported both the early New England missions and a 1653 outreach to Algonquin people at Oyster Bay, Long Island. In 1660, work also began with the Algonquin Montauk people on Long Island. However, the restoration of the Stuart dynasty in that year led to the abolition of the supporting society. It was replaced in 1661 by a Society for Propagating the Gospel Among the Heathen Nations of New England and the Parts Adjacent in America. This was, however, a much weaker society. Its weakness and Indian Wars in the colonies led to a decline in Indian ministry. The Society in Scotland for Propagating Christian Knowledge began in 1709.

Commissioners were set up in America to cooperate with the British societies: in Boston in 1730 (The Company for the Propagation of the Gospel in New England) and in New York in 1741. Their support, and the general Great Awakening, helped revive Indian work among American Calvinists.

In 1733 mission work was strengthened to Mohegans, Narragansetts, Pequots, and Neanticks in Connecticut and Rhode Island. In 1734 a mission was begun to the Stockbridge/Mahican tribe (a wandering branch of the Mohegans, sometimes called Mu-he-ke-ne-ok or Housatonic) in the Berkshires of Massachusetts.

This was followed by a concentrated outreach to other Algonquin tribes in the Middle Atlantic area. Three new recruits who had attended Yale began supported work in conjunction with New Side Presbyterians. Azariah Horton strengthened work to the Long Island tribes from 1741. This work included preaching or churches at seven sites. Samson Occum, a Mohegan Indian from Connecticut, who had been trained by Eleazar Wheelock, joined Horton in 1748/1753 and was later ordained by Suffolk Presbytery. At one time or another, Indian work on the Island served the Montauk, Shinnecock, Rockaway, and people from some of the ten other Island tribes. Peter John Cuffee, a member of the Shinnecock tribe, continued Occum's work on Long Island after Occum left in 1770 to preach in Connecticut.

The Scottish Society also supported David Brainerd, who had worked briefly at Stockbridge. He began a ministry in New Jersey and Pennsylvania that extended from 1740 to his death in 1747, at sites in Northampton and Lehigh Counties, Pennsylvania, Warren County, New Jersey, and a few scattered locations in southern New Jersey. His younger brother, John Brainerd, continued this work in Pennsylvania from 1747 and then in some sites in southern New Jersey, most notably the united settlement at Brotherton from 1759 to 1768. This work was among the various settlements of the Delaware tribe, particularly their Munsee branch.

The Scottish Society also supported Wheelock's work in training Indian missionaries, which expanded into a school that operated at Columbia, Connecticut from 1754 to 1770.

The first missions among Iroquois tribes began just before, during, and following the French and Indian War. Work was begun in Broome County, New York, in 1753. Gideon Hawley served there between 1753 and 1758, and was followed by Ebenezer Moseley, who served under the New England Company for the Propagation of the Gospel Among the Indians from 1767 to 1772. Wheelock's students and the aid of the Scottish Society played key roles in these new endeavors. A mission to the Mohawks existed from 1762 to 1765, and Samuel Kirkland began work with the Oneida tribe in 1764 (a mission conceived in 1759), both in upstate New York.

The Revolutionary War disrupted many mission sites, with the missionaries leaving for various lengths of time. Also, in 1787, the Scottish Society requested that Americans take over the work, and their support stopped.

By this time Americans had already begun plans to organize their own missionary societies to support Indian ministry. A Society for Promoting Christian Knowledge Among the Indians in North America was incorporated in Massachusetts in 1762, but the King interfered with their charter. After the War, in 1787, a new Society for Propagating the Gospel Among the Indians and Others in North America was incorporated in Massachusetts. It soon began work among the revived New York missions. However, it became involved in the debates over Unitarianism, eventually coming under Unitarian control. It turned its primary attention to Maine and the Isles of Shoals, and later to other causes.

In 1778 Occum moved to a new Brothertown track in New York that the Oneidas had created as a refuge for other tribes. Kirkland returned to the Oneida mission in 1785. The new Brothertown settlement welcomed a variety of Algonquin tribes including Mohegan, Mahican (Stockbridge), Narragansett from New England, Wappinger from New England and New York, and Montauk, Shinnecock, and related tribes from Long Island. Occum's work here was connected with the Presbyterian Church, U.S.A..

Work continued on Long Island, now under the Strict Congregationalists. Their Connecticut Convention ordained the Indian preacher Paul Cuffee (the grandson of Peter John Cuffee), in 1790. From 1792 he worked with the Strict Convention of Long Island, preaching in at least five locations. From 1798 he was supported by the New York Missionary Society. The Congregationalists continued to serve congregations at Cold Spring to 1839 and Poosepatuck to 1874. The Shinnecock/Canoe Place congregation was again Presbyterian from 1819 to 1840/1841, then Congregational to 1878. It reorganized as a Presbyterian Church in 1887, but became predominantly European.

In 1785 the Indian members of the Stockbridge Church in Massachusetts organized a new congregation. In 1785/1786 it joined the tribe in a move to New Stockbridge, New York, where they settled on land provided by the Oneidas. The work with this tribe at the new location was divided between two competing missionaries from 1786 to 1792.

The expansion of the frontier encouraged the formation of new missionary societies to serve the Indian population. These included the New York Missionary Society - 1796; the Northern Missionary Society - 1797; and the Western Missionary Society of the Pittsburgh Synod (Presbyterian) - 1802.

The Northern Society took over the work with the Oneidas in 1797. This mission was discontinued in 1808. Some Indians here later joined people from the New Stockbridge settlement in their move west. However, a few Oneida remained and occasional attempts were made afterwards to minister to them.

In 1802 some remnants of the Munsee missions in New Jersey, and much of the Brothertown settlement in New York, moved to New Stockbridge and consolidated with the congregation and tribe there, with the tribe becoming the Stockbridge-Munsee tribe. In 1818 a new Church was organized. It joined with the majority of the tribe in a move west that began that year. After four years in Indiana, the first party settled in Wisconsin (1822). Work there became a mission of the American Board of Commissioners for Foreign Missions from 1826/1828 to 1848. A congregation in Wisconsin survived until 1860. At New Stockbridge, New York, the older church continued to at least 1825, and possibly later serving the few Indians that remained.

The New York Missionary Society supported Cuffee on Long Island from 1799 until his death in 1812. They also began a mission to the Tuscarora tribe in western New York in 1800/1801, and one to the Seneca tribe in 1811.

The Western Missionary Society worked with the Cornplanter Indians, an Iroquois group, primarily Seneca from 1814 to 1818 with General Assembly support.

The need to unify and coordinate Indian mission work was soon seen. The United Foreign Missionary Society was created in 1816/1818 to join the work of the three smaller societies. In 1821 it took over control of the New York Society's Tuscarora and Seneca missions. It began an additional Seneca and mixed Iroquois mission at Cattaraugus in 1822.

However, the dominant force in North American Indian missions and foreign missions during the first half of the nineteenth century was the American Board of Commissioners for Foreign Missions (ABCFM), begun in 1810. Originally designed to be the mission arm of the Congregational General Associations of Ministers in Massachusetts and Connecticut, it was made a freestanding interdenominational agency at the request of the Presbyterians. It first directly impacted Indian missions in New York when Oneidas, Senecas, and Tuscaroras studied at its missionary training school in Cornwall, Connecticut, which operated from 1817 to 1827. In 1826 all the United Foreign Missionary Society missions were taken over by the ABCFM. Additional missions to serve the Seneca and mixed Iroquois population were instituted by the ABCFM at Allegany in 1830 and Corydon, Pennsylvania in 1852. Two of the ABCFM Indian congregations were in Presbyteries in the 1830's. However, in the next two decades four Seneca and one Tuscarora congregations were in Congregational bodies.

In 1860 the ABCFM dropped aid to the Tuscarora mission, and the Church there transferred to the Presbyterians. The Allegany mission to the Seneca also became independent of the ABCFM in 1866, and was then sponsored by the American Home Missionary Society from 1869 to 1870. The ABCFM began a new Seneca/Tonawanda mission in 1870. The same year the Allegany Mission, and all the remaining ABCFM missions were transferred to the support of the Presbyterian Board, giving them responsibility for all the surviving Seneca, Tuscarora, and Tonawanda mission work in western New York. The congregations followed the action of the mission boards, and all these Indian congregations became Presbyterian.

ETHNICITY

In both the Congregational and Presbyterian denominations in this area Indian congregations belonged to the same inter-church bodies as the majority white congregations.

Some small Indian Presbyterian congregations remain. Large parts of other tribes left the region. Among some tribes no lasting sign of this mission work remains.

AFRICAN-AMERICAN CONGREGATIONS

The second major ethnic encounter was with the African population, most of who came to this area as slaves. As was the case in most English colonies, Blacks were brought to worship, often confined to slave galleries, and sometimes admitted to a marginal membership. Lemuel Haynes, America's first ordained Black pastor (1785), served Congregational Churches in New England and at Granville, New York from 1822 to 1833.

Conflicts occurred between European and Black members of Episcopal, Methodist, and other denominations by the 1790's, leading to the formation of independent Black congregations. However, Calvinist congregations were slow to split. A First African Presbyterian Church began in Philadelphia in 1807, and a separate Black congregation began in New York City at the height of the Plan of Union in 1822. It was clear that while the white congregations were enjoying the Era of Good Feeling, the issues of race were proving to be divisive. From these beginnings both Presbyterian and Congregational traditions had strong Black congregations in the Mid-Atlantic States.

In 1846 the American Missionary Association was formed by consolidating several radical mission, liberation, and anti-slavery societies. It chose New York City as its headquarters, bringing several New York Black Presbyterian and Congregational leaders to national prominence, including the Rev.Dr. J.W.C. Pennington.

In both denominations, Black congregations belonged to the same inter-church bodies as white churches. In modern times Black churches of Congregational background have strongly supported the United Church of Christ merger.

In 1931 the Congregationalists merged with the General Convention of the Christian Church, a group which also had Black congregations in the Mid-Atlantic States, but they were in separate racially defined Conferences and Conventions. While the Black Congregational Churches continued in the integrated inter-church bodies, these Christian congregations continued to be part of segregated Afro-Christian bodies until 1960. Interestingly, many of these churches which had experienced segregation, were also less supportive of the United Church of Christ merger than the Congregational Churches.

The Conservative Congregational Christian Conference has also added Black congregations in New York and in Pennsylvania.

WELSH CONGREGATIONS

A new Welsh immigration to Pennsylvania and New York began in the 1790's. During the previous century Calvinism had splintered in Wales, and in addition to the Independent Congregationalists, a new group of Welsh Calvinistic Methodists, a group with Presbyterian polity, had been formed. In America people from both Welsh Calvinist groups and Baptists often formed union Welsh congregations. When populations grew, the churches divided along the denominational lines they had known in Wales.

Congregations with Independent or Congregational background formed Congregational *Gymanfas* (Associations or Conferences). Some of these congregations also joined English Congregational bodies, joined Presbytery under the Plan of Union, or even split or reorganized, choosing a Presbyterian polity within Presbytery. All of these churches spoke Welsh. Later in the nineteenth century Congregational Churches were begun which were English-speaking but sought to retain their Welsh culture and identity.

Welsh Congregationalism, speaking another language, and coming from a strong European church, initially developed almost as a denomination in its own right, and only later affiliated with English-speaking Congregationalists. Those few strong congregations that did join English Congregational or Presbyterian bodies also affiliated with the Welsh bodies. A *Gymanfa* was begun in New York in 1837. An ecumenical *Gymanfa* was started in Pennsylvania in 1838, and then divided denominationally, with a Congregational group operating in 1839. Both of these groups served congregations in adjoining states. The Pennsylvania group divided into Eastern and Western Pennsylvania bodies in 1871/1873. Another new Welsh Association in eastern New York and Vermont functioned 1912 to 1920.

Both of these two major state Welsh groups corresponded with English speaking bodies at an early date. However, the major New York group did not join the New York General Association until 1868/1869 and the two Pennsylvania bodies were seated independently at the National Council of Congregational Churches in 1874. Later, in 1886, they both helped start a general Congregational Association of Pennsylvania. The western Pennsylvania body disbanded in 1902, New York in 1930, and Eastern Pennsylvania in 1931 when churches joined multi-cultural bodies.

The Eastern Ohio Welsh Conference divided 1871 from the 1840 *Gymanfa Ganu* of Ohio. That body and its later divided regional parts participated in the Congregational Conference of Ohio from 1853. The Eastern Ohio body served churches in Pennsylvania from about 1873 to 1930. The Conference survived until 1956.

ETHNICITY

In modern times, a solid core of Welsh and English Welsh Churches has come into the United Church of Christ. However, a very high percentage of Welsh congregations opposed the merger and have become National Association, Conservative Conference, or Schedule I or Schedule II congregations.

Welsh Calvinistic Methodists formed their own congregations from 1824, and synod in 1828, which, after further reorganization, merged with the Presbyterian Church, U.S.A. in 1920.

OTHER ETHNIC CHURCHES IN THE PLAN OF UNION

By 1800 Congregationalism had spread into Scotland, and a few decades later at least one Pennsylvania Church identified itself as Scottish Congregational.

Also in the early Nineteenth Century some Presbyterian Church, U.S.A. congregations were identified as Irish or "Scotch." However, it appears that these identities had more to do with historical connections to Covenanter or Associate Separate historical groups, or ethnic immigrant needs, rather than any use of Celtic languages.

Both Presbyterians and Congregationalists attempted to form French churches before the 1850's, and the Presbyterians also began or received German congregations. The Presbyterian connection to both these groups sank long-term roots, but the French Congregational work soon died.

CONGREGATIONAL ETHNIC CHURCHES AFTER THE END OF THE PLAN OF UNION

After the Civil War Congregationalism tried to reach out to some of the new ethnic groups flooding into America. As indicated, the Welsh churches already had their own *Gymanfas*. However, missions to new immigrant groups not traditionally Congregational did not usually produce enough, or rapidly enough, strong congregations to have their own Conferences and Associations.

A German Congregational Association had begun in the Midwest as early as 1862. This and other Associations formed a General Conference of German Congregational Churches in 1883. In this plan ethnic churches joined a local German Association, and then the Association belonged to both their local state Conference, and the national German Conference. German Congregational Churches appeared in Pennsylvania in 1863, in New Jersey in 1879, and in New York, briefly around 1860, from 1904 to 1908, and again from 1912. However, not enough churches were present in this area to form a German Association. Churches affiliated with English Associations and usually had only a marginal relationship to the national German General Conference. While one German church in New Jersey remains in the United Church of Christ, at least four others in the Middle Atlantic area are still alive outside the United Church of Christ.

Between 1888 and 1892 Southern Congregational bodies began to fracture into racially defined ethnic bodies. However, as reported above, in the North integrated bodies were the rule among formerly Congregational Churches (though not formerly Christian Churches from 1931 to 1960).

As other ethnic ministries were contemplated, organizational questions about how to treat them were often debated. A new strategy was to have ethnic churches join English Conferences and Associations, but also to organize larger regional ethnic bodies for mutual support and guidance, but independent of issues about church and ministerial standing. Some hoped these would eventually develop into ethnic inter-church bodies. Others hoped that the churches would eventually take their English connections as paramount. This plan was put into place for a large ethnic ministry to Scandinavian immigrants.

SCANDINAVIAN CONGREGATIONAL CHURCHES

Swedish Congregational Churches were admitted into local Associations in Pennsylvania in 1883, New York in 1885, and New Jersey in 1893. Closely related to these congregations was a mixed Swedish-Finnish congregation admitted in 1914.

A Scandinavian Free Mission was begun in Massachusetts in 1887, a ministerial Conference in Connecticut in 1888, and an Eastern Missionary Association in 1890. These bodies consolidated under the latter name in 1892/1893 and served a large group of Swedish and Swedish-Finnish congregations, mostly Congregational, but a few independent, in New England, New Jersey, and eastern New York.

M. W. Montgomery of the Congregational Home Missionary Society hoped that this new Swedish body would develop into a full fledged Congregational Conference and join the national church like other Conferences. (*Covenant Memories*) That was not to be the case.

In the meantime two pietist revivalistic Swedish groups had been organized in the Midwest in 1873 and 1874, and gave up their Lutheran confessions and united in 1885 as the Swedish Evangelical Mission Covenant Church of America (now the Evangelical Covenant Church). This group also began to relate to the Eastern Missionary Association, and was better able to provide Swedish resources. Finally, in 1920, after three years of discussion, the Association voted to join the Covenant Church as a district Association, and later became the East Coast Conference of that denomination. At the time the Association affiliated with the Covenant, no more than five congregations were full members of the Covenant denomination, some dual with the Congregationalists, while the vast majority of congregations were full members of Congregational Associations. The new relationship gave these latter congregations a new partial affiliate status to the Covenant. But the die was cast. As time went on, congregation after congregation became full members of the Covenant and dropped their affiliation to the Congregationalists. Almost all those still affiliated with the Congregational Christians in 1957 opposed the United Church of Christ merger. The last Swedish Church in New York in the United Church of Christ died in 1975. A Schedule II Church in that state was carried until 1977, while Swedish churches were gone from New Jersey in 1952 and Pennsylvania in 1953. One even left to a more fundamentalist group.

Similarly, a Southwestern New York and Northwestern Pennsylvania Circuit Association serving Swedes was begun in 1885 and became the Middle East Missionary Association in 1893. It included a smaller percentage of Congregational churches than the eastern body, and eventually was included in the Great Lakes Conference of the Covenant. Churches there also followed the lead of the Association, dropped their Congregational connections and became fully Covenant churches.

What began as an extensive Swedish ministry is now outside the mainstream of Congregational history.

Ministry to Norwegians and Danes had a similar history. A 1900 Danish church in New York was affiliated with the Congregationalists from 1904 to 1936. Norwegian Churches affiliated with the Congregationalists in 1888 in New Jersey, 1891 in Pennsylvania, and 1918 in New York.

In 1891 an Eastern Evangelical Free Church Association (Congregational) was formed to serve these churches. In 1909 it united with the Norwegian Danish Evangelical Free Church of America (1891, formerly the Western Evangelical Free Church Association (Congregational)), as the Norwegian Danish Evangelical Free Church Association. It became the Evangelical Free Church Association in 1943. This became the major body providing resources to these congregations. In 1950 this group merged to the Swedish Evangelical Free Church, an 1884 schism from one of the groups that formed the Covenant Church. The new 1950 body, the Evangelical Free Church of America, became the denominational place of affiliation for the formerly Congregational churches, and those remaining in this area soon transferred there.

A similar pattern developed among Finnish Churches, although no alternative denominational body claimed their loyalty. Finnish Congregational Churches appeared in New York in 1902 and New Jersey in 1926. A Finnish Evangelical Mission Conference of America was begun in 1899. Eventually this became the main body for these churches, and nationally very few Finnish congregations are part of the United Church of Christ, while many more relate to this body, or have joined the Conservative Conference. The last Finnish Church in the Middle Atlantic area is a Schedule II Church in New York.

OTHER CONGREGATIONAL ETHNIC MINISTRIES

Another opportunity to serve the German population came in 1924 when the Evangelical Protestant Church of North America voted to join the Congregational denomination, and was received by the Congregational National Council in 1925 as an ethnic Conference. This denomination of rationalist German congregations had been formed in 1911/1912 replacing two ministerial bodies that had served these congregations. One congregation had been organized as early as 1782. The Church had two Associations, one entirely in western Pennsylvania. After the national merger, some Pennsylvania churches began to transfer to the English Associations, as early as 1929, and in 1935 the Pittsburgh Evangelical Protestant Association merged with the local English body, leaving the Evangelical Protestant Conference with only one Association centered in Ohio. A few Pennsylvania churches wished to continue with the Evangelical Protestant group and transferred to the Cincinnati Association in 1935. That Association gave up its last Pennsylvania Church in 1945, and the Conference died in 1947, transferring all its churches to multi-cultural Associations. These churches also had difficulty with the United Church of Christ merger. Many joined the United Church, but a sizable portion became part of the National Association.

Other ethnic ministries in the Middle Atlantic States were smaller in scope. Protestantism had been established in Armenia because of the ABCFM missions to Armenians, beginning in the Ottoman Empire as early as 1846. As Armenians came to America, Congregational Churches were formed: in New York beginning in 1896, affiliating 1902, and in Pennsylvania from 1920. In the East these Churches were solidly supportive of the United Church of Christ. As international contacts have expanded and become easier, some relation has also existed with the international Union of Armenian Evangelical Congregations.

Slavonic and Slovak Churches affiliated with the Congregationalists in Pennsylvania from 1889. One merged into a continuing United Church of Christ congregation, while the last free standing United Church congregation died in 1989. Another died when a part of the Conservative Conference in 1993.

Italian congregations appeared in New York in 1903 and New Jersey in 1928, the last dying as part of the United Church in 1970.

An Hispanic Church existed in New York from 1898 to 1912. In 1956 an Hispanic Church, which had begun in 1941, joined the Congregational Christians. The United Evangelical Church of Puerto Rico was formed in 1931 by a merger of the Congregationalists, the Christians, and the United Brethren congregations on the island. It has continued as a Congregational Christian and then United Church of Christ Conference, solidly supporting the merger. In 1959 it began mission work in New York. In 1965 this work was consolidated to that already existing in the New York Conference. New Hispanic congregations appeared in Pennsylvania in 1980, and in New Jersey in 1999. The Conservative Congregational Christian Conference has also begun Hispanic work in New York.

NEW UNITED CHURCH OF CHRIST ETHNIC MINISTRIES

The formation of the United Church of Christ spurred an extension of ethnic work. The Evangelical and Reformed Church had been primarily made up of congregations that had been either German speaking or German heritage English-speaking churches at their beginnings. The Evangelical and Reformed Church also had an ethnic Hungarian Magyar Synod, which has continued in the United Church of Christ as the Calvin Synod. New Hungarian Churches have been received into the United Church since the merger.

Another new opening has begun with the German population. The Schwenkfelder Church, a small German denomination that settled in Pennsylvania beginning in 1735, has had the majority of its churches affiliate with the Evangelical and Reformed Church (beginning 1959), or the United Church of Christ. (See Appendix V.).

Another unique change is that some formerly Evangelical and Reformed churches, still culturally German have become parts of the Conservative Conference, beginning in this area in 1994 in Pennsylvania.

Dramatic demographic change in the area has led to outreach to new and growing immigrant groups.

A Haitian Church that began in New York in 1977 affiliated with the United Church of Christ in 1982.

All other new ethnic groups are Asian or Pacific in background.

An existing Church in New York became predominantly a mixed Asian Indian congregation before 1988. Since then other mixed Asian Indian congregations have been formed, as well as ethnically specific congregations such as Tamil or Malayalam. This work extended to Pennsylvania in 1996, and later to New Jersey.

Chinese and Mandarin congregations have arisen in New York from 1969, and one was affiliated in New Jersey 1974 to 1977.

A Korean congregation joined the New York Conference in 1987, and a 1995 congregation joined the New Jersey Association in 1998.

A Filipino congregation began in New York in 1993, and a proposed congregation has been contemplated in New Jersey.

Except for the Hungarian Churches, new United Church of Christ ethnic congregations are part of predominantly English-speaking Associations and Conferences. Many have affiliated with Councils of Ethnic Ministries such as Pacific and Asian American Ministries, United Black Christians, and the Council for Hispanic Ministries.

In the church lists in this book, congregations with no ethnic code are White – European – Anglo-Saxon – English. Multi-Ethnic congregations with White – European membership consistently over fifty percent of the membership are also shown with no ethnic code.

CONGREGATIONAL ORGANIZATION IN THE MIDDLE ATLANTIC STATES

Isolated Puritan congregations in this area were slow to form any inter-church organizations. In the seventeenth century some churches in what is now New York were invited to some of the New England Synods. Those formally in the colonies of Connecticut and New Haven also had to submit to the establishment clauses in their laws, which restricted their church's organization. Some churches throughout the Middle Atlantic area also settled pastors through vicinage councils.

However, few signs appear of standing relationships among pastors or congregations in the earliest years. Some type of ministerial association, at least on Long Island, could be conjectured, but no documentation has been discovered. Some Middle Atlantic pastors may have attended Harvard or Yale graduations and the informal ministerial conventions at the annual election sermons in the New England colonies, but no such meetings are known to have taken place in the Middle Atlantic area.

As political events cut these churches off from the New England colonies they became, more or less, orphans, that is, autonomous churches. Some were tied formally to their local towns, which in some cases provided tax support. Others were fully on their own. Standing rules for mutual recognition did not exist. Some early groups were so isolated that they were able to begin worship and even hire a pastor, but have no vicinage council to settle the pastor or even to recognize the congregation. (That is one reason why dating some early congregations in this area is so difficult. They merely started up, step by step, with no outside recognition.) Fear that royal or Anglican governments might suppress mutual councils, associations, or synods kept many from even attempting such potentially seditious behavior.

After the overthrow of the Stuart dynasty in the Glorious Revolution, ministerial associations began to be organized in the Boston area and other parts of New England (from 1690). More formal plans to organize relationships among the churches were reflected in the Massachusetts proposals suggested in 1704 and promulgated in 1705, the founding of the first Presbytery in Philadelphia in 1706 and the Saybrook Synod in Connecticut in 1708. The original Presbytery was not of the rigid Scottish variety and therefore early attracted many of the Puritan churches in the first union. Many of the Congregational churches staying out of the first union remained completely independent, although some mutual recognition was acknowledged by these churches in vicinage councils. But a few congregations along the Connecticut border became part of adjoining Connecticut Consociations from 1709 and thus became the first churches in Congregational organizations in this area. The first of these was the Church in Bedford, Westchester County. By 1760 at least eight other congregations in Westchester, Putnam, and Dutchess Counties are reported to have been related to Connecticut Consociations. Also by 1760 a pastor in Columbia County was a member of the Hampshire South Association of Massachusetts (ministers). The Berkshire Association in Massachusetts, a ministerial body, also included members serving regularly in New York, after it was formed in 1763. (See below the list of New England bodies serving the Middle Atlantic States).

INDEPENDENT PRESBYTERIES

After the Great Awakening, two Presbyteries were begun in New York by pastors and churches with New England roots. Both of these groups were founded independently, and took on county names in the style of New England associations and consociations. Both then chose to relate to Presbyterian Synods, but in a very marginal and rather independent manner. Both were decimated by the second schism, and were abolished and replaced by their Synods. Because of these peculiarities, they may be considered intermediate between Congregationalism and Presbyterianism. While the member churches eventually were in Presbyterian Synods, churches belonging to these Presbyteries before the Presbyteries joined the Synods are shown here as belonging to Congregational bodies. Membership in these Presbyteries during their Presbyterian phase is noted in the church tables (Column B). Data on these Presbyteries comes primarily from Presbyterian Synod records and secondarily from Trinterud (36) and Cumming (42).

The **Suffolk County Presbytery** (Code: **SUF**) was organized by clergy and six congregations on Long Island in 1747. In 1748 it applied to join the New Side Synod of New York, and was received by them in 1749. Nichols (49) reports that many of this Presbytery's congregations did not have ruling elders. During the period that this Presbytery was part of the New England-oriented New Side New York Synod (1749-1758), some of its ministers attended all but two of the Synod meetings (1755 and 1758). However, in the united years, until 1787, Suffolk failed to have any ministers present at twenty of the thirty Synod meetings, the last attended being 1770. The Presbytery itself was also disrupted by the Revolutionary War, was slow to recover, and did not meet as a Presbytery from 1775 until 1784. Then, in 1787, the Presbytery sent a letter to the Synod asking that "the union between you and us should be dissolved." They told the Synod "that concurrence with the draught of the form of government and discipline for the Presbyterian Church in North America is impracticable" and that the Churches in their limits "will not comply therewith." The Synod dispatched a reconciliation committee to the Presbytery through which a temporary truce was gained. However, the Synod dissolved the Presbytery in 1790, replacing it with one founded on a more solidly Presbyterian foundation.

The **Dutchess County Presbytery** (Code: **DUT**) was also founded independently in 1762. Cumming (42) suggests that it was formed because a legal action in Connecticut had forced congregations not in Connecticut out of the Consociations there. It was formed only by clergy, who described themselves as "not in subjection to any Ecclesiastical Judicatory." In 1763 it asked to join the reunited Synod of New York and Philadelphia. However, there was some uncertainty over whether they met the Synod's standards. The Synod sent some requirements to the Presbytery for membership, including the adoption of the Westminster Confession. Not until 1766 did the Synod acknowledge that they had fulfilled the requirements and were admitted. In the twenty-three years that the Presbytery belonged directly to the Synod of New York and Philadelphia (1766-1788), it sent delegates to only seven meetings (1766,1768,1770,1772,1773,1775, and 1787). It was also disrupted by the Revolutionary War, and did not meet as a Presbytery from 1778 to 1780. Some of its churches had no ruling elders. During the entire life of the Presbytery, it formally received only four congregations into membership, although many more were listed. Near the time of the formation of the General Assembly, this Presbytery suffered many congregational losses in the second schism, and was finally disbanded by its Synod in 1795 and replaced by more Presbyterian bodies.

CONGREGATIONAL INTER-CHURCH BODIES IN THE SECOND SCHISM

Beginning with Green's separation from the New York Presbytery, new inter-church bodies proliferated in the Middle Atlantic area. They also began to have contact with each other and some New England bodies. (See comments on steps to a general body below). Inter-church bodies centered in the Middle Atlantic area formed as part of the second schism: their origins, areas served and the places of their records are as follows:

The **Morris County Presbytery** (Code: **MC**) was the first "Associated" Presbytery, although it began in 1780 without that word in its title. It met in 1820, but was considered to have become extinct by 1821, as noted in the Westchester Associated Presbytery minutes, when the latter group received the remaining Morris County churches and clergy. In 1781 the Presbytery published *A View of a Christian Church and Church Government*... which contains the minutes of the 1780 meeting. Under their sponsorship they formed the *Society, instituted in Morris-County, for the Promotion of Learning and Religion*, which was incorporated by the State of New Jersey in 1787. It continued after the Presbytery's demise, until 1855 or later, as the Morris County Education Society. In 1796 the convention of the three Associated Presbyteries published *A Brief Account of the Associated Presbyteries*..., which includes some notes from Presbytery minutes. Minutes of 1782 and 1787 meetings, and some related correspondence are at the Presbyterian Historical Society in Philadelphia, while minutes of the joint 1806 and 1820 meetings with the Westchester Associated Presbytery can be found in the latter's minutes. Unfortunately Morris County Presbytery records often identify clergy and lay delegate names without specifying congregations served or represented, and not all of these have been assigned. Other information has been reconstructed from scattered sources. This Presbytery included congregations in New Jersey and New York, and sent missionaries to a widespread area.

The **Strict Congregational Convention of Long Island** (Code: **LIS**) was begun in 1791, and was claimed by the Strict Congregational Convention of Connecticut as a constituent part until 1795. It continued until 1840, when it merged to the Long Island Association (see below) to form the Consociation of Long Island. It served congregations in New York (including some upstate), in New Jersey 1795 to 1809, and in Connecticut 1818 to 1834. Its minutes have not been found, but a good review of this body is available in Jere C. Austin's 1964 typescript "*Notes on Early Congregational Churches and Ministers of Suffolk County, Long Island, New York*," and his shorter "*The Strict Congregationalists*," (*Long Island Forum*, May, 1966, pp.90-93). Austin acknowledges two other sources: *The Separates* (1902), by S. Leroy Blake, and another which has not been located, "*A Brief History of the Strict Congregational Convention of Long Island*" (1839).

The **Westchester Associated Presbytery** (Code: **WAP**) was set up by a vote of the Morris County Presbytery in 1791, and organized independently in 1792. In 1822 the Presbytery decided to explore membership in the (Congregational) General Association of Connecticut. However, the General Association, still being only a clergy body, recommended that Westchester reorganize as a purely clergy body and then reapply. Unwilling to cast out the lay delegates, the Presbytery abandoned the plan. The Presbytery voted to dissolve in 1830. Its record book exists at the Presbyterian Historical Society in Philadelphia. It is also covered extensively, but with some errors, in Cumming (42). While centered in New York, it also served churches in Connecticut from time to time, and New Jersey from 1820 on.

The **Northern Associated Presbytery** (Code: **NAP**) was set up by the Westchester Associated Presbytery and the Berkshire Association of Massachusetts (ministers) in 1793. In 1822 the Presbytery proposed a plan for it to join the regular Presbyterian Synod of Albany. Some of the Presbytery's congregations objected, and the plan was abandoned. Thereafter some congregations made the move on their own. The Presbytery disbanded in 1830. Henry Martyn Dodd writing about the church in Windham, New York in 1903, appeared to have access to the Presbytery's minutes, but they are not now available. Running geographically from the Massachusetts and Vermont border across east central New York to the northern reaches of the Susquehanna River and the Pennsylvania border, it held a crucial position in New York Congregationalism. It is also frequently mentioned in the records of other groups existing at this time. The loss of its records is a severe blow to understanding Congregationalism at this point. A list of the member churches has been reconstructed from very feeble and scattered reports. In addition to New York, it served in Vermont at least 1797 to 1806, and possibly elsewhere.

The **Oneida Association** (Code: **OE**) (formally the Association of Pastors and Churches of Oneida County) was begun in 1800, and suspended because of the accommodation plan in 1822. Unfortunately, its records are also missing, and member lists have been pieced together from many sources. It served New York.

The **Ontario Association** (Code: **OA**) was also begun in 1800. It disbanded in 1813 so that its members could join in the accommodation plan. Several sources have reported that its records were given to the Rochester Presbytery, but they also have not been located. Punchard (12) lists the churches that began the Association, and Hotchkin (48) seems to have had access to the minutes from 1804 on, because he gives specific dates of church affiliations with the Association. It served New York.

The **Susquehanna Association** (Code: **SA**) was begun in 1803 and served in New York and Pennsylvania. A high requirement for quorums at meetings made it almost impossible for this body to meet, and it died out after 1807. The records have not been found, but its history has been reconstructed, from information found in Hotchkin (48), Corss (41), and Patterson (1874) and a history of the Lisle, NY, Church.

The **Middle Association** (Code: **ML**) (formally the Middle Association of the Military Tract and Its Vicinity) was planned in 1803 and organized in 1804 between the Oneida and Ontario Associations. Its records were published as edited by the Rev. J. Q. Adams in the *Journal of Presbyterian History* (Vol.X pp.220-229,258-284; Vol.XI pp.20-38, 49-68). It began a correspondence with the Presbyterian Synod of Albany in 1807, and the Synod that year offered to receive the Association on the same basis as a Presbytery. The Association agreed, and in 1808 joined the Synod, thereby becoming a Presbyterian body, but retaining its original name. Thus began the accommodation plan. In 1810 the Synod divided the Association into two Presbyteries, and the name Association disappeared from Presbyterian usage. During the 1808 to 1810 period churches in this Association are shown in both the Congregational and the Presbyterian columns in the text. The Association served in New York.

The **Saratoga Associated Presbytery** (Code: **SAP**) was authorized to be set up by the Northern Associated Presbytery in 1806, and organized in 1807. In 1812 it was proposed that the Presbytery disband so that its churches could join the Albany Presbytery or Vermont (Congregational) Associations. Some churches objected, so the Presbytery continued until it disbanded in 1818. It served in New York and Vermont its entire life. Its records are at the Presbyterian Historical Society in Philadelphia.

The **Black River Association** (Code: **BR**) was planned in 1807 and organized in 1808. Johnson (1878) says that its record book ends in 1811, but Thompson (1860) says that in 1817 it merged to the new 1816 Saint Lawrence Presbytery, which became the Watertown Presbytery in 1829. The records have not been found, but much can be reconstructed from the two articles mentioned and one in a history of Lewis County. It served New York.

The **Union Association** (Code: **UA**) was set off from the Oneida Association in 1808. Hotchkin (48) seems to have had access to the minutes, but they are no longer available. Hotchkin's information has been used. It served New York and disbanded in 1822 (see below).

The **Strict Congregational Convention of New Jersey** (Code: **SNJ**) was set off from the Long Island Convention in 1809. It transferred its members to the New York Independent Association in 1828. It served New Jersey and also New York until 1815. In the absence of any records, information found in Austin's materials has been used (see under the Long Island Convention, above).

The **Luzerne Association** (Code: **LAS**) was organized in 1810. In 1817 it changed its name to **Susquehanna Presbytery**, but remained an independent body serving Congregational churches. In 1821 it joined a Synod of the Presbyterian Church, becoming then a fully Presbyterian body. It served Pennsylvania. The records are at the Presbyterian Historical Society in Philadelphia. It is also discussed in articles by Corss (41), Miller (1873) and Osmond (1897).

EARLY ATTEMPTS TO FORM A GENERAL BODY

New Congregational bodies in the New York area communicated with bodies in New England, and made early attempts to form alliances with each other.

The Strict Congregational Convention of Long Island began in 1791 as a part of the Strict Congregational Convention of Connecticut, and became fully independent by 1795. In 1791 it established a regular correspondence with its parent body and the Morris County Presbytery.

In 1793 the Westchester Associated Presbytery sent a delegation to the Berkshire Association in Massachusetts (ministers), which led to the formation of the Northern Associated Presbytery. The Berkshire Association also agreed to be in connection with the three Associated Presbyteries mentioned above.

In April 1794 the three Presbyteries of Morris County, Westchester Associated, and Northern Associated meeting in Poughkeepsie, New York, decided to have representatives meet annually in what was to be a Convention of Correspondence. Meetings were held in many following years, although Morris County soon was not represented.

Members also attended the meetings of the other groups. In 1801 the Northern Associated Presbytery proposed to the Westchester Associated Presbytery that they seek representation at the Connecticut General Association (Congregational). By 1802 this idea was abandoned, probably in part because the Connecticut organization was only a clergy body (an issue specifically encountered in 1822 when Westchester revived this idea).

At an 1805 convention meeting, also in Poughkeepsie, expansion of the Convention was proposed. Three western New York Associations were invited to meet with the Westchester and Northern Presbyteries in 1806 in Harpersfield (Delaware County), New York to consider such an organization. However, the delegates found it inexpedient at the time to form a general body. At this early date transportation was probably a drawback. Of the four western Congregational Associations at this date (Oneida, Ontario, Susquehanna, and Middle), which one was not involved in the plan, is not clear.

After the failure of the Harpersfield meeting, the Associated Presbyteries dropped the Convention of Correspondence and instead strengthened the practice of sending delegates to the annual meetings of nearby bodies. The Associations followed suit, and minutes reflect neighboring group delegates in most years thereafter. Also the Morris County and Westchester Associated Presbyteries met together in 1806 and 1820.

In 1810 the Saratoga Associated Presbytery asked the help of the Northern Associated Presbytery in again trying to organize a Congregational general body for New York, shortly after the Middle Association entered the Albany Synod on the accommodation plan. In July, 1811, seven Presbyteries and Associations met in Clinton (then in the town of Paris, Oneida County) to consider the proposal. (Those represented were the Saratoga and Northern Associated Presbyteries, and the Oneida, Ontario, Black River, Union, and Luzerne Associations.) Again delegates decided that founding a general body was "inexpedient." This time, the option of the accommodation plan, and the rising era of good feeling probably thwarted the general plan.

The Westchester Associated Presbytery explored a relationship with Connecticut's Congregational churches through discussions with the Fairfield East Consociation of Connecticut in 1822. The Consociation suggested that the Presbytery reorganize as an Association and apply to join the General Association of Connecticut in 1823, but this proposal was abandoned because the Fairfield group's suggestion required that Westchester reorganize as a clergy only body. Loyalty to lay representation thwarted union.

In 1825/1826 the Strict Convention of Long Island began a correspondence with the new New York Independent Association, but withdrew from the relationship in 1830.

The Essex Consociation also became a constituent body in the General Convention of Vermont in 1828/1829.

CONGREGATIONAL INTER-CHURCH BODIES
OUTSIDE GENERAL BODIES
LEADING TO AND PART OF THE THIRD SCHISM

With the exception of the Long Island Strict Convention, which lasted until an 1840 merger, all of the remaining twelve particular groups above gave way in the Plan of Union, the last two dying in 1830. But even as the old organizations were fading, some new Congregational bodies began to appear. Some of these were very radical, and were eventually repudiated. Others became the basis for a restored Congregationalism in the Middle Atlantic area. The first of these could have been included with those above, but because it persisted in its Congregationalism, it is listed here.

The **Essex (County) Consociation** (Code: **EX**) (sometimes called Adirondack Association) was organized in 1817. In 1828/1829 it became a constituent part of the General Convention of Ministers of the State of Vermont. It reported to them regularly until 1832/1833, and was dropped in 1836/1837. It became a founding constituent of the new General Association of New York in 1835. It served New York. Outside of its reports to the General bodies, its records have not been found.

The **Genesee Consociation** (Code: **GC**) was organized in 1818 on liberal theological grounds. It sent delegates to the New York General Association in 1834, and joined in 1835. However in 1843 it was suspended from membership, and continued as an independent body until at least 1848. It served New York. Other than its reports when in the general body, little data has been found.

After the **Union Association** (Code: **UA**) disbanded in 1822, a rump Congregational group claimed to be the continuing Association. No records have been found, but several references occur in the Oneida Association minutes. This group was alive in 1829, and transferred two churches to Oneida in 1830, and one in 1831. This body died probably about 1830. It served New York.

Also in 1822, some Congregationalists reorganized the Black River Association under the name **Black River Consociation** (Code: **BR**). It served New York and became a part of the new New York general body in 1834. Outside the general body reports, information is scanty.

CONGREGATIONAL ORGANIZATION IN THE MIDDLE ATLANTIC STATES

In 1825 a group of Congregationalists reorganized the **Oneida Association** (Code **OE**) using the original group's Constitution. This group served New York. It joined the new New York general body in 1834. The records are at the Congregational Library in Boston.

A **New York Independent Association** (Code: **NYI**) was begun on liberal grounds, probably in 1825. It was in correspondence with the Long Island Strict Convention from 1825 to 1830, and their churches were listed with this Association in the 1834/1835 report. It served New York, New Jersey from 1828, and also Pennsylvania by 1834 and Delaware from 1836. It became part of the New York general body in 1834/1835. It probably became the **New York Congregational Association** by 1835. Records outside the general body have not been found.

The **Saint Lawrence Consociation** (Code: **SL**) was organized in 1825. It served New York. While its records have not been found, much of its information is in *A Breviary of the Doings of the St. Lawrence Consociation*, a copy of which is at the New York Public Library. It sent delegates to the New York general body in 1834 and, after requesting a constitutional amendment or clarification, joined in 1835.

The **Central Evangelical Association of New York** (Code: **CEA**) appears to have been an Association primarily of evangelists and perhaps other clergy. Only one church in New York is known to have been related to it. It is first mentioned in 1834, and in 1836 several clergy from this group joined the new general body on the Western Reserve of Ohio, while in 1841 and 1842 some members were in Wisconsin. No further information is known.

The **Association of West(ern) New York** was organized and joined the New York General body in 1835. Records have not been found. No code has been assigned because of this group's early membership in the general body. It served in New York and Pennsylvania.

The **Long Island Association** (Code: **LIA**) was organized in 1836 and merged in 1840 to the Strict Convention of Long Island to form the Long Island Consociation. It served New York. Only very limited data has been found.

The **New York City Association** was begun on an anti-slavery foundation sometime before 1837, when it merged to form the New York Congregational Association. Churches are not known.

The **New York Welsh *Gymanfa*** (Code: **NYW**) was organized in 1837 (some claim 1834 or even 1810), and acted in some ways as its own denomination. Some data was provided to the 1858 and 1859 *Congregational Yearbooks*, and a general article on Welsh Churches by Thomas appears in the *1860 Congregational Quarterly*. Data was again submitted for 1867/1868, and this body finally joined the New York general body in 1868/1869. Other early data can be reconstructed from the later book by Thomas (68), and those by Hartmann (65) and Williams (70). During the period this group was independent it apparently only served New York, but it later extended into Vermont.

The **Welsh *Gymanfa* of Pennsylvania** (Code: **WP**) was begun in 1838 by Baptists and Independents and reorganized as Congregational in 1839. It was sometimes called the Pennsylvania Welsh Congregational Union Association. It also acted in some ways as its own denomination. It served Pennsylvania, Maryland, New Jersey, and was sometimes visited by representatives of New York and Ohio churches. Some data was provided to the 1858 and 1859 *Congregational Yearbooks* and the *1860 Congregational Quarterly*, and again in 1865 (a late report), and 1866 on. While the records have not been found, much of this group can be reconstructed from Jones (66). The two Thomas' items, and the Hartmann item mentioned under New York above are also helpful. This group never joined a general body, and in 1871/1873 divided into the following two bodies both of which served in Pennsylvania.

The **Eastern Pennsylvania Welsh Association** (Code: **WPE**), sometimes known as the Welsh Quarterly Meeting of Northeastern Pennsylvania was begun in 1871/1873. It submitted reports to national Congregational bodies, was seated as its own body at the 1874 National Congregational Council and from then until 1886 when in joined the new Pennsylvania general body. See also Jones (66).

The **Western Pennsylvania Welsh Association** (Code: **WPW**), was begun in 1871/1873. It submitted reports to national Congregational bodies, was seated as its own body at the 1874 National Congregational Council and from then until 1886 when it joined the new Pennsylvania general body. See also Jones (66). This group also eventually served in Maryland.

The **Whitesboro Association** in New York, an association only of individuals with an unclear faith statement applied to join that state's general body both in 1839 and 1840. It was refused, and disappears after that. No further data known.

The **Congregational Association of Western Pennsylvania**, (Code: **WPA**) was begun in 1840. It was part of the New York general body from 1842 to 1850/1851. It submitted reports to national Congregational bodies on its own, starting with the *1854 Congregational Yearbook*, until 1874 when in joined the Ohio general body. In 1886 it transferred to the new Pennsylvania general body. A copy of the original Constitution and minutes of the organizational meeting are at the Congregational Library in Boston. Other primary records have not been found. It served Pennsylvania.

CONGREGATIONAL ORGANIZATION IN THE MIDDLE ATLANTIC STATES

The **Long Island Consociation** (Code: **LIC**) was an 1840 merger of the Strict Congregational Convention of Long Island and the Long Island Association. This body served New York, and finally joined the state's general body in 1844.

An **Onondaga County Conference** (Code: **OCC**) is mentioned in New York in 1843, but no further information is known.

The **Quarterly Conference of Congregational Churches of Central Pennsylvania** reported directly to national Congregational bodies from 1869 to 1874. No further information is known.

The **Wyoming Conference of Pennsylvania** (Code: **WYO**), initially a group of English speaking Welsh congregations, was begun in 1885 and became part of the new Pennsylvania general body in 1886. It served Pennsylvania.

GENERAL CONGREGATIONAL BODIES IN THE MIDDLE ATLANTIC STATES

Another attempt to organize a general body for New York was requested by the Oneida Association. A convention was held at Clinton (the site of the 1811 meeting) in May, 1834, by representatives from four associations and fourteen individual churches. This time, a plan was finally considered expedient, and a General Association was organized. The Oneida and Black River Associations appear to have joined at the start, and the New York Independent Association, Genesee Consociation, Essex County Consociation, the Association of Western New York, and the Saint Lawrence Consociation had all joined by 1835. Provision was also provided for unassociated churches to be directly represented at the general body.

Nationally, once general associations began to appear, most local bodies belonged to them. The general bodies also usually issued annual reports that provide easily accessible church lists. They also regularly exchanged delegates with similar bodies in other states, and were instrumental in forming the National Council of Congregational Churches in 1871. They, therefore, became the cement that held the denomination together, and replaced the particular regional bodies above as the primary reference points on churches.

The general Congregational, Congregational Christian, and United Church of Christ bodies centered in the Middle Atlantic States are as follows:

The **General Association of New York** was planned and organized in 1834. It became the **Congregational Association of New York** about 1902, and the **Congregational Conference of New York** about 1910. It was incorporated in 1914. The New York Home Missionary Society, organized 1870/1872, was related to the American Home Missionary Society, and was always a full partner, covering all New York mission costs, and apportioning a share of its income to the wider Society. This Society was absorbed by the Conference in 1926. Christian Churches were received in 1931, but the name was not changed to the **New York Congregational Christian Conference** until about 1941. It merged into the new **New York Conference of the United Church of Christ** when that body began in 1963. (Code: **NY**).

The **General Association of Congregational Churches and Ministers of New Jersey** was organized in 1869 with no particular bodies within it. It became a functioning general body to ministerial groups in 1871, and to inter-church bodies after 1877. During the period that it was a body on its own, it served churches in New Jersey, Pennsylvania, Maryland, the District of Columbia, Virginia, and New York, the latter state only until 1877. It became the **Congregational Association of New Jersey** in 1878. A New Jersey Home Missionary Society was organized in 1868 under the American Home Missionary Society, but was never self-supporting. The Association became the **Congregational Conference of New Jersey** in 1909. It became the **Middle Atlantic Conference of Congregational Churches** in 1920 and was incorporated in 1927/1928, at which time it absorbed the New Jersey Home Missionary Society. Christian Churches were received in 1931, when it was renamed and reincorporated as the **Middle Atlantic Conference of Congregational and Christian Churches**. It merged into the **Central Atlantic Conference of the United Church of Christ** when that body was organized in 1964. (Codes: **NJ**; **CAC**).

The **Congregational Association of Pennsylvania** was organized in 1886. A Pennsylvania Home Missionary Society was organized in 1888 under the American Home Missionary Society, but was never self-supporting. It was later absorbed by the incorporated Conference. The Association was renamed and incorporated in 1908 as the **Congregational Conference of Pennsylvania**. It became the **Pennsylvania State Conference of Congregational Churches** about 1915. It received Christian Churches in 1931, and was reorganized that year as the **Congregational Christian Conference of Pennsylvania**. It was discontinued in 1963, when its churches were transferred to four new United Church of Christ Conferences. The **Penn Central Conference of the United Church of Christ**, and the **Penn West Conference of the United Church of Christ** were both organized in 1962, and began to function in 1963. The **Penn Northeast Conference of the United Church of Christ** and the **Pennsylvania Southeast Conference of the United Church of Christ** were both organized and began functioning in 1963. (Codes: **PA,PC,PW,PNE,PSE**).

CONGREGATIONAL ORGANIZATION IN THE MIDDLE ATLANTIC STATES

In 1925 the Evangelical Protestant Church of North America, a previously independent denomination, organized under that name in 1911/1912, was accepted into membership by the National Council of Congregational Churches as the **Evangelical Protestant Conference of Congregational Churches**. It functioned as a general body until 1935, after which it had only one Association. It served in this area until 1945, and disbanded in 1947. (Code: **EP**).

The **United Evangelical Church of Puerto Rico**, a Congregational Christian and United Church of Christ Conference formed in 1931, served in New York from 1959 to 1965. While treated by the denomination as a general body, it never has had any particular associations. (Code: **PR**).

Following the Christian merger in 1931, and following the Evangelical and Reformed merger in 1957, some of their inter-church bodies continued to act in this region as general church bodies, and are discussed separately below.

During their entire histories, the New York and Pennsylvania general bodies were made up of sub-groups to which churches belonged directly. This was also true of the New Jersey/Middle Atlantic general body after 1877, the Evangelical Protestant general body until 1935, and the regional United Church of Christ bodies listed above. Churches belonged directly to the Puerto Rico body, and to one Association (and thereby the Conference) of the Evangelical Protestant body after 1935, and the New Jersey body to after 1877. However, a few exceptions occurred. Information on the listing of unassociated churches can be found in the section on associated and unassociated churches in the Introduction.

PARTICULAR INTER-CHURCH BODIES IN MIDDLE ATLANTIC GENERAL BODIES

The first general body in this region was formed by a joining together of other bodies that became particular constituents of the general bodies. The following list of particular bodies is provided as an aid for studying regional developments.

Particular inter-church bodies part of the New York general body: (These all served in New York unless otherwise specified.)

Essex Consociation from 1835; became Association about 1877; became and continues in United Church of Christ.

Genesee Consociation from 1834/1835 to suspended 1843.

Black River Association from 1834; became Consociation about 1857; merged to St. Lawrence 1873 to form Black River and St. Lawrence.

Oneida Association from 1834; merged 1871 to Chenango to become Oneida and Chenango.

New York Congregational Association (formerly the New York Independent Association) from 1834/1835; served also in New Jersey, Delaware, and Pennsylvania; united to the New York City Association in 1837 to form a new New York Congregational Association.

Saint Lawrence Consociation from 1835; merged 1873 to Black River to form Black River and Saint Lawrence.

Association of West(ern) New York from 1835; became Consociation about 1842; also served Pennsylvania about 1852-1891; merged 1891 to Genesee and two Ontario bodies to form Western New York.

New York Congregational Association formed 1837 by the merger of the former New York Congregational Association and the New York City Association; served in New Jersey, Delaware and Pennsylvania from merger to 1843/1844; charged with perfectionism in 1840 and 1841, was suspended from membership by the general body in 1843, disbanded 1844.

Susquehanna River Association joined 1840; served also in Pennsylvania; it is not listed in the 1843 or 1844 reports, appearing to be replaced by the Association of Southern New York, except that a short report appears in the 1846 minutes (possibly erroneously).

Long Island Consociation joined 1844; reorganized as an Association 1873; became Suffolk Association 1888; became and continues in United Church of Christ.

Association of Southern New York, organized 1843; joined 1843; served also in Pennsylvania; became Susquehanna Association 1851; sometimes called the Bi-State Association; also a part of the Pennsylvania general body by 1910 (q.v.); merged 1926 to Central, and Oneida, Chenango, and Delaware as Union.

Manhattan Association: this is a ministerial body, but the general body listed churches of pastors belonging here in their reports; organized 1841; joined 1842; dropped 1846/1847; also served in New Jersey, Pennsylvania, and Connecticut.

Monroe Association organized 1842 to serve former Genesee churches and ministers adhering to the general body; joined 1842; dropped 1846.

Orleans and Niagara Association joined 1845; dropped 1850/1851.

New York and Brooklyn Association organized and joined 1846; served in New Jersey 1846-1860, and Connecticut 1891-1896; merged 1896 to Manhattan to form Manhattan-Brooklyn.

CONGREGATIONAL ORGANIZATION IN THE MIDDLE ATLANTIC STATES

Ontario Association of Congregational Ministers organized 1848 (sometimes claiming 1818 Genesee date), joined 1848/1849; reported churches to the general body until 1883; merged 1891 to another Ontario body, Genesee, and West(ern) New York to become Western New York.

Puritan Association of Allegany and Wyoming joined 1852/1853; disbanded 1861.

Albany Association organized 1853; joined 1853; replaced by Hudson River Conference 1876.

Delaware Association organized 1858; joined 1858; merged 1875 to Oneida and Chenango to form Oneida, Chenango, and Delaware.

Newark Association organized 1860; served in New Jersey, New York, and Pennsylvania (from 1862); joined 1860/1861; began to function as its own general body 1869.

Oswego Association organized 1863; joined 1863; merged 1874 to Central New York to form Central of New York.

Wyoming Conference (formerly the Wyoming Evangelical Alliance), organized 1858, an informal ecumenical fellowship until joined as Congregational in 1864/1865; became Association about 1879; became Conference about 1881; became Genesee Association of Congregational Churches and Ministers about 1884; merged 1891 to two Ontario bodies and West(ern) New York to form Western New York.

Chenango Association organized 1863 (possibly informal); reorganized 1869; joined 1867/1868; merged 1871 to Oneida to form Oneida and Chenango.

Central New York Association organized 1868; joined 1868/1869; 1874 merged to Oswego to form Central of New York.

New York Welsh Association or Conference; formerly *Gymanfa*; joined 1868/1869; also served Vermont 1880-1883,1902-1913; disbanded 1930.

Oneida and Chenango Association formed 1871 by merger of Chenango and Oneida; merged 1875 to Delaware to form Oneida, Chenango, and Delaware.

Black River and Saint Lawrence Association formed 1873/1875 by merger of Saint Lawrence and Black River; became and continues in United Church of Christ.

Central Association of New York formed 1874 by merger of Central New York and Oswego; merged 1926 to Susquehanna and Oneida, Chenango, and Delaware to form Union.

Oneida, Chenango, and Delaware Association formed 1875 by merger of Delaware and Oneida and Chenango; merged 1926 to Central and Susquehanna to form Union.

Hudson River Conference organized 1876 replacing Albany Association; became Association about 1877; merged 1931 to form Hudson River Congregational Christian.

Ontario Conference of Congregational Churches organized 1866, an informal fellowship until joined about 1883, taking over church relationships from Association; merged 1891 to Ontario Association, Genesee, and West(ern) New York to form Western New York.

Western New York Association formed 1891 by merger of Ontario Association, Ontario Conference, Genesee and West New York; served also in Pennsylvania 1891-1925; received New York Western Christian Conference as a District 1932 to 1947 when integrated into regular membership; received organization of Community Churches 1943; divided 1952 into Genesee Valley and Western.

Manhattan Association organized 1877, began as a ministerial body not part of the general body until 1891, and geographically overlapping the older body in the area; yet its churches were included ion New York reports; by 1885 it had received churches, including some in New Jersey and Connecticut; it was seated directly at the National Congregational Council in 1886; after 1889 it was related to the Manhattan Conference; About 1896 it became a ministerial body only as the Manhattan Minister's Association; merged 1924 to New York City to form New York City Congregational.

Manhattan Conference organized 1889, related to above Association; seated directly at 1889 National Congregational Council, even though informal; joined about 1891; merged 1896 to New York and Brooklyn to form Manhattan-Brooklyn.

Manhattan-Brooklyn Conference formed 1896 by merger of New York and Brooklyn and Manhattan Conference, and taking over the church functions of the Manhattan Congregational Association; became New York City Association about 1910; merged 1924 to Manhattan Minister's Association to form New York City Congregational.

The Welsh Association of Washington County, New York and Rutland County, Vermont organized 1912; joined 1913/1914; served also in Vermont; disbanded 1920.

New York City Congregational Association formed 1924/1927 by merger of Manhattan Minister's Association and New York City; became United Church of Christ; disbanded 1963.

CONGREGATIONAL ORGANIZATION IN THE MIDDLE ATLANTIC STATES

Union Association formed 1926 by merged of Susquehanna, Central, and Oneida, Chenango, and Delaware; sometimes called Bi-State Association; also served in Pennsylvania 1926-1946; also affiliated to Pennsylvania general body 1926-1931/1935; received New York Central Christian Conference as a District 1931 to 1952; divided 1952 into Oneida and Susquehanna.

Hudson River Association of Congregational Christian Churches and Ministers formed 1931 by merger of Hudson River and New York Eastern Christian Conference; became United Church of Christ; disbanded 1963.

Genesee Valley Association of Congregational Christian and Community Churches and Ministers formed 1952 by division from Western New York; became and continues in United Church of Christ.

Western Association of Congregational Christian and Community Churches and Ministers formed 1952 by division from Western New York; became United Church of Christ; disbanded 1963.

Oneida Association of Congregational Christian Churches and Ministers formed 1952 by division from Union; became and continues United Church of Christ.

Susquehanna Association of Congregational Christian Churches and Ministers formed 1952 by division of Union; became and continues United Church of Christ.

Ontario Christian Conference serves Ontario Canada; joined New York Conference 1931; became Ontario Conference of Congregational Christian Churches about 1955; withdrew from New York Conference 1964; affiliated with Conservative Congregational Christian Conference 1964. See below for later information.

Hudson Mohawk Association of the United Church of Christ organized and joined 1963.

Metropolitan New York Association of the United Church of Christ organized and joined 1963.

Western New York Association of the United Church of Christ organized and joined 1963.

Particular inter-church bodies in the New Jersey/Middle Atlantic/Central Atlantic general body: (These all serve in New Jersey unless otherwise specified.)

Newark Association organized 1871; joined 1872; this ministerial body gave up its powers 1880, and disbanded about 1887.

Washington Association organized 1871; joined 1872; a ministerial body serving outside the three states covered in this book; became Washington Minister's Association about 1912; disbanded about 1932/1936.

Philadelphia Association organized and joined 1875; a ministerial body; served in Pennsylvania and New Jersey; merged to Conference 1905.

Newark Conference organized 1877; joined 1882; also served Delaware 1898-1902, 1927-1932, and possibly Pennsylvania before 1901; became Northern New Jersey Conference about 1891; became Northern New Jersey Association about 1908; became New Jersey Association 1920/1930; merged 1932 to form New Jersey Congregational Christian.

Washington Conference organized 1877; joined 1892; sometimes listed as South Conference; served District of Columbia, Maryland, Virginia, Pennsylvania (possibly only in 1901), and West Virginia (1882-1885); became Washington Association about 1912; became United Church of Christ; disbanded 1964.

Philadelphia Conference organized 1898/1901; joined by 1901; served in Pennsylvania; absorbed Association and transferred to Pennsylvania general body 1905.

New Jersey Christian Conference joined 1931; served also in New York, Delaware, and Pennsylvania; 1932 merged to New Jersey to form New Jersey Congregational Christian.

New Jersey Association of Congregational Christian Churches formed 1932 by merger of Christian and Congregational bodies; served also in Delaware, New York (1931-1950), and Pennsylvania (1931-1939); became United Church of Christ; disbanded 1964.

Northern New Jersey Association of the United Church of Christ formed 1964; merged to Southern 1973 to form New Jersey.

Southern New Jersey Association of the United Church of Christ formed 1964; merged to Northern 1973 to form New Jersey.

Catoctin Association of the United Church of Christ formed 1964; serves in Maryland, Pennsylvania, and West Virginia.

New Jersey Association of the United Church of Christ formed 1973 by merger of Northern New Jersey and Southern New Jersey.

Also in the Central Atlantic Conference are three Associations formed 1964 and serving outside the area covered in this book: Chesapeake (serving Maryland and Delaware), Potomac (serving District of Columbia, Maryland, and Virginia) and Shenandoah (serving Virginia, and West Virginia).

CONGREGATIONAL ORGANIZATION IN THE MIDDLE ATLANTIC STATES

Particular inter-church bodies in the Pennsylvania general body: (These all serve Pennsylvania unless otherwise specified).

Eastern Pennsylvania Welsh Association joined 1886; also known as Welsh Quarterly Meeting of Northeastern Pennsylvania; became Welsh Congregational Association of Eastern Pennsylvania 1917/1918; also served in New Jersey 1889; planned 1930, and completed merger 1931 to Wyoming to form Northeastern Pennsylvania.

Western Pennsylvania Welsh Association joined 1886; extinct 1901 (Hartmann (65) says 1910).

Wyoming Conference of Pennsylvania joined 1886; became Wyoming Valley Association 1892/1893; became Wyoming Association 1906/1911; planned 1930, and completed merger 1931 to Welsh of Eastern Pennsylvania to form Northeastern Pennsylvania.

Congregational Association of Western Pennsylvania joined 1886; became Northwestern Association 1888/1890; merged to Pittsburgh 1931 to form Western Pennsylvania.

Philadelphia Association (a merger of former Conference and Association) transferred from New Jersey general body 1905; served in Pennsylvania, and in New Jersey to at least 1913 (although the New Jersey churches still were reported as part of the New Jersey general body); became Delaware Valley Association 1956; became United Church of Christ; disbanded 1963.

Pittsburgh Association joined 1898/1904; merged 1931 to Northwestern to form Western Pennsylvania.

Susquehanna Association (see under New York), also related here by 1910; sometimes called Bi-State Association; 1926 merged to other New York bodies to form the Union Association.

Union Association (see under New York), also related here from 1926 merger; sometimes called Bi-State Association; dropped from relation here 1931/1935.

Association of Northeastern Pennsylvania formed 1930/1931 by merger of Welsh of Eastern Pennsylvania and Wyoming; became United Church of Christ; disbanded 1963.

Western Pennsylvania Association formed 1931 by merger of Northwestern Pennsylvania and Pittsburgh; 1935 merged to Pittsburgh Evangelical Protestant to form Western Pennsylvania.

Rays Hill and Southern Pennsylvania Christian Conference joined 1931, and became 1931 Rays Hill and Southern Pennsylvania Association; also served in Maryland to 1935; became United Church of Christ; disbanded 1963.

Western Pennsylvania Association formed 1935 by merger of Western Pennsylvania and Pittsburgh Evangelical Protestant; became United Church of Christ; disbanded 1963.

Particular inter-church bodies in United Church of Christ Pennsylvania general bodies: (These all serve in Pennsylvania unless otherwise specified).

The Penn Central Conference in 1963 was divided into eight particular Associations: Central, Gettysburg, Harrisburg, Lancaster, Lebanon, Mercersburg, Northern, and York, all of which continue.

The Penn Northeast Conference in 1963 was divided into four particular Associations: Blue Mountain, Eastern Pennsylvania, Lehigh, and Susquehanna. Eastern Pennsylvania also served in New Jersey until 1966, and from 1971. In 1978 all four particular bodies were disbanded, and all work was taken over by the Conference.

The Pennsylvania Southeast Conference in 1963 was divided into seven particular Associations: East Berks, Heidelberg, North Penn, Philadelphia, Reading, Schuylkill, and Ursinus, all of which continue.

The Penn West Conference in 1963 was divided into six particular Associations: Clarion, Juniata, Lake Erie, Pittsburgh, Somerset, and Westmoreland. Somerset also serves in Maryland. All these Associations continue.

Particular inter-church bodies in the Evangelical Protestant Conference:

The Pittsburgh Association was received with the Conference in 1925. It served in Pennsylvania. In 1935 it was merged to the Western Pennsylvania Association to form the Western Pennsylvania Association in the Pennsylvania general body (above).

The Cincinnati Association was received with the Conference in 1925. It served in Ohio, Kentucky, Indiana, Missouri, and in Pennsylvania from 1935 to 1945. The Association disbanded along with the Conference in 1947.

NEW ENGLAND INTER-CHURCH BODIES SERVING IN THE MIDDLE ATLANTIC REGION FROM CONNECTICUT:

The established churches of Connecticut were organized under the Saybrook Platform (1708) which had the force of law in that colony until 1784. Under the Platform regional associations of ministers were formed in 1709, each of which was related to a regional consociation of churches covering the same territory. The associations were also united in a General Association of Connecticut from 1709. The original general body thus, was a ministerial and not a church body.

Many of the consociations became or were replaced by conferences of churches, which later became known as associations of churches and ministers. These particular inter-church bodies planned in 1867 and formed in 1868 a **General Conference of the Congregational Churches of Connecticut**. Many church-related functions which had been performed by the general ministerial body were transferred to the new Conference between 1868 and 1880. The new Conference later merged with the 1798 Missionary Society of Connecticut to become the present **Connecticut Conference of the United Church of Christ** (Code: **CT** from 1819). Records of Connecticut particular and general bodies are held by the Conference. The following particular church bodies centered in Connecticut have served in the Middle Atlantic region:

Fairfield Consociation, formed 1709, probably served in New York from its start to 1720, and from 1723 until it divided about 1734. (Coded with East or West below).

Fairfield East Consociation, divided about 1734 from the above. Served in New York from at least 1743 until 1763, and again from 1809 to after 1810, and from 1832 to 1850. (Cumming (42) also suggests served 1734 to 1743). (Code: **FE**).

Fairfield West Consociation, divided about 1734 from the above. Probably served in New York from 1734 to 1762. (Code: **FW**).

Litchfield Consociation organized 1752, possibly served in New York 1759 to 1763. (Coded with North below).

Litchfield North Consociation divided 1791 from the above, served in New York 1841 to 1858. (Code: **LN**).

New Haven West Consociation, a 1799 division of an earlier body, served in New Jersey 1839 to 1842.

New London Association of Churches and Ministers, a 1911 reorganization of many earlier bodies, has served in New York from 1958 on.

SEPARATE BODIES:

General meetings of Separate Congregationalists ministers and delegates began in Connecticut as early as 1753. **The Strict Congregational Convention of Connecticut** (Code: **SCT**) was planned in 1781 and organized in 1782. It was reorganized by a 1784 plan adopted in 1785 to include churches as members. New York churches are mentioned in its minutes by 1788, and are members by 1789. After it organized a Convention on Long Island in 1791, this body still claimed those churches until 1795. This body disbanded in 1811. Their records are at the Connecticut Historical Society in Hartford.

Little is known about the **Convention of Churches at Bennington** (Code: **CCB**), but it seems that this Vermont based body included at least one New York church 1790 to 1797.

FROM VERMONT:

The **General Convention of Ministers of the State of Vermont** (Code: **VT**) was planned in 1795 and organized in 1796. It was designed to include both associations of ministers and presbyteries, and because of the latter provision could be considered a general inter-church body from its start. However, no presbytery ever joined. Beginning in 1821, it did receive consociations and conferences into membership and evolved into an inter-church body. Before that, some local inter-church bodies covered the same territory as ministerial associations that were part of the general body. New York's Essex Consociation was for a period part of this general body. The Convention later merged with the state's missionary society and is now the **Vermont Conference of the United Church of Christ**. Vermont records are at the Congregational Library in Boston. The following inter-church bodies centered in Vermont served in New York:

The Western Consociation was formed in 1797 and very possibly served in New York before its division in 1808.

The Southwestern Consociation was divided from the above body in 1808. It probably served in New York from its start, but clearly did from 1819. For much of its life this Consociation appears to have related to two ministerial associations (Pawlet and Southern Association of the Western District). This body became the Rutland Consociation in 1825/1826. It continued to serve in New York until 1859/1860.

FROM MASSACHUSETTS:

The first Massachusetts inter-church body to serve in New York was the Berkshire North Conference, organized in 1867, which had an affiliated church in New York (which was also part of a New York body), from 1898 to 1951. The present Berkshire Association, a 1960 merger of several earlier bodies, has served in New York from 1963. These bodies were part of **the General Conference of the Churches of Massachusetts**, organized in 1860, which merged in 1868 to the general ministerial body in the state, the General Association of Massachusetts Proper which had been planned in 1802 and organized in 1803. The merged body later merged with the Massachusetts Missionary Society (1799), and continues as the **Massachusetts Conference of the United Church of Christ** (Code: **MA**).

Before these dates, however, clergy who were part of Massachusetts ministerial bodies (which from 1803 belonged to the general body above), served in New York. The Hampshire South Association, a 1749 division of an earlier body chartered in 1714, was serving in New York by 1760. The Berkshire Association was begun in 1763. It had members serving pastorates in New York at least during the years 1781 to 1793, 1807 to 1820, 1830 to 1837, and 1838 to 1852 when the Association divided into Berkshire North and Berkshire South Associations. The Berkshire North Association served in New York to 1856, and the Berkshire South Association to 1857.

The Berkshire Association published a ministerial directory. Massachusetts' records are at the Congregational Library in Boston.

OHIO INTER-CHURCH BODIES SERVING IN THE MIDDLE ATLANTIC REGION

An **Independent Congregational Union of the Western Reserve** (Code: **IUWR**) was organized in 1834 serving in Ohio and Pennsylvania. It was particularly attractive to churches with direct European connections including Scottish and Welsh. Its 1834 minutes and Constitution are in a pamphlet it published, while its 1835 data is found in Kennedy (1856). No other data has been found, although it is referred to as active as late as 1844.

The **General Association of the Western Reserve** (Code: **GAWR**) was begun in 1836, with several of its members coming from the Central Evangelical Association of New York. While this was a general body, churches were also directly represented at the general as well as the particular bodies. One particular body was the Ashtabula Consociation or Association, which existed by 1839, and is last referred to in 1849. Records of that particular body have not been found, but the general body records are at Oberlin College in Ohio. At least one Pennsylvania church is listed as part of the general body, probably through its Ashtabula particular body. The general group disbanded in 1850/1851.

The **Congregational Conference of Ohio** (Code: **OH**) was planned in 1852, and organized in 1853. It continued as a general body under several names, receiving Christian churches in 1931, and becoming part of the United Church of Christ when it merged into the new **Ohio Conference of the United Church of Christ** in 1963. This body included the Congregational Association of Western Pennsylvania as a particular body from 1874 until it was transferred to the Pennsylvania general body in 1886. The following particular inter-church bodies centered in Ohio also served churches in the Middle Atlantic region:

The Grand River Association organized 1849, joined the Conference 1854, and was serving in Pennsylvania at that time until about 1907.

The Eastern Ohio Welsh Conference was organized in 1871 as part of the Ohio Conference. It was a division of the earlier Welsh *Gymanfa*. Records beginning in 1873 show that it was serving in Pennsylvania at that time, and continued to do so until 1930, when it became a purely Ohio body. For part of its history it was known as the Eastern Ohio and Western Pennsylvania Welsh Association.

The Trumbull and Mahoning Conference began in 1869 and joined the Ohio Conference in 1872. It served in Pennsylvania from about 1870 to about 1873.

ORGANIZATIONAL CHANGE RESULTING FROM THE CONGREGATIONAL CHRISTIAN MERGER

The General Convention of the Christian Church had been reorganized in 1922 into six regional conventions, each of which had several particular bodies that were called conferences. Three of the six conventions were serving the Middle Atlantic region at the time of the 1931 merger with the Congregationalists.

The Central Christian Convention had been organized in 1920, and disbanded in 1931. Its Erie Conference served in Ohio, Pennsylvania and New York. The Erie Conference was merged to the Grand River Association of the Ohio Conference about 1931 under the latter's name. It then served in New York until 1933 and in Pennsylvania until the Association was disbanded in 1963. One Schedule I Congregational Christian Church in Pennsylvania was then transferred to the new Western Reserve Association of the United Church of Christ, a part of the new Ohio United Church of Christ Conference, and continued in that status with these bodies until 1982.

The Afro-Christian Convention, organized in 1892 had a New York, New Jersey, and Pennsylvania Conference (Code: **AC**) which was serving in New York and New Jersey in 1931. The Convention continued as part of the merged denomination on the same basis as a Conference until 1939, with its New York, New Jersey, and Pennsylvania Conference as a particular group. In 1939 that Conference took on the name Afro-Christian Conference, and continued in the denomination as a general body in its own right until 1954 when it became a particular body of a new general body, the Convention of the South, which had been organized in 1950. The Afro-Christian Convention continued as a fellowship body from 1939 until 1950. In 1960 the Afro-Christian Conference disbanded and transferred all its remaining churches to the New York Conference.

The Metropolitan Christian Convention was organized in 1919 and centered in the Middle Atlantic area. When it disbanded in 1931, at the time of the merger, it had ten conferences, each of which related differently to the merger. Four of its Conferences opposed the merger and withdrew from the denomination: Tioga River (serving New York and Pennsylvania) in 1932, Western Pennsylvania in 1932, West Virginia in 1934, and Southwestern West

Virginia in 1935. The Tioga River group picked up some churches from other conferences and has retained visibility as a denomination in its own right. The other six entered the merger. The Rays Hill and Southern Pennsylvania Conference became a part of the Pennsylvania general body in 1931. A group opposed to the merger seceded from it in 1935 and organized an independent Bedford-Fulton Christian Conference. The New Jersey Conference became a constituent part of the Middle Atlantic general body in 1931, and soon merged with the local Congregational body. The Ontario Conference in Canada became a part of the New York general body in 1931, but later opposed the United Church of Christ merger and withdrew. The New York Eastern Conference merged in 1931 to the local Congregational body. The New York Central Conference became a District within the Union Association (Congregational) in 1931, but did not become fully assimilated until 1952. The New York Western Conference stood on its own until 1932 when it became part of the Western New York Association (Congregational), but also only as a District. Its churches became assimilated into the wider group in 1947, but the Conference has maintained a legal existence to this day.

ORGANIZATIONAL CHANGE RESULTING FROM THE EVANGELICAL AND REFORMED MERGER

At the time of the formation of the United Church of Christ in 1957, the Evangelical and Reformed Church was made up of Synods, which were general bodies without particular bodies. Eleven Synods were centered in the Middle Atlantic area: New York (serving New York, New Jersey, and New England), West New York (in New York and Pennsylvania), East Pennsylvania (in Pennsylvania and New Jersey), Philadelphia (in Pennsylvania, and entered New Jersey 1959), Pittsburgh (in Pennsylvania and Maryland), and Central Pennsylvania, Lancaster, Lehigh, Mercersburg, Reading, and Susquehanna, all in Pennsylvania. The Potomac Synod included one church in Pennsylvania, and the non-geographic Magyar Synod included churches in all three states.

The New York and West New York Synods merged into the new New York Conference in 1963.

The Philadelphia Synod's New Jersey churches were transferred to the Middle Atlantic Conference in 1963. In 1964 that Conference united with the Potomac Synod as the new Central Atlantic Conference. It received the New York Conference churches in New Jersey, which had previously been in the New York Synod, in 1965.

The Pennsylvania Congregational Christian Conference and the nine Evangelical and Reformed Synods centered in Pennsylvania were redistricted into four new Conferences centered in that state which began to function in 1963.

The Magyar Synod has continued as a non-geographic conference. In 1964 it became the **Calvin Synod (Acting) Conference of the United Church of Christ** (Affiliation Code: **CAL**). In 1963 its classes began to act as particular associations. The Eastern Classis serves in all three states and elsewhere. The Central Classis serves in Pennsylvania and elsewhere. The Lakeside Classis (formerly Lake) served in New York from 1969 on, and in Pennsylvania from 1963 to 1974.

CONTINUING CONGREGATIONAL CHRISTIAN BODIES IN THE MIDDLE ATLANTIC REGION

REGIONAL FELLOWSHIPS RELATED TO THE CONSERVATIVE CONGREGATIONAL CHRISTIAN CONFERENCE:

Beginning in their *1965 Yearbook* the Conservative Congregational Christian Conference began to list "Regional Associations and Fellowships of Evangelical Congregational Christian and Community Churches." In that issue, for September 1964, these were divided into three categories: Regions in affiliation officially related to the Conservative Conference; Regions in sympathy which had no official tie with the Conference, but had voted that they were in sympathy with its program and purposes; and Regions in Recognition, which had no official relation, but were noted, with a plan, on the Conference's part, not to interfere with their work. By their *1966 Yearbook* these had been combined into two categories: Regions in affiliation; Other Regionals. Regions were not listed in the *1966-1967 Annual Report,* nor the *1968 Yearbook.* In the *1970 Yearbook,* regional fellowships were again listed, but only those officially related to the Conference.

"Other" Regionals, listed, but not affiliated, were:

A Lake Erie Ministers' Fellowship was listed for 1964 and 1965.

A Pennsylvania-Maryland Fellowship was listed for 1964 and 1965.

A Greater New York City Fellowship of Congregational Christians was listed for 1964 and 1965.

Regions officially related to the Conference serving in this area:

The Conference of Christian Churches of Ontario (Canada) was listed for information only for 1964, but affiliated with the Conference later that year. Shortly thereafter it became the Conference of Congregational Christian Churches of Ontario. In 1990 it participated in an expansion of a new Congregational denomination in Canada, becoming the Central Region of the Congregational Christian Churches in Canada. In 1991 it dropped its formal connection to the Conservative Conference, but some of its churches have continued a relation to that body.

CONGREGATIONAL ORGANIZATION IN THE MIDDLE ATLANTIC STATES

The Conservative Congregational Community Churches of Western New York and Pennsylvania was known as the Western New York and Pennsylvania Conservative Congregational Christian Fellowship until 1984. It has been listed since 1979.

The Greater Hudson Valley Congregational Fellowship, which serves part of New England as well as New York, began meeting in 1982, and was organized in 1984. It has been listed since 1985.

The Eastern Pennsylvania Congregational Fellowship has been listed since 1996.

AREA CONGREGATIONAL ASSOCIATIONS AND FELLOWSHIPS LISTED BY THE NATIONAL ASSOCIATION OF CONGREGATIONAL CHRISTIAN CHURCHES (These groups are not members of the Association, but merely reported by them):

The Fellowship of Connecticut Congregational Christian Churches, listed from 1962, has served in both New York and New Jersey.

A Fellowship of New York Congregational Churches was begun by 1958, and listed from 1962 to 1973/1974.

A Pennsylvania Association of Congregational Christian Churches was begun by 1958 as one statewide group with two areas. It was listed from 1962. In 1965 it divided into two Associations.

The Eastern Pennsylvania Association of Congregational Christian Churches has been listed since the division above, but has been inactive since 1993.

The Western Pennsylvania Association of Congregational Christian Churches was listed at the division above, but not listed from 1972 to 1975, but has been again listed since then.

A Western Pennsylvania Congregational Ministers' Association has been listed from 1988 on.

A New York/New Jersey Meeting of Congregational Christian Churches has been listed since 1996.

PRESBYTERIAN ORGANIZATION IN THE MIDDLE ATLANTIC STATES

INITIAL ORGANIZATION:

The first Presbytery was begun at Philadelphia in 1706. In 1716 it voted to divide into four subordinate Presbyteries and to meet each year as a Synod. Eventually the Synod came to be known as the Synod of Philadelphia. The four original Presbyteries authorized in 1716 were Philadelphia, New Castle, Snow Hill, and Long Island. The Snow Hill Presbytery was never actually begun.

A Donegal Presbytery was added in 1732, East Jersey Presbytery in 1733, and Lewes Presbytery in 1735. The Long Island Presbytery was quite weak, and had difficulty functioning. In 1738 it was merged to East Jersey under the name New York Presbytery. Later that year, New Brunswick Presbytery was added in New Jersey.

OLD SIDE/NEW SIDE DIVISION:

The New Brunswick Presbytery came under the censure of the Synod in 1741 and withdrew.

The New Castle Presbytery was divided in 1741, and the Old Side faction reorganized in 1742 by uniting with the Lewes Presbytery under the New Castle name. The New Side faction reorganized as the Londonderry Presbytery, and later known as the New Castle Presbytery (New Side), also continued as an independent presbytery.

The New Brunswick and New Castle (New Side) Presbyteries were known from 1741 to 1745 as the "Conjunct Presbyteries."

In 1745 the New York Presbytery left the Synod. The same year the New Brunswick, New York, and New Castle (New Side) Presbyteries formed a new independent Synod known as the Synod of New York.

The Philadelphia, Donegal, and New Castle (Old Side) Presbyteries stayed with the Philadelphia Synod.

A Presbytery of Suffolk County was organized independently in 1747, and joined the New York Synod in 1749. That Synod also set up an Abington Presbytery in 1751, and a Hanover Presbytery in 1755.

REUNION TO THE GENERAL ASSEMBLY:

The two Synods reunited as the Synod of New York and Philadelphia in 1758. In that year a new Lewiston Presbytery was begun. Also in that year the Abington Presbytery was united to the Philadelphia Presbytery. In 1759 the two New Castle Presbyteries were reunited. This brought the total number of Presbyteries to eight.

A Dutchess County Presbytery was organized independently in 1762, and met conditions for membership in the Synod, probably in 1765 (reported 1766).

Theological strains in the Philadelphia Presbytery, reflecting differences from the Old Side/New Side period, led in 1763 to the organization of a Philadelphia Second Presbytery on theological rather than geographic lines.

A reorganization plan in 1765 abolished the New Castle and Donegal Presbyteries, and set up two new Presbyteries: Carlisle and Lancaster. In 1766, this plan was abandoned, the two new Presbyteries being discontinued and New Castle and Donegal restored.

Additional Presbyteries added were Orange - 1770; Redstone - 1781; South Carolina - 1784; Abingdon - 1785; Lexington - 1785/1786; and Transylvania - 1785/1786. In 1786 the Donegal Presbytery was divided into two Presbyteries: Carlisle and Baltimore. In 1786 the two Philadelphia Presbyteries were reunited.

In 1788 the Synod voted to set up a General Assembly which met for the first time in 1789. The Presbyteries were divided among four new Synods, all of which also met for the first time in 1789. The Synods and their Presbyteries were:

Synod of New York and New Jersey: Presbyteries of New York, New Brunswick, Suffolk County, and Dutchess County.

Synod of Philadelphia: Presbyteries of Philadelphia, New Castle, Lewiston, Carlisle, and Baltimore.

Synod of Virginia: Presbyteries of Hanover, Redstone, Lexington, and Transylvania.

Synod of the Carolinas: Presbyteries of Orange, Abingdon, South Carolina.

DEVELOPMENT FROM THE NEW YORK AND NEW JERSEY SYNOD TO THE EXCISION:

Most of the Presbyterian Churches appearing in this book which were connected with Presbyterian judicatories belonged to those developed from the 1789 Synod of New York and New Jersey. The Synod began with the four Presbyteries mentioned above. Most of the Presbyteries that developed in this area carry the names of counties or major cities in their area; the areas served will not be described in detail.

The Suffolk County Presbytery was disbanded in 1789, and replaced by a new Long Island Presbytery in 1790.

PRESBYTERIAN ORGANIZATION IN THE MIDDLE ATLANTIC STATES

A new Albany Presbytery was begun in 1790. The Dutchess County Presbytery was discontinued in 1795, but a new Hudson Presbytery was begun that year.

In 1802 plans were made for two more Presbyteries, Columbia and Oneida, both of which met for the first time in 1803. In the latter year a new ***Synod of Albany*** was created, including the Albany, Columbia, and Oneida Presbyteries.

The ***Synod of New York and New Jersey*** continued with the Presbyteries of New York, New Brunswick, Long Island, and Hudson. In 1809 the (New) Jersey Presbytery was separated from New York. A division of Hudson in 1819 added a North River Presbytery.

The Newton Presbytery was divided from New Brunswick in 1818.

The New York Presbytery of the Associate Reformed Presbyterian Church merged into the Presbyterian Church (U.S.A.) in 1822 by becoming the New York Second Presbytery.

The previously independent Susquehanna Presbytery (serving mostly northeast Pennsylvania) joined this Synod in 1821.

In 1823 the Presbyteries of Jersey, New Brunswick, Newton, and Susquehanna were set off as a new ***Synod of New Jersey.***

After the 1823 division, the Presbyteries of New York, New York Second, Long Island, Hudson, and North River formed the ***Synod of New York***. A Bedford Presbytery was added in 1829.

Another Presbytery was added along theological rather than geographic lines: New York Third in 1830. The Long Island Presbytery was divided by the organization of Long Island Second in 1833.

This brings to eight the number of Presbyteries in this Synod at the excision.

The ***Synod of New Jersey*** began in 1823 with the four Presbyteries named above.

In 1825 the Jersey Presbytery was divided into the Newark Presbytery and the Elizabeth Presbytery.

In 1832 the Montrose Presbytery was divided from Susquehanna.

This brings to six the number of Presbyteries in this Synod at the time of the excision.

The ***Synod of Albany*** had begun in 1803 with the three Presbyteries of Albany, Columbia, and Oneida. A new Geneva Presbytery was begun in 1805.

The previously independent Middle Association was received by the Synod as if it were a Presbytery in 1808.

In 1810 the Association was discontinued and divided into two new Presbyteries: Onondaga and Cayuga.

The previously independent Londonderry Presbytery (in New England) joined the Synod in 1811. In 1826 the Newburyport Presbytery (also in New England) was set up.

In 1812 the Presbyteries of Geneva, Onondaga, and Cayuga were set off as the new ***Geneva Synod***.

A new Champlain Presbytery was set up in 1813. Others followed at Saint Lawrence - 1816; Otsego - 1819; Troy - 1821; Ogdensburg - 1822; Oswego - 1823.

In 1829 the Presbyteries of Oneida, Saint Lawrence, Otsego, Ogdensburg, and Oswego were set off as a new ***Synod of Utica***.

This left six Presbyteries (two predominantly in New England) in this Synod at the time of the excision.

The ***Synod of Geneva*** began in 1812 with three Presbyteries: Geneva, Onondaga, and Cayuga.

Three Presbyteries were added in 1817: Niagara, Ontario, and Bath. Two more were added in 1819: Genesee and Rochester.

In 1821 the Presbyteries of Niagara, Ontario, Genesee, and Rochester were set off to the new ***Synod of Genesee.***

The ***Geneva Synod*** added Cortland Presbytery in 1825. It added Angelica in 1829, which was transferred to Genesee in 1834. It also added Tioga - 1830; Chenango - 1831; Delaware - 1832; and Chemung - 1837.

This gave the ***Geneva Synod*** nine Presbyteries at the time of the excision.

The ***Synod of Genesee*** began in 1821 with the four Presbyteries mentioned above. The Buffalo Presbytery was added in 1823. It received Angelica from the Geneva Synod in 1834, bringing to six the Presbyteries in this Synod at the excision.

The five Presbyteries mentioned above created the ***Synod of Utica*** in 1829 from the ***Albany Synod***. The Saint Lawrence Presbytery changed its name to Watertown in 1829. The Ogdensburg Presbytery then became Saint Lawrence in 1830. These same five Presbyteries comprised this Synod at the time of the excision.

Thus, by the time of the excision, the original four Presbyteries of the New York and New Jersey Synod had grown into six Synods, and forty Presbyteries. By predominant location, four of these Presbyteries were in New Jersey, two in Pennsylvania, two in New England, and thirty-two in New York.

DEVELOPMENT OF SYNODS AND PRESBYTERIES IN PENNSYLVANIA AND SOUTHERN NEW JERSEY:

When the General Assembly was formed, the ***Philadelphia Synod*** had five Presbyteries covering eastern Pennsylvania, southern New Jersey, Delaware, and much of Maryland. The Redstone Presbytery, primarily in Pennsylvania, was in the ***Synod of Virginia***. Only a few Congregational Churches were in this area.

By the year of the excision, the following Synods were at work in the parts of New Jersey and Pennsylvania not already covered above:

The ***Synod of Philadelphia*** included the Presbyteries of Philadelphia (First), Philadelphia Second, Philadelphia Third, New Castle, Wilmington, Lewes, Baltimore, Carlisle, Huntingdon, and Northumberland. It also included Delaware and parts of Maryland.

The ***Synod of Pittsburgh*** included the Presbyteries of Blairsville, Redstone, Washington, Ohio (along the River, not the state), Allegheny, Steubenville, Beaver, and Erie. (Much of its territory was in the (West) Virginia panhandle, and in the state of Ohio.)

At times these Synods and Presbyteries had also included or given birth to other Presbyteries farther west.

THE NEW SCHOOL FROM THE EXCISION TO THE END OF THE PLAN OF UNION:

Three of the six northern Synods (***Utica, Geneva***, and ***Genesee***) were part of the four Synods cast out of the Church in 1837. (The other was the ***Western Reserve*** in Ohio). These continued in the new New School General Assembly, which was formed in 1838.

However, the other three northern Synods were divided.

The ***Albany Synod***, although it originated the accommodation plan, was still recognized by the Old School. In New England, the Londonderry Presbytery was claimed by the New School until after 1846, but actually continued with the Old School. The Newburyport Presbytery became independent in 1838, was claimed by the New School until 1846, but ceased to exist by 1847.

Of the four New York Presbyteries, Champlain opted for the New School. However, Troy divided by 1839, and Albany and Columbia followed by 1840, the New School parts of which continued in an ***Albany Synod, New School.***

Of the ***New York Synod's*** eight Presbyteries, some were already divided according to theological lines. New York (First), Long Island (Second), and Bedford stayed with the Old School Synod. New York Third opted for the New School. Long Island First was claimed by the Old School, but after a division of Old School churches to the Second Presbytery, the rest remained New School and re-organized by 1840. The other three Presbyteries divided by 1840: New York Second (the New School part was reorganized and named New York Fourth 1845), Hudson, and North River.

Of the six Presbyteries in the ***New Jersey Synod*** in 1837, Newark and Montrose opted for the New School, while Elizabeth, Newton. New Brunswick, and Susquehanna all stayed with the Old School Synod.

The five New School Presbyteries from New York and the two from the former New Jersey Synod united in a New School ***Synod of New York and New Jersey*** in 1840.

From then until the end of the Plan of Union the following changes occurred in the New School:

In ***Albany Synod*** a new Catskill Presbytery was added in 1852.

A Brooklyn Presbytery was begun 1838/1839, and a Rockaway Presbytery in 1839, both in the ***New York and New Jersey Synod***. After the Civil War this Synod also began a mission Presbytery in South Carolina.

In ***Utica Synod***, a new Utica Presbytery began in 1843, and the Oneida Presbytery disbanded by 1846.

In ***Geneva Synod***, an Ithaca Presbytery began 1839. Bath became Steuben in 1862. Delaware was transferred to the Albany Synod in the early 1840's. A Pennsylvania Presbytery was organized to serve congregations in the north central part of that state in 1844. The Lyons Presbytery was added in 1856. Pennsylvania became Wellsborough in 1862.

In ***Genesee Synod***, Angelica Presbytery became Genesee Valley Presbytery in 1858. In 1853 a ***Susquehanna Synod*** was formed taking the Presbyteries of Chenango from ***Geneva Synod***, Otsego from ***Utica Synod***, and Delaware from ***Albany Synod***.

In 1855 an ***Onondaga Synod*** was formed taking the Presbyteries of Cayuga, Cortland, Onondaga, and Tioga, all from ***Geneva Synod***.

In southern New Jersey and the rest of Pennsylvania, however, the New School was left almost destitute of organization. Only the Philadelphia Third Presbytery (Assembly Presbytery), which had been cast out with the New

School, began as an undisputed New School Presbytery. It had been set up in 1832 as Philadelphia Second, and spent its first five years as a political football being created, dissolved, and recreated by the warring political factions in the Church. It came to be called Philadelphia Third in 1836.

Erie Presbytery, which had begun in 1802, was also divided in 1838 into New and Old School Presbyteries.

Other newly begun New School Presbyteries in this area included: Pittsburgh - 1839; Harrisburgh - 1840; Meadville - 1842.

In 1845 the Philadelphia Third Presbytery was divided into a new Philadelphia Third Presbytery and a Philadelphia Fourth Presbytery.

A New School ***Pennsylvania Synod*** was created in 1838, and a ***West Penn*** New School ***Synod*** followed in 1843.

The Delaware-centered New School Presbyteries of Lewes, which had begun by 1826, but died in the late 1840's, and Wilmington, which had begun by 1835, were also added to the New School ***Pennsylvania Synod***. The New School division of the 1831 District of Columbia Presbytery (by 1840) was transferred from the New School Synod of Virginia to the New School ***Pennsylvania Synod*** in 1859.

THE CHURCH LISTS
COLUMNS A THROUGH F EXPLAINED

Each church is located at the city or town in which it worships or worshiped at the time it was part of the fellowship. Where cities or towns have changed their name, the present town name, if known, is used even if it was not the name during the life of the church. Open country churches are located at the name of the nearest town or city used by the congregation for identification.

Churches that have changed their location within a state are located at their last place of worship. Churches that have changed location over state lines are located twice, separately in each state. This, however, does not include mission churches covenanted in one place to be immediately removed to a new location. These are shown only in their new location.

Listings are by state and county. Each state listing begins with the state name followed by its U.S.Census two-digit computer number.

In the main list, under each state, all counties are listed in alphabetical order. Each county is followed by the year in which it was locally organized (sometimes later than being set apart by the state.) A three-digit U.S.Census number then follows it.

Within each county each town or city is listed in alphabetical order. Within each town or city, each church is listed in alphabetical order by name.

The church lists are shown in six columns labeled **A** to **F**.

The consecutive church numbers and town names for alphabetical listing are shown in column B.

However, it is **column D** that provides the research backbone on which the ribs of the churches are attached.

The primary sources for Congregational churches in this study are the church lists published by the national church, the various state or state equivalent bodies, and records of other inter-church bodies.

Listings identified in column D are of two types: Dated listings without letter codes are based on those listings in the national church publications (01) or from earlier state listings (01S). Generally, the earliest listings of this type in the Middle Atlantic area begin with the first listings of the General Association of New York for c.1834, except some listings for churches aligned to other state bodies do begin earlier. Listings including capital letter codes are part of the inter-church body coded, for the years shown. Coded listings are only provided for years not appearing in the primary listings. The lower case code "cl." identifies churches in New York claimed through the 01T study. The code "sv." indicates churches served by pastoral members of a group.

Commas indicate a break in a similar type of listing. Semi-colons indicate a break and change in the type of listing. Dashes within numerical listings indicate from the first year shown to the second. (1917-1918 indicates 1917 to 1918.) Slashes indicate wider periods in year listing ranges as meaning or and between. (For example: 1924/1926-1927/1928 would be read from between 1924 and 1926 to 1927 or 1928.) For clarification of dating before calendar year reporting see the appropriate bibliography.

Congregations with only a dash in column D have never been considered Congregational.

Once a church has been initially listed, periods of not listing indicate that the specific church is not listed. When an entire Association or Conference is not reported, but the church appears on both sides of the missing report, the church is shown as continually listed.

Churches that were never listed in these listings are shown as not listed (nl.) in column D.

Incorrect double or triple listings are shown in the text (column B.) Long periods of not being listed may suggest a temporary withdrawal from the fellowship or being closed for a while, but shorter periods are generally listing errors.

If discrepancies appear between the state and national lists they are treated in one of these ways: problems for the entire state or state body, such as dates of reporting, are discussed in the bibliography; individual church problems are taken up in the text (column B).

In **Appendix I.,** in Column D, following the code letter "U:", listings from national Unitarian yearbooks are shown through the end of the year 1850.

Column E indicates Presbyterian listings. Dates are based on regular General Assembly listings, which begin for c.1773 (75). For colonial churches before that date, we have sought to identify their earliest reference. Colonial churches appearing by 1758 are identified as New Side (NSd) or Old Side (OSd) from 1745 to 1758. Churches in the conjunct Presbyteries between 1741 and 1745 have their New Side reference extended for the appropriate years. All Presbyterian churches listed in reports from 1838 through and including 1869 end with a code NS (New School) or OS (Old School) for the period shown with either General Assembly faction. For clarification of dating before calendar year reporting see the appropriate bibliography. Commas, semi-colons, dashes, and slashes are used in the same way as column D. Semi-colons are also used to separate dates congregations joined Presbytery from their years of listing. A dash in this column indicates that this congregation was never considered Presbyterian.

Column F indicates the current status of the church or its history after listing ended. United Church of Christ churches are shown as such. Congregations listed at any time as Schedule I, Schedule II, National Association or

Conservative Conference are shown here as such with the years listed from 1961 on. For clarification of dating before calendar year reporting see the appropriate bibliography. Corrections regarding actual voting dates are shown here or in the text (column B). Presbyterian churches are shown as such in this column only if that is currently the case.

Churches transferred to other denominations or withdrawn are indicated.

Extinct congregations are identified. It may be assumed that a church became extinct in the year it was dropped from listings (latest figure in column D or column E) unless another date is given here. Dates specifically shown here are clear dates, while dates shown here in parentheses are indicated by some sources but not accepted by this author.

Information on dual alignments with other denominations is also included here, as are debates on subsequent life of the church. Where there is much information for this column, the statement "see text" indicates that further information from this column is printed in column B.

Column A indicates any special ethnic or language group with which the congregation was identified at some part of its history.

Ethnic churches are those where one ethnic group was a clear majority of the congregation's membership.

Language churches are those where the main worship service was held in some language other than English.

Some language churches eventually became English-speaking ethnic.

Ethnic/language abbreviations may be found in the abbreviations section of this book.

Anglo-Saxon identity and English language may be assumed if there is no specific entry here.

Column C shows the year in which the church was organized and also dates of reorganization. Where it is known for a Congregational church, this is the date of the covenanting of the local church, usually as recognized by council. For Presbyterian churches organization is the date the session was organized. If either of these did not happen, the closest parallel date is given.

For churches only Congregational (a dash in column E), the organization is as Congregational unless otherwise specified. For churches only Presbyterian (a dash in column D), the organization is as Presbyterian unless otherwise specified. For churches related to both groups, the organization or reorganization dates are shown with appropriate codes. In churches with both identities, when the initial organization date is not coded, the initial organization is Congregational. In the cases of churches where their form is not clearly known (P or C churches in column B), the type of organization at the date shown can not be identified. Definition of an organizational form is debatable. In most cases the identity shown here conforms to the nineteenth century definition which centered on the presence of a session of ruling elders. Where other issues are known, they are cited in the discussion in column B.

In New Jersey and Long Island some of the early reorganization dates from Congregational to Presbyterian indicate a date after which most sources would recognize the church as Presbyterian, rather than a specific change in the internal structure.

The date of organization for Congregational churches is best found in the records of the local church. For this column we have been forced to use secondary sources. The first date given is the best possible date (indicated as directly from the church records, or the most widely used date in the most responsible sources.) If the overwhelming majority of references or the only reference indicate a specific date, it is shown first without indicating the reference. Other alternative dates follow with references. If a more detailed history indicates the origin of these dates, that designation is given. If the reason for a conflicting date is not given, we merely indicate its source.

When the date shown is for a specific reason (such as Society organized, preaching begun, etc.) a colon (:) before the source indicates that they say that this date is for the reason shown. When a semicolon (;) separates special information from a source, it indicates that while the date is for the reason shown, the source mentioned sees that date as the church organization date.

Merged churches are so noted. The date here is the date of the merger, although most of these churches prefer to use the age of their earlier part in describing their age.

When there is too much information for this column, "see text" indicates it is described in column B.

Column B is the main text for each church.

The first item given after the church's number code, is the town or city name in which the church is located (or nearest if in the open country), either at present, at the time of the 1934 change in listings, or when the church was dropped. Location means primary place of worship.

This is followed by the current legal name of the church (except that since the listing of new Congregational churches ended in 1933, in some cases the name at that time is inserted to make sense of the order of the listings. This is noted if not otherwise obvious. Similarly, Presbyterian churches merged or changed are listed under the name which qualifies the church for a listing in this directory with later merged names following in the column B discussion.) Churches which were never incorporated or for whom legal status is obscure are listed by their best-known name. The word "church" or the listings of the town of its location are generally eliminated from the printed church name in the list unless needed to make sense. (For example: Springfield, First Cong., would normally be incorporated as the First Congregational Church of Springfield.)

Following in parentheses is this information:

Popular current or historic alternative names for the church are shown, including translations of ethnic names when known.

Former formal names of the church are also noted if substantially different than the present name. Minor rearrangements of words are not shown. The most recent name is given first; following in reverse chronological order until the most ancient name which is given last. We have uniformly not included changes from Congregational to Congregational Christian or United Church of Christ, or from Congregational Christian to United Church of Christ, which would be obvious where the latter name is used in a given historical setting. If the town name changed that is shown here.

Information on the origin of merged churches is given. Information on intra-Presbyterian mergers is given.

Information on Federations is given.

Post office addresses, and notes and corrections to the listing and post merger listings are noted here.

Branches, when known, are discussed.

Information on confusing treatments in various references, exclusion in exhaustive references, and any confusing factor in the church's history are discussed here. Information from other columns too extensive to fit there, is often shifted to this column.

Churches in the Suffolk or Dutchess Presbyteries are noted.

An underlined place or post office name indicates that the church at some point appeared in the listings alphabetically under that name.

Information on minor civil divisions, if different from the location shown, is provided.

Churches within each county are numbered consecutively.

Notes are shown alphabetically between churches. These usually regard missions or claimed churches that can not be fully recognized as Congregational or Presbyterian churches.

Merged Congregational churches formed 1934 or later deriving from a congregation in the main lists are shown under their older partner (except where they maintain the location or sometimes name of the newer partner, then there) with the designation of "M.".

Appendix V. Covers the Schwenkfelder Church. The Schwenkfelders settled in Pennsylvania in 1734 and 1735. Meetings were held in homes and often led by lay people. In 1762 meeting places were divided into two districts: Upper and Lower. The group was organized in 1782 as the *Schwenkfelder Gemeinde.* The denomination was incorporated in 1909 as The Schwenkfelder Church. In 1764 a schoolhouse was built which was also used for worship services. Eventually most home worship services were phased out as other meeting houses were also built. Dates shown in this Appendix in Column C before 1895 are the dates that meeting houses were built. A Board of Home and Foreign Missions of the Schwenkfelder Church in the U.S.A. was organized in 1895. It took a lead in organizing new churches. In that year new work in Philadelphia was designated the Lower District, while the former Lower District became the Central District. From this date on, data in Column C more closely resembles organizational data as in the other Appendices. In 1904 the Board began to conduct its foreign work through the Congregational American Board of Commissioners for Foreign Missions. In 1963 a committee of the General Conference recommended that all congregations seek associate membership with the United Church of Christ. Four of the then existing five churches did so, and that is why this report is included here. The plan, however, collapsed when rejected by the largest congregation in 1965.

Calendar Dating:

In all cases, dating up to 1752, when the British Empire changed their calendars, preferentially the New Style (modern equivalent) date is shown. If a church or body claim an Old Style date, it is shown as an alternative claim.

Location and Minor Civil Divisions:

All three states in this area are divided into minor civil divisions. In New Jersey and Pennsylvania all of these are directly incorporated. In New York some incorporated villages are still within an incorporated township. In such cases both the village and township name are given, although not repeated when the village and township have the same name. Most churches in this study are or have been traditionally identified by the name of their incorporated minor civil division. In the case of a few churches in small-unincorporated villages or in the open country, we have inserted the name of the proper minor civil division. The location given for the church is the same as the incorporated minor civil division, unless otherwise specified. Where a city or village is now incorporated, but was previously not incorporated, that information is not shown unless the name of the village, city or minor civil division was changed. An asterisk (*) in the church listings indicates that this location name was never used in church lists for the church.

The Middle Atlantic colonies resisted granting charters to communities, and therefore incorporated names during the colonial period are not specified.

New York City now covers five entire counties. City or Township information for congregations begun before incorporation into New York City has that data revealed in their column B entry. In all New York City counties, the location is given as the city, followed by the Borough, then the name of the Church, except in Queens and Richmond Counties, where an alphabetical village or section name follows the Borough name, and then the church names are given.

Official names of New York communities have appeared to change spellings over time. This is further complicated by wrong spellings often appearing in the church lists. To compensate for these confusions, we have listed alternative spellings in the index and church lists. In cases where the change is minor (such as placing a concluding "h" on the suffix "burg"), one entry is made with the disputed letter in parentheses. In more complicated situations alternative spellings are shown.

Computer coded Identification:

Any church may be identified by a ten-digit code as follows: Listing (one digit - zero or appendix numeral); State (two digits); County (three digits); and church (four digits - three for the consecutive number and one for a letter M.) Churches with two or more mergers under the number (shown as M1, M2 etc. in the text) can be identified as N,O, etc. here for complete coding.

In all columns, numbers shown with the pound symbol # refer to the one-, two-, or three-digit numbers of churches in the county being discussed (if not otherwise noted.) All unexplained two-digit numbers are bibliographic references, as are the forms "01K," "01S," "01T," and "01N." (See annotated bibliography.)

ABBREVIATIONS USED IN THE TEXT

ab.	absorbed
ABCFM	American Board of Commissioners for Foreign Missions
AC	Afro-Christian Convention
af.	after
affl.	affiliated
AHMS	American Home Missionary Society
AI	Asian Indian
ALC	American Lutheran Church
AMA	American Missionary Association
Amer.	America(n)
Ar	Armenian
AR	Associate Reformed
Ash.	Ashtabula Assn. (OH)
Assn.	Association
Assns.	Associations
Asso.	Associate
assod.	associated
Ave.	Avenue
bA	became predominantly Asian/Pacific Islander
Bapt.	Baptist
bB	became Black (African American)
Bd.	Board
bec.	became
bf.	before
Bl	Black (African American)
bldg.	building
bM	became Multi-Ethnic
BR	Black River Association/ Consociation
Brk.	Berkshire Association
bS	became Hispanic
btwn.	between
c.	*circa* (about)
CAC	Central Atlantic Conference
CAL	Calvin Synod
CC	Congregational Christian
CCB	Convention of Churches at Bennington
CCCC	Conservative Congregational Christian Conference
CEA	Central Evangelical Association of New York
CG	Congregational (forms)
cgn./ Cgn.	congregation
Ch	Chinese
ch./ Ch.	church
Chap.	Chapel
Chr.	Christian
chs./ Chs.	churches
cl.	claimed (01T study)
Co.	County
C of C	Church of Christ
Com.	Community
Conf.	Conference
Cong.	Congregational
Constit.	Constitution
Conv.	Convention
Cos.	Counties
Counc.Com.Chs.	Council of Community Churches
CT	Connecticut
Ctr.	Center
Da	Danish
denom.	denomination
Disc.	Christian Church (Disciples of Christ)
Dist.	District
DUT	Dutchess County Presbytery
EC	Evangelical Covenant Church (Swedish Evangelical Mission Covenant Church)
Ed.	Editor(s)
EF	Evangelical Free Church
e.g.	for example
ELCA	Evangelical Lutheran Church in America
Eng.	English
EP	Evangelical Protestant Conference
Epis.	Episcopal
E&R	Evangelical and Reformed
ER	German – Evangelical and Reformed
et al.	and others
etc.	*et cetera* (and so forth)
Evan.	Evangelical
EW	English-Welsh
EX	Essex Consociation
f.	formerly
FE	Fairfield East Consociation
Fed.	Federated
ff.	following
Fi	Finnish
Fl	Filipino
f.l.	formerly listed
Flfd.	Fairfield Consociation
Fr	French
FW	Fairfield West Consociation
GAWR	General Association of the Western Reserve
GC	Genesee Consociation
GCLuth.	General Council Lutheran
Gen.	General
Ger.	German
GP	German – Evangelical Protestant
Gr	German
GS	German – Schwenkfelder
GSLuth.	General Synod Lutheran
Ha	Haitian
Hgts.	Heights
Hu	Hungarian
IFCA	Independent Fundamental Churches of America

ABBREVIATIONS USED IN THE TEXT

IM	Indian Mission
In	American Indian (all tribes)
IN	Indiana
inclu.	included/including
incor.	incorrect/incorrectly
incp.	incorporated
indep./ Indep.	Independent
Intl.	International
It	Italian
IUWR	Independent Congregational Union of the Western Reserve
j	joined
Ko	Korean
l.	listed/listing
LAS	Luzerne Association/ Susquehanna Presbytery
LIA	Long Island Association
LIC	Long Island Consociation
LIS	Strict Congregational Convention of Long Island
LN	Litchfield North Consociation
lt.	listed twice
Luth.	Lutheran
m.	mentioned
M.	Merger
MA	Massachusetts
MC	Morris County Presbytery
Mem.	Memorial
Meth.	Methodist
min.	minutes
ML	Middle Association
mnd.	mentioned, no date
Mr.	Mister
Mt.	Mount
mtg.	meeting
mtghse.	meetinghouse
Mtn.	Mountain
NA	National Association of Congregational Christian Churches
NAP	Northern Associated Presbytery
natl.	national
n.d.	no date
NJ	New Jersey
nl.	not listed
no.	number
n.p.	no place
nr.	near
Nr	Norwegian
NS	New School
NSd	New Side
Nt	Note
NY	New York
NYI	New York Independent Association
NYW	New York Welsh *Gymanfa*
OA	Ontario Association
OCC	Onondaga County Conference

OE	Oneida Association
OH	Ohio
org.	organized/organization
Orth.	Orthodox
OS	Old School
OSd	Old Side
p.	page
PA	Pennsylvania
Par.	Parish
pb.	probably
pB	possibly Black (African American)
Pby.	Presbytery
Pbys.	Presbyteries
PC	Penn Central Conference
PCA	Presbyterian Church in America
Pct.	Precinct
Pkwy.	Parkway
pl.	place
pltn.	plantation
PNE	Penn Northeast Conference
PO	Post Office
P or C	Presbyterian or Congregational
pp.	pages
pr.	preaching
PR	Presbyterian (forms)
PR	Puerto Rico
Pres.	Presbyterian
Prot.	Protestant
pr.pl.	preaching place
prps.	proposed
ps.	possibly
PSE	Pennsylvania Southeast Conference
Pt.	Point
PV	Pawlet Association (VT)
PW	Penn West Conference
q.v.	which see
r.	reorganized/ reorganization
RCA	Reformed Church in America
Rd./ Rds.	Road/ Roads
Ref.	Reformed
reg.	regular
Relg.	Religious
Rgn.	Region
RPGS	Reformed Presbyterian General Synod
s.	sometime/ sometimes
SA	Susquehanna Association
SAP	Saratoga Associated Presbytery
Sc	Scandinavian
SCT	Strict Congregational Convention of Connecticut
Sch.	Schedule
sett.	settled
SF	Swedish-Finnish
Sh	Scottish
sic	thus so (literal quote)

ABBREVIATIONS USED IN THE TEXT

Sk	Slovak/ Slavonic
SL	Saint Lawrence Consociation
SNJ	Strict Congregational Convention of New Jersey
Soc.	Society
Sp	Hispanic
Sq.	Square
sr	sources
SS	Sunday School
SS.	Saints
St.	Saint or Street
Sts.	Streets
SUF	Suffolk County Presbytery
sv.	served
Sw	Swedish
SWVC	Southwestern Consociation (VT)
Terr.	Terrace
Tm	Tamil
T of	Town of
Tr.	Transferred
Twn.	Township
U:	Unitarian listing
UA	Union Association
UCC	United Church of Christ
UDMS	United Domestic Missionary Society
UFMS	United Foreign Missionary Society
U.Meth.	United Methodist
unassod.	unassociated
Undenom.	Undenominational
Unitar.	Unitarian
Univ.	Universalist
unorg.	unorganized
UPNA	United Presbyterian Church of North America
U.S.	United States
U.S.A.	United States of America
UUA	Unitarian Universalist Association
Vol.	Volume
VT	Vermont
w	withdrew
WAP	Westchester Associated Presbytery
We	Welsh
WI	Wisconsin
WNYCCC	West New York Council of Community Churches
WP	Welsh *Gymanfa* of Pennsylvania
WPA	Congregational Association of Western Pennsylvania
WPE	Eastern Pennsylvania Welsh Association
WPW	Western Pennsylvania Welsh Association
WYO	Wyoming Conference
X	Extinct

SYMBOLS

&	and
?	unknown or possibly
#	number (used for one, two, or three digit number of a church)
*	location not used in church name designation

THE CHURCHES

NEW JERSEY (34)

ATLANTIC COUNTY (org.1837) (001)

	1.	Egg Harbor City, Emmanuel Cong.(f.Intl.Gospel Ch.Assn.to 1910;s.m.Philadelphia PA Assn. 1913)	1903(24,04)	1905-1965	-	Sch.II 1961-1965; NA by 1961-1979; withdrew
We	2.	Richland, Cong.(mnd.66;nl.65;*Buena Vista Twn.)	1889(01N)	1889-1912	-	X
	3.	Ventnor City, Com.Cong.(f.Ventnor Union to 1918; SS:1911)	1914(24) 1918(2 sr) 1915	1919-on	-	Sch.II 1961-1963; UCC 1963-on NA 2000(j2001)-on

BERGEN COUNTY (1675 court bec.Co.1682/1683) (003)

	1.	Cliffside Park, Grantwood Cong.(f.Grantwood Union to 1908;SS:1905:see also #2)	1907(01) 1908(24)	1908-on	-	UCC
It	2.	Cliffside Park, UCC (f.Italian Cong.;f.branch of #1 1912-1928)	1912(24)	1928-1970	-	UCC; X
	3.	Closter, First Cong.UCC (f.Peoples to 1878;f.l. Harrington Twn.;s.m.Manhattan NY Assn.1885-1893/1894)	1877(4 sr) 1879	1877-on	-	UCC
	4.	Coytesville, Cong.(f.Linwood;in Fort Lee)	1888(01N)	1888-1899	-	X
	5.	Cresskill, CC of UCC (f.Gospel Cong.)	1907(24)	1910-on	-	UCC
Fi	6.	Englewood, Finnish Bethel Cong.	1918(24)	1926-1958	-	X
	7.	Fort Lee, Cong.	1867	1866-1870	-	X
	8.	Garfield, Cong.	1891(01N)	nl.	-	X pb. soon
	9.	Hackensack, First Cong.UCC (f.Fairmount Union Chap.Assn.to 1917)	1907(24) r.1917(24,01)	1918-1999	-	UCC; X
	10.	Haworth, First Cong.	1893(01N,24) 1894(s.01)	1893-on	-	UCC
Gr	11.	Little Ferry, Evan.Cong.(l.01K by 1904-1926/ 1938;Tr.Ger.to Eng.Assn.1926)	1897(4 sr) 1896(s.01)	1897-1994	-	UCC 1961-1994; withdrew
	12.	Lodi, Free Ch. (bec.Hasbrouck Heights, Ref. (RCA)1893-on)	1846(01) 1845(98)	1860-1868, 1870-1889	-	Tr.to RCA 1893 (see text)
	13.	Park Ridge, First Cong.UCC (f.First Cong.Soc.to 1913;f.Union Cong.;f.First Cong.Chap.to 1909; f.Cong.Chap.of Pascack)	1875(01) 1873(24) 1895(s.01) r.1910(s.01) 1909	1874-on	-	UCC
	14.	Ridgefield Park, People's Cong.	1906	1906-1928	-	X
	15.	River Edge, First Cong.(in 1897 bldg.)	1899(24) 1846(s.01)	1899-on	-	UCC
	16.	Rutherford, Cong.(f.Union Twn.;l.only by 98)	1878(98)	nl.	-	X af.1882(98)

NEW JERSEY – BERGEN COUNTY – continued

A	B	C	D	E	F
17.	Rutherford, Cong.(f.Emanuel Pres.;f.West End Chap.;SS:1893)	1896(Soc.:PR) 1901(Ch.:24) r.1907(CG;24)	1907-on	1894-1907	UCC

BURLINGTON COUNTY (1681 court bec.Co.1694) (005)

A	B	C	D	E	F
1.	Maple Shade, Cong.(s.m.Philadelphia PA Assn. 1913)	1909(01,24)	1909-on	–	UCC

CAMDEN COUNTY (org.1844) (007)

A	B	C	D	E	F
Nt	Blackwood, First Pres.(f.Blackwell town;f.Timber Creek,Gloucester Twn.;indep.ch.1720-1740 which suggests ps.CG)	1718(14) r.1750(25,46) r.1770(98) r.1828(98)	nl.	1750-1758NSd; by 1773-1788/ 1793,1794/ 1797-1814/ 1819,1825-onOS	Pres.
Sc Nt	Camden, Scand.Mission (l.EC:Rgn.:by 1910-1912)	by 1910	nl.	–	EC; X
1.	Lindenwold, Cong.(in 1890 bldg.;f.in *Gloucester Twn.;s.m.Philadelphia PA Assn.1913)	1912	1914-1930	–	X
Nt	West Berlin, Cong.(m.Philadelphia Assn.,PA 1913; *Voorhees Twn.)	1911	nl.	–	X af.1913

CAPE MAY COUNTY (1685 court bec.Co.1692) (009)

A	B	C	D	E	F
1.	Cape May, <u>Cold Spring</u> Pres.(f.Portsmouth;j Pby. 1714:46;CG:36;indep.ch.1721-1740;*Lower Twn.)	1706/1718 (CG:36) 1714(4 sr) r.af.1740(PR)	nl. sv.1726-1727	j1715-1721; j1740;Indep. Pby.:1741-1745;NSd: 1745-1758; by 1773-onOS	Pres.

CUMBERLAND COUNTY (org.1748) (011)

A	B	C	D	E	F
1.	Fairfield, Fairton Pres.(f.C of C of Fairfield at New England Crossroads at Cohansey (nr. River,not modern village);moved 1780;1850 merged to Second Pres.of Fairfield in Fairton (Osborne Mem.;1838,l.75:1838-1850NS),at Fairton;had a NSd schism 1744-1745(1775:14); CG:36,46)	1680(CG;3 sr) 1692(34) 1694(14) 1697(30) r.1709(PR:36) 1783(incp.) r.1850 M	nl.	j1708;OSd: 1745-1756; NSd:1756-1758; by 1773-1839OS, 1839-1972NS	Tr.to PCA 1979-on
2.	North Vineland, Cong.(Vineland Twn.;f.*Landis Twn.)	1867	1867-1877	–	X
3.	Vineland, Ch.of Pilgrims,Cong.(f.Trinitarian;f. *Landis Twn.;s.m.Philadelphia PA Assn.1913)	1871(4 sr)	1870-1982	–	UCC; X

A		B	C	D	E	F
		NEW JERSEY - ESSEX COUNTY	(1675 court bec.Co.1682/1683)		(013)	
	1.	Bloomfield, Bloomfield Ch.on the Green,Pres. (Bloomfield Pres.Soc.;First;f.Third Pres.of Newark;1966 ab.Park Ave.Pres.(f.German, 1855(98),l.75:1862-1966NS;nl.25);1966 ab. Westminster Pres.(1870:18,98;1869:25),l.75: 1869-1966N;& Ampere Pkwy.Pres.(1925:25)l.75: 1924-1966;25 says 1794 is Soc.,1796:Ch.;18 says 1798 is Ch.;98 says 1794 is ch.,1796: Soc.,1798:ecclesiastical body;l.here as to what would be normal process;pb.PR forms in MC)	(see text) 1796(Ch.: incp.) 1798(Ch.full) 1794(Soc.) r.1966 M	MC: 1800-1811	1794/1797- 1798/1802, 1810-onNS	Pres.
	2.	Caldwell, First Pres.(First Ch.;First Eng.Pres. Cgn.;Pres.Cgn.of Horseneck;C of C at Horseneck (CG:12,18);m.on Pby.l.as CG 1828-1829;1956 ab.First Magyar Pres.(1919:25); l.75:1919-1956))	1779(PR;2 sr) r.1779(CG;25) 1784(18) 1785(99) 1788(incp.) r.1831(PR) r.1956 M	MC:1784-1820; WAP:m.1801, j1820- pb.1830	1830(j1831)-onNS	Pres.
	3.	Cedar Grove, Union Cong.(bec.Old First Ch.1948)	1889(01N,01) 1888(24)	1888-1948	-	withdrew
	4.	East Orange, First Cong.(f.Grove St.;Groveland; f.l.Orange Valley)	1868(5 sr) 1867(24) 1866(plan:98)	1867-1953	-	Merged to form M.
	4M.	East Orange, CC (merger of #4 & #7;closed 1976)	1953 M	1953-1979	-	UCC 1961-1971; Sch.II 1971-1979; NA 1971(j1972)-1978; X 1979
	5.	East Orange, Franklin Dist.Cong.(f.l.Orange Valley)	1868	1867-1869	-	X
Sw	6.	East Orange, Swedish Free (bec.Trinity Evan. Covenant;EC:Rgn.:by 1910-1919;full 1919-on; moved to Livingston 1953)	1893(01,01N)	1893-1919	-	Tr.to EC
	7.	East Orange, Trinity Cong.(Brick Ch.;f.l.Orange Valley)	1870(5 sr)	1869-1953	-	Merged to #4 (q.v.)
	8.	Glen Ridge, Cong.(f.of Bloomfield)	1888(3 sr)	1888-on	-	UCC
	9.	Maplewood, Central Cong.	1924	1926-1927	-	X
	10.	Montclair, First Cong.(First Cong.C of C)	1870(6 sr)	1869-on	-	UCC
	11.	Montclair, Pilgrim Cong.(in 1892 bldg.)	1901(01)	1907-1913	-	X
	12.	Montclair, Union Cong.of Upper Montclair (f.Chr. Union)	1882(4 sr) 1880(24) 1881(Soc.:98)	1882-on	-	UCC

NEW JERSEY - ESSEX COUNTY - continued

A	B	C	D	E	F
Sw 13.	Montclair, Valley Rd.Covenant Cong.(f.Swedish Chr.Mission;EC:Rgn.:by 1910-1953;full:1953-on)	1895(24) 1892(pr.:24)	1897-1921, 1931-1952	-	Tr.to EC
14.	Montclair, Watchung Ave.Cong.	1903(01,24)	1903-1977	-	UCC; X
Nr 15.	Newark, Bethlehem Cong.(f.Third)	1887(01N) 1888	1888-1909	-	X
Bl 16.	Newark, Cong.(unnamed;60 cites this cgn.,nl. elsewhere)	1886	nl.	-	X pb.soon
17.	Newark, First Cong.Jube Mem.(formed at mtg.where #18 disbanded;Fed.to Meth.c.1946-1954)	1851(4 sr)	1851-1954	-	X
18.	Newark, First Free Pres.(thrown out of NS Pby. 1840;pb.CG forms;disbanded at same mtg.where #17 org.in 1851(incor.:1840:25))	1834(3 sr) 1833(25)	1835-1839	1834-1839NS	(dual 1835-1839); X 1851
19.	Newark, Old First Pres.(First Ch.;Cong.;CG:12, 14,18,19,24,30,36,84;f.of New Ark;f.of Milford to 1667;claim is as continuation of First Ch.,Branford,New Haven Co.,CT,removed here 1666/1667;1951 ab.Olivet Italian Pres.(1903,l.75:1908-1951);1945 ab.High St.Sixth Pres.(1941 merger,l.75:1941-1945) of Sixth Pres.(1848(25;1847:98)l.75:1847-1941NS) & High St.Pres.(1849:98,25)l.75:1849-1941NS))	1666(6 sr) 1667(5 sr) 1644(claim) r.1720(PR:31) 1753(charter) r.1945 M r.1951 M	nl.	j1719; NSd: 1745-1758; by 1773-onNS	Pres.
20.	Newark, Second Ave.Cong.(f.Belleville Ave.;affl. Manhattan NY Assn.1890-1896)	1868(3 sr)	1867-1938	-	X
21.	Newark, Second Free Pres.(Cong.in some sources)	1836	nl.	1836-1839NS	X 1839
22.	Nutley, St.Paul's Cong.	1894(3 sr)	1894-on	-	UCC
23.	Orange, Christ Cong.	1916	1921-1938	-	X
24.	Orange, First Pres.(First Ch.;Orangedale;f.West Second of Newark to 1811;Newark Mtn.;Mtn. Soc.;CG:12,18,19,24,98;1969 ab.Williams St. Pres.(f.First Ger.Pres.(f.Orange Valley Ger. Pres.,1866:18,98;(1859:25)l.75:1866-1969NS))	1719(CG;4 sr) 1718(24) r.af.1748(PR) r.1969 M	nl.	j1748; NSd: 1748-1758; by 1773-onNS	Pres.
25.	Orange, Highland Ave.Cong.(f.Orange Valley Cong.;f.First)	1860(5 sr)	1859-1985	-	UCC; X
Nr 26.	Orange, Norwegian Cong.(Norwegian Evan.Free;pr. 1904;in Evan.Free Ch.Assn.;moved to <u>Essex Fells</u> 1959)	1909(24) 1907(67B)	1912-1954	-	Tr.to EF Ch. 1950(l.1949)
27.	Short Hills, Cong.(l.as "deceased" 1897-1898; *Millburn Twn.)	1890(01N)	1889-1898	-	X
28.	Verona, First Cong.	1896(01,24)	1897-on	-	UCC
29.	West Orange, Second Cong.of Orange Valley	1867(01N)	1866-1883	-	X

A		B	C	D	E	F
		NEW JERSEY - GLOUCESTER COUNTY	(1686 court	bec.Co.1694)	(015)	
	1.	Forest Grove, Cong.(*Franklin Twn.)	1865(01N)	1865-1866	-	X
	2.	Franklinville, Cong.(*Franklin Twn.)	1867	1867-1885	-	X
	3.	Newfield, Cong.	1867	1867-1889, 1891-1893	-	X
		HUDSON COUNTY	(org.1840)	(017)		
	1.	Guttenburg, Cong.	1888(01N)	1888-1896	-	X
Nr	2.	Hoboken, Norwegian Evan.Free (f.Norwegian Evan. Cong.;Norwegian Free to 1890;pr.1888;bec. Trinity Evan.Free at move;EC:Rgn.by 1910-1912; in Evan.Free Ch.Assn.;two branches 1925-1934, other in Teaneck,Bergen Co.;moved there 1934)	1890(3 sr) 1889(24,66B)	1890-1959	-	s.EC; Tr.to EF Ch. 1950(l.1949)
Bl	3.	Jersey City, Com.Cong.	1928(24)	1930-1941	-	X
	4.	Jersey City, First Cong.(f.Tabernacle)	1858(24,98)	1857-1896	-	Merged to form #5 (q.v.)
	5.	Jersey City, First Cong.(merger of #4 & South Bergen Dutch Ref.(RCA,1874-1896))	1896 M	1896-1970	-	UCC; X
	6.	Jersey City, Free Ch.	1842 m.1841(24)	1842-1843, m.1843-1847	-	X
Nr	7.	Jersey City, Norwegian Evan.Cong.(l.01N;r.as Vroom St.Evan.Free;in Evan.Free Ch.Assn.)	1889(3 sr) r.1891	nl.	-	Tr.to EF Ch. 1950(l.1949)
	8.	Jersey City, Pres.Soc.(Tr.to RCA as First Ref. (Grand St.,Paulus Hook)(sv.Ref.:1822-1823,r. 1830);1886 merged to Wayne St.Ref.(f.Second Ref.,First Ref.of Van Vorst;RCA,1846)as Wayne St.Ref.;1923 merged to Faith Ref.(RCA, 1909) as Faith Van Vorst Ref.;1973 merged to Lafayette Ref.(RCA,1863) & Greenville Ref. (RCA,1871) as United Ref.)	1809(PR)	WAP: 1821-1822	1808-1837	Tr.to RCA (see text)
	9.	Jersey City, Second Cong.	1869 1870(01N)	1868-1882	-	Merged to form #11 (q.v.)
	10.	Jersey City, Third Cong.	1880	1880-1882	-	X
	11.	Jersey City, Waverly Cong.(merger of #9 & Waverly Meth.Epis.(1870);in 1873 bldg.)	1883 M(3 sr)	1882-1968	-	UCC; X
Sw	12.	Weehawken, Union Hill Cong.(Swedish Evan. Mission;f.West New York PO;EC:Rgn.1911-1917/ 1921)	1904(01) 1905(06)	1904-1908	-	Tr.to EC; X

HUNTERDON COUNTY (org.1714) (019)

NEW JERSEY - MERCER COUNTY (org.1838) (021)

A		B	C	D	E	F
Nt		Pennington, First Pres.(12 says this is CG, actually part of a group of three early chs., Puritan in 98, but early PR,see notes a,b,& c as follows;all three in New Brunswick Pby. 1738,but returned to OSd when it bec.Indep. Pby.1741)				
	a.	Ewing, Ewing Pres.(f.Ewing of Trenton;f.First, Old House, or Twn.of Trenton to 1849;f.of Hopewell to 1719(46))	1709(3 sr) 1715(14)	nl. (see text)	j1709;OSd: 1741-1758; by 1773-1794/ 1797,1798/ 1802-onOS	Pres.
	b.	Lawrenceville, Pres.(Maidenhead Ch.)	1699(99; land:98) 1698(25) 1709(46) 1712(14)	nl. (see text)	j1709;OSd: 1741-1758; by 1773-onOS	Pres.
	c.	Pennington, First Pres.(f.of Hopewell to 1774/ 1787;14 & 25 dates based on founding of first Hopewell which bec.Ewing;had a NSd schism, 1741(14;pr.:1738)-1760)	1723(46) 1724/1725(98) 1715(14) 1709(25)	nl. (see text)	j1723(46); OSd:1741-1758; by 1773-onOS	Pres.
	1.	Trenton, St.Mark's Cong.	1906	1906-1909	-	X

MIDDLESEX COUNTY (1675 court bec.Co.1682/1683) (023)

A		B	C	D	E	F
	1.	Monmouth Junction, Cong.(*South Brunswick Twn.)	1875	1875-1876	-	X
	2.	New Brunswick, Free Cong.Pres.(apply to j NSPby. 1840,instead Pby.org.#2Nt)	1836	1836-1839	(see text)	X 1840
Nt		New Brunswick, Second Pres.(see #2;1907 merged to First Pres.(1726(14,25,98),j1727,Indep. Pby.1741-1745,NSd:1745-1758,l.75:by 1773-1907OS,as New Brunswick Pres.(f.First,l.75: 1907-on)	1840	-	1839-1845NS, 1845-1907OS	Pres.,merged (see text)
	3.	Perth Amboy, Amboy Ch.(period bf.jPby.,suggests CG;25 says this continued as First Pres. through house mtgs.till new bldg.plan 1801,m. 75:1802,l.1803/1805-onOS)	1731(land, 14) 1735(pastor) 1708(pr.)	nl.	j1738; Indep. Pby.:1741-1745; NSd: 1745-1758	X af.1764 (see text)
Sw	4.	Perth Amboy, Swedish Cong.Mission (EC:Rgn.:by 1910-1945)	1881(24,s.01) 1893(06,s.01) 1892(01N) 1891(s.01)	1892-1938	-	Tr.to EC; X
	5.	Piscataway, Puritan sett.(sett.:1666/1668;CG Ch.:18,m.as Puritan sett.:84)	by 1700	nl.	-	X soon

A		B	C	D	E	F
		NEW JERSEY – MIDDLESEX COUNTY – continued				
	6.	Woodbridge, First Cong.	1874(4 sr) 1880(s.01)	1874-on	-	UCC
	7.	Woodbridge, First Pres.(First Ch.;f.C of C in Woodbridge;sett.:1664;town (in New England fashion)tried to call pastor 1669,1670,1674; CG:12,14,18,19,24,30,36,84;bldg.1675;Ch. j Pby.1710(24,25,84))	1675(24,84) 1669(14) 1680(34) 1686(30) r.1710(PR; 3 sr) 1708(46)	nl.	j1708(min); NSd:1745-1758; by 1773-onOS	Pres.
		MONMOUTH COUNTY (1675 court bec.Co.1682/1683) (025)				
	1.	Asbury Park, Cong.	1896(01) 1897	1896-1917	-	X
Sh	Nt	Freehold, Old Tennent Ch.(l.Tennent;f.Old Scots Ch.of Frehill(now Marlborough Twn.);Pres.Cgn. of Freehold;s.First;Scots Mtghse.site 1692-1760(early date doubted by 36);Ref.Pres. Covenanter sett.:31,46,though that denomination not yet functioning in America; CG:12,Union 98,always PR in 30:ps.mixed in sett.;j Pby.1706:Union 98;branch at White Hill,Manalpan Twn.,1727/1731-on(af.1760 only branch);do not confuse with First Village Pres.of Freehold,(1836:98)l.1837-onOS)	1692(5 sr) 1690(25)	-	j1711; Indep. Pby.:1741-1745; NSd: 1745-1758; by 1773-onOS	Pres.
	2.	Long Branch, Cong.	1887(01N)	1886-1891	-	X
	3.	Manasquan, Cong.(in 1860 bldg.)	1904	1904-1923	-	X
	4.	Middletown, Middletown Ch.(84:union mtghse.of Puritan,Pres.,& Bapt.(Appendix III.#2);CG:84; Ch.at Matawan,Middletown Point (1763:25;1766: 14,98;supplied from here,it r.& l.as First Pres.of Matawan,Middletown Point,l.75:1794/1798-onOS)	1706(25,98) 1711(14) 1691(30)	nl.	j1711; Indep. Pby.:1741-1745; NSd: 1745-1758; by 1773-1774/1787	X 1790 (see text)
	5.	Shrewsbury, Shrewsbury Pres.(f.Cong.at Rumson; CG:18,36,84,98;bldg.by 1672;CG & PR separate in same bldg.:84)	by 1672(CG;98) 1705(14) 1706(pr.:36, 98) r.1727(PR;98) 1732(25)	nl.	j1735; Indep. Pby.1741-1745; NSd: 1745-1758; by 1773-onOS	Pres.
	6.	Union Beach, First Cong.	1926(24)	1927-1960	-	X;ab.by Meth.
		MORRIS COUNTY (org.1738/1739) (027)				
	1.	Boonton, Free Ch.(m.07,2 local sources)	1839	nl.	-	X af.1852
	2.	Chatham, Stanley Cong.UCC	1873(01,24)	1872-on	-	UCC

NEW JERSEY - MORRIS COUNTY - continued

A		B	C	D	E	F
	3.	Chester, First Cong.(f.First of Roxbury to 1822; f.Strict Cong.,nl.10;1779-1782/1785 united to Pres.(f.Black River,Pleasant Hill,Hill Ch.;f. First of Roxbury;1752(25,1745:14,98)NSd:1752-1758;l.75:by 1773-onOS(lt.75:1822-1823)),as C of C,Cong.;Fed.to Pres.(above) & Meth.(by 1868) 1918-1920,some Cong.withdrew 1920 to Fed. which continued to af.1921 when Meth.ab. by Pres.as Com.Pres.;see also Mount Olive Nt)	1740(3 sr) r.1779 r.1782/1785	MC:by 1791-1795; SLI:1795-1809; SNJ:1809-1828; NYI:1828-1834; 1834-1835, 1838-1843; m.1843-1846; 1846-1971	(see text)	UCC 1961-1971; NA 1975-2003; withdrew
Sw	4.	Dover, Bethlehem Swedish Cong.(f.Swedish Free Mission to 1900;EC:Rgn.by 1910-1947)	1894(01,06) 1890(24) 1872/1874 (pr.:98)	1894-1948	-	s.EC; Tr.to IFCA
We	5.	Dover, Welsh Cong.at Thomaston (r.as Welsh Pres.of Thomaston (or Richards Mines:25); branch of Dover Pres.(First Mem.,1835,l.75: 1835-onNS)1863-1869;*Rockaway Twn.)	1857(CG;2 sr) 1850(25) r.1869(PR; 2 sr)	nl. m.WP:1863	1869-1900NS	X 1903
	6.	East Hanover, First Pres.(f.First Pres.of Hanover (East);Hanover Neck;f.at Whippany to 1755;CG:12,19,MC;elders when in MC;voted 1783 still in NY Pby.,though nl.there,& pastor in MC;see also #7 & #10;some oppostion 1791 to hiring a PR pastor)	1718(land; CG;98) 1719(25) 1727(46) 1746(14) pb.r.1791(PR)	MC: 1780-1790	j1727; NSd: 1745-1758; by 1773-1774/1787; j1791; 1788/1793-onNS	Pres.
	7.	Madison, Madison Pres.(First;f.First of Chatham Village to 1846;f.South Hanover (Bottle Hill) to 1817;CG:19;m.37:1740;branch of #6 1747-1755;l.PR through MC period;PR forms in MC)	1747(3 sr) 1746(?)	MC: 1780-1782	j1747; NSd: 1747-1758;by 1773-1843OS, 1843-onNS	Pres.
	8.	Mendham, First Pres.(Hilltop;Rocksiticus; Roxiticus;Rocsiticus;1738 bldg.;CG:12,18,19, 98;1904 ab.Second Pres.(1859,l.75:1859-1902NS))	1738(CG;2 sr) 1744(pb.PR:2 sr) r.1904 M	nl.	Indep.Pby.: ? -1743; NSd:1745-1758;by 1773-1840OS, 1842-onNS	Pres.
	9.	Morristown, First Cong.(affl.Manhattan Assn.NY 1893-1896)	1882(01N) 1880(98)	1882-1900	-	X

NEW JERSEY - MORRIS COUNTY - continued

A	B	C	D	E	F
10.	Morristown, Morristown Pres.(First;f.West Hanover;branch of #6 1727-1733/1739;CG:12, 18,19;37:m.1742/1743;1926 ab.Second South St.Pres.(1841,l.75:1841-1865OS,1865-1926NS))	1738(25,s.98) 1735(s.98) 1732(Soc.) 1727(branch) 1742(14) 1733(46) r.af.1745(PR) 1756(incp.) r.1926 M	nl.	j1745; NSd: 1745-1758; by 1773-onOS	Pres.
Nt	Mount Olive, Pres.(f.of Schooley's Mtn.to 1786; Both CG and PR branches of #3 in 1768 union mtghse.here,also with Epis.& Bapt.;CG branch X af.1812;new mtghse.1808/1818 Pres.& Bapt. only;see also #13;Pres.branch bec.this Ch.; 1960 merged to Pres.of Flanders (1852,l.1851-1960OS) as United Pres.of Flanders (l.1960-on);do not confuse with later Schooley's Mtn. Pres.in *Washington Twn.s.l.Lower German Valley (1825,l.75:1841-1857OS,r.1875,l.1875-on))	1834 1752(14)	nl.	1806-1807, 1834-1960OS	Merged, see text
11.	Parsippany, Parsippany Pres.(f.Second of Hanover;in 1755 bldg.;1870(25) ab.First Pres.of Parsippany(c.1858,l.75:1858-1868NS); *Parsippany-Troy-Hills)	1755(25,99) 1760(14,98) 1746(pr.) 1787(incp.) pb.r.1815 or 1870(PR) r.1870 M	MC: 1780-1815	jby 1755; NSd 1755-1758;by 1773-1774/ 1787; 1815-onNS	Pres.
12.	Rockaway, First Pres.	1758(3 sr) 1752(14) 1787(incp.) r.af.1792(PR)	MC: 1783-1792	j1768-1771; 1788/1793-on NS	Pres.
13.	Roxbury Twn., Strict Cong.(nl.14;bec.Roxbury Bapt.(Rocksbury) 1753,bec.Schooley's Mtn. Bapt.of Mount Olive Twn.1786;bec.Mt.Olive Bapt.1890;in union bldg.,see #10Nt,1768-1810,& new union bldg.with Pres.to c.1834; jBapt.Assn.1753)	by 1750(10) r.1753(Bapt.)	nl.	-	1753 Tr.to Bapt.
14.	Succasunna, First Pres.(Roxbury Twn.;Suckasunny Plains;37:jPby.af.1758)	1756(land,25) 1745(claim:14) 1765(25: incor.) r.af.1787(PR)	MC: 1780-1782	jby 1756; NSd 1756-1758; by 1773 (j1787)-1798/ 1802,1803/ 1805-onNS	Pres.

A	B	C	D	E	F
	NEW JERSEY - MORRIS COUNTY - continued				
	15. Wharton (PO), Berkshire Valley Pres.(First;s.l. Buckshire Valley;PR branch of Passaic Co.#2 1822-1829;Jefferson Twn.)	1803(CG;25, 99:incp.) 1827(incp.r.) r.1828(PR)	nl.; pb.MC or SNJ	1803/1805-1807, m.1822;l. 1828-onNS	Pres.
	16. Whippany, First Pres.(f.Free Ch.;Hanover Twn.)	1833(PR;25) r.1836(CG) r.1845(PR)	1836-1843	1833-1836, 1845-onNS	Pres.
	OCEAN COUNTY (org.1850) (029)				
	1. Manchester, Cong.	1886(01N)	1886-1891	-	X
	PASSAIC COUNTY (org.1837) (031)				
	1. Little Falls, Com.Cong.	1927(24)	1927-1947	-	X
	2. Oak Ridge, Oak Ridge Pres.(f.First Pres.Cgn.of Newfoundland;f.Split Rock & Newfoundland Cong.;*West Milford Twn.(Newfoundland extends into *Jefferson Twn.,Morris Co.;Split Rock is in *Rockaway Twn.,Morris Co.))	by 1812(CG;98) r.1818(PR;25) 1816 (?)	nl.; pb.SNJ or MC	1817(j1818)-1839,1840-on NS	Pres.
	3. Passaic, First Cong.(bec.Inclusive Com. 1986/1996;f.of Passaic Bridge;moved to Nutley, Essex Co. 1994)	1885(3 sr) 1872(s.01)	1885-on	-	UCC
	4. Paterson, First Cong.(f.Auburn St.Cong.;f. Broadway Tabernacle;f.First Free Indep.Pres. (CG forms)to 1853;applied to be org.by NS Pby.1836,& to j 1839,rejected both times)	1836(24,99) 1837(98) r.1853(CG name)	1836-1839, 1851-1973	(see text)	UCC; X
	5. Paterson, Second Cong.	1917	nl.	-	X 1918
Sw	6. Paterson, Swedish Cong.(Bethany;in 1864 bldg.; EC:Rgn.by 1910-1922)	1903(01)	1907-1921	-	s.EC; X
	7. West Milford, West Milford Pres.(f.l.Long Pond to 1825;f.New Milford Eng.Pres.Mtghse.to 1834/1835)	1806(CG;25) 1807(incp.:99) r.1819(PR;25)	nl.; pb.MC or SNJ	1819-onNS	Pres.
	SALEM COUNTY (1681 court bec.Co.1694) (033)				
	1. Daretown, Pittsgrove Pres.(Upper Pittsgrove Twn.;f.l.Pilesgrove to 1770;CG:36;indep.1722-1741)	1706/1718 (CG:36) m.1720(46) r.1741(PR; 4 sr)	nl.	j1720-1722; j1741;OSd: 1745-1752; NSd:1752-1758; by 1773-onOS	Pres.
	SOMERSET COUNTY (org.1688,full 1714) (035)				
	1. Bernardsville, Cong.	1909(01)	1911-1928	-	X

NEW JERSEY - SOMERSET COUNTY - continued

A		B	C	D	E	F
	2.	Bound Brook, Cong.(Round Brook:01N;f.l. Bridgewater Twn.)	1876(5 sr)	1875-1985	-	Sch.I 1961-1962; Sch.II 1962-1985; NA 1963-on
Gr	3.	Warren, Warrenville Cong.(Tr.Ger.to Eng.Assn. 1938;l.01K by 1904-1926/1938;f.Ref.Prot.Dutch Ch.(Ger.)at Warren(RCA,1856-1872);f.Ger.Luth. at Coontown,Warren Twn.1847-1856;24 s.incor. says j Cong.1879;bec.Trinity United 1970,by ab.Pres.new Ch.start to be dual)	1847(Luth.:24) 1849(98,99) Tr.1856(RCA) Tr.1871(CG: 3 sr) 1872(24) r.1970 M	1871-1947, 1948-on	1970-on	UCC & Pres.
		SUSSEX COUNTY	(org.1753)	(037)		
	1.	Branchville, First Pres.(f.First Pres.of Frankford (Twn.) at Augusta (moved 1854);f. Strict Cong.of Augusta (Frankford Twn.))	c.1800(CG) r.1819(PR; 2 sr) r.1854(25)	SLI:1808-1809; SNJ:1809-1815	1818-1820, 1821-onNS	Pres.
	2.	Frankford Plains, Free Ch.(f.Strict Cong.of Frankford;in 1810 bldg.)	c.1800	SLI:1808-1809;- SNJ:1809-1815		1869 lost land title fight to Meth.;X
	3.	Hardyston Twn., Strict Cong.of Newton (not city of Newton);bec.Newton Bapt.1756;bec.Bapt.of Hardyston,Wantage & Newton 1769;bec.Bapt.of Wantage 1790;bec.First Bapt.of Deckertown 1883;bec.First Bapt.of Sussex 1907;s.l.as Papakating Bapt.;split 1751:98(1756:10) from Strict Cong.of Mansfield (s.l.as Newfield), Tolland Co.,CT(org.1745(s.1749)),& moved to Hardyston Twn.at split;had branches in Hardyston Twn.(Newton,then Hamburg 1770) 1751-1798,Augusta 1770-?,& Wantage 1782-on; claim is as CT Ch.;jBapt.Assn.1759:98)	1751(98) r.1756(Bapt., 2 sr) 1758(10) 1759(98) r.1769 1745(claim)	nl.	-	Tr.to Bapt.: 1756(2 sr) 1758(10)
	4.	Wantage Twn., Papakating Strict Cong.of Frankford & Wantage Twns.(or Wantage & Frankford);Beemer Mtghse.;lt.14 as Cong.& (incor.)Pres.;1844(24) merged to Second Pres.of Wantage(Twn.)at Beemerville(Sussex PO;1834(25),l.75:1835-onNS);r.as Papakating Pres.;25 says org.as Pres.,then united with a CT Assn.& bec.CG,not supported elsewhere;had a Pepecoton branch (org.?) which merged 1817 (s.25,98;1818:s.25,85) to Clove Dutch Ref. (f.Pres.,l.75:1774/1787-1788/1793),r.Ref.1788 (85,98),to form First Pres.of Wantage (Clove; Sussex PO,j1818;l.1818-1964NS,X))	1744(CG;2 sr) 1742(24) 1740(14:PR) r.1882(PR)	SLI:1805-1809; SNJ:1809-1828; NYI:1828-1834; 1834-1843	1882-1894	1844 merged (see text); r.; X 1896

NEW JERSEY – UNION COUNTY (org.1857) (039)

A		B	C	D	E	F
	1.	Elizabeth, First Cong.(f.First Cong.Soc.of Elizabethport;s.affl.Manhattan Assn.NY 1885-1887)	1864(4 sr)	1863-1954	-	X
	2.	Elizabeth, First Pres.(First Ch.of Elizabethtown;f.Cong.;CG:12,14,18,19,24,36, 84;98 says j Pby.1716;internal division 1797-1802)	1665(CG;3 sr) 1664(4 sr) 1666(s.36) 1668(3 sr) r.1716/1717 (PR) 1753(incp.)	nl. m.MC 1784	j1717; NSd: 1745-1758; by 1773-onOS	Pres.
	3.	Elizabeth, Greystone Pres.(f.Marshall St.Pres.; f.First Pres.of Elizabethport;f.Cong.of Elizabethport,affl.CT to 1842)	1839(CG;2 sr) r.1846(PR;25)	1839-1842, m.1843-1846	j1846; 1845-onOS	Pres.
	4.	Grasselli Park, Com.Cong.(Linden PO)	1920	1920-1936	-	X
	5.	New Providence, New Providence Pres.(f.Turkey Chr.to 1778;CG:19;98 says ch.sought aid of NY Pby.in 1737,it did not exist then;37:jPby. 1750)	1737(25,98) pb.r.af.1750 (PR)	nl.	j1741; NSd: 1745-1758; by 1773-onOS	Pres.
	6.	Plainfield, Cong.(division of Central Ref.(RCA, 1863))	1872 r.1879(4 sr) 1880(01N) 1878(plan:24)	1871-on	-	UCC
Sw	7.	Plainfield, Swedish Pilgrim Covenant Cong.(f. Swedish Mission Soc.;moved to <u>South Plainfield</u>,*Piscataway Twn.,<u>Middlesex Co.</u>, 1948/1964;EC:Rgn.by 1910-1946;full 1946-on)	1901(01,24) 1900(06) 1889(Soc.)	1902-1947	-	Tr.to EC
	8.	Rahway, First Pres.(always Pres.in 98;Pastor install by Pby.1748:98;CG:19)	1741(CG;2 sr) 1742(s.14) pb.r.af.1750 (PR)	nl.	j1749; NSd: 1749-1758; by 1773-onOS	Pres.
	9.	Springfield, First Pres.(Pastor install by Pby.: 1746:98;37:jPby.af.1758;CG:12,19)	1746(18,25) 1745(14) pb.r.af.1758 (PR)	nl.	j1747; NSd: 1747-1758; by 1773-onOS	Pres.
	10.	Union, <u>Connecticut Farms</u> Pres.(Pastor install by Pby.1734:98;CG:12,18,19;f.Elizabeth Twn.)	1730(CG;2 sr) 1725(s.14) pb.r.af.1735 (PR)	nl.	j1735; NSd: 1745-1758; by 1773-onOS	Pres.
	11.	Union, First Cong.(f.<u>Unionville</u> Union Chap.to 1915)	1895(incp., 24) 1892(pr.) r.1915(CG)	1915-2002	-	Sch.I 1961-1965; UCC 1965-2002; Merge to form M.(q.v.)

A	B	C	D	E	F
	NEW JERSEY - UNION COUNTY - continued				
11M.	Union, Faith UCC (merger of #11 & Emanuel UCC of Irvington, Essex Co.(f.Evan.,E&R,1897))	2002 M	2002-on	-	UCC
12.	Westfield, First Cong.(First Cong.C of C)	1880(3 sr)	1880-on	-	UCC
13.	Westfield, Westfield Pres.(First;Old Westfield Ch.;CG:12,19)	1727(min;14) 1728(25) 1730(pb.r.PR; 18,98)	nl.	j1727; NSd: 1745-1758; by 1773-onOS	Pres.
	WARREN COUNTY	(org.1824)	(041)		
1.	Johnsonburg, Log Gaol Strict Cong.(First Cong. (Strict) of Hardwick Twn.;now *Frelinghuysen Twn.)	1786/1787 (MC:min.)	MC:by 1787-af.1792; WAP:m.1792; SLI:1808-1809; SNJ:1809-1815	-	X 1820
2.	Marksboro, Marksboro Pres.(f.Second Pres.of Hardwick;f.Second Cong.of Hardwick Twn.(now *Frelinghuysen Twn.);moved to village 1816; Blairstown PO)	1811(CG;25) r.1814(PR; 2 sr) 1815(25)	nl.; ps.SNJ	1813-onOS	Pres.

NEW YORK - ALBANY COUNTY (org.1683) (001)

A	B	C	D	E	F
1.	Albany, Clinton Ave.Cong.	1887(01N)	1886-1897	-	X
2.	Albany, Fifth Pres.	1831(98)	-	1831-1834/ 1835	X
3.	Albany, First Cong.(lt.01S:1852-1853)	1850(22,98)	1851-1956	-	Merged to form M.
3M.	Albany, First Cong.(merger of #3 & Second Cong. (f.First Chr.,1881))	1956 M	1956-on	-	UCC
4.	Albany, First Pres.(withdrew from Pby.1795, (incor.1801:47),but l.again by 1798;DUT 1764/ 1766-1785(1775:49))	1762(4 sr) 1763(46A) 1760(14)	-	m.1764/1766; by 1773-onOS	Pres.
5.	Albany, Fourth Pres.(1931/1932 ab.Sixth Pres. (1869/1870,l.75:1869-1932NS)as Fourth Pres.; 1959 ab.Park United Pres.(f.Asso.,1800,affl. Asso.Pby.of Montreal 1800-1820;Asso.Ch.1820-1858;UPNA 1858-1958;l.75:1958-1959) as United Fourth Pres.;1992 ab.Madison Ave.Pres.(1888, l.75:1887-1992)as New Covenant Pres.)	1828(98) 1829(2 sr) r.1932 M r.1959 M r.1992 M	-	1828-onNS	Pres.
6.	Albany, Second Cong.	1862(01N,98)	1862-1864	-	X
7.	Albany, Second Pres.(1909/1910 ab.#8 as Second Pres.;1919 ab.State St.Pres.(1860/1861,l.75: 1860-1920OS) as Westminster Pres.)	1813(4 sr) r.1909 M r.1919 M	-	1814/1818-onOS	Pres.
8.	Albany, Third Pres.(f.Asso.Ref.)	c.1796(AR) Tr.1817(PR: 26,98)	-	j1823(26); 1819/1824-1909OS	Merged to #7(q.v.)
9.	Berne, P or C Ch. (l.Bern)	by 1803	nl.	1798/1802-1819/1824	X
10.	Bethlehem, First Pres.(Philadelphia Ch.;North Bethlehem branch of #12 1833-1835;s.l.Albany PO)	1835(2 sr)	-	1834/1835-1851NS, 1850-1940OS	X
11.	Cohoes, First Pres.,Silliman Mem.(1969/1970 merged to First Ref.(RCA,1837),as United (Pres.))	1839(2 sr) r.1969/1970 M	-	1839-1840OS, 1840/1842-on NS	Pres.
Sc Nt	Cohoes, Scandinavian Pilgrim Covenant (EC:Rgn.by 1910-1932)	1898(06)	nl.	-	EC; X
12.	Guilderland, Hamilton Union Pres.(in 1797 bldg.; see also #10;Fed.to Meth.(1852)1920-1944)	1812(2 sr) r.1824(PR)	nl.	1809/1813-onOS	Pres.
13.	Knox, Pres.(Tr.to Ref.(RCA) as Altamont Ref. 1841/1842-on)	by 1825	-	1819/1824-1842OS	Tr.to Ref. (see text)
Sh 14.	New Scotland, New Scotland Pres.(Scotch:49; Slingerlands PO;SUF 1787-1790;withdrew from Pby.1801,but l.by 1802;1949 ab.Pres.of Voorheesville (1885,l.75:1885-1949))	1787(3 sr) 1791(incp.) r.1949 M	-	1774/1787 (j1787)-1807,1808-onOS	Pres.
15.	Onesquethaw, P or C Ch.(*New Scotland)	by 1825	nl.	1819/1824-1837	X

NEW YORK - ALBANY COUNTY - continued

A	B	C	D	E	F
16.	Rensselaerville, Rensselaerville Pres.(f.First Pres.or Cong.Soc.;f.Cong.)	1793(CG;3 sr) 1794(11,22) 1792(Soc.:99) 1795(?) r.1827(PR)	NAP 1793-af.1805, by 1815-af.1818	j1827; 1827-onNS	Pres.
17.	Watervliet, First Pres.(f.West Troy Cong.;f. Pres.or Cong.Soc.of West Troy;nl.01T;1962 ab.First Pres.of Green Island (1853,l.75: 1853-1963OS) as First Pres.of Watervliet)	1834(CG) r.1835(PR:98) r.1836/1837 (CG:98) r.1839/1840 (PR:98) r.1962 M	1836-1839	j1840; 1840/1842-on NS	Pres.
18.	Watervliet, Pres.Soc.of Pine Grove (f.Pine Grove Cong.;bec.Roessleville Pres.,Albany PO;f.West Albany PO;nl.01T;*Colonie)	1854(CG) r.1865(PR:98) 1867(46A)	1855-1866	j1867; 1866-1919NS, 1921-on	Pres.
Sw 19.	Watervliet, Swedish Cong.Fed.(EC:Rgn.1917/1921-1956;pb.l.Fed.because of EC connection)	1897(01)	1907-1954	-	EC; X
20.	Westerlo, P or C Ch.	by 1819	nl.	1814/1818-1831	X

NEW YORK - ALLEGANY COUNTY (org.1806) (003)

A	B	C	D	E	F
1.	Alfred, Pres.	by 1853	-	1852-1855NS	X
2.	Allen, Cong.(f.Pres.)	1826(PR;2 sr) 1830(90) r.1839(PR:48) r.1851(CG:98)	cl.1853-1858	j1826; 1826- 1836,1837/ 1838-1855NS	X c.1836; r.; X af.1858 (bldg. sold 1868)
3.	Almond, First Pres.(f.Cong.forms;f.Ref.(RCA, 1797-1817(85);r.PR:1812(48,98);f.of Alfred to 1821;Fed.to Bapt.1924-on as United)	1797(Ref.:85, 90) 1798/1799(98) Tr.1812(CG) r.bf.1854(PR; 01T)	nl.	j1812; 1809/ 1811-onNS	Pres.
4.	Andover, First Pres.(f.First Cong.)	1824(CG) r.1874(PR)	cl.1853-1858	j1827; 1826-onNS	Pres.
5.	Angelica, First Pres.Ch.& Soc.(f.Cong.;org.as PR:48;X af.1827:98,but l.to 1846;services end 1912(26),but l.to 1935)	1812(CG;4 sr) 1811(90) r.1827(PR) r.1846(CG) r.1851(PR) r.1857(CG) r.1859(PR)	nl.	j1812; 1809/ 1811-1935NS	X
6.	Belfast, Cong.	1854(CG)	cl.1853-1854; 1854-1860, 1865-1866, 1877-1881	1862-1871NS	X
7.	Belfast, P or C Ch. (Pres.:98)	1830(26,98)	nl.	j1830; 1830-1831	X
8.	Belmont, First Pres.(f.of Phillipsville (or Philipsburg);First Cgn.in Amity;lt.75: 1833-1834;1854 asso.CG:01T;1972 merged to Belmont United Meth.(f.First,1834) as United(dual 1972-2000);2000 dropped Pres. affl.& bec.Belmont United Meth.)	1832(PR;4 sr) r.1854(CG) r.1866(PR) r.1972 M	cl.1853-1855; 1855-1860	j1832; 1831-1855NS, 1861-2000NS	X (see text)
9.	Black Creek, Cong.(f.named Pres.;in New Hudson; f.of *Haight to 1837;f.of *Rushford to 1822)	1822(CG;2 sr)	nl.	j1822; 1821/ 1822-1837/ 1838	1837 Merged to #21 to form #20(q.v.)
10.	Black Creek, Pres.(in New Hudson;CG in 01T)	by 1844(PR) 1846(48) r.1852(pb.CG)	cl.1853-1858	1843-1849OS, 1852-1857NS	X
11.	Burns, First Pres.	1833(98)	-	j1837; 1834/ 1835-1873NS	X

NEW YORK - ALLEGANY COUNTY - continued

A		B	C	D	E	F
	12.	Centerville, Cong.(Indep.in 01T,but l.in Pby.)	1824(CG;2 sr) 1834(?) r.af.1858(PR; 01T)	cl.1853-1858	j1824; 1819/ 1824-1897NS, 1901-1914	X
	13.	Cuba, First Pres.(s.named Pres.when Cong.forms; left Pby.1842,& j again 1842)	1827(CG;4 sr) r.1833(PR:98) r.1835(CG) r.1842(PR)	nl.	j1829; 1828-onNS (see text)	Pres.
We	14.	Fairview, Welsh Cong.(in Centerville, at Farmersville, Cattaraugus Co.line;f.l. Farmersville Station, Cattaraugus Co.PO;Tr. to Eng.Assn.1905;nl.01T,68)	1846(s.01,98) 1845(s.01) 1858(?) 1868(s.01)	NYW ?-1867; 1867-1895, 1896-1899, 1900-1936	-	X (1900:65)
	15.	Friendship, First Cong. (f.a branch of unknown 1815-1835,PR in 90;nl.01S 1852-1853;f.Fed. by 1919-1926,pb.to Bapt.)	1835(CG;4 sr) 1833(?) 1855(s.01) 1815(branch) 1813(90)	1851-1860, 1865-1963	j1835; 1834/ 1835-1853NS, 1858-1859NS	Sch.I 1961-1963; X
	16.	Grove, P or C Ch.(Pres.:98)	1836(98)	nl.	j1836; 1834/ 1835-1840/ 1842NS	X 1840(98)
	17.	Hume, <u>Cold Creek</u> Pres.(f.Cong.;in 1841 bldg.)	by 1834(CG)	cl.1853-1858	j1834; 1833- 1834/1835, 1837/1838- 1858NS, 1867-1872NS	X (ps.by 1871)
	18.	Independence, Pres.	1833	-	j1833; 1832-1858NS	X
	19.	Mixville, Cong.(not.in Pby.:48;*Hume)	1842(48)	nl.	-	X (pb.af.1848)
	20.	New Hudson, <u>Black Creek</u> Cong.(f.Pres.;merger of #9 & #21;lt.1865-1866)	1837 M(PR) r.1844(CG)	cl.1853-1854; 1854-1856; cl.1856-1858; 1861-1951	j1837; 1837/ 1838-1852NS	X
	21.	New Hudson, Cong.of Haight (at Belleville in North Valley;f.of Haight to 1837/1838)	1828(CG;48) 1831(98)	nl.	j1832(48); 1828-1837/ 1838	1837 Merged to #9 to form #20(q.v.)
	22.	Oramel, First Cong.C of C (f.First Cong.of Caneadea)	1842(CG;2 sr)	cl.1853-1854; 1854-1856; cl.1856-1858; 1865-1866, 1875-1909	j1846; 1843/ 1845-1854NS	X
	23.	Rushford, First Pres.(f.Cong.)	1838(PR;4 sr) r.1853(CG:98) r.1867(PR:98)	cl.1853-1854; 1854-1860	j1838; 1837/ 1838-1855NS, 1867-1897NS	X

NEW YORK - ALLEGANY COUNTY - continued

A	B	C	D	E	F
24.	Wellsville, First Cong.Soc.(f.of Scio to 1855; lt.01T:both unassod.;lt.cl.1853-1858;incor. l.UCC late 1961-1962,j 1962)	1841(PR;3 sr) r.1856(CG) r.1874(01N)	cl.1853-1856; 1856-1860, 1861-1866, 1873-on	j1841;1840/ 1842-1857NS	Sch.I 1961; UCC late 1961-on

NEW YORK - BRONX COUNTY (org.1914) (005)

A		B	C	D	E	F
	1.	New York City, Bronx, Beck Mem.Pres.(f.First Pres.of West Farms;f.in West Farms to 1874;f. in *Westchester to 1846)	1814(3 sr)	-	1815-1816, 1818-onOS	Pres.
	2.	New York City, Bronx, Bedford Park Cong.(l. thrice:01N)	1889(01,21) 1894(s.01N) 1892(s.01N) 1890(s.01)	1894-on	-	UCC
SF	3.	New York City, Bronx, Bethlehem Covenant Swedish-Finnish (f.in New York City, Manhattan,New York Co. to 1925;EC:Rgn.by 1910-1946,full 1946-1969)	1902(01,21) 1901(06) 1906(s.01)	1914-1946	-	Tr.to EC; X
	4.	New York City, Bronx, C of C in Westchester (s. l.White Plains,Westchester Co.;sett.1642;f. in New Haven Colony 1642-1656,as part of Stamford,claimed there to 1662;f.in New Netherland 1656-1664;attempt to j CT 1662-1664;org.dates are"pr.by",ps.not fully org.; pastor by 1674(s.98),1678(s.98),1684(49);in Par.with Eastchester,Westchester Co. from 1693;1702 submitted to St.Peter's Epis.Ch. (1701:98;branch of St.Pauls Epis.of Eastchester to 1762(14));f.of Westchester to 1898)	1654(98) 1655(49)	nl.	-	Submitted to Epis.1702
	5.	New York City, Bronx, Christ Cong.(f.Mt.Hope)	1892(01N,01) 1895(s.01)	1892-1918	-	Merged to New York Co.#63 to form #10(q.v.)
	6.	New York City, Bronx, Claremont Park Cong.	1903(01) 1902	1903-1920	-	X
bB	7.	New York City, Bronx, First Cong.of Morrisania (f.Forest Ave.;bec.predominantly Black by 1988;f.of Morrisania to 1874;f.of *West Farms to 1855)	1851(4 sr)	1851-1860, 1862-on	-	Sch.I 1961-1963; UCC 1963-on
Sw	8.	New York City, Bronx, Immanuel Covenant (f. Swedish Evan.;bec.Fellowship Covenant 1982;f. of New York City,Manhattan,New York Co. to 1924;EC:Rgn.by 1910-1961,full 1961-on)	1900(3 sr) 1901 1906 r.1982	1901-1977	-	Sch.II 1961-1977; Tr.to EC
bB	9.	New York City, Bronx, Cong.of North New York (bec.predominantly Black by 1975)	1890(01N,01) 1889(s.01) 1888(s.01) 1883(21)	1890-on	-	UCC
bA	10.	New York City, Bronx, Pilgrim UCC (merger of #5 & New York Co.#63;bec.predominantly mixed Asian Indian by 1988)	1918 M	1918-1961, 1962-on	-	UCC 1962-on

NEW YORK - BRONX COUNTY - continued

A	B	C	D	E	F
11.	New York City, Bronx, Port Morris Cong.	1901	1901-1903	-	X
12.	New York City, Bronx, Second Cong.of Morrisania (f.of Morrisania to 1874)	1868(01)	1873-1878	-	X
13.	New York City, Bronx, Williams Bridge Cong.(f.of West Farms to 1874)	1864 1865(01N)	1864-1870	-	X

NEW YORK - BROOME COUNTY (org.1806) (007)

		C	D	E	F
1.	Binghamton, East Side Cong.	1905(01,22)	1905-on	-	UCC
2.	Binghamton, First Cong.UCC (Central Binghamton; f.of Chenango to 1855;1.75 as specifically CG 1840/1842-1843/1845,1846/1848-1849,1850-1851)	1836(CG;3 sr)	j1851; 1850-on	j1839; 1839-1851NS	UCC
3.	Binghamton, First Pres.(First Ch.;f.Chenango Point;f.of Conklin & Chenango;f.of Chenango to 1855;44 incor.confuses this with #5:as Tr.from RCA 1817)	1817(CG;5 sr) r.1820(PR)	LAS:1817-1820	j1820;1820/ 1821-onNS	Pres.
4.	Binghamton, Plymouth Cong.	1890(3 sr) 1888(?)	1890-1944	-	X
5.	Castle Creek, Pres.(in Chenango;f.Chenango Ref. (RCA,1794-1831(85),1798-X bf.1817(51B);51B: Ref.not r.as PR);see also #3)	1794(Ref.) Tr.1833(PR)	-	j1833/1834; 1833-1870NS	X
6.	Centre Lisle, Cong.(f.West;Yorkshire Par.;in Lisle)	1830(CG;01) 1831	1840-on; (j1843)	j1830; 1830-1833, 1834/1835- 1837/1838	Sch.II 1961-1983; UCC 1983-on
7.	Chenango Forks, First Cong.(f.First of Barker; (in Barker);f.of Barker & Greene(Chenango Co.);f.Third of Lisle to 1831)	1821(CG:2 sr) 1822(98) 1832(Soc.)	UA:pb.by 1822-ps.to 1829; cl.1853-1858; 1862-on	j1831; 1830-1865NS	UCC
8.	Colesville, Cong.(Cambridge Soc.;Cole's Hill;f. North of Windsor to 1821;f.Eastern Pres.of Chenango to 1807,but nl.PR;two branches 1800-1812,other at Oquago (or Ouquaga,now Windsor village),& there to 1800;j Pby.1826 (44;pb.Tr);left Pby.1840;see also #20)	1793(PR;3 sr) r.1800(CG:MC) 1803(Soc.)	MC:1800-? SA:1803-1809; UA: ? -1816; LAS:1816-1821	j1821; 1821-1834/ 1836,1837/ 1838-1840/ 1842NS	X (1834:51B; 1836/1837:44)
9.	Conklin, Conklin Pres.(First)	1825(46A) r.1839	-	j1826; 1825-onNS	Pres.
10.	Endicott, Union Pres.(f.First Pres.of Union; Union Village;f.Union Village Ref.of Tioga (RCA);r.PR 1822:3 sr;75H incor.connects to Oneida Co.#54)	1794(Ref.:85) 1791(2 sr) 1796(44) 1789(90) 1819(Soc.) Tr.1822(PR) 1824(85)	-	j1822; 1822/ 1823-onNS	Pres.
11.	Endicott, UCC (f.Cong.;in Union)	1920(01)	1920-1993	-	UCC 1961-1993; X
12.	Harpersville, Cong.(in Colesville)	1827(CG)	nl.	j1828; 1827- 1837/1838	X 1841(51B)

NEW YORK - BROOME COUNTY - continued

A	B	C	D	E	F
13.	Lisle, Associate Cong.(s.l.Pres.;f.Second Forks of Chenango in Union to 1801;two branches 1842-1854;Fed.to First Meth.1919/1937-on as Associate Fed.;see also #19)	1797(CG) 1795(Soc.) 1799(2 sr) 1798(s.48) 1803(99)	SA:1803-1809; ps.NAP UA:1820-1829; cl.1853-1858; 1867-on	j1813; 1812-1820; j1834; 1833-1868NS	UCC
14.	Maine, First Cong.(f.First Central Cong.of Union to 1848;f.First of Nanticoke to 1833;f.l. Central Union;l.by Pby.as specifically CG 1833-1836,1840/1842-1843/1845;48 says j Pby. 1817,not otherwise supported;1868 r.from accommodation to full CG;Fed.to Meth.1928/1929-on as Fed.)	1819(CG;3 sr) by 1817(48) r.1868	LAS:1819-1821 cl.1853-1858; 1866-on	j1821; 1821-1836, 1837/1838-1868NS	UCC
15.	Nineveh, Nineveh Pres.(in Colesville;f.of Bainbridge (Chenango Co.) & Nineveh;51B connects to Chenango Co.#1)	1831	-	j1831; 1831-1834/1836, 1837/1838-1846/1848NS, 1851-onNS	Pres.
16.	Sanford, P or C Ch. (nl.48)	by 1830	nl.	1829-1833	X
17.	Triangle, Cong.(Clark's Settlement;f.Second of Lisle to 1831;assod.1854 in 01T)	1819(CG;2 sr)	UA:pb.by 1822-ps.to 1829; cl.1853-1858; 1863-1906	j1832; 1831-1864NS	X
18.	Union Center, Cong.(in Union;in 1827/1840 bldg.; lt.01:1842-1846;m.on Pby.l.as CG 1840/1842-1843/1845)	1841(01) 1851(98)	1841-1964 (j1843)	-	Sch.I 1961-1964; X
19.	Whitney Point, Cobblestone Hill Pres.(f.First Pres.;Lisle PO;f.Whitney's Point Cong.;s.l. Whiting's Point;f.a branch of #13 1842-1854; assod.in 1854:01T;in Triangle;f.Fed.to unknown 1931-1952)	1854(CG;98) 1842(branch) r.1873(PR)	cl.1853-1858; 1861-1866	1854-onNS	Pres.
In 20.	Windsor, Oquaga Indian Mission (not org.as a ch.;mission of New England Co.for Propagation of Gospel Among the Indians;sv.Six Nations (Iroquois)tribes)	1753	nl.	nl.	X af.1772
21.	Windsor, Windsor Pres.(f.South Cong.;f.branch of #8 to 1812,which began at this site 1793;1852 ab.Pres.(1837:44;1839:48;1840:98),l.75:1840-1852OS)	1812(CG) r.1827(PR) r.1852 M	LAS:1813-1821	j1821; 1821-1852NS, 1852-onOS	Pres.

NEW YORK - CATTARAUGUS COUNTY (org.1808) (009)

	1.	Allegany, First Pres.(f.Cong.Soc.;f.of Burton to 1851)	1852(CG;3 sr) 1851(?) r.1858(PR)	1851-1857; cl.1857-1858	1857-onNS	Pres.
In	2.	Allegany & Cornplanter Indian Reservation, Indian Pres.(f.Allegany Indian Cong.Mission; served Seneca tribe(& mixed Iroquois); Salamanca PO:at Lower Allegany 1830-1866, second branch at Upper Allegany(or Bucktown, Bucktooth,Jimerstown,Shongo)1860-1889;1889 divided into three cgns.:Corn Planter Indian Pres.(Salamanca PO,l.75:1889-1954,X);Old Town Indian Pres.(Salamanca PO,l.75:1889-1905,X); Jimerstown Indian Pres.(Salamanca PO,l.75: 1889-1964);the latter ch.merged 1964 to Onoville Indian Pres.at Allegany Reservation (1890(22,26),l.75:1906-1964)to form Jimersontown Pres.at Salamanca(l.75:1964-on), which continues original ch.;Western Missionary Soc.(Pres.;which work s.l.Warren Co.PA)1814-1818;ABCFM 1830-1870;AHMS 1870; Pres.Bd.1870(or 1891);two other Pres.Chs. developed from this root:Cold Spring Pres., Salamanca (l.75:1905-1960);& Tunessassa Pres.,Salamanca (l.75:1905-1923,X:1919:26))	1830(CG;67) 1831(22) by 1832(48) 1834(3 sr) 1835(s.01) r.1886(PR:26) 1883(75H) 1881(22) r.1889 (divided) r.1964 M	1840/1841-1878	1883-on (see text)	divided; merged; (see text); Pres.
	3.	Ashford, Pres.of East Ashford (see also #7)	1832	-	j1832; 1832-1855NS	r.as #7
	4.	Burton, Cong.(ps.f.Peth village(98);left Pby. 1840:48;f.of Great Valley to 1831)	1825(CG;98) 1827(26)	nl.	j1830; 1830-1837/1838	1843 merged to #23(q.v.)
	5.	Clear Creek, First Cong.C of C (in Conewango)	1876(3 sr)	1875-1895	-	X
	6.	Conewango Valley, Cong.(in Conewango;at Ellington,Erie Co.line)	1894(01N)	1894-1897	-	X
	7.	East Ashford, Cong.(f.l.Ashford;Delevan PO;r.of #3;nl.01T)	1854(01,98) 1858(s.01)	1860-1884, 1885-1925	-	X
	8.	East Otto, Cong.(f.Pres.(name only);f.of Otto to 1854)	1834(CG;3 sr) 1836(?)	cl.1853-1857; 1857-1884, 1885-1891	j1834; 1834/1835-1857NS	X
	9.	East Randolph, Cong.(in Randolph;f.incor.l.East Lebanon)	1885(01N)	1884-1890	-	X
	10.	Ellicottville, Cong.(nl.01T,but l.cl.)	by 1853	1853-1854; cl.1854-1858	-	X

NEW YORK - CATTARAUGUS COUNTY - continued

A		B	C	D	E	F
	11.	Ellicottville, First Pres.(f.Cong.;nl.01T;lt.75: 1836-1837/1838(two Pbys.);1976 ab.First U.Meth.(1845) as United Pres.)	1818(CG;26) 1822(90) r.1829(PR) r.1976 M	nl.	j1822; 1819/ 1824-onNS	Pres.
	12.	Farmersville, P or C Ch.	1830	nl.	j1830; 1830-1840/1842NS	1844 merged to #14(q.v.)
We	13.	Farmersville, Siloam Welsh Cong.(in Farmersville;Elton PO;lt.1915-1916;Tr.to Eng. Assn.1905;incor.l.in Madison Co.by 65)	1856(3 sr)	NYW ? -1867; 1867-1936	-	X
	14.	Franklinville, First Pres.(f.Cong.Soc.;f.of Ischua to 1824;f.of Hebe to 1816;f.of T#4R4; 1844 ab.#11;98 says r.1828,then r.PR 1829; 26,46A,& 99:r.PR 1828;01T pb.incor.r.PR af. 1858;1960 merged to First United Pres.(1867, UPNA 1867-1958,l.75:1958-1960) as Franklinville Pres.)	1813(CG) r.1828(PR) 1829(PR) r.1844 M r.1960 M	cl.1853-1858	j1829/1830; 1830-onNS	X c.1825; r.; Pres.
Nt		Freedom, First Pres.(l.by 98 as if regular Pres.,actually Asso.Ref.Pres.)	1827(98) 1834(32,75H)	-	nl.	X 1856(32,75H)
	15.	Gowanda, First Pres.(in Persia;f.of Perrysburgh to 1835;f.Cong.;f.Lodi Soc.;village extends into Collins,Erie Co.,& ch.s.located there)	1828(CG;3 sr) 1827(3 sr) 1826(90) r.bf.1854(PR) (01T)	nl.	j1827/1828; 1828-onNS	Pres.
	16.	Great Valley, Cong.(ps.same as #17;l.only by 90)	1817(90)	nl.	-	X pb.soon
	17.	Great Valley, Pres.(ps.same as #16)	by 1842	-	j1842; 1840/ 1842-1855NS	X
	18.	Leon, Cong.(assod.1854:01T;f.branch of #27)	1845	1844/1845-1853; cl.1853-1858	-	X af.1858
	19.	Little Valley, First Cong.	1840(3 sr)	1840/1841-on	-	UCC
	20.	Little Valley, Second Cong.	by 1853	1852-1853	-	X af.1853
Nt		Machias, First Pres.Soc.(l.only in 26,nl.32,48; ps.only a branch or not fully org.)	1831	-	nl.	X (unknown date)
	21.	Napoli, Cong.(f.Pres.;f.First of Cold Spring to 1828;f.First of Little Valley to 1823;left Pby.(first time)1840;left Assn.(first time) 1843)	1821(CG) 1820(90) 1823(Soc.) r.1826	j1840; 1839-1842; cl.1853-1858; 1862-1923	j1821; 1819/ 1824-1839; j1843; 1846/ 1848-1861NS	X 1825; r.; X
	22.	Olean, Cong.	1889 1891(s.01N)	1889-1906	-	X

NEW YORK - CATTARAUGUS COUNTY - continued

		B	C	D	E	F
	23.	Olean, First Pres.(f.Cong.;left Pby.1840;1843 ab.#4)	1822(PR) r.1838 r.1840(CG) 1841(Soc.) r.1843 M r.1851(PR)	nl.	j1822; 1821/ 1822-1829, 1837/1838- 1840/1842NS, 1851-onNS	X 1830; r.; Pres.
	24.	Otto, First Cong.(West Otto;f.First Pres.;Fed.to Evan.Meth.(1826/1840)1908/1912(s.1914:01)-1969 as Fed.;merged to Meth.)	1828(PR) r.1858(CG)	j1862; 1861-1898, 1902-1969	j1829; 1828-1862NS	Sch.I 1961-1969; Merged (see text)
	25.	Portville, First Pres.	1849	-	1849-onNS	Pres.
	26.	Randolph, Cong.(ab.Chautauqua Co.#33 in 1836; left Pby.1840;Fed.to First Meth.(1830)1929-1967)	1836(CG;4 sr) 1834(s.01) 1839(?)	j1840; 1839-1967	j1836; 1834/ 1835-1840/ 1842NS	UCC 1961-1967; Merged to form M.(q.v.)
	26M.	Randolph, Pres.(merger of #26 & First Meth. (1830))	1967 M	(see text)	1967-on	Pres.
	27.	Rutledge, First Pres.of Conewango (f.First Cong.;f.Second of Little Valley to 1823;1816 PR not supported by 48 or minutes;see also #18)	1823(CG) 1816(PR:90) r.1839(PR)	nl.	j1823; 1825-1965NS	X
	28.	Salamanca, First Cong.(ps.a r.of Pres.,l.75: 1865-1874NS)	1875(4 sr)	1874-2000	(see text)	UCC; Merged to form M.(q.v.)
	28M.	Salamanca, United Cong.Meth.(merger (informally 1991,l.1995) of #28 & U.Meth.(1992 merger of Kissinger Meth.(f.Kissinger United Brethren (1885)), Peoples Meth.Epis.(1904) & First United Meth.(1984 merger of West Meth.Epis. (1875) & First Meth.Epis.(1867)));dual)	2000 M	2000-on	-	UCC (dual, see text)
We	29.	Sandusky, Carmel Welsh Cong.of Cattaraugus Co. (in Freedom)	by 1850(68)	cl.1856-1858; WP:m.1860	-	X af.1860
	30.	Versailles, First Cong.(in Perrysburgh;assod. 1854:01T)	by 1842 1846(incp.)	1840/1841-1850,1851-1853; cl.1853-1858	-	X af.1858
In	31.	Versailles, Indian Cong.(f.l.Cattaraugus Station;Lower Cattaraugus Indian Reservation; 1850/1853 ab.Erie Co.#24;served Seneca tribe (& mixed Iroquois);UFMS 1822-1826;ABCFM 1826-1870;Pres.Bd.1870-1964;af.1870 r.bec.Iroquois Wright Mem.Pres.,l.Irving,Chautauqua Co.,& Hanover,Chautauqua Co.)	1827(CG;67) 1822(mission) r.1850/1853 M r.1870(PR)	1844/1845-1857; cl.1857-1858; 1865-1867	1834/1835-1837/1838; 1870-1964	X
	32.	Waverly, Cong.(in Otto)	by 1854	cl.1853-1858	-	X af.1858
	33.	West Salamanca, Bethel Cong.(in Salamanca)	1877(01N,01) 1875(98)	1876-1881	-	X

NEW YORK - CAYUGA COUNTY (org.1799) (011)

A	B	C	D	E	F
1.	Auburn, First Pres.(f.First Cong.Soc.;f.of Auburn in Aurelius to 1823;f.a branch of #23)	1811(CG) 1810(Soc.) r.1814(PR)	nl.	j1811; 1809/ 1811-onNS	Pres.
2.	Auburn, Second Pres.(Western Exchange;1921 merged to Central Pres.(1861/1862,l.75:1861-1922NS)as Second Central Pres.;1968 merged to Westminster Pres.(1885,l.75:1885-1968) as Westminster United Pres.)	1830 1829(Soc.) r.1921 M r.1968 M	-	j1830; 1830-onNS	Pres.
3.	Aurelius, Pres.	by 1842	-	j1842; 1840/ 1842-1871NS	X
4.	Aurora, First Pres.(in Ledyard;f.in *Scipio to 1823;98 says a r.of #17;Fed.to St.Paul's Prot.Epis.(1835)1969-on as United Ministry)	1818	-	j1818(48); 1818-onNS	Pres.
5.	Cato, First Pres.Ch.& Soc.of <u>Meridian</u> (First Pres.of Cato;Cato Four Corners;f.Fed.to Meridian Bapt.(f.First Bapt.Ch.& Soc.of Cato, 1810) 1932/1933-1948)	1836	-	1834/1835-1971NS	X
6.	Cayuga, Pres.(f.Cong.:01T;in Aurelius;elders 1820;"Pres." Soc.:1819)	1819(CG) r.1820(PR)	nl.	j1819; 1819-1962NS	1961 merged to #23(q.v.)
7.	Genoa, First Free Cong.of Genoa,at Five Corners	1831(2 sr) 1830(s.48)	nl.	-	1842 merged to Tompkins Co.#13 to form #10(q.v.)
8.	Genoa, First Pres.of <u>King's Ferry</u> (f.First of Genoa;Northville;f.First Cong.Ch.& Soc.of Milton to 1808;in 1804 Union Soc.)	1798(CG;3 sr) r.1820(PR) r.1831(CG: 2 sr) 1830(CG:48) r.1868(PR)	ML:1804-1810; cl.1853-1858	j1808; 1809/ 1811-onNS	Pres.
9.	Genoa, Second Pres.(Union,Village,East;f. Northeast Cong.;01T & cl.:r.PR af.1858 pb. incor.;1970 merged to First Bapt.(1881) as United Ch.(dual),f.Fed.1929-1970)	1817(CG;98) r.1821(PR;98, 99) r.1970 M	cl.1853-1858	j1817; 1817-onNS	Pres.(dual, see text)
10.	Genoa, Third Pres.(Five Corners Pres.;f.First Cong.of Genoa;f.Ref.Cong.of Genoa & Lansing (Tompkins Co.);Atwater PO;merger of #7 & Tompkins Co.#13;specifically CG on Pby.l. 1846/1848-1869)	1842 M(CG) r.1871(PR)	cl.1853-1858	1843/1845-1935NS	X
11.	Ira, Pres.(f.First Cong.of Cato to 1821)	1807(CG) r.1823(PR)	nl.	j1812; 1809/ 1811-1867NS	X
12.	Locke, First Cong.of Locke,West Locke (f.of Milton to 1802;see also #13)	1799(CG)	ML:1804-1810	j1808; nl.	X 1809/1810: min.

NEW YORK - CAYUGA COUNTY - continued

		C	D	E	F
13.	Milan, P or C Ch.(f.West of Locke;a r.of #12:48)	1816	nl.	j1816/1817; 1815/1816-1850NS	X
14.	Montezuma, P or C Ch.(f.of Mentz(to 1859))	by 1825	nl.	j1825; 1824-1834/1835	X
15.	Moravia, First Cong.(f.Pres.;f.First Cong.Ch.& Soc.of Sempronius to 1833(l.later);unassod.in 01T but l.by Pby.to 1854 & l.affl.CG by 1852/1853;left Pby.1859(first time:98))	1806(CG;3 sr) 1808(s.48)	ML:1806-1810; 1852-1865; j1870; 1870-on	j1808; 1809/1811-1854NS, j1864;1864-1869NS	UCC
16.	Port Byron, First Pres.of Mentz at Port Byron (First Cong.Soc.of Mentz;f.of Jefferson;moved 1820 to Owasco village,which bec.Port Byron 1825;divided to Port Byron Pres.,l.75:1840-onOS)	1801(CG) r.1811(PR) r.1820(CG) r.1824(PR) r.1839(CG)	ML:1804-1810; cl.1853-1858	j1808; 1809/1811-1856NS	X (1850:98)
17.	Scipio, First Cong.(s.First Pres.;see also #4; two branches at Aurora & Ridge 1803-1813)	1794(PR;44) r.1800(CG;48) 1803(46A)	ML:1804-1810	j1808; 1809/1811-1821	1821/1823 merged to #19 to form #18 (q.v.)
18.	Scipio, First Pres.(99:merger of #17 & Associate Pres.(pb.#19);48:three way merger of #17,#19 & Associate Ref.(nl.32))	1821 M(99) 1823 M(48)	-	j1821; 1821-1843/1845NS	X
19.	Scipio, Second Pres.(Scipio Center;f.Associate Pres.(11,99);1816 ps.new org.;see also #18)	1811(Asso.:11) r.1816(PR)	-	j1816; 1815/1816-1821	1821 Merged to #17 to form #18(q.v.)
20.	Scipio, Second Pres.(f.l.Fleming to 1826;f. United Pres.Soc.of Scipio,Fleming & Ledyard; Mapleton PO)	1823(99) 1825(Soc.)	-	j1823; 1822/1823-1942NS	X
21.	Sennett, Pres.(f.First Cong.Soc.of Brutus to 1827(l.later);Fed.to First Calvinistic Bapt. Ch.& Soc.(1799,incp.1834)1928-on,as Fed.)	1806(CG) 1805(Soc.:48) r.1873(PR) 1870(s.99)	ML:1806-1810; cl.1853-1858	j1808; 1809/1811-onNS	Pres.
22.	Summer Hill, Cong.(f.of Plato to 1832;f.East of Locke to 1831)	1827(CG;3 sr)	cl.1853-1858; 1868-1974	j1827; 1827-1868NS	UCC 1961-1974; X
23.	Union Springs, First Pres.Ch.& Soc.of Springport (f.C of C;1811:refused juridiction of Pby.; later 1811 accepted Pby.membership;f.First of Aurelius to 1823(in name to 1834);01T & cl.: r.PR af.1858,pb.incor.;see also #1 & #6;1961 ab.#6;Fed. 1968-1994,see under #23M.)	1799(CG;2 sr) 1798(s.48) 1801(3 sr) 1802(Soc.) r.1822(PR) r.1961 M	ML:1804-1810; cl.1853-1858	j1810; 1809/1811-1994NS	Merged to form M.(q.v.)
23M.	Union Springs, Trinity UCC (merger of #23, Grace Epis.of Springport (1866),& Union Springs United Meth.(1843);f.Fed.1968-1994; *Springport)	1994 M	1994-on	(see text)	UCC 1994-on [Count as UCC]
24.	Victory, Pres.(f.Second of Cato to 1821)	1820	-	1825-1915NS	X

NEW YORK - CAYUGA COUNTY - continued

A	B	C	D	E	F
25.	Weedsport, First Pres.Soc.of Brutus	1825 1841(incp.)	-	j1826; 1825-onNS	Pres.

NEW YORK - CHAUTAUQUA COUNTY (org.1808) (013)

A		B	C	D	E	F
	1.	Ashville, Cong.(in North Harmony;f.First of Harmony;lt.75:1825-1826)	1820(CG)	j1839; 1838-1911	j1822; 1819/ 1824-1839	X
	2.	Busti, Cong.(l.only 01S 1856-1857)	1819(CG;90)	1835-1857	j1826;1825- 1834/1835	X
Sw	3.	Busti, Swedish Cong.(EC:Rgn.1924-1938,full 1941-1957)	1893(01N) 1877(01) 1876(06)	1897-1925	-	Tr.to EC; X
	4.	Charlotte, Cong.(left Pby.(first time)1840;nl. 01T)	1831(CG)	1840/1841- 1842	j1831; 1831- 1840/1842NS, 1852-1854NS	X
	5.	Chautauqua, P or C Ch.(left Pby.1826)	by 1818	nl.	j1818; 1818-1825	X
	6.	Cherry Creek, P or C Ch.(Pres.:48)	1842	nl.	1840/1842- 1846/1848NS	X
	7.	Clymer, Clymer Hill Cong.Ref.(divided 1853, majority Tr.to Ref.(RCA,1853-on:85))	1847 r.1853	1848-1852, 1853-1870	-	X
	8.	Dunkirk, First Pres.(mixed org.at start,bec. gradually PR;f.of Pomfret;nl.01T)	1830(mixed) r.(see text)	nl.	j1830; 1830-onNS	Pres.
	9.	Ellery, P or C Ch.	by 1824	nl.	j1824; 1825-1836	1836 merged to #18(q.v.)
	10.	Ellington, First Cong.Ch.& Soc.(f.Pres.;left Pby.(first time)1836;1836 Tr.to a CG Assn., but not received by them)	1828(CG) r.1845(PR) r.1858(CG)	1859-1984	j1828; 1828-1839NS; j1846; 1843/ 1845-1859NS	UCC 1961-1984; CCCC 1995-on
	11.	Forestville, Cong.(f.of Hanover;lt.75:1829-1830; 01T says r.PR bf.1854,but CG af.left Pby., then X)	by 1822(CG) r.c.1830 (48,98)	1840/1841- 1846	j1822; 1819/ 1824-1837/ 1838	X
	12.	Fredonia, First Pres.(f.Pomfret Relg.Soc.;f. First Cong.Soc.;f.First of Pomfret)	1810(CG;4 sr) r.1817(PR) 1819(Soc.)	nl.	j1817; 1815/ 1816-onNS	Pres.
	13.	Frewsburg, Cong.(f.incor.l.Trewsbury;in Carroll; lt.(natl.)1856-1858)	1856	1855-1892	-	X
	14.	Harmony, Second Ch.,P or C	by 1822	nl.	j1822; 1819/ 1824-1826	X
	15.	Hartfield, Cong.(in Chautauqua;assod.CG 1854: 01T)	by 1853(CG)	cl.1853-1858	1852-1858NS	X
Da	16.	Jamestown, Danish Cong.(Danish-Norwegian Zion Free Cgn.)	1900	1904-1936	-	X
	17.	Jamestown, First Cong.UCC (f.First Ch.in Jamestown,Cong.;f.First of Ellicott;f.Second of Ellicott to 1825)	1816(CG;3 sr) 1815(22) 1821(Soc.)	1835-on	j1818;1818- 1834/1835	UCC
	18.	Jamestown, First Pres.(1836 ab.#9)	1834 r.1836 M	-	j1834;1834/ 1835-onNS	Pres.

NEW YORK - CHAUTAUQUA COUNTY - continued

A		B	C	D	E	F
	19.	Jamestown, Pilgrim Mem.Cong.(in 1888 bldg.)	1901(s.01,22) 1907(s.01) 1902(?)	1908-on	-	UCC
	20.	Kiantone, First Cong.(f.First of Carroll to 1853;f.First of Ellicott to 1825;f.l.Jones Settlement;s.Jamestown PO)	1815(CG;4 sr) 1850(s.01)	1835-1962	j1818;1818-1834/1835	Sch.II 1961-1962; CCCC 1960 (j1961)-on
	21.	Lakewood, Cong.(in Busti)	1893(01N)	1894-1914	-	X
	22.	Mayville, Pres.(in Chautauqua)	by 1824	-	j1824; 1825-1858NS	X
	23.	Omar, Cong.(f.of Villenova;l.01T assod.1854,but nl.cl.)	by 1829(CG)	1846-1853	j1829; 1828-1846/1848NS	X
	24.	Panama, First Pres.(f.First Cong.;in Harmony)	1830(CG) r.bf.1854(PR; 01T)	nl.	j1833; 1834/1835-1896NS	X (1892:26)
	25.	Portland, First Cong.(48 says not in Pby.(X),af. 1825-1833 & 98 agress (X period:1828-1833), l.through:75)	1818(CG;3 sr) 1817(48,90) 1822(Soc.) r.1833	cl.1853-1858; 1870-1978	j1818; 1818-1879NS	X 1828; r.; UCC 1961-1978; CCCC 1979-on
	26.	Portland, Pres.(affl.PA;ps.lt.of #25 1820-1822)	by 1806	-	1803/1805-1807, 1820-1822	X
	27.	Ripley, First Pres.,East Ripley (at Quincy;1870/1871 merged to Second Pres.(Village,1853/1854,l.75:1854-1871NS)as First Pres.;48 says drop Pby.1843,not supported in min.;affl.PA to 1830)	1818(2 sr) r.1871 M 1870(46A)	-	j1821; 1817-1819, 1820-onNS	Pres.
??	28.	Sheridan, Cong.(Canadaway;f.First of Pomfret to 1827;lt.75:1827-1830(both names);ps.dual or divided 1835-1844)	bf.1810(CG)	1834-1844/1845, 1850-1851; cl.1853-1858	j1818; 1817-1846/1848NS	X af.1858(bldg. sold 1874)
	29.	Sherman, First Pres.(f.First Cong.Relg.Soc.;f.of Mina to 1832)	1827(CG) 1826(90) 1833(Soc.) r.1871(PR)	1836-1870	j1827; 1828-1836; j1871; 1871-1919	Merged to form M.(q.v.)
	29M.	Sherman, Com.(merger of #30,Meth.Epis.(by 1868) & Univ.;in WNYCCC to 1943)	1919 M(22) 1918 M(26)	1943-1950	-	Tr.to Counc. Com.Chs. [Count as CC]
	30.	Silver Creek, First Pres.(First Cong.Soc.;PR Ch. with CG Soc.,Soc.still alive 1876;nl.01T;in Hanover;1969 merged to First Meth.(1812) as First United Pres.)	1831(PR) 1831(CG Soc.) r.1969 M	nl.	j1831; 1831-onNS	Pres.

NEW YORK - CHAUTAUQUA COUNTY - continued

A	B	C	D	E	F
31.	Sinclairville, Cong.(Sinclearville;f.l.Gerry; lt.cl.1857-1858;Fed.to Meth.(1812) 1917-1945 as Fed.)	1842(01) 1830(22)	1842-1851, 1852-1945	-	X
32.	Stockton, Cong.(f.of Stockton & Gerry to 1833;f. of Gerry & Chautauqua to 1821;left Pby.1840)	by 1815(CG)	1842-1843, 1844/1845-1858	j1821; 1819/ 1824-1840/ 1842NS	X
33.	Waterloo, P or C Ch.(Waterborough;in Poland;f. in Ellicott to 1832;left Pby.1836)	1828	nl.	j1828;1828- 1834/1835	1836 merged to Cattaraugus Co. #26(q.v.)
34.	Westfield, First Pres.(f.Cong.;s.considered PR from org.,though no elders;f.The Chautauque Ch.,Chautauqua Cross Rds.,Chataque;affl.PA to 1822/1824;f.Ripley Ch.1817-1819;f.of Ripley to 1829;l.CG when sv.by CG pastor)	1808(CG) 1807(90) 1817(Soc.) r.1817(PR)	1852-1853; cl.1853-1858	j1808; 1809-1818, 1819-onNS	Pres.

NEW YORK - CHEMUNG COUNTY (org.1836) (015)

A		B	C	D	E	F
Sh	1.	Big Flats, First Pres.(began with no elders,but s.called "Scotch Covenanter")	1825(3 sr) 1826(46A) 1827(48)	-	j1827; 1827-onNS	Pres.
	2.	Chemung, P or C Ch.(nl.01T;1854 ab.by Second Pres.of Southport (j1854,l.75:1854-1857NS,X 1860))	by 1840	nl.	j1840; 1839-1854NS	X; Merged, (see text)
	3.	Elmira, First Pres.(f.First Ch.;f.Chemung & Newtown;f.of Newtown to 1808;PR pr.1790:from General Assembly:45,99;org.PR not in a Pby.; dissolved by Pby.1810,but ch.continued,two factions 1810-1811;l.Pby.(not natl.75)1813-1814)	1795(PR;5 sr) 1790(PR:pr.) r.1810(CG:min) af.1805(CG: 48,98) r.1824(PR)	MC:mnd.; OA:1810-1813	j1805-1810, (nl.); j1814; 1814-onNS	Pres.
	4.	Elmira, Park Ch.,Cong.(f.Indep.;rejoin Cong. 1920)	1846(org.) 1845(plan)	1850-1865, 1867-1897, 1919-on	-	Sch.II 1961-1984; UCC 1984-on
	5.	Elmira, St.Luke's Cong.(Fed.to Northside Bapt. (1865)1965-1974 as Northside Com.)	1890(2 sr)	1890-1974	-	UCC 1961-1974; X
	6.	Elmira, South Pres.(Second;f.Cong.of Southport; bec.First Pres.of Southport to 1899;1961 merged to Franklin St.Pres.(1881,l.75: 1881-1961)as Westminster Pres.)	1821(CG) 1814(Soc.) 1815(Soc.s.48) r.1829(PR) r.1961 M	nl.	j1822; 1821/ 1822-onNS	Pres.
We	7.	Elmira, United Welsh Cong.	1874(01)	1873-1878	-	X (1880:65)
Nt		Erin, Pres.(l.98 as if Pres.,actually Asso.Ref.)	1831(AR:32) c.1849(98)	-	nl.	X 1854
	8.	Horseheads, First Pres.(f.First in Fairport;f.of Elmira to 1854;ab.#11 at start)	1832(3 sr)	-	j1832; 1832-onNS	Pres.
	9.	Millport, Pres.(in Veteran)	1836(2 sr)	-	j1837; 1836-1865NS	X (c.1860:26; bldg.sold 1867)
	10.	Post Creek, P or C Ch.(in Catlin)	by 1847	nl.	1846-1850NS	X
	11.	Veteran, Pres.(f.Second Pres.of Catherine (Schuyler Co.) to 1823)	1822	-	j1822; 1821-1832	Ab.by #8(q.v.)
	12.	Wellsburg, Cong.(in Ashland;f.of Southport)	1865 1866(01N)	1865-1870	-	X

NEW YORK - CHENANGO COUNTY (org.1798) (017)

A	B	C	D	E	F
1.	Afton, Pres.(f.South of Bainbridge at Bettsville (to 1857);f.South of Jericho to 1814;48 says j Pby.1840,not otherwise supported;Ch.r.1875 PR,l.75:1875-on)	1802(CG;2 sr) 1803(44) 1819(Soc.) 1825(98)	SA:mnd.; UA:1819-1822/ 1829	1837/1838- 1840/1842NS	X 1840(44) (see text)
2.	Bainbridge, First Pres.(f.Cong.or Pres.,at Bainbridge Green;Cong.Soc.of Cilicia;Ch.in Silesia;s.Selicia;f.of Jericho to 1814)	1793(CG;3 sr) 1792(s.44) 1797(2 sr) 1798(2 sr) c.1790(90) 1799(?) 1814(Soc.r.) 1816(Soc.r.) r.1817(Ch.) r.1833(PR) r.1837(CG) r.1854(PR) r.1863(CG) r.1873(PR)	NAP:by 1798- 1803; SA:1803-1809; UA:1818-1822/ 1829; 1839-1846; cl.1853-1858; j1864; 1863-1873	j1828/1829; 1828-1864NS, 1873-on	Pres.
3.	Columbus, First Cong.Soc.(Sherburne PO;l.by Pby. as specifically CG 1830-1831)	1806(CG;2 sr) 1814(Soc.)	OE: ? -1808; UA:1808- pb.1829; OE:j1830-1834; 1834-1929	1830-1831	X 1926(99)
4.	Coventry, First Cong.of Coventryville (f.l.East Coventry;f.Pres.;Bainbridge PO;f.First Cong. Soc.of Greene to 1806)	1807(CG;2 sr) 1804(Soc.) 1805(?) 1809(s.01)	NAP:by 1812- 1815;UA:1815- 1822/1827; 1839-1842/ 1845(w 1842); cl.1853-1858; 1878-2001	j1827; 1827- 1840/1842NS, j1845; 1843/ 1845-1879NS	NA by 1961-1962; UCC 1961-2001; withdrew
5.	Coventry, Second West Pres.(at Village;f.Second Cong.Soc.;f.l.West Coventry)	1825(CG;2 sr) 1822(Soc.;98) 1845[sic](98) r.af.1876(PR; 51B)	cl.1853-1858; 1863-1866	j1825; 1826-1919NS	X
6.	East Guilford, East Guilford Pres.(First Pres.; in Guilford;f.Unadilla & Rockdale Soc.;f.l. Rockdale;Bainbridge PO)	1831	-	j1832; 1831-onNS	Pres.
7.	East McDonough, Cong.(*McDonough)	1896	1896-1905	-	X
8.	East Pharsalia, Free Cong.Ch.of God (f.First Pres.Soc.;in Pharsalia;nl.01T)	1838(PR;2 sr) r.1850(CG) 1853(s.98) 1860(?)	j1858; 1858-1961	j1838; 1837/ 1838-1846/ 1848NS, 1850-1851NS	X

NEW YORK - CHENANGO COUNTY - continued

A	B	C	D	E	F
9.	Greene, First Cong.(UCC;f.Pres.;f.Cong.Soc.of Greene & Smithville to 1828;m.on Pby.l.as CG 1828-1829;1835 ab.#30;nl.98)	1811(CG;2 sr) r.1835 M	UA:1819-1822/ 1829; cl.1853-1858; 1863-on	j1832; 1831-1862NS	UCC
10.	Guilford, Guilford Center Pres.(Pres.Soc.;f. Cong.-Pres.;f.First Cong.of Guilford Center; f.of Eastern to 1817;f.Second Associated Pres.of Oxford to 1813)	1812(CG) 1807(Soc.) r.af.1932(PR; 46A)	ps.NAP; UA:1812-1824; cl.1853-1858; 1864-1866	j1824/1825; 1819/1824-onNS	Pres.
11.	Lincklaen, Cong.(at Catlin;bldg.of #13;see also #12)	1859(3 sr)	1861-1884	-	X
12.	Lincklaen, First Cong.(in 1894 bldg.;s.l.as r. of #11)	1897(01,99) 1896(?)	1896-1910, 1913-on	-	Sch.I
13.	Lincklaen, Pres.(Cong.forms;Union Pres.Soc.of German;f.Second of German to 1823;left Soc. c.1840(98);left Pby.(first time)1846;see also #11)	by 1818(CG) 1819(Soc.)	cl.1853-1858	j1818; 1815/ 1816-1843/ 1845NS,1846/ 1848-1857NS	X
14.	McDonough, Cong.(f.First Pres.of McDonough,East McDonough;f.of Preston to 1816)	1814(CG;2 sr) r.1826(PR) 1827(Soc.) r.c.1853(CG; 01T)	UA:1817-1822; cl.1853-1858	j1826; 1828-1853NS	Indep.; X af.1858
15.	New Berlin, Cong.(later called Lancaster(pb.not Erie Co.);cited by 48 in UA,not otherwise known)	pb.by 1818	UA:pb.1818- pb.1822	-	X
16.	New Berlin, Pres.(f.Cong.;nl.48 as f.in non-western Pby.;lt.1839-1840;see also #33)	1839(CG:99) 1838(Soc.) r.1844(PR) r.by 1853(CG) r.1873(PR)	cl.1853-1858	1839-1937NS	X
17.	North Guilford, First Cong.Soc.of Guilford & Nineveh(at Little Four Corners (or Van Buren Corners);f.of Guilford & Norwich;nl.01T; nl.48)	1843(CG:2 sr) 1842(s.01) 1838(s.01) r.1873(PR) r.1895(CG)	1849-1850, 1895-on	1852-1895NS	Sch.I
18.	North Norwich, First Associated Pres.Soc.& Cgn. in Norwich Soc.(f.of No.10;f.of Norwich to 1849)	1799(44) 1800(Soc.:98)	ps.NAP; OE: ? -1808; UA:1808-1814	-	X; r.as #20(q.v.)
19.	North Pitcher, First Cong.(in Pitcher;f.First East of Lincklaen to 1833(l.as Lincklaen to 1854);apply to j OE 1831 but refused;lt.cl. 1853-1858;withdrew 1965,l.incor.1965-1987)	1827(CG;2 sr) 1837(s.01)	(see text) 1836-1987	j1833;1831- 1834/1835	Sch.I 1961-1987; withdrew 1965
Nt	North Pitcher, Schismatic Cong.(from #24;in *Lincklaen to 1833;f.of *German to 1823)	1821	nl.	-	X 1821

NEW YORK - CHENANGO COUNTY - continued

A	B	C	D	E	F
20.	Norwich, UCC First Cong.(f.l.North Norwich;r.of #18;l.specifically as CG in 1819 Pby.l.;left Pby.1861(98);48:not in Pby.1834-1837,75 l. through;incor.as Litchfield Soc.,confused with Herkimer Co.#14)	1814(CG;4 sr) 1813(?) 1816(Soc.r.) r.1835(PR) r.1857(CG)	UA:1814-1822; cl.1853-1858; 1863-on	1814/1818-1819/1824; j1826/1827; 1826-1833, 1836-1862NS	UCC
21.	Otselic, Cong.(s.l.Otselie;assod.in 01T:1854)	by 1830(CG)	1849-1852; cl.1853-1858	j1830;1830-1834/1835	X
22.	Oxford, First Cong.(f.First Associated Pres.)	1799(CG;6 sr) 1797(?) 1790(s.01) 1808(Soc.r.) r.1812(?) 1818(Soc.r.)	ps.NAP UA:1812-1822/1827; cl.1853-1858; 1864-1865, 1881-1976	j1822/1827; 1827-1881NS	UCC 1961-1976; merged to form M.
22M.	Oxford, United (merger of #22 & First Bapt.C of C(1815),dual)	1976 M	1976-on	-	UCC (dual, see text)
23.	Pharsalia, First Cong.(assod.in 01T)	1814(48,98)	OE:mnd.; 1836-1844/1845, 1846-1853; cl.1853-1858	-	X
24.	Pitcher, Union Cong.(f.First of German to 1827; f.C of C of DeRuyter(Madison Co.)to 1806;Fed. to Bapt.(1805) 1929-on,as Fed.)	1805(CG;3 sr) 1815(s.01)	ML:1807-1810; cl.1853-1858; 1864-on	j1808; 1809/1811-1862NS	UCC
25.	Plymouth, First Cong.	1814(CG;48) 1819(Soc.:98)	UA:1814-1822; 1836-1869	j1829;1828-1834/1835	X (bldg. sold 1878)
26.	Preston, First Cong.Union Soc.(Pres.:name only)	1822(CG;2 sr) 1836(Soc.r.)	UA:pb.by 1822; cl.1853-1858	j1830/1831; 1830-1869NS	X
27.	Sherburne, First Cong.UCC (f.l.Pres.; specifically CG on Pby.l.bf.1809)	1794(CG;5 sr) 1798(Soc.) 1793(?) 1802(s.44)	OE: ? -1808; UA:1808-1824; cl.1853-1858; j1869; 1868-on	1806-1807/1808; 1829-1868NS	UCC
28.	Sherburne, Free Ch.,Cong.	1845(48,s.99) 1854(s.99)	nl.	-	X c.1849(bldg. sold 1856)
29.	Sherburne, Second Cong.(West Hill;specifically CG in Pby.l.)	1802(CG;2 sr)	OE: ? -1808; UA:1808-1822	1803/1805-1806	X 1827(48)
30.	Smithville, Cong.(s.Pres.name;1834 request Pby.to merge to #9,done 1835)	1827(CG;51B)	nl.	j1828;1827-1834/1835	1835 merged to #9(q.v.)
31.	Smithville, First Pres.of Smithville Flats (f. Cong.of Smithville Flats)	1855(CG) 1863(46A) r.1865(PR)	nl.	1865-onOS	Pres.

NEW YORK - CHENANGO COUNTY - continued

A	B	C	D	E	F
32.	Smyrna, First Cong.	1824(CG;2 sr)	j1835; 1834-1926	j1829; 1828-1835	X
33.	South New Berlin, P or C (in New Berlin;lt.75: as South New (& as Berlin) 1834/1836-1837/ 1838;nl.01T)	1833(48)	nl.	j1833; 1832-1850NS	X

NEW YORK - CLINTON COUNTY (org.1788) (019)

	B	C	D	E	F
1.	AuSable, <u>Clintonville</u> Pres. (see also Essex Co. #1;f.of *Peru to 1839)	1828 1825(Soc.) r.1859(26)	-	j1828; 1827-1863NS	X
2.	Beekmantown, First Pres.Ch.& Soc.(f.Second of Plattsburgh to 1820)	1817(40,98) 1820(26)	-	j1817;1814/ 1818-1825, 1826-1950NS	X
3.	Champlain, Champlain Pres.(f.First Pres.Cong.Ch. & Soc.;still mixed name 1932(46A);f.First Cong.Ch.& Soc.;1997 merged to First Pres.of Rouse Point (*Champlain;l.75:1890-1997) as First Pres.of Rouse Point in Champlain,l.75: 1997-on)	1802(CG;3 sr) 1805(26) r.1830(26: mixed) r.af.1932(PR: see text)	cl.1853-1858	j1817; 1814/1818- 1997NS	X; Merged (see text)
4.	Chazy, Chazy Pres.(Pres.Ch.of Chazy & Cong.Soc. (incp.1854);f.First Pres.& Cong.Ch.& Soc.; still mixed name 1932(46A);m.on Pby.l.as CG 1829-1832;l.specifically as CG on Pby.l.1832-1833;no session but a "ch.court" from 1845)	1805(CG;2 sr) r.af.1932(PR: see text)	cl.1853-1858	1814/1818- 1819/1824; j1833; 1832-onNS	Pres.
5.	Ellensburgh, Pres.(f.Cong.;f.of Mooers to 1830; incor.l.Edinburg:75H;nl.01T)	by 1830(CG) r.1857(PR)	nl.	j1830; 1830-1839, 1857-1883NS	X
6.	Keeseville, Pres.(Cong.Ch.& Soc.;still CG name 1932(46A);f.First Cong.;f.C of C;Ch.of Emanuel;Anderson Falls PO;in *Peru;village extends into <u>Chesterfield</u>,Essex Co.;org.& in Essex Co.to 1828/1830;l.in Essex Co.by CG & 01T;m.on Pby.l.as CG 1828-1832;s.l.AuSable; 26 says closed 1915/1916,l.to 1954;lt.01: 1834/1835-1836)	1806(CG;5 sr) 1829(Soc.r.) r.af.1932(PR: see text)	EX: ? -1828, 1828-1844/ 1845, cl.1853-1858	j1845; 1846/ 1848-1954NS	X
7.	Mooers, First Pres.Cong.Soc.(f.First Cong.)	1807(CG;4 sr) 1832(incp.) r.1876(PR)	cl.1853-1858	j1828; 1827-1984NS	X
8.	Peru, First Cong.(98 says left EX 1830,but nl. there 1828-1830;Ch.voted to change name to Pres.1869,but legally First Cong.Soc.to 1944 Fed.incp.;Fed.to Meth.Epis.(1807) 1938/1944-on as Peru Com.)	1822(CG;98) r.1869(PR:40)	EX:1822- ? ; 1832/1834- 1839, cl.1853-1858	1819/1824- 1825; j1830; 1829-1837/ 1838,1839- onNS	Pres.
9.	Plattsburgh, First Pres.Ch.& Cgn.	1797(PR;3 sr) 1796(98) 1792(Soc.) 1803(Soc.r.) r.1810(Ch.)	-	j1793; 1788/1793- 1809/1813, j1814; 1814/1818- onNS	Pres.

NEW YORK - COLUMBIA COUNTY (org.1786) (021)

A	B	C	D	E	F
1.	Austerlitz, Cong.(indep.:1854:01T,pb.because in MA body;75H suggests that NS l.is for #6)	1792(CG;98) 1780(pr.) r.1872 r.c.1884(PR)	pb.NAP; MA:1844-1857; cl.1857-1858; NY:1873-1884	1830-1846/ 1847NS, 1884-1924	X
2.	Canaan, <u>Canaan Center</u> Pres.(f.First)	1829(2 sr)	-	1830-1963NS	X
3.	Canaan, Cong.(Canaan Four Corners;f.l.New Canaan;lt.1852(01S,1853:natl.)-1856;had a dual relation to MA 1898-1951)	1772(CG;3 sr) 1780(s.01) 1785(s.01) 1783(?) 1740[sic](11)	sv.Brk(MA): c.1781-1793, 1807-c.1820; NAP:1793- af.1797; MA:1830-1837, 1839-1856, NY:1852-1963, MA:1963-on	1819/1824- 1830	UCC
4.	Canaan, Strict Cong.(s.New Canaan)	1770(10)	nl.	-	1778 Tr.to Bapt.
5.	Chatham, <u>New Concord</u> C of C (East Chatham PO;Tr. to Ref.(RCA,1857-on(85))	1771(CG;14) r.1815(PR:98) r.1835(CG:98) Tr.1856(Ref.)	sv.Brk(MA): 1781-1793; NAP:1793- ? ; MA:1838-1840, 1841-1852 cl.1853-1858	j1815; 1809/ 1813-1814/ 1818,1819/ 1824-1837/ 1838	Tr.to Ref. (see text)
6.	Hillsdale, Cong.at <u>Green River</u> (Austerlitz PO; see also #1;nl.01T;f.of *Claverack to 1782)	1765(CG;14) 1792(land) 1801(Soc.)	pb.NAP	1809/1813- 1814/1818, 1819/1824- 1830	Indep.to af.1856; X
7.	Hillsdale, Pres.	1831(98)	-	1831-1928NS	X
8.	Hudson, First Pres.(period bf.l.implies Cong.)	1790(pb.PR; 3 sr)	nl.	j1794; nl.; 1798/1802- 1846/1847NS	Merged to #10 to form #9(q.v.)
9.	Hudson, Hudson Pres.(f.First Parish Ch.,Pres.; First Pres.Soc.;merger of #8 & #10)	1848 M 1845 M	-	1846/1847- onNS	Pres.
10.	Hudson, Second Pres.(divided 1839 to OS,which moved to Stockport 1844(l.75:1839-1870OS))	1831(98)	-	1830-1846/ 1847NS	Merged to #8 to form #9(q.v.)
11.	New Lebanon, Cong.(s.Pres.(name);f.of *Canaan to 1818;First Relg.Soc.of King's Dist.,Lebanon Soc.;Fed.to #12 1848-1884(q.v.);specifically Cong.in 1819 Pres.l.)	1772(CG;3 sr) r.1820(PR:98) r.1839(CG) r.1887	sv.Brk(MA): by 1792-1793; NAP:1793- ? ; MA:1839-1848; cl.1853-1858; NY:1884-1983	1809/1813 (j1820)- 1839NS	UCC 1961-1983; CCCC 1984 (j1983/1984)- on
12.	New Lebanon, Pres.Soc.(Fed.to #11 1848-1884)	1838(98) 1840(Soc.)	-	1839-1884NS	X (most ab.by #11)
13.	North Chatham, Cong.(*Chatham)	1877(01N)	nl.	-	X pb.soon

NEW YORK - COLUMBIA COUNTY - continued

A		B	C	D	E	F
	14.	Spencertown, St.Peter's Pres.(specifically CG in Pby.l.bf.1824;nl.01T;in Austerlitz)	1760(CG;3 sr) 1750(90) 1803(incp.) r.1827(PR)	sv.Hmp(MA): 1760- ? ; sv.Brk(MA): 1790-1793; NAP:1793- pb.1824	j1824; 1809/1813- onNS	Pres.
Gr	15.	Stuyvesant Falls, Emanuel Ger.Luth.Cong.(s.l. 01K:Schuylkill Falls;Tr.to Amer.Luth.Ch. 1946,now ELCA;l.01K:1919-1944/1948; *Stuyvesant)	1919	1919-1945	-	Tr.to Luth. (see text)
	16.	Valatie, Valatie Pres.(f.First Pres.of Kinderhook;f.Second Prot.Ref.Dutch of Kinderhook(RCA,1833-1835(85))	1833(Ref.) r.1835(PR) 1834(46A)	-	1834/1835- onNS	Pres.

NEW YORK - CORTLAND COUNTY (org.1808) (023)

A	B	C	D	E	F
1.	Cincinnatus, Union Cong.Soc.of Cincinnatus & Solon (s.l.Pres.;m.on Pby.l.as CG 1829-1830; voted 1838 to leave Pby.when a CG Assn.could be formed)	1819(CG;2 sr) 1822(Soc.:98)	cl.1853-1858; 1863-1866, 1912-1970	j1831; 1831-1874NS	Sch.I 1961-1970; Merged to form M.
1M.	Cincinnatus, United Ch.(merger of #1 & unknown)	1970 M	1970-1971	1971-on	Sch.I 1970-1971; Pres.
2.	Cortland, First Cong.of Cortlandville	1881(3 sr) 1882(01,s.98)	1880-1980	-	UCC 1961-1980; Merged to form M.
2M.	Cortland, United Com.(Merger of #2 & First Bapt. C of C(1801),dual)	1980 M	1980-on	-	UCC (dual, see text)
3.	Cortland, First Pres.(f.of Cortlandville;f.of Homer to 1829;1969 merged to North Pres. (1916,l.75:1916-1969)as United Pres.)	1825 1824(Soc.) r.1969 M	-	j1825; 1825-onNS	Pres.
4.	Cortland, Free Cong.	1840's	nl.	-	X (pb.soon)
5.	Cortland, Second Cong.	1907(01)	1907-1987	-	UCC 1961-1987; X
6.	Freetown, Pres.(East;f.First of Cincinnatus to 1825;48 says in ML,but not in minutes)	1794(CG;11) by 1812(min) 1818(?) r.af.1858(PR:01T)	cl.1853-1858	j1812; 1809/1811-1934NS	X
7.	Harford, Cong.(f.Pres.;f.Second of Virgil to 1845;l.in Tioga Pby.,when another Second of Virgil l.in Cortland Pby.:see #19)	1831(CG;01) 1832(48)	1851-1858, 1869-1898	j1832; 1831-1854NS	X
8.	Homer, Cong.(UCC) on the Green (First Relg.Soc. 1799 ab.First Pres.Soc.;f.Calvinistic Cong.; asso.1854:01T,but nl.cl.)	1801(CG;90) 1799(CG Soc.) 1797(PR Soc.) 1793(pr.)	SA:1803- ? ; ML:1804-1810; 1863-1866, 1867-on	j1808; 1809/1811-1868NS	UCC
9.	Marathon, Marathon Pres.(First;f.of Harrison to 1827;f.Second Cong.of Cincinnatus to 1818;f. Union Soc.of Lisle(Broome Co.),Cincinnatus & Virgil;l.Pby.(not natl.):1813-1814)	1812(CG;51B) 1814(2 sr) r.af.1858(PR:01T)	cl.1853-1858	j1814; 1814-onNS	Pres.
10.	McGraw, McGraw Pres.(f.McGrawville;f.Cong.;f. Second Pres.in Cortlandville)	1833(PR) r.1838(CG) r.1868(PR)	cl.1853-1858	j1834; 1834/1835-2001NS	X
11.	Preble, First Free Ch.(l.is 01S;nl.01T)	1841(48,98)	1856-1857	-	X af.1857
12.	Preble, Pres.(Relg.Soc.of Preble;f.Cong.& Pres. of Preble & Tully;f.C of C of Preble & Tully (Onondaga Co.);f.First Cong.of Tully;f.in Tully to 1808;moved 1859 to Preble Corners; Fed.to Meth.(by 1821) 1946/1947-1951)	1804(CG;2 sr) 1810(Soc.) r.1811(PR)	ML:1807-1810	j1808; 1809/1811-1952NS	Merged to form M.
12M.	Preble, Com.UCC (merger of #11 & Meth.(by 1821))	1950/1951 M	1950-on	-	UCC [count as CC]

NEW YORK - CORTLAND COUNTY - continued

A	B	C	D	E	F
13.	Preble Corners, P or C Ch.(in Preble;left Pby. at 1834 X)	by 1828	nl.	j1828; 1828-1833	X 1834(48)
14.	Scott, Cong.(f.Pres.)	1818(PR) r.1825(CG)	cl.1853-1858	j1818; 1818-1866NS	X
15.	Taylor, Cong.of Solon (f.of Solon to 1849)	by 1809(CG) ps.bf.1807 c.1810(98) r.1827(98)	ps.SA bf.1807	j1827; 1827-1830	X af.1810; r.; X 1831(48,98)
16.	Truxton, Pres.(Cong.forms;ps.never r.PR)	1811(CG)	cl.1853-1858	j1813; 1814-1889NS	X
17.	Union Valley, Cong.(in Taylor;f.Free Cong.of Solon to 1849;lt.01T;s.incor.l.Union Village)	1845(01)	1852-1855; cl.1855-1858; 1867-1898, 1899-1906, 1913-1915	-	X
18.	Virgil, Pres.(f.Cong.;in Pby.1854:01T,l.01:1852-1854,pastor in Assn.,Ch.in Pby.)	1805(CG;3 sr) 1804(s.48) r.1870(PR)	ML:1806-1810; 1852-1854; cl.1854-1858	j1808; 1809/ 1811-1890NS	X
19.	Virgil, Second Pres.(l.Cortland Pby.,see also #7)	by 1833	-	j1833; 1832-1840/1842NS	X 1846(48)
20.	Willett, Cong.(s.named Pres.)	1851(CG:51B) ps.r.af.1876 (PR:51B)	cl.1853-1858	1854-1897NS	X

NEW YORK - DELAWARE COUNTY (org.1797) (025)

A	B	C	D	E	F
1.	Andes, Pres.(Cong.forms;nl.98;nl.01T,but l.cl.)	by 1832(CG)	cl.1854-1858	1831-1872NS	X
2.	Colchester, Downsville Pres.(f.Cong.at Downsville;nl.01T,but l.cl.)	1825(CG;2 sr) r.af.1858(PR: cl.)	NAP 1825-? ; cl.1854-1858	j1833; 1831-1969NS	Merged to Meth. 1967/1968
3.	Croton, Cong.(now *Treadwell;f.in *Franklin)	by 1866	1865-1874	-	X
4.	Davenport, First Cong.(1854:unassod.01T)	1830(CG:98)	cl.1853-1858	1832-1870NS	X
5.	Delhi, Cong.(l.only by 90)	1798(90)	ps.NAP	-	X pb.soon
6.	Delhi, First Pres.(f.First Asso.Ref.,Tr.1822; 98 incor.f.First Ref.Pres.)	1804(AR:2 sr) 1805(2 sr) 1809(2 sr) Tr.1822(PR)	-	j1822; 1825-onOS	Pres.
7.	Delhi, Second Pres.(West Delhi;Fed.to Meth.as United Ministry 1972-on)	1831(2 sr) 1833(2 sr)	-	1830-onNS	Pres.
8.	Deposit, First Pres.(f.First Pres.Soc.of Tompkins;f.First Cong.;f.of Cookhouse (village),s.l.Cookhaven;village now extends into Sanford,Broome Co.;lt.cl.1854-1858)	1812(CG;4 sr) 1813(?) 1818(Soc.) r.1832/1835 (PR:98) r.1844(CG) r.af.1876(PR: 51B)	ps.NAP; cl.1853-1858	1810-1812, 1813-1815, 1830-onNS	Pres.
9.	Franklin, Cong.Bapt.Fed.(merger of #10 & #11; Fed.to Bapt.(1793)1921/1923-1994)	1878 M	1878-1994	-	Sch.I 1961-1966; UCC 1966-1994; withdrew
10.	Franklin, First Cong.(44:j Pby.1839,not supported by min.)	1793(CG;3 sr) 1792(s.01) 1798(s.01)	NAP:by 1794-af.1807; WAP:m.1794, 1807; 1842-1850; cl.1853-1857; 1857-1878	1826-1841NS	Merged to #11 to form #9(q.v.)
11.	Franklin, First Pres.(f.Second Cong.;f.First Orth.Relg.Soc.)	1841(CG;s.98) 1842(s.98) r.1862(PR)	cl.1853-1858	1841-1878NS	Merged to #10 to form #9(q.v.)
12.	Hamden, Hamden Pres.(First;f.Cong.;f.of Hampden to 1826;in 1827 Union Soc.)	1835(CG) r.1855(PR:98)	cl.1853-1858	1833-onNS	Pres.
13.	Hancock, First Pres.(f.Cong.;1854:assod.:01T; f.of Chehocton)	1831(CG;98) 1830(2 sr) r.1898(PR)	1849-1851; cl.1853-1858; 1864-1898	1830-1840/ 1842NS, 1843/1845-1864NS, 1897-on	Pres.

NEW YORK – DELAWARE COUNTY – continued

		C	D	E	F
14.	Harpersfield, Cong.(f.Pres.;pb.Ch.m.1802 by WAP as Harford;l.PR bf.Ch.fully org.;s.l. Harpersville)	1793(CG;44) 1787(Soc.: 11,98) 1796(s.01) 1798(s.01) 1771(ch.land) r.1831(PR) r.1844(CG)	NAP:1798-1830; 1842-1846; cl.1853-1858; 1858-1860, 1863-1899, 1900-1905	l.1774/1787-1791/1793; j1787-1792; j1830;1831-1860NS	X
Nt	Hobart, Pres.Soc.(initially indep.,r.Asso.Ref. 1851/1852;affl.AR & UPNA to 1868;r.PR 1868)	1829(46A)	-	1868-onOS	Pres.
15.	Masonville, Masonville Pres.(f.Cong.;left Pby. first time 1847(48);s.m.in SA,but since it X bf.this ch.org.,ps.means NAP;1854:unassod.: 01T;Fed.to Bapt.(1810) 1919-on)	1818(CG:98) 1822(99) 1820(Soc.) r.af.1876(PR: 51B)	ps.NAP; 1839-1843/1845;j1844; 1845/1846-1850; cl.1853-1858	j1846; 1843/1845-1846/1848NS, 1851-onNS	Pres.
16.	Meredith, Cong.(f.l.Ouleout;North Franklin PO)	1909	1912-1922	-	X
17.	Meredith, Meredith Sq.Cong.(l.by Pby.as specifically CG 1830-1831;Tr.to UPNA 1870 (1874:46A)-1894)	1807(CG) 1815(Soc.)	NAP by 1823-af.1825; cl.1853-1858; 1861-1869	1830-1862NS	Tr.to UPNA (see text); X (1893:46A)
18.	Middletown, Pres.(Cong.forms;f.Middletown Ref.of Coshington (RCA,bf.1790(98,1794:85))	1794(Ref.:85) by 1790(98) r.1835(CG:98)	cl.1853-1858	1834/1835-1860NS	X
Nt	Moresville, Pres.(only in 98;in 1832 bldg.;ps. branch or other PR type,nl.32;*Roxbury)				
19.	Northfield, Cong.(New Road;f.Second of <u>Walton</u>; North Walton PO;in Walton;Columbia Soc.;cl. lt.1855-1856,1857-1858)	1816(01,98) 1815	ps.NAP; 1839-1842/1845;j1843; 1846-1850; cl.1853-1857; 1857-1962	-	Sch.I 1961-1962; X
20.	Shaver Town, First Pres.(nl.01T,but l.cl.; *Andes;1968 merged to United Pres.of Andes (f.Asso.Ref.,1834(32,75H),affl.AR to 1858; UPNA 1858-1958;l.75:1958-1968)as Pres.of Andes,l.75:1968-on)	1851(CG:2 sr) r.af.1858(PR: cl.) r.1968 M	cl.1854-1858	1852-1968NS	Merged, see text
21.	Sidney, First Cong.(First C of C;Sidney Plains; f.named Pres.;in 1807 bldg.;m.on Pby.l.as CG 1829-1830;lt.75:1840/1842-1843/1845NS)	1808(CG:2 sr)	NAP 1808-pb.1830; cl.1853-1858; 1876-on	1830-1878NS	UCC
22.	Sidney Center, Cong.	1851	cl.1853-1857; 1857-1888	-	X

NEW YORK - DELAWARE COUNTY - continued

A	B	C	D	E	F
23.	South Franklin, P or C Ch.(Second of Franklin; Arabia)	by 1832(98)	nl.	1831-1837/ 1838	X c.1842(98)
24.	Stamford, First Pres.(f.Head of Delaware;f.of New Stamford)	1834(3 sr) 1841(Soc.)	-	1834/1835- onNS	Pres.
25.	Tompkins, Pres.at Cannonsville (f.Second Pres.of Tompkins;Cong.;nl.01T,but l.cl.;af.r.PR 1836, had a period in Pby.without any elders in office:to 1855,& none installed to 1866, therefore cl.says r.PR af.1858)	1828(CG;2 sr) 1830(Soc.) r.1836(PR) (see text)	cl.1854-1858	1830-1958NS	X
26.	Tompkins, Third Pres.	by 1831	-	1830-1851NS	X
27.	Walton, First Cong.(left Pby.1843;Union Soc.;f. of *Franklin to 1797)	1793(CG;3 sr)	NAP:1796- m.1803; WAP:m.1796- 1800; SA:1803- c.1809; cl.1853-1857; 1857-on	j1834; 1834/ 1835-1843/ 1845NS	UCC
28.	West Brook, Plymouth Cong.(Walton PO;in Franklin)	1857(01,22) 1856(98) 1858(s.01)	1857-1861, 1869-1962	-	Sch.I 1961-1962; X

NEW YORK - DUTCHESS COUNTY (org.1683) (027)

A	B	C	D	E	F
1.	Amenia, First Pres.(North Ch.& Soc.;First Cong. Relg.Soc.;Carmel C of C in Nine Partners; Northeast Pct.;Ameniaville;Red Mtghse.;Great Nine Partners at Oblong:10;moved 1833;1854: unassod.in 01T,but affl.CT;X & replaced by United Pres.of Amenia (1992,l.1991-on) which also replaced First Pres.of Wassaic(*Amenia; 1896,l.75:1896-1991))	1748(CG;5 sr; Soc.:98) 1752(14) 1760(11) 1750(10,98) 1762(Soc.) r.1815(PR) r.c.1840(CG) r.1855(PR) r.1992(see text)	WAP:1797-1801;FE(CT): 1814-1816; 1839-1843, m.1843-1846; (CT) 1844-1854, cl.1854-1858	j1815;1815-1816,1818-1840/1841NS 1854-1991NS; 1991-on	X & replaced (see text), Pres.
2.	Amenia, Smithfield Ch.at The City (Relg.Soc. (Cong.)of Smithfield)	1742(CG;4 sr) 1750(98) 1760(14)	nl.	-	1787 merged to #20 to form #3(q.v.) (1812 in 38)
3.	Amenia, Smithfield Pres.(f.Smithfield United Cong.C of C of Amenia,Washington & Stanford in Westfield Soc.(United Cong.Soc.of Smithfield);merger of #2 & #20;two branches 1787-1812/1814;s.l.Stanford;f.Indep.;f. Stanford & Nine Partners;f.Oblong Little Nine Partners (CT Strict);f.Millerton PO;jPby. 1824:98;Tr.to NS 1859)	1787 M(CG) r.1812 M(38) r.1824(PR: 26,98)	CT Strict: 1789-1790; NAP:j1793; WAP:1792/1795 -1812	j1814; 1813-1840/ 1841NS, 1841-1860OS, 1859-1869NS 1863-onOS	Pres.
4.	Amenia, South Amenia Pres.(South Pres.Ch.& Soc. of Union;Union Soc.of South Amenia;1786 moved Amenia Union to South Amenia;Oblong Soc.; Round Top Mtghse.;f.Wassaic PO;DUT 1777-1780; cl.l.incor.as already PR;nl.14;1755 bldg.)	1759(CG;2 sr) 1749(Soc.:45) r.1827(PR:99)	FE(CT):1759-1763; WAP:1806-1813; cl.1853-1858	1777-1780; j1814; 1813-1840/ 1841NS, 1838-1842OS, 1842-onNS	Pres.
5.	Beacon, First Pres.(f.of Matteawan to 1913;f.of *Fishkill)	1833(4 sr) 1832(Soc.)	-	1832-1840/ 1841NS 1840-onOS	Pres.
6.	Beekman, Union Ch.(P or C)	by 1834 1812(pr.:45)	nl.	1833-1839NS	X
7.	Dover, Pres.(f.Ref.,RCA 1769-af.1774(85);DUT 1777-1778)	1769(Ref.) 1770(22) Tr.1777(PR)	-	1777-1778 (nl.)	X af.1778
8.	Fishkill, Rombout Pres.(First;Middle;Rumbout; Brinkerhoffsville;in 1748 bldg.:45;DUT 1763-af.1777;pastor ord.by Cong.Council 1749 [old calendar,now 1750]:45;nl.01T;attempt r.,l.75: 1968-1970,X)	1746(PR;2 sr) 1747(38,49) 1748(14) 1744(22) 1750(53)	FE(CT):1749-1751; WAP:1792-1801	j1751; NSd1751-1758; by 1773-1774/1787, 1794/1797-1885OS	X (1885:26; 1866:98; c.1870:38)
9.	Fishkill, Strict Cong. (Bapt.in some sources)	1745(10)	nl.	-	X pb.bf.1760

NEW YORK - DUTCHESS COUNTY - continued

A	B	C	D	E	F
10.	Freedom Plains, Pres.(LaGrangeville;Ch.of Freedom;in LaGrange;s.Pleasant Valley PO)	1827(2 sr) 1828(full: 2 sr)	-	1827-onNS	Pres.
11.	Millerton, First Pres.(f.Cong.of Millerton;Pres. Cong.Soc.of Northeast;f.Union Mtghse.;f.Cong. Mtghse.;pb.m.Pby.l.as CG at North Amenia 1829-1832;unassod.1854:01T,but affl.CT;1866/1867 moved Northeast Center to Millerton;CG 1834-1873:98)	1829(CG;4 sr) 1827(Soc.:38) r.1873(PR)	(CT)1841-1860,1861-1869,1870-1872	j1873; 1872-on	Pres.
12.	New Hamburgh, First Pres.(f.of Wappingers Creek; *Poughkeepsie;had a branch at Hughsonville 1840/1843-1850/1851;also l.Pby 1808-1809)	1809(38,45) 1810(22,26) 1811(2 sr) 1803(11)	-	1809-1941OS, 1837-1838NS, 1839-1840/1841NS	X
13.	Pine Plains, First Pres.(f.Union Mtghse.;f.of *Northeast to 1823)	1813(2 sr) 1815(26) 1816(98) 1834(full: 3 sr)	-	j1818/1819; 1817-onNS	Pres.
14.	Pittsburgh, Washington Hollow Soc.of Charlotte Pct.(Pleasant Valley);Pittsberry:98;DUT 1764-1791;had #16 as a branch to 1785;united by yoke to #16 1805-1814;nl.01T;f.of *Clinton to 1821)	1747(4 sr) 1746 (46A) 1764/1765(98) r.1813(45)	WAP:mnd.(42)	j1764; by 1773-1788/1793,1798/1802-1862NS	X (1848:38)
15.	Pleasant Plains, Pres.(Clinton Trustees of Pres. Soc.;Westminster & Providence Soc.(Dutch & Scotch)in Charlotte Pct.,in Clinton; Staatsburg PO;DUT 1787-1789;X 1790;Tr.to Ref. (RCA,1816-1823(85)) & back to Pres.)	1784(38,98) 1785(26) r.1816(Ref.) Tr.1837(PR: 3 sr)	-	1774/1787-1788/1793, j1837; 1837-onNS	X 1790 (26); r.; Pres.
16.	Pleasant Valley, First Pres.(f.a branch of #14 to 1785;in 1770 bldg.;united by yoke to #14 1805-1814;46A:this continues #14;DUT 1770-1791(with #14,nl.),DUT (on own) 1791-1795; nl.01T)	1765(branch: 5 sr) 1788(elders) 1785(incp.)	WAP:m.1805 (42)	(see text) j1791;nl.; 1794/1797-onNS	Pres.
17.	Poughkeepsie, First Cong.(lt.01S:1852-1853;r.of #19:46A)	1837(01,22) 1838(98) r.1851	1836-1841, m.1843-1846, 1850-on	-	UCC

NEW YORK - DUTCHESS COUNTY - continued

A	B	C	D	E	F
18.	Poughkeepsie, First Pres.(DUT 1763-af.1774; 99:incor.l.in NAP,when in WAP;nl.01T)	1749(PR;5 sr) 1750(14) r.1791(CG:38) r.1817(PR:38) 1826(99)	ps.MC: 1786-1792; WAP: 1792-1803; NAP:(see text)	j1750; NSd 1750-1758;by 1773-1774/ 1787;j1817; 1817-1819, 1820-1821; j1826; 1826-onNS	Pres.
19.	Poughkeepsie, Second Pres.	by 1834(min) 1835/1836(98)	-	1833-1839NS	X 1838(38) (r.as #17:46A)
20.	Stanford, Strict Cong.(at "Separate," two miles South of Smithfield;ps.in Amenia)	bf.1787	nl.	-	1787 merged to #2 to form #3(1812:38)

NEW YORK - ERIE COUNTY (org.1821) (029)

A		B	C	D	E	F
	1.	Alden, First Pres.(f.Cong.Soc.;f.Clarence Union, of Clarence to 1823;lt.75:1825-1826;nl.01T)	1813(CG) r.1817(PR)	nl.	j1817; 1817-1846/1848NS, 1846-onOS	Pres.
	2.	Angola, First Cong.(in Evans)	1863	1863-on	-	UCC
	3.	Black Rock, First Pres.(f.of Buffalo to 1837;l. <u>Buffalo</u> again 1853;bec.Breckenridge St.Pres. of Buffalo c.1870,bec.West Ave.Pres.of Buffalo c.1887)	1831(2 sr)	-	j1831; 1831-1839, 1840/1842-1846/1848NS, 1845-1887OS, 1888-on	Pres.
	4.	Boston, Pres.(Cong.forms;left Pby.(first time) 1846)	1837(CG)	cl.1853-1858	j1835; 1834/1835-1843/1845NS, 1849-1856NS	X (bldg.sold 1857)
	5.	Buffalo, Buffalo City Cong.(f.Free Cong.;ps.f. Second Pres.;left Pby.1837;26 says r.1839 as #18)	1832(CG;2 sr) 1831(?)	1839-1840	j1832; 1831-1837/1838	X (or r., see text)
	6.	Buffalo, <u>East Buffalo</u> Cong.(ps.in Cheektowaga; Sloan PO)	1891(01N) 1892(01)	1891-1914	-	X
	7.	Buffalo, East Pres.	by 1851	-	1850-1861NS	X
	8.	Buffalo, First Cong.	1880(81)	1879-1928	-	Merged to #20 to form #9(q.v.)
	9.	Buffalo, First Pilgrim Cong.(merger of #8 & #20)	1928 M(81)	1928-1968	-	UCC 1961-1968; Merged to form M. UCC
	9M.	Buffalo, Pilrgim St.Luke UCC (merger of #9 & St.Luke UCC (f.Evan.,E&R,1870/1872))	1968 M	1968-on	-	UCC
	10.	Buffalo, First Pres.(f.First Ch.of Buffalo,Pres. & Cong.;1959 ab.First United Pres.(f. Caledonia Asso.Ref.,1848(32),affl.AR to 1858, UPNA 1858-1958;l.75:1958-1959)	1812(mixed: 5 sr) by 1810(22) 1809(?) r.1816(PR: 2 sr) 1815(PR:48) r.1959 M	nl.	j1816; 1815/1816-onNS	Pres.
	11.	Buffalo, Fitch Mem.Cong.	1894(01N) 1892(01,22) 1891(s.01,81) 1890(?)	1894-1947	-	X
Fr	12.	Buffalo, French Prot.	by 1844(min) af.1830(?)	-	j1844; 1843/1845-1855NS	Indep.; X af.1860

NEW YORK - ERIE COUNTY - continued

A		B	C	D	E	F
Gr	13.	Buffalo, Ger.Evan.Pres.(Tr.to OS:48;divided,l. 1837-1848OS)	1832(48)	-	j1832/1833; 1832-1840/ 1842NS,1843/ 1845-1855NS	X
	14.	Buffalo, Lafayette St.Pres.(98 says a r.of #18; bec.Lafayette Ave.Pres.)	1845(4 sr)	-	j1846; 1843/ 1845-onNS	Pres.
Bl	15.	Buffalo, Lloyds Mem.Cong.	1920(01,81) 1914(22)	1922-1974	-	UCC 1961-1974; Merged to form M.
Bl	15M.	Buffalo, New Covenant UCC (merger of #15 & St. Peter UCC (Evan.,E&R,1845))	1974 M	1974-on	-	UCC
	16.	Buffalo, Niagara Sq.Cong.(f.Peoples;in 1850 bldg.)	1890(01)	1890-1911	-	X
	17.	Buffalo, North Pres.(moved to <u>Amherst</u> 1959;s.l. Williamsville)	1846(3 sr) 1847(3 sr)	-	1846/1848- onNS	Pres.
	18.	Buffalo, Park Ch.Soc.(ps.a r.of #5;26 & 46A:PR form;98:CG form;drop Pby.:1846:48;98:r.as #14)	1839 (see text)	nl.	j1839; 1837/ 1838-1843/ 1845NS	X 1845 (or r., see text)
	19.	Buffalo, Pearl St.Pres.(Tr.to OS 1842;bec. Central Pres.1848;1909 ab.Park Pres.(1893,l. 75:1893-1911) as Central Park Pres.,later bec.Central Pres.)	1835(5 sr) 1836(s.81) r.1909 M	-	j1836; 1834/ 1835-1840/ 1842NS, 1841-onOS	Pres.
	20.	Buffalo, Pilgrim Cong.	1886(81)	1885-1928	-	Merged to #8 to form #9(q.v.)
	21.	Buffalo, Plymouth Chap.Cong.	1895	1895-1897	-	X
	22.	Buffalo, Plymouth Cong.UCC	1908(3 sr) 1891(s.01)	1908-on	-	UCC
	23.	Buffalo, Prospect Ave.Cong.	1892	1892-1894	-	X
In	24.	Buffalo, Seneca Indian Mission Cong.(served Seneca tribe;f.Seneca Indian Reservation,West Seneca.;s.l.Seneca Indian Mission,Cazenove Creek;f.l.Seneca Station (75);moved 1843/1846 to <u>Upper Cattaraugus</u> at Erie & Cattaraugus Co.line,in Cattaraugus Co.,Cattaraugus Reservation,l.as <u>Cattaraugus</u> Indian Mission; NY Missionary Soc.1811-1821;UFMS 1821-1826; ABCFM 1826-merger;still l.in Erie Co.& as CG by 01T)	1823(CG;67) by 1826(48) 1827(?) 1811(mission: 08,32,69) 1821(mission: 67) 1822(mission: 48) r.1846(67) 1843(48)	1849-1850; cl.1853-1858	1831-1839	1850/1853 Ch. merged to Cattaraugus Co. #31(q.v.)
	25.	Buffalo, Winchester Cong.of <u>Gardenville</u> (in West Seneca)	1928 1918(22)	1928-1955	-	X
	26.	Clarence, First Pres.(Clarence Hollow;s.l.in Newstead:98;divided to #41 1839)	1817(3 sr) 1821(Soc.:98) c.1820(98)	-	j1818; 1817-onNS	Pres.

NEW YORK - ERIE COUNTY - continued

A	B	C	D	E	F
27.	East Aurora, First Pres.(in Aurora;s.claims to continue #28)	1838	-	1837-onOS	Pres.
28.	East Aurora, Pres.(f.Cong.;in Aurora;f.of Willink to 1818;nl.01T;see also #27)	1818(CG) r.1843(PR)	nl.	j1818; 1818-1854NS	X
29.	Eden, Cong.(f.First Pres.)	1817(CG:2 sr)	cl.1853-1858; 1863-1880, 1883-1885, 1886-1890	j1820; 1818-1863NS	X
30.	Elma, Spring Brook Cong.(nl.01T)	by 1851(CG)	nl.	1850-1873NS	X (by 1868:98)
31.	Evans, First Ch.of Evans (f.First Cong.of East Evans;f.Evan.;f.Second of Eden to 1821;Derby PO;indep.1910:26)	1818(CG) 1822(incp.) r.1833(98)	1835-1880, 1881-1884, 1885-1915	j1818;1818-1834/1835	withdrew; Tr. to Coun.Com. Chs.by 2002
32.	Evans, Third Cong.,Evans Ctr.	1835	1835-1849, 1850-1875	-	X
33.	Glenwood, Pres.(f.Cong.;in Colden;1847 moved from Colden (village);nl.01T)	1829(CG) r.1878(PR:98) 1875(?)	nl.	j1832; 1830-1946NS	X
34.	Grand Island, First Cong.(l.22 & 01N;nl.01T; f.of Tonawanda to 1852)	1865(01N) 1849(22)	nl.	-	X 1880(22)
35.	Grand Island, First Cong.(Island PO)	1892(01) 1893(?)	1894-1928	-	X
36.	Griffins Mills, Pres.(s.l.Griffiths Mills;in Aurora;f.First Cong.Soc.of Aurora;f.l.West Aurora;f.of Willink to 1818;West Falls PO;lt. as West Willink 1818-1819/1824:75;never PR forms,1875 a r.at end of accomodation plan)	1810(CG;98) 1818(?) r.1875 r.1906(PR)	cl.1853-1858; 1875-1906	j1819; 1818-1874NS, 1906-on	Pres.
37.	Holland, Cong.(left Pby.1837)	by 1821(CG)	1840/1841-1850, 1851-1852, 1853-1861, 1864-1872	j1821; 1819/ 1824-1837/ 1838	X
38.	Lackawanna, Cong.(f.l.Roland;West Seneca PO)	1903(01)	1903-1923	-	X
39.	Lake View, Cong.(in Hamburg)	1891(05,22) 1897(s.05) 1894(s.01)	1900-1951	-	Tr.to IFCA:l.1965; CCCC 1967 (j1966)-on
40.	Lancaster, Lancaster Pres.(f.Cayuga Creek Pres.; f.Cong.;f.of Clarence to 1833)	1818(CG;4 sr) r.1827(PR;26)	nl.	j1819; 1818-onNS	Pres.
41.	Newstead, Pres.(at Akron;l.Akron from 1874;f. Newstead Village;98:ab.part of #26 in 1839, 26 puts movement from here to there)	1835 1836(Soc.) r.1839(48)	-	j1839; 1837/ 1838-1928NS	X (1933:26)
42.	North Collins, First Cong.Ch.& Soc.of Collins (f.Second of Concord to 1821;f.Evan.Cong.Free (at 1835 r.);left Pby.1836(1835:26))	1817(4 sr) 1827(incp.) r.1835	1835-1917	j1821; 1819/ 1824-1834/ 1835	Merged to form #42(q.v.)

NEW YORK - ERIE COUNTY - continued

A	B	C	D	E	F
43.	North Collins, First Cong.(merger of #41 & Meth. Epis.)	1917 M	1917-1951	-	CCCC:by 1958 (j1949)-on
44.	North Evans, Cong.(f.Second of Evans;lt.(natl.) cl.1853-1858)	1834(01,98) 1837(?)	1835-1953	-	CCCC 1962 (j1963)-1976; X
45.	Orchard Park, Orchard Park Pres.(f.First Pres. Soc.of <u>East Hamburg</u>;f.First Free Cong.of East Hamburg 1853-1859;f.of Ellicott to 1852;f.of <u>Hamburg</u> to 1850;f.at Abbott's Corners to bf. 1850;l.Pres.when Free Cong.)	1817(CG;4 sr) r.1835(?) r.1853 r.1859(PR)	cl.1853-1858	j1817; 1815/ 1816-onNS	Pres.
46.	South Wales, South Wales Pres.(f.Cong.;in Wales; left Pby.1846;99 says 1841 is new ch.,divided from #28)	by 1820(pb.PR) r.1841(CG) r.1867(PR)	1840/1841-1850; cl.1853-1858	j1820; 1819/ 1824-1843/ 1845NS;j1851; 1851-onNS	Pres.
47.	Springville, First Pres.(f.Cong.;f.First of Concord;lt.48,s.j1842)	1816(CG;4 sr) r.1844(PR:26) 1840(98)	nl.	j1818; 1818-onNS	Pres.

NEW YORK - ESSEX COUNTY (org.1799) (031)

A	B	C	D	E	F
1.	AuSable Forks, Pres.(1837 bldg.;*Jay;village crosses into *Black Brook,Clinton Co.,had a branch there 1840-?;1831 org.date may be #11; 26:X 1867,pb.Clinton Co.#1)	1839(40,98) 1831(26)	-	j1839; 1839-1899NS	X (see text)
2.	Brookfield, Cong.(*Essex)	by 1809 (claim:98)	1831-1850	-	X
3.	Chesterfield, <u>Port Kent</u> Pres.(in union bldg. which was abandoned c.1884(26))	1841(26)	-	j1844; 1850-1857NS	X
4.	Crown Point, C of C at <u>Hammondville</u>	1879(01N,98) 1875(?)	1878-1894	-	X
5.	Crown Point, First Cong.	1804(5 sr)	EX: ? -1828; 1828-1982	-	UCC 1961-1982; NA 1982(j1981)-on
6.	Crown Point, Second Cong.(West Par.;<u>Ironville</u>)	1846 1843(Soc.) 1845(s.01)	1843-on	-	UCC
7.	Elizabethtown, UCC (ab.First Meth.Epis.1938;Fed. to Bapt.(1797,r.1834) 1957-1964 as United Cgns.;ab.Bapt.1964)	1821(s.01,98) 1844(s.01) r.1938 r.1964	EX: ? -1828; 1828-1860, 1861-on	-	UCC
8.	Essex, Com.Pres.(f.First Cong.Soc.of Essex & Willsborough;begun in Willsborough in Willsborough Soc.(bf.1800);sett.here 1818, with some pr.there;divided 1830/1831 to #23; lt.1828-1829 both names;nl.01T;Fed.to Meth. (1834) & Bapt.(1838) 1922/1923-1993;1993 merged to Meth.& Bapt. as Essex Com.United Meth.)	1815(CG;4 sr) 1817(Soc.) bf.1800(W. Soc.:2 sr) r.1833(PR)	EX: ? -1828; 1828-1829	1825-1827; j1832; 1831-1993NS	X (see text)
9.	Essex, <u>Whallonsburgh</u> Pres.	by 1840	-	j1840; 1839-1863NS	X
10.	Hoffman, First Cong.of <u>Schroon</u> (lt.01:1831-1832/ 1834)	by 1829(CG)	EX: ? -1828; 1828-1832/ 1834	1831-1834/ 1835	X
11.	Jay, Pres.(26 ps.suggests bec.#1)	1831(22)	-	j1832; 1831-1839	X
12.	Keene Valley, First Cong.(f.of Keene Flats;in Keene;nl.98)	1828(s.01,22) 1829(?) 1815(90) r.1873(01N) 1872(s.01)	EX: ? -1828; 1828-1856, cl.1856-1858, 1872-on	-	UCC
13.	Lewis, First Cong.(Lewisville;f.of *Willsborough to 1805;m.as CG on Pby.l.1828-1829;f.Fed.to Meth.1923-1926)	1804(CG;3 sr) 1807(s.01) r.1812(01,99)	EX: ? -1828; 1828-1857, cl.1857-1858, 1858-on	1814/1818- 1819/1824, 1825-1827	UCC

NEW YORK - ESSEX COUNTY - continued

14.	Moriah, Cong.(f.East Moriah;s.Pres.;m.on Pby.l. as CG 1828-1830(pb.incor.1829-1830,pb.should be Franklin Co.#12))	1808(CG;2 sr)	EX: ? -1828; 1828-1839, 1844/1845-1873, 1874-1911	(see text) 1832-1840/1842NS	X
15.	Moriah, First Pres.of Mineville (f.First Cong.of Mineville;merged 1988 to Port Henry Pres. (1860,l.75:1860-1988NS,in *Moriah) as Mt. Moriah Pres.of Port Henry)	1874(CG;3 sr) 1875(3 sr) r.1878(PR;22) r.1988 M	1874-1877	1878-on	Pres.
16.	North Elba, Cong.(f.Keene Plains;f.of Keene to 1849;1854:assod.01T)	1840(s.01) 1824(90) r.1853	1839-1844/1845, cl.1853-1854, 1854-1874	-	X
17.	North Hudson, Cong.(unassod.1854:01T)	by 1854	cl.1853-1854; 1854-1856; cl.1856-1858	-	X af.1858
18.	Schroon Lake, First Cong.Ch.& Soc.of Schroon (f. First Pres.(in name to 1878);f.Second Cong. Ch.& Soc.to 1834;in EX to 1834(99);26 suggests a merger of two chs.in 1878,not otherwise supported;Fed.to First Meth.Epis. (1809/1834) 1907-on;r.1951 as Com.(still Fed. form))	1829(CG) r.1834(PR) r.1844(CG)	1829-1832/1834; j1844; 1844/1845-1857; cl.1857-1858; 1858-on	j1834;1837/1838-1843/1845NS	UCC
19.	Ticonderoga, First Cong.UCC (in union bldg.1819-1874)	1809(s.01,98) 1808(s.01) 1813(s.01)	EX: ? -1828; 1828-1832/1834, 1835-1857; cl.1857-1858; 1858-1860, 1861-1981	-	UCC 1961-1981; pb.X
20.	Upper Jay, Cong.(l.Jay;nl.98;m.on Pby.l.as CG 1828-1830)	1814 1813(s.01)	EX: ? -1828; 1828-1857; cl.1857-1858; 1858-1880	1819/1824-1827	X
21.	Wadhams, UCC (Wadhams Falls;Wadhams Mills;f.l. Westport;West Port;s.l.incor.West Point;m.on Pby.l.as CG 1828-1830,1831-1832;lt.1854-1855, lt.01S:1855-1856,lt.:l.& cl.1853-1854,1857-1858;f.of *Elizabethtown to 1815)	1827(CG;3 sr) 1821(s.01) 1813(s.01) 1808(?) 1835(s.01)	EX: ? -1828; 1828-on	- (see text)	UCC
22.	West Moriah, Cong.(1854:asso.:01T;*Moriah)	by 1829	EX: ? -1828; 1828-1849, 1851-1854; cl.1854-1858	-	X

NEW YORK - ESSEX COUNTY - continued

A	B	C	D	E	F
23.	Willsborough, Cong.UCC (Old Stone;1830/1833 division of (& claim) #8,l.as Essex & Willsboro[ugh] 1829-1832/1834 & continuing its EX membership to 1834;lt.1837-1838)	1833(s.01,98) 1832(Soc.) 1834(s.01) 1815(claim)	j1834; 1829-on	-	UCC
24.	Wilmington, Cong.	1834(s.01) 1833(s.01)	1832/1834- 1911, 1916-1930	-	X

NEW YORK - FRANKLIN COUNTY (org.1808) (033)

	1.	Bangor, Cong.	1826(CG;01) 1833(Soc.)	1853-1977	j1827; 1826-1856NS	Sch.I; X
Fr	2.	Bangor, French Pres.	by 1851	-	j1851; 1851-1863NS	X
	3.	Bombay, Cong.(l.by Pby.bf.j;f.of Fort Covington to 1833)	by 1827	nl.	j1831;1826- 1834/1836	X
	4.	Burke, Pres.(f.C of C;f.First Cong.;1968 merged to North Burke Pres.(l.75:1935-1968) as Burke Center Pres.)	1845(CG;3 sr) r.1875(PR;98) r.1968 M	cl.1853-1858	j1846;1846/ 1848-1998NS	X
	5.	Chateaugay, First Pres.(f.Cong.;l.by Pby.bf.j; mission pr.:1800:46A)	1816(CG;40) 1817(46A) r.1842(PR)	nl.	j1827; 1825-onNS	Pres.
	6.	Constable, Pres.(f.Cong.;Fed.to unknown 1923-1953)	1821(CG;40) 1822 1817(Soc.:90) r.1847(PR;40)	nl.	j1822; 1819/1824- 1953NS	X
	7.	Duane, P or C Ch.(f.of *Malone to 1828)	by 1827	nl.	j1827;1830- 1834/1836	X
	8.	Fort Covington, Cong.Soc.	c.1821(CG) r.1827(PR;40)	nl.	j1827; 1826-1831	Merged to #9 to form #10(q.v.)
	9.	Fort Covington, First Pres.(f.Asso.Ref.;nl.40;32 l.as AR to 1834)	1827(AR;2 sr) 1824(32) Tr.1830(PR)	-	j1830; 1830-1831	Merged to #8 to form #10(q.v.)
	10.	Fort Covington, Fort Covington Pres.(f.United Pres.;merger of #8 & #9)	1830 M(PR)	-	1831-onNS	Pres.
	11.	Malone, First Cong.(f.Cong.-Pres.;retained CG forms;l.by Pby.specifically as CG:1833-1834/1835;f.of *Ezraville to 1812;f.of *Harrison to 1808)	1807(CG;3 sr) 1809(?) r.1962(UCC)	cl.1853-1858 1962-on	j1817;1814/ 1818-1962NS	UCC 1962-on
	12.	Moira, Cong.(s.l.Pres.;pb.m.as CG in Pby., incor.as Moriah Essex Co.1828-1829;f.of *Dickinson to 1828;f.Fed.1920-1922 to unknown)	1823(CG;2 sr) 1830(?)	cl.1853-1858 1866-1898, 1899-1909, 1913-1948	j1827;1827- 1828,1829- 1840/1842NS, 1846/1848- 1866NS	X
	13.	North Bangor, Cong.(in f.Chr.bldg.;*Bangor)	1928	1929-1944	-	X
	14.	Skerry, Cong.(f.l.Brandon;North Bangor PO;in 1890 bldg.)	1891(01N,01)	1891-1970	-	Sch.I; X
	15.	Westville, P or C Ch.(nl.01T;but time outside Pby.suggests CG forms)	by 1842	nl.	j1842;1840/ 1842-1849NS, 1859-1863NS	X

NEW YORK - FULTON COUNTY (org.1838) (035)

A		B	C	D	E	F
	1.	Broadalbin, First Pres.(f.First of Mayfield to 1850;f.Ref.Prot.Dutch of New Harlem;f.Fonda's Bush;(RCA)1795-1823:85(1794-1822:99);f.a branch of #9 1792-1794)	1794(Ref.:99) 1795(85) 1792(3 sr) 1798(s.98) 1800(incp.) Tr.1823(PR)	-	j1823; 1819/ 1824-onOS	Pres.
Sh	2.	Broadalbin, Pres.(Breadlbin;Breadalbane;Scotch Ch.:49)	by 1797	-	1794/1797- 1803/1805	X
	3.	Ephrata, Pres.& Ref.Dutch Ch.(f.First Pres.Ch.& Soc.of Palatine;RCA:1825-1832:85,pb.dual, divided to First Ref.(RCA):1832;f.l.Palatine, Montgomery Co.;lt.75:1827-1828)	1823 r.1832	-	1819/1824- 1839OS	X (f.dual, see text)
	4.	Gloversville, First Cong.Soc.UCC (f.in Johnstown)	1852(01,98) 1851(22)	1852-on	-	UCC
	5.	Gloversville, Kingsborough Ave.Pres.(f.Cong.of Kingsborough;merger of #7 & #8;l.by Pby. specifically as CG 1837-1838;f.of *Johnstown; 98:NAP:1806-1807,SAP:1807-1821;1976 X in Pres.Ch.,U.S.A.,who sold bldg.1985)	1804 M (CG) r.1853(PR: 3 sr)	NAP: 1804-1807; SAP: 1807-1818	j1821; 1819/ 1824-1838OS; 1853-1976OS	1976 Tr.to Asso. Ref.Gen.Synod
	6.	Johnstown, First Pres.(m.1776 as "Tryon Co. supply";f.of *Caughnawaga to 1793;1957 ab.SS. Cyril & Methodius Pres.(Slovak,1923,r.1937 (PR),l.75:1937-1957;always Pres.in 98))	1765(3 sr) 1764(incp.) 1763(s.49) 1762(99) 1785(r.incp.: 2 sr) r.1957 M	-	j1787; 1774/ 1787-onOS	Pres.
	7.	Kingsborough, First Cong.Soc.(1797 specifically vote,not under NAP,but CT type Assn.;in *Gloversville;f.of *Johnstown;f.of *Caughnawaga to 1793;incor.Washington Co.:12)	1793(6 sr; Soc.:99) by 1792(?) 1794(incp.)	nl.	-	1804 merged to #8 to form #5(q.v.)
	8.	Kingsborough, Pres.(nl.47;in *Gloversville;f.of *Johnstown)	by 1796(98)	-	1794/1797- 1803/1805	1804 merged to #7 to form #5(q.v.)
	9.	Mayfield, Central Pres.(f.First;f.Second to 1841;f.Dutch Ref.of Mayfield & Broadalbin (see also #1);RCA:1793-1826:85(1792-1811:11); 99:vote to be PR 1826,Tr.1827)	1792(Ref.: 2 sr) 1793(85,98) Tr.1827(PR: 2 sr) 1826(3 sr) 1821(11)	-	1827-1837/ 1838NS, 1840-onOS	Pres.
	10.	Northampton, Pres.at Fish House	1824(98)	-	1819/1824- 1919OS	X
	11.	Stratford, P or C Ch.	by 1825	nl.	1819/1824- 1834/1835	X

NEW YORK - FULTON COUNTY - continued

A	B	C	D	E	F
Sh 12.	West Galway, West Galway Pres.(First Pres.of Galway;s.Galloway;Scotch Ch.:49;in Perth;f. of *Amsterdam,Montgomery Co.to 1831;l.in Saratoga Co.:47;nl.01T)	1790(CG;3 sr) r.1793(PR; 4 sr)	nl.	j1791; 1788/1793-on OS	Pres.

NEW YORK – GENESEE COUNTY (org.1802) (037)

A	B	C	D	E	F
1.	Alabama, P or C Ch.(f.of Gerrysville to 1828;f. of Shelby(Orleans Co.)to 1826;merger incor. 1824:48)	1824(48)	nl.	j1824(48); 1833-1834/ 1835	Merged to #18(q.v.)
2.	Alexander, Pres.(f.First Cong.;f.of Batavia to 1812;1836 ab.#3;s.l.Alexandria;01T l.in Pby., but temporarily nl.1852-1855)	1818(CG) 1807(Soc.) r.1836 M r.af.1858(PR: 01T)	1848-1852; cl.1853-1858	j1819; 1818-1852, 1855-1869NS, 1875-1893	X
3.	Alexander, Union Ch.of Alexander & Darien (Cong. forms)	1835(CG)	nl.	j1835; nl.	1836 merged to #2(q.v.)
In Nt	Basom, Indian Pres.(served Seneca tribe;33 says this was an ABCFM mission Tr.to Pres.Bd.1870; nl.67;*Alabama)	1870	-	1870-on	Pres.
4.	Batavia, First Pres.(f.Cong.)	1809(CG;4 sr) r.1818(PR)	nl.	j1818; 1817-onNS	Pres.
5.	Bergen, First Pres.(f.First Cong.Ch.& Soc.;lt. cl.1853-1858;f.l.Northampton:98;see also #8)	1807(CG) 1808(Soc.) r.1910(PR)	OA:1812-1813; 1853-1854; cl.1854-1857; 1857-1863	j1808-1812, nl.; j1817/1819; 1817-onNS	Pres.
6.	Bergen, Free Cong.	by 1854	cl.1853-1856	-	X af.1856
7.	Bergen, North Bergen Pres. (<u>Lyme</u>(or Lime) Relg. Soc.;f.Cong.of Byron,Bergen,& Clarendon (Orleans Co.);s.Byron PO)	1823(CG:3 sr) 1827 r.1833(PR) 1828(99) 1841(Soc.r.)	nl.	j1828; 1829-onNS	Pres.
8.	Bergen, <u>Stone Church</u> Pres.(f.Second Cong.of Bergen & Leroy;46A:a r.of #5;still CG in name 1932:46A)	1828(CG;3 sr) 1829(48) r.1882(PR) (see text)	GC: ? -1834; 1834-1842; GC:1842-by 1848; cl.1853-1858; 1860-1874	1881-on	Pres.
9.	Bethany, <u>East Bethany</u> Pres.(f.First Pres.of Bethany;f.Cong.Soc.;Tr.to OS 1842(1853:51); nl.01T;l.cl.when in OS,but sv.CG;still CG in name 1932:46A)	1817(CG) r.1824(PR)	cl.1856-1858	j1827; 1826-1831; j1834; 1833-1840/1842NS, 1842-onOS	Pres.
10.	Bethany Centre, Pres.(in Bethany;Tr.to OS 1844)	1829	-	j1830; 1829-1843/1845NS, 1843-1905OS	X

NEW YORK - GENESEE COUNTY - continued

A	B	C	D	E	F
11.	Byron, First Pres.at Byron Ctr.(f.First Cong. Soc.;moved 1823 from site in Stafford,f.of Batavia to 1820, to site f.in Bergen to 1820; if 1845 r.PR(48) correct,then pb.CG bf.1854)	1818(CG) 1827(Soc.) r.1896(PR; 2 sr) 1845(2 sr)	GC:1824-1831; cl.1853-1858	j1831; 1830-onNS	Pres.
12.	Darien, First Cong.Soc.(Darien Center;f.South of Pembroke to 1832;1834 ab.#13;unassod.in 01T, but l.by Pby.to 1856)	1823(CG) r.1834 M	cl.1853-1858	j1824; 1819/ 1824-1831, 1833-1856NS	X c.1860 (bldg.sold 1880)
13.	Darien Village, P or C Ch.(in Darien)	by 1833	nl.	j1833;1833-1834/1835	1834 merged to #12(q.v.)
14.	Elba, Elba Pres.(First;f.Cong.)	1822(CG) r.1867(PR)	GC:1822-1834; 1834-1838; GC(nl.):1838-1840; cl.1853-1858	j1840; 1839-onNS	Pres.
15.	Elba Plains, P or C Ch.(in Elba;ps.#18)	by 1834	nl.	1833-1834/ 1835	X
16.	Leroy, Cong.	1843	cl.1853-1858	-	af.1861 ab.by #17
17.	Leroy, First Pres.(f.Cong.;f.of Bellona to 1813; f.Second C of C of Caledonia(Livingston Co.) (First Cong.Soc.of Caledonia) to 1812;voted PR 1814,j Pby.1815 on accomodation plan; elected elders later 1815;af.1861 ab.#16)	1812(CG) r.1814(PR) (see text) r.af.1861 M	nl.	j1815; 1814-onNS	Pres.
18.	Oakfield, First Pres.(f.of Elba to 1842;ab.#1 1834(incor.:1824:48))	1833(4 sr) r.1834 M	-	j1836; 1834/ 1835-onNS	Pres.
19.	Pavilion, Pres.(f.of Covington (Wyoming Co.) to 1841)	1840	-	j1840; 1839-1885NS	X
20.	Pembroke, First Pres.(Corfu PO;f.Pres.of North Pembroke (from 1831);First Pres.Soc.;f.Cong. at Long's Corners;Pby.directed that ch. records bf.1831 be burned!;f.in *Batavia to 1812)	1810(CG;2 sr) r.1817(2 sr) r.1831(PR)	nl.	j1817; 1817-onNS	Pres.
21.	Stafford, Cong.(left Pby.(first time)1824)	1821(CG)	GC:1824-1834; 1834-1842; GC:1842-1846	j1821; 1819/ 1824-1825; j1846; 1843/ 1845-1849NS	X

NEW YORK - GREENE COUNTY (org.1800) (039)

A	B	C	D	E	F
1.	Ashland, First Pres.(f.First Cong.of Windham to 1848;in 1799 bldg.;moved 1842 to Scienceville in Ashland;see also #9;nl.01T;Fed.1934-1936 to unknown)	1803(CG;99) c.1799(99) 1808(Soc.) r.1826(PR)	NAP:1803-1826	j1826; 1826-1936NS	X
2.	Athens, P or C Ch.	by 1815	nl.	j1815; 1814/1818-1819/1824	X
3.	Cairo, Pres.C of C of Canton (f.Cong.;f.in Canton to 1808;nl.01T;pb.ab.by United Ch.of Cairo (Meth.))	1799(CG;2 sr) r.af.1812(PR)	NAP:1799-af.1803	j1812; 1809/1813-1953NS	X (see text)
4.	Catskill, Christs Pres.(Pres.Soc.;f.Cong.; nl.01T)	1803(CG;3 sr) r.af.1811(PR)	NAP:by 1805-?	j1811; 1809/1813-1995NS	X
5.	Durham, First Pres.(New Durham;f.Cong.;f.of *Freehold to 1805)	1792(CG;2 sr) r.1830(PR) r.1847(CG) r.1857(PR)	NAP j1799-1830; WAP m.1801; cl.1853-1858	j1830; 1830-1961NS	X
6.	Durham, Second Pres.of West Durham (f.Cong.;in 1808 bldg.)	1816(CG;2 sr) 1814(Soc.) r.1861(PR)	NAP:1816-1830; cl.1853-1858	j1830; 1830-1887NS	X
7.	Greenville, Greenville North Pres.(f.Cong.; f.C of C of Freehold to 1808-1809,& to 1803; f.of Greenfield 1803-1808;f.*Newry (village))	1790(CG;2 sr) 1789(2 sr; pr.:98) 1814(Soc.) r.1824(PR:99)	NAP ? -1824/1825	jc.1825; 1819/1824-2000NS	X
8.	Hunter, Pres.(Edwardsville;org.PR forms in NAP; Fed.1939-1953 to Meth.(1825);1953 merged to Meth.as United Meth.)	1822	NAP:1822-pb.1822	(pb.j1822); 1819/1824-1953NS	X (see text)
9.	Jewett, Jewett Pres.(f.First Cong.of Lexington Heights;f.of Lexington to 1849;f.of *New Goshen to 1813;f.Second Cong.Soc.of Windham to 1813;nl.01T;pr.by 1800 as a branch of #1; lt.75:1852-1853OS)	1813(CG) r.1827(PR)	NAP:1813-1827	j1831; 1827-1865OS, 1865-onNS	Pres.
10.	Lexington, Lexington Flats Cong.(specifically Plan of Union;nl.01T)	1833(CG)	nl.	1832-1833, 1837/1838-1846/1847NS	X
11.	Sunside (PO), <u>Centerville</u> Pres.(*Durham)	1834(98)	-	1834/1835-1929NS	X
12.	Tannersville, Peoples Cong.(*Hunter)	1893(01N)	1894-1903	-	X
13.	Windham, Big Hollow Cong.	1802	NAP 1802- ?	-	X pb.soon

14.	Windham, Big Hollow Pres.(East;f.Second Pres.;f. Second Cong.;Maplecrest PO;claimed OS & NS: 1839-1846/1847;nl.01T)	1822(CG) r.1826(PR)	NAP 1822-?	1828-1846/ 1847NS, 1839-1857OS, 1857-1940NS	X
15.	Windham, Centre Pres.of Windham (Osbornville; Fed.to Meth.(1843) 1968-1972;1972 merged to U.Meth.as Windham Com.U.Meth.)	1834(2 sr)	-	1834/1835- 1973NS	X (see text)

NEW YORK - HAMILTON COUNTY (org.1816) (041)

A	B	C	D	E	F
1.	Long Lake, First Cong.	1842(98)	nl.	-	X by 1846(98)

NEW YORK - HERKIMER COUNTY (org.1791) (043)

A		B	C	D	E	F
	1.	Columbia, Cong.(1830 jPby.without dismissal from OE;in 1799 Ref.(RCA) bldg.)	by 1825(CG)	OE:1825-1831	j1830;1832-1843/1845NS	X
	2.	Danube, P or C Ch.	by 1834	nl.	1833-1843/1845NS	X
	3.	Fairfield, Cong.(nl.01T)	by 1819(CG)	nl.	j1819;1814/1818-1869NS	X
	4.	Frankfort, Pres.(Tr.to Ref.1829,(RCA,1830-1858 (85));1825 bldg.sold to Meth.1865)	1826	-	j1826; 1826-1829	Tr.to Ref.; X (see text)
	[5.	Glen's Purchase, Pres.(ps.in *Herkimer)	by 1793	-	j1793; nl.	X by 1794]
	6.	Herkimer, Pres.(79:in Ref.(RCA)bldg.)	by 1812	-	j1812;1809/1813-1834/1835	X
	[7.	Jersey Settlement, Pres.(on Mohawk River,seventy miles from Albany;ps.f.*Jerseyfield Patent, town uncertain)	by 1774	-	m.1774 (Synod min.)	X pb.soon]
	8.	Litchfield, Jerusalem Hill Pres.(f.First Cong.; nl.01T)	1796(CG;98) 1804(Soc.;98) r.1813(PR;98) 1811(22)	OE: ? -1812	j1812/1813; 1809/1813-1863NS	1876 merged to #15 as #17(q.v.)
	9.	Little Falls, First United Pres.(f.Ch.of Concord Union Soc.;f.1796 bldg.:98(1792:79);44:Ch.X bf.1813 & r.,but l.through;98:j Pby.1815,ps. af.r.;ch.left Soc.1831;f.village of Rockton 1850-1852;f.in Little Falls village pb.in *Herkimer to 1829;nl.01T)	1793(mixed: 2 sr) r.1800(44; PR:49) r.1805(Soc.) r.1812(2 sr) 1813(44) r.1823(Soc.: 98)	nl.	1794/1797-1840/1842NS 1842-onOS	Pres.
	10.	Manheim, P or C Ch.	by 1831	nl.	1830-1833	X
We	11.	Newport, *Bryn Scion* Welsh (Mt.Zion;l.only 70; nl.01T)	1830(70)	NYW: mnd.	-	X 1875(70)
	12.	Newport, Pres.(in 1844 union bldg.)	by 1852	-	1851-1869NS	X
	13.	Norway, Ch.in Calvary Soc.(f.Cong.;Union;Pres.: 98;nl.01T)	1798(CG;98)	MC:1798-?; pb.OE	j1819;1819/1824-1861NS	X
	14.	Norwich Corners, Cong.(division of #16:two factions:"Ch."&"Schlhse.";nl.01T;*Litchfield)	1846(CG:79)	nl.	-	1866 Merged to #16 to form #15(q.v.)
	15.	Norwich Corners, Cong.(merger of #14 & #16; *Litchfield)	1866 M(CG)	nl.	1866-1876NS	Merged to #8 to form #17(q.v.)

NEW YORK - HERKIMER COUNTY - continued

A	B	C	D	E	F
16.	Norwich Corners, Norwich Ch.& Soc.,Cong.(s. incor.1.Litchfield Soc.;specifically CG in Pby.bf.1824;see also #14;*Litchfield)	1798(CG;2 sr) 1799(98)	pb.OE:bf.1822; OE:1825-1834; 1834-1843, 1849-1852; cl.1853-1858	1814/1818-1819/1824, 1858-1866NS	1866 merged to #14 to form #15(q.v.)
17.	Norwich Corners, Pres.(f.Cong.;merger of #8 & #15;*Litchfield)	1876(CG) M r.af.1895 (PR:79)	nl.	1876-2002	X
18.	Ohio, Pres.(f.of West Brunswick to 1836)	by 1824	-	j1824; 1819/1824-1860NS, 1868-1869NS 1870-1890	X
[19.	Royal Grant, Pres.(ps.in *Norway)	by 1793	-	j1793; nl.	X by 1794]
20.	Russia, Pres.(Union Ch.:22;in Russia Union Soc.: 1818;f.town of *Union to 1808)	by 1809	-	j1809;1803/1808-1867NS	X 1875(22)
21.	Salisbury, First Pres.(f.Ref.,RCA 1822-1824:85; f.Cong.(99))	bf.1822(CG) Tr.1822(Ref.) Tr.1824(PR)	nl.	j1824; 1825-1860NS	X
22.	Salisbury, Second Pres.(f.Cong.;in 1795 bldg.; moved 1831;f.of *Palatine,Montgomery Co.to 1797)	1795(CG:98)	NAP m.1801	1843/1845-1846/1848NS	X 1845(98)
23.	Salisbury Center, Cong.(*Salisbury)	1910(01)	1910-1914	-	X
[24.	Spruce Creek, Pres.(pb.in *Salisbury)	by 1793	-	j1793; nl.	X by 1794]
25.	Warren, Cong.	by 1803(CG;44)	ps.OE bf.1822	1809/1813-1814/1818, 1829-1840/1842NS	X
26.	Warren, Cong.	1872(01N)	nl.	-	X pb.soon UCC
27.	West Winfield, Immanuel Cong.(f.First;f.Harmony Soc.;f.Summer Soc.to 1820;f.at (East)Winfield Center to 1876;moved 1816;f.l.Winfield; Second of Litchfield to 1816;Fed.to Bapt. (1796) & Meth.(1827)1945/1946-on as Fed.)	1799(01,98) 1791 1801(Soc.)	pb.OE bf. 1822; OE:1825-1834; 1834-on	-	

NEW YORK - JEFFERSON COUNTY (org.1805) (045)

A	B	C	D	E	F
1.	Adams, First Pres.(f.First Cong.Soc.;01T & cl. incor.:r.PR af.1858)	1804(CG;2 sr) 1800(11) 1803(?) 1805(Soc.) r.1821(PR; 2 sr)	BR:j1808-pb.1817; cl.1853-1858	j1821; 1819/1824-1951NS	X 1950
2.	Alexandria, First Pres.(Alexandria Bay Cong.;see also #28)	1821(CG;98) 1823(?)	nl.	1819/1824-1833	X
3.	Antwerp, First CC (reaffirm vote to be CG (r.) 1854;incor.l.UCC,had not voted)	1819(PR;2 sr) r.1849(CG)	cl.1853-1858; 1863-on	1819/1824-1854NS	UCC 1961;Sch.I late 1961-on
4.	Belleville, First Pres.of Ellisburgh	1829(99) 1820(Soc.) 1830(Soc.r.)	-	1829-1871NS	X
5.	Brownville, First Pres.	1818(3 sr)	-	1814/1818-1961NS	X
6.	Burrville, Cong.UCC (f.Burr Mills;in Watertown; claim is as #37 which was f.at this location)	1834(2 sr) 1833(Soc.) 1836(s.98) 1817(s.01) 1803(claim)	BR:j1834; 1834-on	-	UCC
7.	Cape Vincent, First Pres.(Fed.to U.Meth.1952-1994;1994 merged to Meth.as U.Meth.)	1823 1832(Soc.)	-	1819/1824-1994NS	X (see text)
8.	Carthage, First Cong.(West Carthage in *Champion;f.in East Carthage in *Wilna to 1852;see #9;Fed.to First Union Univ.(1902/1904)1922-1966 as United Chr.)	1835 1852(r.Soc.)	j1835; 1834-1966	-	Sch.I; merged to form M.
8M.	Carthage, United Com.(merger of #8 & First Union Univ.(1902/1904,left UUA 1965);in *Champion)	1966 M 1968(s.01)	1966-on	-	UCC
9.	Carthage, First Pres.(46A:r.of part of #8; *Wilna)	1851	(see text)	1851-1969NS	X
10.	Champion, Cong.(specifically Cong.in Pres.l.; also m.on Pby.l.as CG 1828-1829)	1801(CG;2 sr) 1805(Soc.;90) 1830(?)	BR:j1808-pb.1817; BR:1822-1834; 1834-1898; 1907-1909	1814/1818-1819/1824	X
11.	Chaumont, Pres.Soc.(First;*Lyme;f.Fed.to U.Meth. 1947-1956)	1831(98)	-	1831-onNS	Pres.
12.	Clayton, Cong.	1890(01N) 1891(s.01)	1890-1912	-	X
13.	Clayton, Pres.(f.Clayton & Orleans Cong.;nl.01T)	1835(CG;98)	cl.1853-1858	1839-1865NS	X
14.	DePauville, Cong.(at 1838 union bldg.;*Clayton)	by 1854	cl.1853-1858	-	X af.1858
15.	Dexter, First Pres.(*Brownville)	1839(98)	-	1839-onNS	Pres.

NEW YORK - JEFFERSON COUNTY - continued

A	B	C	D	E	F
16.	Ellisburgh, First Cong.	1817(CG;2 sr) 1823(Soc.)	ps.BR bf.1817	1819/1824-1851NS	X 1844:98
17.	Evans Mills, First Pres.of <u>LeRay</u> (f.Cong.;nl. 01T)	1814(CG;98) r.1825(PR)	ps.BR bf.1817 BR:1822-c.1825	j1825; 1819/1824-1837/1838, 1840-1861OS, 1861-onNS	Pres.
18.	Fineview, Cong.(*Orleans)	1894	1894-1895	-	X
19.	French Creek, P or C Ch.(pb.location;pb. *Clayton;Watertown Pby.)	by 1839	nl.	1837/1838-1839NS	X
20.	Henderson, Cong.(Pres.:98)	1819(CG) c.1820(s.98)	BR:1822-1823, by 1824-1834; 1834-1835/1836	j1823; nl. gone 1824	X
21.	LeRay, P or C Ch.(f.l.Evans Mills to 1839;nl. 01T)	by 1839	nl.	1837/1838-1852NS	X
22.	Lorraine, Cong.(specifically Cong.in Pres.l.)	by 1808(CG) 1829(98)	BR:j1808-ps. 1817; BR:1822-1834; 1834-1842, 1843-1856; cl.1856-1858	1814/1818-1819/1824	X (closed by 1854; bldg. sold 1858)
23.	Mannsville, Cong.(f.Second C of C & Soc.of Ellisburgh;s.incor.l.Morrisville;f.union to Bapt.(1831 merger of Lorraine Bapt.Soc.& Second Bapt.of Ellisburgh (1817))1833-1854; f.Fed.by 1919-1930 to unknown)	1833(2 sr) r.1834(2 sr) 1835(s.01)	BR:j1833-1834 1834-1950	-	X
24.	North Adams, Second Cong.of Adams (specifically Cong.on Pres.l.)	1809(CG:98) 1816(Soc.) 1839(r.Soc.)	ps.BR bf.1817 BR:1822-1834; 1834-1861	1814/1818-1819/1824	X
25.	Orleans, First Pres.of <u>LaFargeville</u> (f.Cong.;nl. 01T;X 1861:98)	1823(CG;98) r.1839(PR) r.1848(CG) r. ? (PR) 1854(Soc.r.)	BR:1822-bf. 1825	1819/1824-1837/1838, 1839-1898NS	X
26.	Oxbow, Oxbow Pres.Soc.of Antwerp (f.of Antwerp & Rossie (St.Lawrence Co.) to 1834 (see St. Lawrence Co.#48);s.l.Rossie & Oxbow;r.Asso. Ref.in 1837,affl.to 1858;l.Asso.Ref.1834(32); affl.Asso.Ref.NY 1858-1869;75H:Fed.to unknown 1962-1968,Ch.says never Fed.)	1820(PR;2 sr) r.1837(AR;2 sr) r.1869(PR)	-	1819/1824-1834; 1869-onOS	Tr.to AR; Tr.back; Pres.

A B C D E F

NEW YORK - JEFFERSON COUNTY - continued

27.	Philadelphia, Cong.(1854:asso.01T)	1841(CG;98) 1840(?) r.1859/1860 (PR) r.1868(CG)	j1841; 1840-1842, 1843-1853; cl.1853-1858; 1869-1975	1854-1871NS	Sch.I 1961-1975; X
28.	Plessis, Pres.(ps.#2;*Alexandria)	by 1834	-	1833-1909NS	X
29.	Rodman, Cong.UCC (Harrison Soc.;specifically CG on Pby.l.;f.of *Harrison to 1808)	1805(CG;2 sr) 1809(Soc.) 1834(r.Soc.) 1905[sic:s.01]	BR:1808-pb.1817; BR:1822-1834; 1834-1842, 1843-on	1814/1818-1819/1824	UCC
30.	Rutland, First Cong.UCC (First Relg.Soc.; specifically CG on 1819 Pby.l.;left Pby.1834)	1808(CG;2 sr) 1807(plan)	BR:j1808-pb.1817; BR:j1834; 1834-1842, 1843-on	j1824; 1814/1818-1833	UCC
31.	Sackets Harbor, Pres.(Fed.to Grace U.Meth.(1842) 1947-1982;merged to U.Meth.as United Pres.; *Hounsfield)	1816(2 sr) r.1982 M	-	1814/1818-onNS	Pres.
32.	Smithville, Cong. (left Pby.1829:98;*Henderson)	1824(CG) 1823(Soc.)	BR:j1829-1834; 1834-1842, 1843-1874	j1823/1824; 1819/1824-1833	X
33.	Theresa, Theresa Pres.(f.Flower Mem.)	1825 1835(Soc.)	-	1825-onNS	Pres.
34.	Thurso, Cong.(town uncertain)	1893(01N) 1892	1894-1895	-	X
35.	Watertown, Cong.	1830(98)	BR:1830-by 1831	-	X
36.	Watertown, Emmanuel Cong.UCC	1887(3 sr) 1886(s.01)	1886-on	-	Sch.I 1961-1965; UCC 1965-on
37.	Watertown, First Pres.(f.First Cong.;Watertown Eccles.Soc.;f.First Pres.-Cong.;Relg.Soc.of Watertown (Ctr.;1811),X by 1814;moved Burrville to Watertown 1815;specifically Cong.in 1819 Pres.l.;1968 ab.Faith Pres. (1959,l.75:1959-1968))	1803(CG;5 sr) 1801(pr.;22) 1811(Soc.) 1814(Soc.r.) 1817(?) r.1821(PR) r.1968 M	BR:j1808-pb.1817	j1821; 1814/1818-onNS	Pres.
38.	Watertown, Second Orth.Cong.Soc.(nl.01T)	1842	nl.	-	X af.1854
39.	Watertown, Stone Pres.(f.Second)	1831(4 sr)	-	1831-onNS	Pres.
40.	Wilna, First Pres.at Natural Bridge	by 1826(min) 1830(98)	-	1825-1840/1842NS; 1838-1876OS	X

NEW YORK - JEFFERSON COUNTY - continued

A	B	C	D	E	F
41.	Woodville, Cong.(f.l.Fed.,actually f.yoked to Meth.;*Ellisburgh)	1836(01,98)	j1837; 1835/1836-on	-	Sch.I 1961-1966; Sch.II 1966-on

NEW YORK - KINGS COUNTY (org.1683) (047)

A		B	C	D	E	F
	1.	New York City, Brooklyn, Bedford Ave.Cong.(f.of Brooklyn to 1898)	1849(01)	1851-1860, 1861-1883	-	X
	2.	New York City, Brooklyn, Beecher Mem.Cong.(f. Tabernacle;f.of Brooklyn to 1898)	1888(01) 1890(01N)	1889-1893	-	Merged to #41 to form #3(q.v.)
	3.	New York City, Brooklyn, Beecher Mem.Cong. (merger of #2 & #41;f.of Brooklyn to 1898)	1893 M	1893-1920	-	X
SF	Nt	New York City, Brooklyn, Bethel Cong.Swedish Finnish (EC:Rgn.:by 1910-1934)	1900(06)	nl.	-	EC; X
	4.	New York City, Brooklyn, Bethesda Cong.(f.of Brooklyn to 1898)	1897(01)	1897-1912	-	Merged to #32 to form #56(q.v.)
	5.	New York City, Brooklyn, Borough Park Cong. (Martense)	1901(s.01,21) 1903(s.01)	1903-1936	-	X (1924:21)
	6.	New York City, Brooklyn, Bushwick Ave.Cong.(f. Peoples Union;f.of Brooklyn to 1898)	1885(3 sr) 1891(s.01)	1884-1967	-	UCC 1961-1967; X
Bl	7.	New York City, Brooklyn, <u>Carrsville</u> Pres.(f. Colored;nl.27;pb.f.of Brooklyn to 1898)	by 1845	-	1843/1844-1855NS	X
	8.	New York City, Brooklyn, Central Cong.(f.of Brooklyn to 1898)	1854(01,21)	1853-1871	-	Merged to form #9
	9.	New York City, Brooklyn, Central Cong.(merger of #8 & Lee Ave.Ref.Prot.Dutch (RCA,1855-1871 (85));see also #57;f.of Brooklyn to 1898)	1871 M	1871-1937	-	Merged to #57 to form M.(q.v.)
	9M.	New York City, Brooklyn, Central Cong.(merger of #9 & #57)	1937 M	1937-1943	-	Merged to #10(q.v.)
	10.	New York City, Brooklyn, Clinton Ave.Cong.(f. Fed.to Simpson Meth.Epis.(1850)1935-ps.1937; f.of Brooklyn to 1898)	1847(01) 1854(21)	1847-1943	-	Merged to #9M. to form M.(q.v.)
	10M.	New York City, Brooklyn, Cadman Mem.Ch.,Cong. (merger of #9M. & #10;incor.l.as Fed.1960-1962)	1943 M	1943-1962	-	Sch.II 1961-1962; NA by 1961-on
	11.	New York City, Brooklyn, <u>Coney Island</u> Cong.(f.of *Gravesend to 1894;f.of Brooklyn to 1898)	1886(01N)	1885-1897, 1898-1901	-	X
	12.	New York City, Brooklyn, Ch.of Covenant,Cong. (bec.Trinity Cong.1892;r.as Bedford Pres.; merged 1944 to Central Pres.(f.First Ref. Pres.,1848,claimed by Ref.Pres.General Synod 1848-1899,Tr.to Pres.& r.1892,l.75:1891-1944),as Bedford-Central Pres.;merged 1961 to Classon Ave.Pres.(1867,l.75:1867-1961NS) as Bedford-Central Pres.;f.of Brooklyn to 1898)	1868(CG;2 sr) r.1894(PR) r.1944 M r.1961 M	1867-1894	j1896; 1893-on	Pres.
Sw	13.	New York City, Brooklyn, Covenant Cong.(f. Tabernacle Swedish Cong.;f.Swedish Evan. Mission;South Brooklyn;EC:Rgn.by 1910-1947, full 1947-1951)	1901(3 sr) 1902(?) r.1935	1902-1951	-	s.EC; X

NEW YORK - KINGS COUNTY - continued

A	B	C	D	E	F
14.	New York City, Brooklyn, Debevoise Pl.Cong.(f.of Brooklyn to 1898)	by 1851	1850-1851	-	X
15.	New York City, Brooklyn, Dyker Heights Cong. (f.incor.l.in Queens Co. 1915-1916)	1913	1915-1919	-	X
16.	New York City, Brooklyn, East Cong.(f.of Brooklyn to 1898)	1877(01)	1877-1900	-	X
17.	New York City, Brooklyn, Elm Pl.Cong.(merger of #28 & #59;f.of Brooklyn to 1898)	1853 M	1853-1874	-	Merged to #65 to form #70(q.v.)
bB 18.	New York City, Brooklyn, Ch.of Evangel,UCC (bec. predominantly Black by 1988)	1907(01)	1907-on	-	Sch.I 1961-1967; UCC 1967-on
19.	New York City, Brooklyn, Fifth Ave.Cong.(f.of Brooklyn to 1898)	1866(01N) 1868	1865-1868	-	X
20.	New York City, Brooklyn, Fifth Pres.(f.Cong., majority divided 1840 to #27;f.of Brooklyn to 1898)	1838(CG) r.1841(PR;27)	nl.	j1839; 1837/1838-1847NS	X (1842:27)
Fn 21.	New York City, Brooklyn, Finnish Golgotha Cong. (f.American Finnish Calvary Evan.)	1912(01,21)	1912-1989, 1990-on	-	Sch.II 1961-1989, 1990-on
22.	New York City, Brooklyn, First Pres.of Brooklyn (Cranberry St.;see also #23;f.of Brooklyn to 1898)	1822(3 sr)	-	1821-onNS	Pres.
23.	New York City, Brooklyn, First Pres.of Brooklyn (Remsen St.;claim is as #22;1875 ab.#64 as Clinton St.Pres.;1882 ab.#60 as New Second Pres.;1927 ab.Westminster Pres.(1856,l.75: 1855-1927NS) as Spencer Mem.Pres.;f.of Brooklyn to 1898)	1838 1822(claim) r.1875 M r.1882 M r.1927 M	-	1838-1979OS	X
24.	New York City, Brooklyn, First Pres.of Williamsburgh (E.D.);f.of Williamsburg to 1855;f.of Brooklyn to 1898;confused with South Third St.Pres.(1843/1844,l.1844-1946OS)by 27)	1843	-	1840/1842-1886NS	X
25.	New York City, Brooklyn, <u>Flatbush</u> Cong.	1899(01,21)	1899-1942	-	Merged to #68 to form M1.(q.v.)
25M1.	New York City, Brooklyn, Flatbush Tompkins Cong. (merger of #25 & #68)	1942 M	1942-1961	-	NA bf.1961; Merged to #40M. to form M2.(q.v.)
25M2.	New York City, Brooklyn, Flatbush Tompkins Cong. (merger of #25M1. & #40M.)	1961 M	1961-1979	-	Sch.II 1961-1979; NA 1961-on
26.	New York City, Brooklyn, Fourth Pres.(Gowanus; lt.by 27 as Gouanus;f.of Brooklyn to 1898)	1838(27)	-	1837/1838-1840/1842NS	X 1842(s.27; s.1838)

NEW YORK - KINGS COUNTY - continued

A	#	B	C	D	E	F
	27.	New York City, Brooklyn, Free Cong.(pb.continues Pearl & Willoughby St.division of #20 sv.by H.P.Tappen;later sv.by Mr.Sprague;f.of Brooklyn to 1898)	1840	m.1843-1845	-	X
	28.	New York City, Brooklyn, Fulton Ave.Cong.(f.of Brooklyn to 1898)	1851	1851-1853	-	Merged to #59 to form #17(q.v.)
Gr	29.	New York City, Brooklyn, Ger.Cong.(f.of Brooklyn to 1898)	1860(01N)	nl.	-	X pb.soon
Gr	30.	New York City, Brooklyn, Ger.Cong.Luth.(Ger. American Settlement;l.01K:1905/1906-1907/1910)	1904	1905-1909	-	X
Sp	31.	New York City, Brooklyn, Hispano-American Cong. (f.of Brooklyn to 1898)	1898(01)	1898-1912	-	X
	32.	New York City, Brooklyn, Immanuel Cong.(Patchen Ave.;merger of #45 & #53;f.of Brooklyn to 1898)	1897 M	1897-1912	-	Merged to #4 to form #56(q.v.)
	33.	New York City, Brooklyn, Kings Highway Cong. (Little Ch.in the Woods)	1911(s.01,21) 1910(s.01)	1911-1942	-	Merged to #40(q.v.)
	34.	New York City, Brooklyn, Lee Ave.Cong.(f.Chr. Endeavour;f.of Brooklyn to 1898)	1872(01N)	1871-1874, 1879-1901	-	Merged to #39 to form #71(q.v.)
	35.	New York City, Brooklyn, Lewis Ave.Cong.(Grace Cong.;f.of Brooklyn to 1898)	1877(s.01,21) 1880(01N) 1882(s.01)	1880-1951	-	X
	36.	New York City, Brooklyn, Mapleton Park Cong.(l. Sch.I incor.late 1961-1962,was Sch.II)	1911(01,21) 1912(s.05)	1914-1981	-	Sch.II 1961; Sch.I late 1961-1962; Sch.II 1962-1981; NA 1962-1980; X
	37.	New York City, Brooklyn, Navy Mission Cong.(f.of Brooklyn to 1898)	1867(01N)	1870-1872	-	X
Bl	38.	New York City, Brooklyn, Nazarene Cong.(f.of Brooklyn to 1898)	1873(several) 1872(s.01) 1883(s.01N)	1883-on	-	UCC
	39.	New York City, Brooklyn, New England Cong.of Williamsburgh (E.D.;f.of Williamsburg to 1855;f.of Brooklyn to 1898)	1851 1857(s.01)	1851-1901	-	Merged to #34 to form #71(q.v.)
	40.	New York City, Brooklyn, Ocean Ave.Cong.(f. Manhattan Terr.)	1903(01,21)	1903-1942	-	Merged to #33 to form M.(q.v.)
	40M.	New York City, Brooklyn, Ocean Ave.Cong.(merger of #33 & #40)	1942 M	1942-1961	-	NA by 1958-1961; Merged to #25M1. to form #25M2.(q.v.)
	41.	New York City, Brooklyn, Orient Ave.Union Cong. (f.Union Cong.of East New York to 1887/1888; f.of Brooklyn to 1898)	1883(01N)	1882-1893	-	Merged to #2 to form #3(q.v.)

NEW YORK - KINGS COUNTY - continued

A	B	C	D	E	F
	42. New York City, Brooklyn, Park Cong.(Park Pres. bought land 1857 (s.considered a r.of CG), PR bec.Lafayette Ave.Pres.1862(1857,j1857, 1.75:1857-onNS),but CG continued;f.of Brooklyn to 1898)	1854(CG)	1853-1856, 1862-1863	(see text)	X
	43. New York City, Brooklyn, Park Slope Cong.Fed. (f.Park Cong.;Fed.to First Ref.of Brooklyn (Midwout,RCA,1660-on:85) 1963-1970;& Mem. Pres.(1867,1.75:1866-onNS) 1961-1971;f.of Brooklyn to 1898)	1868(01N,21) 1867(s.01) 1866(s.01)	1867-1971	(see text)	Sch.I 1961-1962; UCC 1962-1971; X
	44. New York City, Brooklyn, Parkville CC (f. Greenfield Ch.of <u>Parkville</u>;f.Cong.of Cresco in <u>Greenfield</u> to 1868;f.of *Flatbush to 1894; f.of Brooklyn to 1898)	1866(3 sr) 1865(s.01) 1868(s.01)	1865-on	-	Sch.I 1961-1962; UCC 1962-on
	45. New York City, Brooklyn, Patchen Ave.Cong.(f.of Brooklyn to 1898)	1894 1899(21)	1894-1897	-	Merged to #53 to form #32(q.v.)
	46. New York City, Brooklyn, Pennsylvania Ave.Cong. (f.of Brooklyn to 1898)	1896	1896-1901	-	X
Sw	47. New York City, Brooklyn, Pilgrim Swedish Cong. Evan.(f.of Brooklyn to 1898;EC:Rgn.by 1910-1951,full 1951-1999)	1883(01,21) 1886(01N)	1885-1951	-	Tr.to EC; X
	48. New York City, Brooklyn, Ch.of Pilgrims,Cong. (f.of Brooklyn to 1898)	1844(01,21)	1846-1934	-	Merged to #49(q.v.)
	49. New York City, Brooklyn, Plymouth Cong.(f.of Brooklyn to 1898)	1847(01,21)	1847-1934	-	Merged to #48 to form M.
	49M. New York City, Brooklyn, Plymouth Ch.of the Pilgrims,Cong.(merger of #48 & #49)	1934 M(21)	1934-on	-	Sch.I 1961-1962; Sch.II 1962-on; NA 1961(j1962)-on
Bl	50. New York City, Brooklyn, Plymouth Cong.of <u>Canarsie</u> (Rockaway Ave.of Canarsie;f.l. Canarsie;f.of *Flatlands to 1896;f.of Brooklyn to 1898)	1888(s.01,21) 1886(s.01)	1887-on	-	Sch.I
	51. New York City, Brooklyn, Puritan Cong.(East Brooklyn;f.of Brooklyn to 1898)	1864(3 sr)	1864-1915	-	X
It	52. New York City, Brooklyn, Ch.of Redeemer,Italian Evan.	1903 1900	1903-1927	-	X
	53. New York City, Brooklyn, Rochester Ave.Cong.(f. Ch.of Mediator;f.of Brooklyn to 1898)	1866(s.01) 1861	1866-1897	-	Merged to #45 to form #32(q.v.)
	54. New York City, Brooklyn, Rugby Cong.	1912(s.01) 1913	1912-on	-	Sch.I 1961-on; NA by 1961-on

NEW YORK - KINGS COUNTY - continued

A		B	C	D	E	F
bB	55.	New York City, Brooklyn, St.Luke's Com.Fed.(f. Rockaway Ave.Cong.;bec.predominantly Black by 1975;Fed.to Brownsville Pres.(1.75:1958-1997) 1963-1997;f.of New Lots to 1886;f.of Brooklyn to 1898)	1868(01) 1839(?)	1870-1997	(see text)	Sch.I 1961-1968; UCC 1968-1997; Merged to form M.
	55M.	New York City, Brooklyn, St.Luke's UCC (merger of #55 & Brownsville Pres.(see above))	1997 M	1997-on	(see text)	UCC 1997-on
	56.	New York City, Brooklyn, St.Mark's Cong.(merger of #4 & #32)	1912 M	1912-1944	-	X
	57.	New York City, Brooklyn, St.Paul's Cong.(f.a branch of #9 1903-1916)	1903(01)	1916-1937	-	Merged to #9(q.v.)
Bl	58.	New York City, Brooklyn, St.Paul's Cong.of Flatbush (Colored;f.of Flatbush to 1898)	1857	cl.1856-1857, 1857-1863, 1864-1890	-	X
	59.	New York City, Brooklyn, Second Cong.(f.Bridge St.;f.First Free Cong.to 1847;Tr.from Pres. 1845;f.First Free Pres.to r.(Rev.Judd, Military & Lawrence Sts.);f.of Brooklyn to 1898)	1841(PR;27) Tr.1845 r.1847(CG)	1846-1853	nl.	Merged to #28 to form #17(q.v.)
	60.	New York City, Brooklyn, Second Pres.(1870 ab. #67 as Second Pres.;f.of Brooklyn to 1898)	1831 r.1870 M	-	j1831; 1831-1882OS	Merged to #23(q.v.)
Bl	61.	New York City, Brooklyn, Siloam Pres.(f.Colored; lt.27 as Silvan;f.of Brooklyn to 1898)	1847(2 sr) 1849(2 sr)	-	1848-onNS	Pres.
	62.	New York City, Brooklyn, Sixth Pres.(f.of Brooklyn to 1898)	1840(27)	-	1839-1840/ 1842NS	X 1843(27)
bB	63.	New York City, Brooklyn, South Cong.(bec. predominantly Black by 1975;f.of Brooklyn to 1898)	1851(01,09) 1850(21)	1851-1994	-	UCC; X
	64.	New York City, Brooklyn, South Pres.(f.of Brooklyn to 1898)	1842(21,27)	-	1840/1842-1875NS	Merged to #23(q.v.)
	65.	New York City, Brooklyn, State St.Cong.(f.First Cong.Meth.to 1861;f.of Brooklyn to 1898)	1848(C.Meth.) r.1861(CG)	1861-1874	-	Merged to #17 to form #70(q.v.)
	66.	New York City, Brooklyn, Stuyvesant Ave.Cong.(f. of Brooklyn to 1898)	1885(CG:01N)	1884-1894	-	X
	67.	New York City, Brooklyn, Third Pres.(f.of Brooklyn to 1898)	1835	-	j1835; 1834-1870NS	Merged to #60(q.v.)
	68.	New York City, Brooklyn, Tompkins Ave.Cong.(f. of Brooklyn to 1898)	1875(3 sr) 1877(01N)	1875-1942	-	Merged to #25(q.v.)
	69.	New York City, Brooklyn, Union Cong.(f.of Brooklyn to 1898)	1858	1861-1869	-	X
	70.	New York City, Brooklyn, Union Cong.(merger of #17 & #65;f.of Brooklyn to 1898)	1874 M	1874-1887	-	X

NEW YORK - KINGS COUNTY - continued

A	B	C	D	E	F
71.	New York City, Brooklyn, United Cong.(merger of #34 & #39)	1901 M	1901-1914	-	X
72.	New York City, Brooklyn, Warren St.Cong.(f. Mission Chap.;nl.01T;f.of Brooklyn to 1898)	1854	1853-1875	-	X
73.	New York City, Brooklyn, Williamsburgh Cong.(f. First Cong.of Williamsburg;f.of Williamsburg to 1855;f.of Brooklyn to 1898)	1843	cl.1853-1854, 1854-1865	-	X

NEW YORK - LEWIS COUNTY (org.1805) (049)

A	B	C	D	E	F
1.	Copenhagen, First Cong.(f.Cong.-Pres.Ch.;First Pres.of Denmark;f.Harrisburgh Eccles.Soc.of Harrisburgh to 1807)	1807(CG) 1805(Soc.) 1810(Soc.r.) r.1815(PR) 1825(01) 1839(new Soc.) r.1841(CG:98)	BR:1807/1808- ps.1817 j1839; 1838-1858	1819/1824- 1839NS	Merged to form #2(q.v.)
2.	Copenhagen, First Cong.(f.C of C;1857/1858 merger of #1 & Chr.Union (by 1852);Fed.to Meth.Epis.(1841) 1967-on as United;*Denmark)	1857 M(99) 1858(98,s.01) r.1868(CG) 1870(s.01) r.1880(98)	1869-on	-	UCC
3.	Deer River, First Cong.(1857 moved Denmark to Deer River(in Denmark);f.Second Pres.of Denmark;s.incor.l.Deep River;lt.1856-1858)	1826(PR;2 sr) 1827(s.98) 1828(s.01) r.1833(CG)	BR:j1834; 1834-1842, 1843-on	1826-1833	UCC
4.	Denmark, Union Cong.(in 1848/1849 bldg.)	1896(01)	1896-1992	-	Sch.I 1961-1992; X
Nt	Greig, Pres.(l.only 90;ps.bec.#11;ps.a branch or other type of Pres.;nl.32)	1807(90)			
5.	Harrisville, Cong.(*Diana)	1864(01) 1865(98)	1867-1894	-	X
6.	Houseville, Cong.(f.Second of Turin)	by 1808	BR:1807/1808- pb.1817; BR:j1833-1834 1834-1837	-	X
7.	Lewis, Second West Cong.of Leyden (f.of Leyden to 1852;lt.75:1825-1828;nl.01T)	1806(CG;98) 1826(90)	BR:1807/1808- pb.1817	j1826; 1825-1856NS	X
8.	Leyden, First Cong.(Leyden Hill;specifically CG in 1819 Pby.;left Pby.1835)	1803(98) 1807(?) 1826(Soc.) r.1836(98)	BR:1807/1808- pb.1817; j1835; 1834- 1835/1836, 1837-1842, 1843-1858	1814/1818- 1834/1835	X
9.	Lowville, First Cong.(North;Stowe's Sq.; specifically CG on 1819 Pby.l.;nl.01T;ps.r.PR 1819)	1803(CG;3 sr) (see text)	BR:1807/1808- pb.1817 (to 1819:98)	j1819; 1814/ 1818-1862NS	X
10.	Lowville, First Pres.(f.Village Ch.,Cong.)	1807(CG;2 sr) 1805(Soc.) r.1808(98) r.1820(98) r.1822(PR)	ps.BR bf.1817	1819/1824- onNS	Pres.

NEW YORK - LEWIS COUNTY - continued

A	B	C	D	E	F
11.	Lyons Falls, Forest Pres.(1893 moved from Lyons Falls in Lyonsdale to Lyons Falls in *West Turin;f.in Brantingham in Greig(s.l.Gregg)to 1849/1854(l.to 1843/1845);f.First Pres.of Watson to 1830;lt.75:1826-1828)	1826(4 sr)	-	1825-onNS	Pres.
12.	Martinsburg(h), Pres.(f.Cong.;nl.01T;in 1806 bldg.)	1809(CG;2 sr) 1804(90) 1810(Soc.:98) r.1812(PR;98)	ps.BR bf.1812	j1812; 1809/ 1813-1961NS	X 1960
13.	North Greig, Cong.(*Greig;in 1859 union Soc.)	1877(01N,98)	1876-1880	-	X
14.	Osceola, First Cong.(Camden,Oneida Co.,PO;nl. 01T)	1853(CG;2 sr) r.1872(01N)	1872-1980, 1984-on	1862-1872NS	UCC 1961-1980, 1984-on
15.	Port Leyden, First Cong.(f.of Port Leyden & Greig;nl.01T;f.Fed.to Meth.1922-1930;in *Leyden)	1854(01,98) 1851(Soc.:99) 1853(Soc.) 1859(Soc.r.) 1834(s.01)	1858-1963, 1964-1967	-	Sch.II 1961-1963, 1964-1967; CCCC 1965(j1966)-1980;pb.withdrew
We 16.	Tug Hill, Nebo Welsh Cong.(Welsh Hill;s.l.Tuck Hill;nl.01T;town uncertain,pb.*Montague)	1843(01,70)	NYW ? -1867; 1867-1884	-	X 1886:65 (1880:70)
17.	Turin, First Pres.(f.Cong.;in a union Soc.1827-1842;bf.1852 moved from West Turin to Turin Corners)	1802(CG;5 sr) 1801(12) 1803(44,s.98) r.1824(PR) r.1831(CG) r.1852(PR)	BR:1807/1808- pb.1817 BR:j1832- 1834; 1834-1842, 1843-1852	j1824; 1819/ 1824-1829; j1852; 1852- 1959NS	X 1958
We 18.	Turin, Welsh Cong.	1843(3 sr) 1848(full:70) 1861(65) 1868(Soc.)	NYW ? -1867; cl.1856-1858 1867-1884	-	X 1886:65 (1885:70)
19.	West Turin, Pres.Soc.at Constableville (f.Cong.; nl.01T)	1838(CG) 1835(Soc.) r.1843(PR)	nl.	1843/1845- 1877NS	X

NEW YORK - LIVINGSTON COUNTY (org.1821) (051)

A	B	C	D	E	F
1.	Avon, Free Ch.(Littleville;South Avon;Cong. forms;nl.01T)	1834(CG)	nl.	j1834; 1834/ 1835-1858NS	X 1856(51)
2.	Caledonia, First Pres.(Pres.Relg.Soc.;Tr.to OS 1837;f.of Southampton to 1806)	1805 1802(Soc.) r.1808	-	j1806/1809; 1803/1808-onOS	Pres.
3.	Conesus, P or C Ch.(1.75 af.X)	1831	nl.	j1832; 1833-1850NS	X 1839
4.	Dansville, Dansville Pres.(f.Dansville Village; in North Dansville;incor.OS in 98 to 1861;f. of Sparta to 1846;1861 ab.#6)	1825 r.1861 M	-	j1825; 1825-onNS	Pres.
5.	Dansville, First Pres.of Sparta & Dansville(f. United Cgn.of Dansville & Sparta;s.1.Sparta; f.United Cgn.of Ontario & Steuben;51:Pres. settlement at Williamsburg in Groveland 1795,Tr.to Ref.1805(RCA),Tr.to Pres.1805,nl. 75;98 does not connect Groveland sett.to this Ch.;51 also 1.a separate Ref.(RCA)sett.by 1795(1.as Dansville Ref.,Allegany Co.);85: says only one Ref.:1797-1819;98 says a c.1800 Dutch Ref.,Tr.to Pres.1806;98 says divided 1814,reunited 1828;1t.75:1819-1820/1824;f.in Sparta to 1846)	1797(85) 1795(51) 1800(90,98) Tr.1805(51) 1806(98) r.1819(98) 1820(s.48)	-	j1820; 1819-1828	Replaced by #25 & #4
6.	Dansville, Free Pres.(Second of Dansville;at Dansville village,in North Dansville;f.of Sparta to 1846)	1840	-	j1840; 1840/ 1842-1862NS	1861 merged to #4(q.v.)
7.	East Avon, First Pres.(f.Cong.Soc.;in Avon;f.of Hartford to 1808)	1795(PR;3 sr) r.1810(CG) r.1842(PR)	nl.	nl.; j1822; 1820/ 1824-onNS	X soon; r.; Pres.
8.	Fowlerville, Pres.(f.Cong.;f.Second of York; unassod.1854:01T)	1826(CG;98) 1832(51) r.1878(PR)	cl.1853-1855; 1855-1877	j1829(48,51); 1826-1856NS, 1878-1922	X
9.	Geneseo, Second Pres.(White Ch.;f.First of Geneseo at Geneseo village;f.Geneseo Gospel Soc.;f.First Cong.;1880(1870:51) merged to Central Pres.(1858,1.75:1858-1880OS) as Central Pres.)	1810(CG;5 sr) 1809(48) 1815(Soc.) r.1817(PR:26, 51) 1818(PR:s.48) 1814(99) r.1834(PR:98, s.51) r.1880 M 1870(51)	OA:1811-1813	j1814; 1813-onNS	Pres.

NEW YORK - LIVINGSTON COUNTY - continued

A	B	C	D	E	F
10.	Groveland, Groveland Pres.(left NS Pby.1838,l. through to #11;98 says 1842 merged to #11, which makes no sense;Fed.to Meth.1985-on as Groveland Fed.Par.)	1809(PR) 1829(99) 1795(claim: 98:as #5)	-	j1819; 1818-1840/1845NS; j1842; 1841-onOS	Pres.
11.	Groveland, Pres.(98 says merged to #10 1842, which makes no sense)	1842(51)	-	j1842; 1840/1845-1850NS	X
12.	Lakeville, Cong. (*Livonia)	by 1853	cl.1853-1858	-	X
13.	Lakeville, Pres.(*Livonia;f.First Pres.of Geneseo;moved 1824;moved over town line 1855 (99;by 1848(48));f.Cong.;nl.01T;l.by Pres.af. merged)	1795(PR) r.c.1806(CG) r.1810(PR)	nl.	j1802; 1803/1808-1931NS	1922 Merged to form M.(q.v.)
13M.	Lakeville, Com.Cong.(f.Com.to 1928;j CG 1928;in *Livonia;merger of #13 & Chr.of Lakeville (1818,*Livonia;f.of South Lima in *Lima to 1850;l.by Chr.to 1923,1927-1930))	1922 M 1928(s.01)	1929-on	(see text of #13)	UCC
14.	Leicester, Pres.of Moscow (1845 merged to Pres. (1837/1838,l.75:1837-1845OS) as Leicester Pres.)	1817 1818(Soc.) r.1845 M	-	j1818; 1818-1850NS 1845-onOS	Pres.
15.	Lima, Lima Pres.(f.named Cong.to 1851;Charleston Relg.Soc.;f.of Charleston to 1808)	1795(PR) r.1799(CG) 1802(Soc.) r.1820(PR)	OA:j1800-1813	j1820; 1819-onNS	X c.1797; r.; Pres.
16.	Livonia, Com.Cong.	1925 1924(?)	1925-1972	-	UCC 1961-1972; X
17.	Livonia Center, First Pres.of Livonia (f.Cong.; f.Second Cong.of Pittstown to 1808;voted CG form 1830,but not approved to 1832;01T:PR form by 1854,pb.aware of 1813 vote & not 1830/1832)	1806(CG) r.1813(PR) r.1832(CG) r.af.1881(PR: 98)	OA:j1807-1813	j1813; 1812-onNS	Pres.
18.	Mount Morris, Mount Morris United Pres.(f.First; f.of Leicester to 1818)	1814	-	j1817; 1815/1816-onNS	Pres.
19.	Mount Morris, Second Pres.(drop from Pby.1840: 48)	1830(3 sr) 1831(s.48)	-	j1831; 1830-1840/1845NS	X 1839(46A,51)
20.	North Avon, P or C Ch.(in Avon)	by 1818	nl.	j1818; 1817-1818	X
21.	Nunda, Pres.(First;98 says 1835 r.is as PR, which would indicate f.Cong.,51 says PR at start;nl.01T;Fed.to Amer.Bapt.1967-on as Trinity Fed.)	1831(pb.CG; 4 sr) 1832(s.48) r.1835(PR)	nl.	j1832; 1831-onNS	Pres.

NEW YORK - LIVINGSTON COUNTY - continued

A	B	C	D	E	F
22.	Ossian, Ossian Pres.	1818	-	j1825(48); 1819-1858NS; j1868; 1868-onNS	Pres.
23.	Portage, Pres.(Oakland;f.First of Nunda to 1827; had a branch at Hunt's Hollow 1830-1848;1848 merged to Nunda Pres.(by 1847,l.75: 1846-1848OS) as Portage OS at Oakland)	1819(2 sr) 1820(s.98) r.1848 M	-	j1820; 1819-1852NS 1848-1870OS	X
24.	South Livonia, Cong.(in Livonia)	1930	1930-on	-	UCC
25.	Sparta, First Pres.(Haven's Corners;Groveland PO;merged to Pres.(l.1838-1852OS))	1828 r.1852 M	-	1828-1852NS, 1852-onOS	Pres.
26.	Springwater, Pres.(f.Cong.;01T:PR form by 1854, pb.aware of 1827 vote & not 1837;01T l.as Springfield)	1821(CG) r.1827(PR) r.1837(CG) r.1870(PR:51)	nl.	j1827/1829; 1826-1920NS	X
27.	Tuscarora, First Pres.(f.Second Pres.of Mount Morris to 1852;f.First Prot.Ref.Dutch Ch.of Mount Morris (RCA,1839-1847:85))	1839(Ref.) Tr.1846(PR:98)	-	j1846; 1840/ 1845-1853NS, 1852-onOS	Pres.
28.	Tuscarora, <u>Union Corners</u> Pres.(incor.l.OS:75H)	1851	-	1851-1890NS	X
29.	West Sparta, Pres.(f.Second of Sparta to 1846 (48);not to be confused with Second Pres.of Sparta (Groveland Station PO,1847,l.75:1847-1907OS))	1825	-	j1825; 1825-1851NS	X
30.	York, First Cong.(s.First Pres.;York Ctr.)	by 1825(CG)	cl.1853-1858	j1828/1830; 1820/1824-1851NS	X af.1860's

NEW YORK - MADISON COUNTY (org.1806) (053)

A	B	C	D	E	F
1.	Canaseraga, P or C Ch.(s.confused with #5; s.confused with village in Burns,Allegany Co.;*Lenox)	by 1832	nl.	j1832; 1831-1834/1835	X
2.	Canastota, Indep.(Free Ch.;CG,but l.26;*Lenox)	1845(26)	cl.1853-1858	-	X af.1858
3.	Cazenovia, First Free Ch.(First Cong.;Free Cong.)	by 1834	OE:j1834; 1834-1836, 1837-1838, 1839-1840, cl.1853-1858	-	X 1858/1872
4.	Cazenovia, First Pres.(f.Cong.;01T & cl.:r.PR af.1858,pb.incor.)	1799(CG;5 sr) 1798(Soc.) 1796(39) r.1834/1841 (PR:99) 1709[sic:44]	ps.OE bf.1807; ML 1807-1810; cl.1853-1858	j1808; 1809/1811-onNS, 1840-1843OS	Pres.
5.	Chittenango, Cong.(Pres.in 98;see also #1,#23; in Sullivan)	c.1831(CG;98)	CEA:1834-1835	j1835; nl. left 1835	X (bldg.sold 1844)
6.	DeRuyter, Cong.(Fed.to Meth.Epis.(1817/1830) 1946-1968)	1896(01) 1890 1898	1896-1968	-	Sch.I 1961; UCC late 1961-1968; Merged to form M.
6M.	DeRuyter, United Ch.of DeRuyter,UCC (merger of #6 & Meth.Epis.(1817/1830))	1968 M	1968-on	-	UCC
7.	DeRuyter, Cong.(s.named Pres.)	1804(CG;2 sr) 1805(s.48) c.1830(99)	ps.OE bf.1811; UA:1811-1822; cl.1853-1858	1819-1880NS	X
8.	Eaton, Com.(f.Village Cong.;bec.Com.1961;bec. Bible 1998)	1831(s.01,98) 1833(s.01)	OE:j1833-1834; 1834-1848, 1849-1912, 1913-on	-	Sch.II
9.	Georgetown, Cong.Free (98 says this Ch.was Pres.,and later a Free Cong.was org.,minutes do not support this;nl.48:f.of *DeRuyter to 1815)	1810(CG)	UA ? -1822/1829; OE:j1831-1834; 1834-1866	nl.	X (bldg. sold 1874)
10.	Hamilton, Cong.(Second,Village;apply OE 1826,not j to 1828)	1824 1828(01,98)	(see text) OE:j1828-1834 1834-1866, 1867-1929	-	X

NEW YORK - MADISON COUNTY - continued

A	B	C	D	E	F
11.	Lebanon, Cong.(Third Cong.C of C of Hamilton to 1807;Fed.to Bapt.(1816) 1920-on as Fed.; lt.1850-1851;assod.1854:01T)	1802(01,98) 1806 1709[sic:44]	OE ? -1808; UA:1808-pb. 1829; OE:j1830-1834 1834-1853; cl.1853-1858; 1861-1862, 1870-on	-	Sch.I 1961-1962; UCC 1962-on
12.	Lenox, Cong.of Lenox & <u>Sullivan</u> (First of Lenox; f.East of Sullivan to 1809;48 says pb.in ML, but nl.minutes)	1804/1805(CG; 48) 1810(98)	nl.	1809/1811- 1815/1816	1817 merged to #27 to form #13(q.v.)
13.	Lenox, First Pres.at Quality Hill (merger of #12 & #27;nl.48)	1817 M(CG) r.af.1858(PR: 01T)	cl.1853-1858	1815/1816- 1906NS, 1912-1918	X
14.	Lenox, Second Ch.(P or C;see also #23)	by 1820	nl.	1819-1831	X
15.	Madison, Cong.(f.First of Hamilton to 1808)	1796(01,98) 1795(90)	OE ? -1808; UA 1808-1826; OE:1826-1834; 1834-1908	-	X
16.	Morrisville, Cong.(f.Morris Flats;in Eaton;f. Fourth Ch.of Hamilton to 1807;left Pby.1842; jUCC 1962,incor.l.UCC late 1961-1962; Fed.to Bapt.(1809) 1925-1968 as United Fed.;nl.48)	1805(CG;3 sr) 1817(Soc.) 1818(Soc.r.) r.1819(PR) r.1821(CG) 1709[sic:44]	OE:j1805- 1808; UA:1808-1819/ 1822; j1842 1841-1968	j1819; 1819/ 1824-1831, 1833-1840/ 1842NS	Sch.I 1961; UCC late 1961-1968; Merged to form M.(q.v.)
16M.	Morrisville, Com.Pres.(merger of #16, Bapt. (1809) & Meth.(1834))	1968 M	(see text)	1968-on	Pres.
17.	Munnsville, First Cong.(in Stockbridge;f.Pres.; f.l.New Stockbridge,f.l.West Stockbridge;f.of Augusta(Oneida Co.)& Smithfield to 1836,see Oneida Co.#3;see also #26;left Pby.1842; assod.1854:01T;nl.48)	1818(CG;2 sr) 1828(s.01,98) r.1829(PR) r.1836(CG: 98,99) 1820(?) 1833(?)	OE ? bf.1821; 1841-1844/ 1845, 1852-1853; cl.1853-1856; 1856-on	j1821; 1819/ 1824-1840/ 1842NS	Sch.I 1961-1962; Sch.II 1962-1986; UCC 1986-on
18.	Nelson, Cong.(s.l.Pres.)	by 1813(CG) 1794/1813 (48)	UA 1813-1822	j1825; 1822/ 1824-1846/ 1848NS	X 1848(98)
We 19.	Nelson, Peniel Welsh Com.(First Welsh;Nelson Flats;Cazenovia PO;Fed.1922-1963 to unknown; l.as Com.1962-1987;Tr.to Eng.Assn.1930; nl.01T)	1850(5 sr)	NYW ? -1867; 1867-1987	-	Sch.I 1961-1969; Sch.II 1969-1987; X (alive in 70:1993)

NEW YORK - MADISON COUNTY - continued

A	B	C	D	E	F
In 20.	New Stockbridge, Indian Ch.(Ch.org.1734 at Stockbridge,Berkshire Co.MA was org.to sv. Stockbridge (Mahican) tribe;it bec.mostly European, Native Americans r.as this Ch. & immediately moved here;divided into two factions 1786-1792,one faction SUF 1774/1787-1788/1793;r.1802 by ab.group from Delaware (Munsee)tribe of NJ(f.sv.by Pres.),& a group from the mixed Indian sett.in Brotherton, Oneida Co.;tribe bec.Stockbridge-Munsee tribe; r.1818 in order to be removed to West; joined in move by some of Oneida tribe;af. pausing 1818-1821 nr.White River at Pequot, IN, sett.1821/1822 at Statesburgh,nr.South Kaukauna,Outagamie Co.,WI;again moved 1834 to Stockbridge,Calumet Co.WI;cgn.died there 1859;nl.48)	1785(CG:MA) 1786(sett.) r.1802 r.1818	nl.	1774/1787-1788/1793	majority removed 1818, part here to af.1825; X
In 21.	Oneida, Indian Ch.(sv.Oneida tribe;aided by Scottish Soc.1764-Revolutionary War;mission r.1785;under Northern Missionary Soc.1797-1808;pb.not fully org.;nl.48;most of tribe moved to WI by 1840)	1759(pr.) 1764(69) 1766(08)	nl.	nl.	X af.1808 (some j to Stockbridge migration;Epis. mission here 1816)
22.	Oneida Depot, Cong.(in Oneida)	by 1854	cl.1853-1858	-	X af.1858
23.	Oneida Lake, First Cong.(at Lakeport in Sullivan (from 1846);f.Union Cong.Soc.of Lenox & Sullivan(1814,Soc.r.in Lenox 1824,Soc. X 1842);f.Sullivan Cong.Soc.(1813),Second Ch.of Sullivan;Chittenango Station PO;Canastota PO; Soc.vote 1909 to reaffirm CG form,l.75 af. withdrew;nl.01T;f.l.Fed.1922-1946,but ch.says yoked,not Fed.;48 confuses with #5 & #14)	1813(CG;s01) 1809(s.01) 1812(?) 1814(Soc.r.) 1824(Soc.r.) 1826(s.01) 1846(Ch.& Soc.r.)	1857-1859, 1909-1984	j1819; 1819-1840/1841NS, 1842-1854NS, 1859-1918NS	Sch.I 1961-1963; UCC 1963-1984; withdrew
24.	Peterborough, Pres.(f.Cong.;in Smithfield;01T: unassod.1854,but l.in Pby.;48 says ps.in ML, but not in min.)	1806(CG;98) 1820(?)	cl.1853-1858; 1863-1867	1809/1811-1862NS	X 1870
25.	Poolville, Cong.(First of Hamilton;moved Hamilton Ctr.to Poolville 1840/1842;f.Second Cong.Soc.of Hamilton to 1807)	1798(98)	OE ? -1808; UA:1808-1829; OE:1829-1834; 1834-1866	-	X
26.	Stockbridge, Cong.(f.a branch of #17 to 1834)	1834(98)	OE:j1834; 1834-1863	-	X (by 1872:98)
27.	Sullivan, Bethzura Pres.(only in 98;nl.32,48,75; ps.only a branch of another Ch.f.of *Cazenovia to 1803)	c.1802(98)	-	nl.	1817 merged to #12 to form #13(q.v.)

NEW YORK - MADISON COUNTY - continued

A	B	C	D	E	F
28.	Wampsville, Wampsville Pres.(in Oneida;f.Fourth Ch.of Lenox to af.1860;Tr.to OS 1841,Tr.to NS 1844)	1828(3 sr) 1832(39) 1829(Soc.)	-	j1829; 1828-1840/1841NS, 1840-1843OS, 1843/1845-1994NS	X
We 29.	West Eaton, Welsh Cong.(Leeville;*Eaton;union to Welsh Calvinistic Meth.to 1851;nl.68,01T)	1850(70)	NYW:mnd.	-	X 1860(70)
30.	Whitelaw, First Pres.(division of #23;Canastota PO;f.First Pres.of Ridgeville;First Pres.Soc. of Lenox;f.Third of Lenox)	1826(4 sr) 1827(48) r.1878	-	j1827; 1826-1860NS, 1878-on	Pres.

NEW YORK – MONROE COUNTY (org.1821) (055)

A	B	C	D	E	F
1.	Adams Basin, P or C Ch.(in Ogden;1813 date in 98 only,ps.confused with #23;nl.51)	1837(48) 1813(98)	nl.	j1837; 1839/ 1845-1853NS	X
2.	Brighton, Brighton Pres.(First Cong.Soc.;in Rochester from 1857;left GC 1842)	1817(CG;4 sr) 1816(22) r.1870(PR)	GC:j1829(ps. by 1825)- 1834; 1834-1842, 1850-1869	j1846; 1839/ 1845-1846/ 1848NS; j1870; 1870-on	Pres.
Nt	Brighton, Free Pby.(apply to j Pres.,not admitted nor fully org.;now in *Rochester)	1833	-	(see text)	X
3.	Brockport, Cong.(in Sweden)	1834	nl.	-	X by 1841
4.	Brockport, First Pres.(f.First Cong.Soc.;in Sweden;af.1841 CG vote X & r.PR same year)	1828(CG) 1827(Soc.) r.1834(PR) r.1841(CG) r.1841(PR)	nl.	j1828; 1829-1841NS; j1841; 1841-1857NS; j1864; 1864-onNS	Pres.
5.	Bushnell's Basin, P or C Ch.(1831 bldg.;incor.l. j Pby.1843(51),but implies 1833;in Perinton; in Irondequoit in 51)	1833(2 sr) 1832(s.48)	nl.	j1833/1834; 1832-1834/ 1835	X 1834
6.	Carthage, P or C Ch.(location uncertain)	by 1819	nl.	j1819; 1819- 1820/1824	X 1822
7.	Chili, First Pres.(f.Cong.;Rochester PO;f.East Pres.of Riga to 1822;f.Coldwater PO)	1816(CG) r.1833(PR) r.bf.1841(CG) r.1874(PR)	cl.1853-1858	j1819; 1818-onNS	Pres.
8.	Churchville, Pres.(in Riga)	1832(51) 1833(?)	-	j1832/1833; 1832-1846/ 1848NS, 1851-1853NS	r.as #9
9.	Churchville, UCC Union Cong.(in Riga;r.of #8)	1852	cl.1853-1855; 1855-on	-	UCC
10.	Clarkson, CC (r.of #11,hence claim;1825 bldg.)	1910 1816(claim)	1910-1974	-	Sch.I 1961-1974; pb.withdrew
11.	Clarkson, Pres.of Clarkson Corners (f.Cong.;f. First Cong.Soc.of Murray (Orleans Co.)to 1819;98:j Pby.1830,pb.means r.)	1816(CG) r.1825(PR:s. 98) 1830(s.98) r.1853(CG) r.1869(PR:98) 1868(51)	cl.1853-1858	j1819; 1818-1852NS, 1869-1909	r.as #10

NEW YORK – MONROE COUNTY – continued

12.	Fairport, First Cong.in Perinton (s.incor.l. Perington)	1824(4 sr)	GC:(ps.1824)- -1834; 1834-1842; GC:1842- ? by 1848; 1849-1852; cl.1853-1854; 1854-1855; cl.1855-1858; j1864; 1861-on	-	UCC
13.	Gates, Gates Pres.(First;Rochester PO;f. Coldwater PO;nl.01T)	1831(CG) 1828(Soc.) r.1834(PR:51, 98)	nl.	j1831; 1831-onNS	Pres.
14.	Greece, Parma & Greece Pres.(f.First Cong.of <u>Parma</u> & Greece;f.of Parma & Gates to 1822; org.in Parma,at Parma Corners;open bldg.in Greece at Parma line 1825;lt.75:1819-1820/1824(both names);j Pby.by 1817:51;Tr.to OS 1854;nl.01T;see also #15)	1819(CG) r.1846(PR)	GC:1830-1834; 1834-1842; GC:1842- by 1848	j1819/1820; 1818-1830; j1844; 1839/1845-1856NS, 1853-1862OS	X 1861
15.	Greece, <u>West Greece</u> Cong.(<u>Parma</u> & Greece Cong.; claim is as #14)	1846 1819(claim)	1848-1890	-	X (c.1885:98)
16.	Henrietta, UCC (f.East;f.of Pittsford to 1818)	1816(CG;3 sr) 1818(s.01,09) 1867(?)	GC:j1835; 1834-1841, 1851-on	j1833-1835, nl.	UCC
17.	Honeoye Falls, First Pres.(f.of Nortons Mills;f. West of Mendon;s.l.<u>West Mendon</u>;Weston;no CG period in 51)	1828(CG;22) r.1831(PR)	nl.	j1831; 1831-onNS	Pres.
18.	Irondequoit, Cong.	1903	1903-1909	-	X
19.	Irondequoit, United (f.Union Cong.;Rochester PO; SS:1850(99;1851:22))	1911(01,99) 1912(s.01)	1911-on	-	UCC
20.	Mendon, Central Cong.Soc.(see also #21;moved 1839)	1815(Soc.) 1818(?) 1820(Soc.r.)	GC:1818-1834; 1834-1842; GC:1842- by 1848	-	X af.1842
21.	Mendon, Mendon Pres.(First,East Mendon;s.claim to continue #20 af.1820 division)	1822(2 sr) 1823(48)	-	j1823; 1820/1824-onNS	Pres.
22.	Mumford, Mumfordville Cong.(in Wheatland)	by 1840	1839-1842; GC:1842- by 1848	-	X af.1842

NEW YORK – MONROE COUNTY – continued

A	B	C	D	E	F
23.	Ogden, Pres.(First;at Ogden Ctr.;Spencerport PO; f.Cong.;f.of Parma to 1817;51 says org.as PR;left Pby.first time 1826;m.on Pby.l.as CG: 1828-1829;left GC 1835;see also #1)	1811(CG) r.1835(PR) 1836(?)	GC:1826-1834; 1834-1838	j1815; 1814-1825; j1835; 1834/ 1835-onNS	Pres.
24.	Ogden, Stone Ch.Cong.	1867	1867-1870	-	X
25.	Parma, Parma Ctr.Cong.(98 says majority of #26)	1842	pb.GC:1842- by 1848	-	X af.1844
26.	Parma, Pres.(Parma Ctr.;pb.Cong.to r.;see also #25;nl.01T)	1829(pb.CG) r.1842(pb.PR)	nl.	j1829; 1827-1969NS	X
27.	Parma Corners, P or C Ch.(in Parma)	1830	nl.	j1830; 1830-1831	X
28.	Penfield, First Pres.(South Pres.;f.First Cong.; f.of Boyle to 1810;f.Northfield Soc.;named Pres.1806,but no elders to 1814;Tr.to OS 1850;Tr.to NS 1857)	1804(CG) 1806(51,98) r.1814(PR)	OA:1806-1813	j1814; 1813-1850NS, 1849-1856OS, 1857-1883NS	X
29.	Pittsford, First Pres.(f.Second Cong.Ch.of Northfield;f.Cong.Soc.of Stonetown;f.of Smallwood to 1814;f.of Boyle to 1813;f.of Northampton to 1808;98:r.PR 1814,pb.means j Pby.)	1809(CG;90) 1807(Soc.) r.1869(PR) (see text)	OA:1809-1813; cl.1853-1858	j1814; 1813-onNS	Pres.
30.	Riga, First Cong.(f.Pres.;Riga Corners;West Riga;Churchville PO;left Pby.(first time) 1838,ps.re-j by 1845,l.through;1854:in Pby.: 01T;22 says f.First Cong.of West Pulteney (Steuben Co.;Bergen,Genesee Co.PO) which makes no sense)	1809(CG;2 sr) 1800(12) 1806(s.01,90) 1810(s.48)	OA:1812-1813; 1838-1842; GC:1842- by 1848; 1853-on	j1817; 1817- 1846/1848NS, 1852-1856NS	UCC
31.	Rochester, Brick Pres.(f.Second;f.in Gates to 1834;divided to Second Pres.1848,l.75:1848- 1853OS,Tr.to Ref.1854(51)(RCA,First Ref., 1852-on:85))	1825(2 sr)	-	j1825; 1825-1974NS	Merged to #32 & #34, See #34.
32.	Rochester, Central Pres.(f.Washington St.Pres.; f.Bethel;not in Pby.1843-1844)	1836(4 sr) 1837(48)	-	j1836; 1836-1974NS	Merged to #31 & #34, See #34.
33.	Rochester, Durand Cong.(f.l.Seabreeze;f.l.Point Pleasant;in Irondequoit)	1918 1916(s.01)	1918-on	-	UCC
34.	Rochester, First Pres.(f.First Pres.of Gates in Rochesterville to 1822;f.in Gates to 1834;Tr. 1854 to OS;if org.1810,ps.CG to 1815,no CG period in 51;nl.01T;1974 merged to #31 & #32 as Downtown Pres.)	1815(PR;2 sr) 1810(22) r.1974 M	nl.	j1816; 1815/ 1816-1854NS, 1853-onOS	Pres.
35.	Rochester, First Pres.Free Ch.& Soc.(f.in Gates to 1834;nl.86)	1832	-	j1832; 1832-1839/ 1845NS	X 1838

NEW YORK - MONROE COUNTY - continued

36.	Rochester, Fourth Pres.(f.Fifth Pres.to 1844; nl.86;s.confused with Fourth Pres.,which bec. North Rochester Pres.(1884,SS:1869(22),l. 75:1882-1959),merged to Ch.of Evangel(Italian Pres.1909,l.75:1909-1959)as Christ Pres.(l. 75:1959-1989,X))	1838(51)	-	j1838; nl.(long Pby.lacuna)	X 1848
37.	Rochester, Free Cong.(f.of Gates & Brighton to 1834)	1836(86)	1836-1840	-	X
38.	Rochester, Lakeside Pres.(f.Charlotte Pres.to 1916;in Greece;Tr.to OS 1855)	1852(51,98) 1851(22)	-	j1852; 1852-1854NS; j1855; 1854-onOS	Pres.
Nt	Rochester, Mount Hor Pres.(incor.l.by 22 as org. 1823;org.1893,l.75:1893-on;bec.New Life Com. Ch.1974)				
39.	Rochester, North Cong.	1918	1918-1927	-	X
40.	Rochester, Plymouth Cong.(in 1853 bldg.;1854: assod.:01T)	1853(s.86,98) 1855(01,s.86) 1854(Soc.) 1851(?)	cl.1853-1854; 1854-1904	-	X
41.	Rochester, Saint Paul St.Cong.(1854:unassod.: 01T;r.as Calvary Pres.,a new org.in most sources;f.Fed.to St.Andrews Epis.1968-2001; 2001 merged to Epis.to form Calvary-St. Andrews Pres.Par.)	1848(CG) 1837(22) r.1856(PR) r.2001 M	cl.1853-1854; 1854-1855; cl.1855-1856	1856-onOS	Pres.
42.	Rochester, South Ave.Cong.(nl.86)	1847	nl.	-	X pb.soon
43.	Rochester, South Cong.UCC	1886	1885-1987	-	UCC 1961-1987; Merged to form M1.
43M1.	Rochester, South Emmanuel UCC (merger of #44 & Evan.Ref.Emmanuel (UCC,f.Free Ger.Cath.,1848, r.1852))	1987 M	1987-1996	-	UCC 1987-1996; Merged to form M2.
43M2.	Rochester, Trinity South Emmanuel UCC (merger of Trinity Ger.Evan.(E&R,UCC,1842) & #43M1.)	1996 M	1996-on	-	UCC
44.	Rochester, State St.Cong.(North Cong.;First Cong.:86)	1841(Soc.) c.1842(86)	cl.1853-1856	-	X 1856
45.	Rochester, Third Pres.(f.of Brighton to 1834)	1827 1826(incp.)	-	j1827; 1826-1850NS, 1849-onOS	Pres.
46.	Rochester, Winton Cong.	1928	1928-1951	-	X
47.	Rush, Cong.(same as #48:51;left Pby.1823)	by 1818(CG)	nl.	j1818; 1818-1820/1824	X 1823

NEW YORK - MONROE COUNTY - continued

A	B	C	D	E	F
48.	Rush, Cong.(same as #47:51)	by 1830(CG)	nl.	j1829/1830; 1829-1846/ 1848NS	X 1843
49.	Spencerport, First Cong.(in Ogden;22 calls First Pres.& early date,not otherwise supported)	1850(01,98) 1805(22)	1850-on	-	UCC
50.	Sweden, First Pres.,Sweden Ctr.(f.First Cong. Soc.;nl.01T)	1817(CG) 1816(Soc.) r.1833(PR)	nl.	j1819; 1818-1936NS	X
51.	Webster, Webster Pres.(f.Cong.;Second of Penfield to 1840;f.North Penfield & Ontario; 51 says PR at start,98 & 46A say CG, r.PR; 1840 pastor called by Soc.,not session;Tr.to OS 1849;nl.01T)	1825(CG) c.1820(99) r.1829(PR) 1829(Soc.)	nl.	j1825; 1834/ 1835-1850NS, 1849-onOS	Pres.
Nt	Wheatland, Big Spring Pres.at Mumford(m.in Genesee 98,as if Pres.)	1803		nl.	
52.	Wheatland, Pres.(f.Cong.;lt.75:1825-1826,1839/ 1845-1846/1848NS in Scottsville;f.of Inverness to 1825;f.of Caledonia(Livingston Co.)to 1825;Tr.to OS 1853;1859 merged to First Pres.of Scottsville(in Wheatland,1837, l.75:1839-1859OS(lt.75:1841-1843OS)as Union Pres.of Scottsville;1970 merged to Ballantyne Pres.(f.Scottsville or Rochester PO,1948, l.75:1948-1970) as Union Pres.of Scottsville)	1822(CG) 1820(99) r.1832(PR) r.1859 M r.1970 M	nl.	j1822; 1820/ 1824-1853NS, 1852-onOS	Pres.

NEW YORK - MONTGOMERY COUNTY (org.1784) (057)

A	B	C	D	E	F
1.	Amsterdam, Cong.	1884	1883-1884	-	X
2.	Amsterdam, First Pres.(f.Albany Bush Ref.(RCA) s.say had a branch at Manny's Corner (RCA,l. 85:1800-1802);98:one Ch.moved from Amsterdam to Manny's Corner by 1800;see also #6 & #3; ab.#6 in 1812 or 1814/1816)	1795(Ref.:4 sr) 1792(2 sr) Tr.1803(PR) r.1812 M(98) 1814/1818 (min)	-	1798/1802-1885OS	X
3.	Amsterdam, Second Pres.(Village Pres.;46A:claim as successor to #2;1962 ab.Zion E&R (f.Evan. 1902);1995 merged to Emmanuel Pres.(1887, l.75:1886-1995 as United Pres.)	1832 1800(claim) r.1962 M r.1995 M	-	1831-onOS	Pres.
4.	Bowmans Creek, P or C Ch.(in Canajoharie;s.l. Canajoharry)	by 1814	WAP:m.1817	1809/1813-1835	X
5.	Buel, First Pres.(f.Bowmans Kill;f.Ref.RCA; *Canajoharie)	1802(Ref.) Tr.1847(PR:85) 1844(46A)	-	1844-1870NS, 1880-1973	X
6.	Veddersburgh, Pres.(Weddersburgh;Teddersburgh; s.l.as a branch of #2;f.Ref.RCA;Twn. uncertain)	1800(Ref.:98) 1799(85) Tr.by 1807 (PR:min) Tr.1812(85,98)	-	1803/1806-1807,1808-1814/1818	1812(98) or 1814/1818 merged to #2(q.v.)

NEW YORK – NASSAU COUNTY (org.1899) (059)

A	B	C	D	E	F
1.	East Rockaway, Bethany Cong.UCC (incor.l.UCC 1961-late 1961,had not voted;*Hempstead)	1885(3 sr) 1889	1884-on	–	UCC 1961-late 1961; Sch.I late 1961-1963; UCC 1963-on
Nt	Freeport, First Pres.(f.Christ;f.of Raynortown; f.South of Raynor;1849 date would exclude from this l.,shown because of 1835 date; *Hempstead)	1849(98) 1835(22)	–	1849-onOS	Pres.
2.	Garden City, Com.(f.l.incor.New York City, Queens,Queens Co.1933-1934;*Hempstead,village extends into *North Hempstead)	1932(01)	1933-on	–	UCC
3.	Hempstead, Christ's First Pres.(f.First;f.C of C;sett.1643(90,98),1644(49);lt.14 at Foster's Meadow 1721(pb.a branch);f.in New Netherland to 1663;in CT 1663-1664;submitted to St. George Epis.(1704)in 1705,mixed Epis.& Puritan forms to 1724;divided c.1717 & ch.in Pby.begun;SUF 1765/1772-1790;nl.01T)	1644(CG;6 sr) 1643(2 sr) 1648(90) 1672(30) r.c.1717(98) r.1721(PR:49) . 1728(?)	nl.	j1717-1725/ 1736; j1758;by 1773-1803/ 1806,1807-onOS	Submitted to Epis.1705; r. Pres.
4.	Oyster Bay, C of C (sett.1653;f.in New Haven Colony 1655-1662;in CT 1662-1664;98 says r. as Suffolk Co.#25)	1653(14,98)	nl.	–	X af.1658
In Nt	Oyster Bay, Indian pr.(pb.Ch.m.in Suffolk 98;ps. not fully org.;pb.sv.Mattineock tribe)	1653	IM: (nl.)	nl.	X af.1715
In Nt	Rockaway, Indian pr.(pb.not fully org.;sv. Rockaway tribe;town uncertain)	by 1741	nl.	IM: (nl.) af.1741	X
5.	Rockville Centre, Cong.(*Hempstead)	1895	1895-1898	–	X
6.	Rockville Centre, Cong.(*Hempstead)	1925(22) 1926(01)	1926-1973	–	UCC; Merged to form M.(q.v.)
6M.	Rockville Centre, United Chr.(merger of #6 & First Pres.of Rockville (1909,l.75:1909-1973),dual(Fed.in 75)to 1997;*Hempstead)	1973 M	1973-on	1973-1997	UCC (f.dual)
7.	Roslyn Highlands, Cong.(*North Hempstead)	1894	1894-1897	–	X
8.	Wantagh, Mem.Cong.(f.l.Ridgewood;in 1885 bldg.; *Hempstead)	1889(01N,01) 1888(22)	1890-on	–	UCC

NEW YORK - NEW YORK COUNTY (org.as a city 1652,functioning also as a county by 1683) (061)

A		B	C	D	E	F
	1.	New York City, Manhattan, Allen St.Pres.(f. Madison St.;f.Mission Ch.of Argyle Female Mission (Bancker St.))	1819(50,82) 1821(21,27) 1816(37)	-	1820-1899NS	Merged to #37(q.v.)
	2.	New York City, Manhattan, Ch.of the Alliance, Cong.	1874(01N) 1775[sic:01]	1875-1876	-	X
Ar	3.	New York City, Manhattan, Armenian Evan.	1896(3 sr)	1902-on	-	UCC
	4.	New York City, Manhattan, Bethany Cong.	1877(01,01N)	1889-1929	-	X
Bl	5.	New York City, Manhattan, Bethesda Cong.(f. Colored Ch.)	1845(s.01,82) 1847(s.01)	1848-1861, 1865-1870	-	X
Sw	Nt	New York City, Manhattan, Bethesda Covenant Cong.(EC:Rgn.:by 1910-1958;full 1958-2001)	1878	nl.	-	EC; X
	6.	New York City, Manhattan, <u>Bloomingdale</u> Pres.	1845	-	1843/1844-1855NS	X 1856
	7.	New York City, Manhattan, Bowery Pres.(f.Fourth Mission Ch.)	1822	-	1821-1837/1838	X 1841
	8.	New York City, Manhattan, Brainerd Pres. (Brainard)	1834 1833(pr.)	-	1833-1852NS	Merged to #74 to form #37(q.v.)
	9.	New York City, Manhattan, Brick Pres.(f.a branch of #33 to 1809,l.75 as a branch:by 1773-1774/1787,1788/1793-1803/1805,l.by Pby.1808-1809; Beekman St.;1894/1895 ab.Ch.of Covenant,Pres.(1862/1866,l.75:1861-1895NS);1937/1938 ab. Park Ave.Pres.(f.First Union Pres.,f.First Pres.of Yorkville(1846,r.1870,l.75:1845-1937OS)))	1766(branch: 27) 1767(14,46A) 1768(3 sr) r.1809 r.1894/1895 M r.1937/1938 M	-	(see text) 1809-onOS	Pres.
	10.	New York City, Manhattan, Broadway Cong.	c.1817(82)	nl.	-	X c.1820(82)
	11.	New York City, Manhattan, Broadway Pres.(f. Fourth Ave.to 1912,f.Bleecker St.to 1854)	1825	-	j1825; 1824-onNS	Pres.
	12.	New York City, Manhattan, Broadway Tabernacle, Cong.(f.Tabernacle Cong.;r.of minority of #13)	1840(several)	m.1842-1843, 1846-1962	-	UCC 1961-1962; Merged to form M1.
	12M1.	New York City, Manhattan, Broadway UCC (merger of #12 & Appendix II.,#1)	1962 M	1962-1965	-	UCC 1962-1965; Merged to form M2.
	12M2.	New York City, Manhattan, Broadway UCC (merger of #12M1.& Appendix II.,#3)	1965 M	1965-on	-	UCC
	13.	New York City, Manhattan, Broadway Tabernacle, Pres.(merger of #29 & #77;27 starts this ch.1834 as Pres.,& merged to #29,1838,with no m.of #77;see also #12)	1838 M 1834(27)	-	j1838; 1837/1838-1840/1842NS	X 1840(82; 1841:27)
	14.	New York City, Manhattan, Broome St.Cong.(f.in a bldg.on Rose St.;tried to j Pby.1821,refused)	1819(82)	nl.	(see text)	X 1822(82)

NEW YORK - NEW YORK COUNTY - continued

A		B	C	D	E	F
	15.	New York City, Manhattan, Camp Mem.Cong.(f. Center St.Mission;f.l.in Brooklyn,Kings Co. 1860-1863)	1859(01) r.1890(01N)	1858-1863, 1889-1924	-	X
Ir	16.	New York City, Manhattan, Canal St.Pres.(f. Orange St.to 1825;f.Irish Pres.to 1815)	1808(27) 1809(50,82)	-	j1808; 1807-1894OS	X (1893:27)
	17.	New York City, Manhattan, Central Cong.	1881	1880-1897	-	X
	18.	New York City, Manhattan, Central Pres.(f.Broome St.;1853 ab.#62;1866 ab.(legal 1869:27) West Fiftieth St.Pres.(1863,l.75:1863-1869NS))	1821(6 sr) 1822(27) r.1853 M r.1866 M	-	1821-onNS	Pres.
	19.	New York City, Manhattan, Eastern Cong.(f. Madison St.Pres.)	1836(PR) r.1848(CG) 1845(s.01)	1847-1859	1836-1847NS	X
	20.	New York City, Manhattan, Eighth Pres.(at Greenwich)	1819	-	j1819; 1818/ 1819-1843OS	X 1843(3 sr) (1842:82)
	21.	New York City, Manhattan, Eighth St.Pres.(f. Astor Pl.;f.Murray St.;f.Third Asso.Ref.to 1822;affl.AR 1810-1822;withdrew from Pby. 1845-1846)	1810(AR:2 sr) 1812(82) Tr.1822(PR)	-	1822/1824- 1851NS	X 1852
	22.	New York City, Manhattan, Eng.Presbiterians for the Public Worship of God (Second)	1722(3 sr) 1721(21)	-	nl.	X 1723(3 sr; 1722:21)
	23.	New York City, Manhattan, Fifth Ave.Pres.(f. Duane St.to 1852;f.Cedar St.to 1834)	1808	-	j1808; 1807-onOS	Pres.
	24.	New York City, Manhattan, Fifth Cong.	1844(82)	nl.	-	X af.1846(82)
	25.	New York City, Manhattan, Fifth Ward Mission, Cong.	1840(82)	nl.	-	X 1843(82)
Fn	26.	New York City, Manhattan, Finnish Evan.Cong. (incor.l.at drop as if in Brooklyn,Kings Co.)	1902(01)	1902-1912	-	X
	27.	New York City, Manhattan, First Cong.(First Indep.Cong.;bec.Elizabeth St.Pres.1811)	1801(CG;min) 1804(82) r.1811(PR:82)	WAP:1801- af.1809 (pb.1811)	j1811; 1810-1813	X 1813 (1816: s.82;1819:37)
	28.	New York City, Manhattan, First Free Cong.(from 1841,at Chrystie St.;l.as Free Cong.(1850's); 82:l.as Second Free Cong.:1842-1844;left Pby. as Second Free Ch.1836[indep.of Pby.:mixed forms];f.Chatham St.Chap.;f.Second Free Pres. to 1832)	1832(PR) r.1836(CG) r.1841(full CG) r.1842(82)	1836-1839, 1840-1843, 1846-1849, 1851-1856	j1832; 1831-1836	X
	29.	New York City, Manhattan, First Free Pres.(Dey St.;Free Ch.of First Ward;The Free Pres.)	1830(several)	-	j1830; 1830- 1837/1838NS	1838 merged to #77 to form #13(q.v.) (X:21)
Gr	30.	New York City, Manhattan, First Ger.Pres.	1852	-	j1853; 1852-1870NS	X 1872(21,27)

NEW YORK - NEW YORK COUNTY - continued

A	B	C	D	E	F
Gr 31.	New York City, Manhattan, First Ger.Ref.(Tr.to Epis.as St.Timothy Epis.,X 1840)	1834	-	j1834; 1833-1837/1838	1837 withdrew, see text
32.	New York City, Manhattan, First Indep.Ch.& Soc., Cong.(Indep.Cong.;apply to j Pby.1820,not received;ch.divided,part jPby.1821,other part X;r.as Vandewater Pl.Pres.;withdrew from Pby. 1822/1823,first time;Tr.to Ref.(RCA) as Vandewater St.Ref.)	1817(CG;2 sr) r.1821(PR:27) 1820(85) Tr.1829(Ref.)	MC:mnd.; WAP:1818-1821	(see text) j1821; 1820-1822; j1825/1826; 1825-1829	Tr.to Ref.; X
33.	New York City, Manhattan, First Pres.(f.Eng. Pres.;Old First;Wall St.;f.Collegiate Pres., with branches at #9 & #68 to 1809;closed c.1776-1783;property assigned to Ch.of Scotland 1730,though few Scots;1918/1919 ab. University Pl.Pres.(1871 merger,l.75:1871-1919,of #55 & University Pl.Pres.(1844/1845, l.75:1844-1871OS)) & Madison Sq.Pres.(1853, l.75:1852-1871NS) as First Pres.)	1716 1774(charter) r.1918/1919 M	-	j1717; NSd 1745-1758; by 1773-onOS	Pres.
34.	New York City, Manhattan, First St.Pres.(f.Sixth St.to 1859;division of #74)	1853(27)	-	1852-1866NS	X
Bl 35.	New York City, Manhattan, First Union CC (f. Union)	1920(3 sr) 1921(s.01)	1921-on	-	Sch.I 1961-1968; UCC 1968-on
36.	New York City, Manhattan, Fourteenth Pres. (Provost St.)	1823(82) 1822(27)	-	j1823; 1822-1825	X
37.	New York City, Manhattan, Fourteenth St.Pres. (merger of #8 & #74;1899 ab.#1;1910 ab.#84 as Greenwich Pres.;1947 ab.#92 as Village Pres.)	1851 M r.1899 M r.1910/1911 M r.1947 M		1852-1975NS	X
38.	New York City, Manhattan, Fourth Cong.(division of Sullivan St.Meth.Prot.(1839))	1843(82) 1842(pr.:01S)	m.1844/1845-1846, 1847-1853	-	X
39.	New York City, Manhattan, Fourth Free Pres.	1834(pb.mixed)	nl.	j1834; 1833-1840/1842NS	withdrew 1840; X 1842
Fr 40.	New York City, Manhattan, French Evan.Cong.(org. not complete)	1846(82)	nl.	-	not fully org.; X
Fr 41.	New York City, Manhattan, French Evan.Pres. (27 says dismiss & rejoin Pby.:1886)	1848	-	1852-onNS	Pres.
Bl 42.	New York City, Manhattan, Grace Cong.(in 1892 bldg.)	1923(01)	1923-on	-	UCC
43.	New York City, Manhattan, Hammond St.Cong. (r.of members of f.Hammond St.Pres.)	1845(PR) r.1848(CG)	1848-1851	1845-1848OS	X
pB 44.	New York City, Manhattan, Harlem Cong.	1911	1912-1923	-	X

NEW YORK – NEW YORK COUNTY – continued

A	B	C	D	E	F
45.	New York City, Manhattan, Harlem Pres.(f.First Pres.of Harlem)	1844	–	1843/1844-1915NS	Merged to New York Pres.(see #68)
46.	New York City, Manhattan, Indep.Ch.on Rose St. (nl.27)	1818(CG) 1819 r.1821(PR)	WAP:1819-1821	1821-1822	X
47.	New York City, Manhattan, Jane St.Pres.	1842	–	nl.;pb.NS	X 1844
48.	New York City, Manhattan, Laight St.Pres.(f. Spring St.to 1825;withdrew 1837(37) still l.; r.1840 by merger to a faction of Franklin St. Ref.(RCA,Madison Ave.,Northwest,1808-1915: 85))	1811(3 sr) 1810(pr.) r.1840	–	1810-1843OS	X
49.	New York City, Manhattan, Longwood Cong.	1905(01)	1905-1911	–	X
50.	New York City, Manhattan, Madison Ave.Cong. (merger of #56 & Ch.of Disc.)	1871 M 1872(01)	1871-1887	–	X
51.	New York City, Manhattan, Madison Ave.Pres.(f. Mem.to 1887;f.Eleventh Pres.to 1872;see also #53;1899 ab.Phillips Pres.(f.Fifteenth St., 1843/1844,l.75:1844-1899OS))	1839 r.1899 M	–	1839-onNS	Pres.
52.	New York City, Manhattan, Manhattan Cong.	1896(01)	1896-1935	–	X
53.	New York City, Manhattan, Manhattan Island Pres. (Ch.in Swamp)	1834	–	1834-1837/1838	X 1838(27,82) (37 says pb. ab.by #51)
54.	New York City, Manhattan, Manhattanville Pres.	1853(27) 1852	–	1852-1876NS	X
55.	New York City, Manhattan, Mercer St.Pres.	1835(37) 1834(s.82)	–	1835-1871NS	1870/1871 merged to two other chs.;see #33
56.	New York City, Manhattan, New England Cong.	1866(01N)	1865-1871	–	Merged to #50(q.v.)
57.	New York City, Manhattan, New York Cong.	1837(82)	m.1843-1846	–	X (1840:82)
58.	New York City, Manhattan, New York Cong.	1885(01N)	1884-1887	–	X
59.	New York City, Manhattan, Ninth Pres.	1836	–	j1837; 1836-1839OS	X 1838(82; 1839:27,37)
60.	New York City, Manhattan, North Pres.(division of #91)	1831(r.)	–	1831-1834	X 1835(37,min.)
61.	New York City, Manhattan, North Pres.(1904/1905 ab.#90;1926/1927 ab.St.Nicholas Ave.Pres.(f. Lenox,1891,l.75:1891-1926))	1847 r.1904/1905 M r.1926/1927 M	–	1846-onNS	Pres.
62.	New York City, Manhattan, Pearl St.Pres.(f. Second Asso.Ref.(Magazine;branch of #69 1797-1800;affl.AR 1800-1822)	1800(AR:50) 1797(branch, 21,82) Tr.1822(PR)	–	1822/1824-1852NS	1853 merged to #18(q.v.)

NEW YORK - NEW YORK COUNTY - continued

A	B	C	D	E	F
63.	New York City, Manhattan, Pilgrim Cong.(f. Harlem)	1862(01N,01)	1862-1918	-	Merged to Bronx Co. #5 to form Bronx Co.#10(q.v.)
64.	New York City, Manhattan, Ch.of Pilgrims,Cong.	1866(01N) 1862	1865-1870	-	X
65.	New York City, Manhattan, Providence Chap. (Strict Cong.;1854:asso.:01T)	1819(82)	WAP:m.1824-1825; NYI: ? -1834 1834-1843, m.1843-1846, 1846-1847, 1848-1853, cl.1853-1854	-	X c.1854
66.	New York City, Manhattan, Ch.of Puritans,Cong.in Union Sq.(1874 Merged to Second Pres.of Harlem(1872,l.75:1871-1874)as Ch.of Puritans, Pres.(l.75:1874-1937(X 1936))	1846(82) r.1874 M	1846-1861, 1862-1867	- (see text)	1874 Merged, see text; X
67.	New York City, Manhattan, Robinson Cong.	1845(82)	nl.	-	X 1845(82)
68.	New York City, Manhattan, Rutgers Pres.(f. Rutgers St.;f.Rutgers-Riverside;branch of #33 to 1809,l.as a branch,75:1788/1793-1803/1805; 1863 ab.Madison Ave.Pres.(1848,l.75:1845-1866OS);1942 ab.Harlem-New York Pres.(1915 merger,l.75:1915-1942,of #45 & New York Pres. (f.Thompson & Houston Sts.Sts.Pres.:1867, l.75:1867-1915OS,f.Twenty-Eighth St.Asso.Ref. (pb.United Pres.),1831(f.Fourth Asso.Ref.to 1847),Tr.1867))	1796(branch: 27,37) 1798(3 sr) r.1863 M r.1942 M	-	(see text) 1808-onOS	Pres.
Sh 69.	New York City, Manhattan, Second Pres.(f.Scotch Pres.on Cedar St.;f.First Asso.Ref.1782-1822; f.First Asso.to 1782;affl.Asso.to 1782;affl. AR 1782-1822;1907 ab.First Ref.Pres.(1797, affl.RPGS 1797-1907);1910 ab.Knox Pres.(1884, l.75:1885-1903(X 1910:27);see also #62)	1756(AR) 1757(49) Tr.1822(PR) r.1907 M r.1910 M	-	1822/1824-onOS	Pres.
70.	New York City, Manhattan, Seventh Free Ch.	by 1837	1836-1837	-	X

NEW YORK – NEW YORK COUNTY – continued

A	B	C	D	E	F
	71. New York City, Manhattan, Seventh Pres.Ch.of Jesus Christ (1912(21)ab.Madison St.Second Ger.Pres.(l.75:1894-1913;pb.1894 merger of Second Ger.Pres.(l.75:1881-1894)& Madison St. Ger.Pres.(1852,l.75:1852-1894OS,(a division of Second Ger.Evan.Ref.(Grand St.RCA,1848), other part continued as Ref.1848-1865,X (85)));1934/1935 merged to Sea & Land Pres. (1864,l.75:1864-1934OS)as Sea & Land Pres.)	1818 r.1912 M r.1934/1935 M	–	j1818; 1817-1972NS	X
Bl	72. New York City, Manhattan, Shiloh Pres.(f.Prince St.;f.First Colored Pres.)	1822	–	j1822; 1822-1840OS, j1839; 1839-1891NS	X 1888
	73. New York City, Manhattan, Sixth Ave.Pres.	1835	–	j1835; 1834-1838OS	X
	74. New York City, Manhattan, Sixth St.Pres.(f. Second Ave.(or Branch Ch.)to 1843)	1831	–	1830-1852NS	Merged to #8 to form #37(q.v.),divided to #34(q.v.)
We	75. New York City, Manhattan, Smyrna Welsh Cong. (f.Welsh Pres.in name to 1893;f.Broome St. St.Welsh Ch.,f.Mott St.;ps.not fully org. 1801;f.a union ch.to 1826;Bapt.schism 1806/ 1807;divided 1826 to Welsh Calvinistic Meth.; f.l.,pb.incor.:Brooklyn,Kings Co.1861-1863;s. dual Pres.;also affl.NYW 1867-1876,1877-1883, 1912-1923,NY(Eng.)1853-1863,1865-1872,1892- 1896,1919-1953,(often dual Welsh & Eng.);nl. 01S:1852-1853)	1801(CG) r.1813 r.1820(99) 1819 1822(82) 1824(s.82: full) 1825(65, s.82:full) r.1833(PR) r.1851(CG:37)	pb.m.WAP:1825; WP:1840-1863; NYW:j1852- -1867; 1852-1863, 1865-1953	j1833; 1833-1837/ 1838,1839- 1851NS	X 1812; r.; X af.1817; r.; X no services af.1955 (alive:1969:99)
	76. New York City, Manhattan, Spring St.Pres.(f.New Spring St.)	1825	–	j1826; 1825-1963NS	X
	77. New York City, Manhattan, Tabernacle Free Ch.(f. First Free Cong.;s.Broadway Tabernacle;82 s. l.this as Pres.because it had a session of deacons)	1811(46A) 1836(82)	1836-1837	–	1838 merged to #29 to form #13
	78. New York City, Manhattan, Tabernacle Pres.(f. Village Ch.;82 says jPby 1822,not supported by minutes)	bf.1822 Indep.:82) 1822(27)	–	j1828(37); 1827-1830	X 1830
	79. New York City, Manhattan, Tabernacle Pres. (Catherine St.;seek to be org.1833,put off to 1834;37 suggests Tr.to North River Pby.& alive af.1834,nl.(lacuna),gone by 1836)	1834(37,82)	–	j1834; nl.	X 1834 (see text)
	80. New York City, Manhattan, Tenth Pres.(Rose Hill)	1837	–	1836-1852NS	X

NEW YORK - NEW YORK COUNTY - continued

A	B	C	D	E	F
81.	New York City, Manhattan, Third Cong.	c.1824(82)	nl.	-	X c.1826(82)
82.	New York City, Manhattan, Third Free Pres.(bec. Houston St.Pres.1839)	1832(several) 1833(37)	-	1831-1857NS	X 1858
83.	New York City, Manhattan, Thirteenth St. Associate Ref.Pres.(Tr.to Pres.1822:32)	1820(AR:32) Tr.1822(PR)	-	j1822; nl.	X pb.soon
84.	New York City, Manhattan, Thirteenth St.Pres. (1892 ab.Chalmers Pres.(1889,l.75:1888-1892))	1846 r.1892 M	-	1845-1911NS	1910 Merged to #37(q.v.)
85.	New York City, Manhattan, Twentieth St.Cong.	by 1854	1853-1858	-	X
86.	New York City, Manhattan, Union Cong.	1850	1850-1857, cl.1857-1858	-	X
87.	New York City, Manhattan, Union Pres.	1829	-	1829-1837/ 1838	X 1838(27,82) (1839:37)
88.	New York City, Manhattan, University (Pres.Ch. Mtg.in the University)	1836	-	1836-1837	X 1837(82) (1838:27,37)
89.	New York City, Manhattan, Village Pres.	1833	-	j1834; 1833-1840/1842NS	X 1841(82) (1843:2 sr)
90.	New York City, Manhattan, Washington Heights Cong.(bec.Washington Heights Pres.)	1855(CG;27) r.1859(PR)	1854-1856	1859-1904OS	Merged to #61(q.v.)
91.	New York City, Manhattan, West Pres.(f.North Pres.to 1831;s.l.Carmine St.;1911 merged to Park Pres.(f.Eighty Fourth St.,1854,l.75: 1853-1912OS),as West-Park Pres.;see also #60)	1829 r.1831 r.1911/1912 M	-	j1829; 1829-onNS	Pres.
92.	New York City, Manhattan, West Twenty Third St. Pres.(f.Eighth Ave.to 1852;Tr.NS to OS 1858; 1889/1890 merged to Westminster Pres.(1856, l.75:1856-1889OS;merger of Westminster Pres. (1852,l.75:1851-1856OS),& West Twenty Fifth St.Asso.Ref.(1851;X:75H:1858));as Westminster Pres.of Twenty Third St.;bec.Westminster Pres.1903;bec.Chelsea West Twenty Third St. Pres.1909)	1834(3 sr) 1835(50) r.1889/1890 M	-	j1834; 1833-1859NS, 1859-1947OS	Merged to #37(q.v.)

NEW YORK - NIAGARA COUNTY (org.1808) (063)

A		B	C	D	E	F
	1.	Cambria, UCC Cong.(First Cong.;Lockport PO;left Pby.(first time)1834;f.Fed.1919-1921,to Meth. Epis.of Pekin)	1817(CG;3 sr) 1818(s.01) 1821(incp.) 1824(Soc.) 1827(?)	1839-1840, 1845/1846-on	j1823; 1819/ 1824-1834/ 1835;j1846; 1843/1845- 1847NS,1850- 1855NS	Sch.I 1961-1967; UCC 1967-on
	2.	Chalmers, P or C Ch.(in Niagara)	by 1837(?)	nl.	j1840; 1837/ 1838-1847NS	X
	3.	Gasport, Cong.UCC (First Cong.of Royalton;f.in Hartland to 1817)	1817(CG;4 sr) 1814(?)	1836-1841, 1845/1846- 1850; cl.1853-1858; 1859-1975	j1820; 1819/ 1824-1836	UCC 1961-1975; 1974 merged to form M.
	3M.	Gasport, Covenant UCC (merger of #3 & First Chr. Soc.of Royalton in Orangeport(1813))	1974 M	1975-on	-	UCC
	4.	LaSalle, Cong.(in Niagara)	1917	1918-1928	-	X
	5.	Lewiston, First Pres.(f.First Relg.Soc.;f.of Cambria to 1818;original name & later r. suggest ps.CG,nl.01T)	1817(4 sr, see text) r.1854(26)	nl.	j1817; 1815/ 1816-onNS	Pres.
In	6.	Lewiston, <u>Tuscarora</u> Indian Mission (sv. Tuscarora tribe;NY Missionary Soc.1801-1821, UFMS 1821-1826,ABCFM 1826-1860,Pres.Bd.1860-1919)	by 1826(CG) 1801(Mission, 67,s.48) 1800(Mission, 08,s.48) 1805(98) r.c.1861(PR)	1845/1846- 1850, 1851-1852, 1853-1861	1861-1919NS	X
	7.	Lockport, East Ave.Cong.	1890(3 sr)	1890-1920	-	Merged to #8 to form #10(q.v.)
	8.	Lockport, First Cong.(First Free:98)	1838(3 sr) 1836(48)	1839-1840, 1845/1846- 1920	-	Merged to #7 to form #10(q.v.)
	9.	Lockport, First Pres.(ab.#13 1935)	1823(2 sr) r.1935 M	-	j1823; 1819/ 1824-onNS	Pres.
	10.	Lockport, Plymouth Cong.(merger of #7 & #8)	1920 M	1920-2002	-	UCC; Merged to form M.(q.v.)
	10M.	Lockport, Lockport UCC (merger of #10 & St.Peters UCC (f.Evan.,E&R;1861/1863))	2002 M	2002-on	-	UCC
	11.	Lockport, Second Ch.(Free Ch.)	by 1832	BR:j1832-1834; 1834-1835/ 1836	-	X

NEW YORK – NIAGARA COUNTY – continued

12.	Lockport, Second Pres.(s.Second Ward Pres.)	1832	-	j1832; 1831-1850NS, 1850-1865OS, 1863-onNS	Pres.
13.	Mapleton, Mapleton Ch.of Pendleton Twn.(f.at Shawnee in Wheatfield 1844-1847,f.at Beech (or Beach) Ridge at Pendleton/Wheatfield line to 1844;First Pres.of Pendleton & Wheatfield)	1833(min) 1835(2 sr) 1847(Soc.) 1846(46A)	-	j1833; 1832-1837/1838, 1839-1843/1845NS,1846-1867OS,1867-1935NS	Ab.by #9(q.v.)
14.	Middleport, Pres.(in Royalton)	1833(2 sr)	-	j1833; 1832-1872NS	X (bldg. sold 1875)
15.	Niagara, Pres.(left Pby.1796;f.of *Schlosser to 1816;f.of *Cambria to 1813;f.of *Willink(Erie Co.)to 1808;f.of *Batavia(Genesee Co.)to 1804;unorg.land to 1802;land under British control to 1796)	by 1790	-	j1790; 1788/1793-1794/1797	1796 Tr.to Montreal Pby.; pb.later X
16.	Niagara Falls, Central Cong.(f.Ch.of Pilgrims)	1908(01) 1907(?)	1910-1923	-	X
17.	Niagara Falls, First Cong.(f.of Niagara City;f. of Suspension Bridge)	1855(s.01,98) 1853(s.01,22) 1854(s.01)	1854-on	-	UCC
18.	Niagara Falls, First Pres.(f.of Niagara;f.in Manchester (village) to 1840;withdrew from Pby.(first time)1841;withdrawal suggests Cong.period;nl.01T;1931 ab.Third Pres.(1905, 1.75:1905-1931))	1824(PR;4 sr) r.1931 M	nl.	j1824; 1819/1824-1840/1842NS,1848-onNS	Pres.
19.	Pekin, Cong.(in Cambria;1854:asso.:01T)	1843	1845/1846-1850, 1851-1853; cl.1853-1854; 1854-1862	-	X
20.	Somerset, Pres.	1824(2 sr)	-	j1824; 1819/1824-1917NS	Merged to Meth.Epis.
21.	Wilson, First Pres.	1819	-	j1819; 1818-1931NS	X (1930:26)
22.	Youngstown, First Pres.(f.First of Porter)	1823(3 sr)	-	j1824; 1819/1824-onNS	Pres.

NEW YORK – ONEIDA COUNTY (org.1798) (065)

A		B	C	D	E	F
We	1.	Alder Creek, Bethel Welsh Cong.(f.Second Indep. Cong.of Remsen;Pres.in 198;nl.01T;f.Fed. 1919-1963 to unknown;Tr.to Eng.Assn.1930;only annual services af.1943)	1838(3 sr) 1839(s.01,65) 1842(incp.)	NYW: ? -1867; cl.1856-1858; 1867-1963	-	Sch.I 1961-1963; X 1992
	2.	Annsville, Cong.(f.a branch of #9;s.incor.l. Armsville;nl.01T)	c.1825(CG) 1820(branch)	nl.	1825-1839NS, 1843/1845-1860NS	X
	3.	Augusta, First Pres.(f.First Cong.Soc.of Augusta Ctr.;f.Oriskany Falls PO;f.New Petersburgh of Whitestown to 1798;1827 plan to j OE or Pby. led to split;applied to jOE 1829,OE favored reunion,even if in Pby.;united to Madison Co. #17 in yoke 1822-1827,nl.)	1797(CG;2 sr) 1793(99) r.1866(PR)	pb.NAP; OE:pb.by 1804-1822; 1839-1840; cl.1853-1858; 1861-1865	j1822; nl. j1828/1829; 1829-1839; j1866; 1866-onNS	Pres.
	4.	Boonville, First Pres.(f.Cong.;nl.01T)	1805(CG;3 sr) r.1853(PR;99) 1856(46A)	ps.OE bf.1821	j1821; 1819/ 1824-onNS	Pres.
	5.	Bridgewater, First Cong.(North;f.of *Sangerfield to 1797;f.of *Paris to 1795;f.of *Whitestown to 1792)	1798(CG;4 sr) 1790(?)	ps.OE bf.1819; 1836-on	j1819; 1814/ 1818-1837/ 1838	UCC
In	6.	Brothertown, Indian Ch.(sv.united settlement of Mohegan,Mahican (Stockbridge),Wappinger, Narragansett,& Montauk (inclu.Shinnecock) tribes;SUF 1774/1787-1788/1793;in *Marshall)	1778(pb.PR)	nl.	1774/1787-1788/1793	X
	7.	Camden, First Ch.(East Camden;f.Fish Creek of Mexico to 1799;98:f.in Paris)	1798(s.01,98) 1796(s.01)	OE by 1813-1815	-	1815 merged to #8 to form #9(q.v.)
	8.	Camden, Second Cong.(West;at the "Seventh")	1803(98)	ps.OE bf.1815	-	1815 merged to #7 to form #9(q.v.)
	9.	Camden, Union Cong.C of C (merger of #7 & #8;two branches 1815-pb.1825;see also #2;98:jPby. 1823;Fed.to First Pres.(1867,l.75:1867-1951NS)1930-1951 as United Ch.;Merged to that Ch.1951 as United Pres.(l.75:1951-on))	1815 M(CG)	OE:1815-1818; cl.1853-1858; 1867-1951	j1819; 1814/ 1818-1867NS (see text)	Merged, see text
	10.	Cassville, Pres.(*Paris)	1834	-	1834/1835-1856NS	X
	11.	Clayville, Pilgrim Cong.(f.Pres.;*Paris)	1856(PR;2 sr) 1857(22) r.1890(CG) 1891(s.01)	1900-1999	1857-1899NS	Sch.I 1961-1962; UCC 1962-1999; X
	12.	Clinton, Hamilton College Ch.(*Kirkland;f.of *Paris to 1827)	1825(98) r.1861	-	j1825; 1825-1833; 1862-1931NS	X 1831; r.; X

NEW YORK - ONEIDA COUNTY - continued

A		B	C	D	E	F
	13.	Clinton, Stone Pres.(f.First Cong.;1788 date is a covenant planning ch.,but no ch.org.; Clinton Soc.in Kirkland;f.of *Paris to 1827; f.of *Whitestown to 1792)	1791(CG;4 sr) 1788(3 sr) 1787(pr.,s.49 r.1864(PR)	pb.OE bf.1822; OE:1825-1834; 1834-1864	1864-onNS	Pres.
We	14.	Clinton, Welsh Cong.(*Kirkland)	1886(70) 1887(?)	nl.	-	X 1887 (70)
	15.	Deansboro, Cong.UCC (f.l.Deansville;*Marshall)	1853(s.01) 1852(s.01) 1851(?) 1854(?) 1835[sic:s.01]	cl.1853-1858; 1867-1868, 1871-on	-	UCC
	16.	Deerfield, Pres.	by 1830	-	1829-1846/ 1848NS, 1849-1887NS	X
We	17.	Deerfield, Salem Welsh Cong.(First Welsh Cong. Soc.;in Marcy from 1832;f.a branch of #63 by 1823-1833:68;nl.01T;only annual services af. c.1925;l.by 01S to 1907)	1833(full:68) 1830(70) 1823(pr.:70) 1832(s.01) 1831(65)	NYW: ? -1867; cl.1856-1858; 1867-1898	-	(see text) X 1950/1953(70)
	18.	Delta, Pres.(*Lee)	by 1853	-	1852-1861NS	X
	19.	Durhamville, Pres.(at Madison Co.line;*Verona)	by 1836	-	1834/1835- 1851NS, 1849-1877OS	X
	20.	Elpis, Cong.(*Vienna)	by 1854	cl.1853-1858	-	X af.1858
	21.	Florence, Cong.	1859(CG;01)	1874-1883	1859-1875NS	X
	22.	Florence, Florence Hill Cong.(nl.01T)	1816(CG;2 sr) 1826(Soc.:98)	ps.OE bf.1822	j1822; 1819/ 1824-1854NS	X
We	23.	Floyd, Camroden Welsh Cong.(*Cymmrodorian*;Upper Ch.;*Capel Goch*,Red Chap.;union ch.divided 1839;nl.01T;Pres.in 98;Rome PO)	1834(union) 1836(68) r.1839(70) r.1843(65)	NYW: ? -1867; 1867-1912, 1913-1920	-	X 1920
	24.	Floyd, Cong.(Pby.min.:Tr.from RCA,but nl.85; nl.01T)	.? (Ref.) Tr.1824(CG)	1839-1840	j1824; 1819/1824- 1840/1842NS, 1846/1848- 1860NS	X
	25.	Holland Patent, Cong.(*Trenton)	1812(98)	ps.OE bf.1822	-	1821/1822 merged to #27 to form #26(q.v.)
	26.	Holland Patent, First Pres.(C of C;merger of #25 & #27;*Trenton)	1822 M(98) 1821 M(?)	-	1819/1824- onNS	Pres.

NEW YORK - ONEIDA COUNTY - continued

A		B	C	D	E	F
	27.	Holland Patent, United Ch.& Cgn.,First Pres.Soc. (f.branch of #60 & #61 to 1812/1813(44;1816: min);*Trenton)	1816(min) 1812/1813(44) 1799(46A) 1797(branch: 98)	-	1814/1818-1819/1824	1821/1822 merged to #25 to form #26
We	28.	Holland Patent, Welsh Cong.(in Trenton;nl.01T; Tr.to Eng.Assn.1930;1905 ab.members of Welsh Calvinistic Meth.(1840))	1843(68,70) 1842(s.01,65) 1840(s.01) 1835(?)	NYW ? -1867; 1867-1958	-	X 1956(70) (alive: 65:1967)
	29.	Kirkland, Cong.(f.Second of Clinton to 1835)	1834(3 sr) 1835(s.98)	OE j1834; 1834-1864, 1867-1883	-	X
	30.	Lee, Cong.(98:r.PR bf.X,ps.only j Pby.;f.of *Western to 1811)	1797(CG;2 sr) by 1803(44)	ps.OE bf.1822; OE:1825-1828	1829-1834/ 1835	X
We	31.	Marcy, Bethania Welsh Cong.(First Welsh Cong. Soc.;Plank Rd.Welsh Pres.,Second Welsh (98); Welsh Calvinistic Meth.also on site 1839-1848;in 1839 bldg.;lt.98;nl.01T;l.by 01S to 1914)	1840(3 sr) r.1848 1854(Soc.)	NYW ? -1867; 1867-1912	-	X 1910(70; 1913:65)
	32.	Marshall, Cong.(f.Hanover Soc.;f.of *Kirkland to 1829;f.of *Paris to 1827)	1797(3 sr) 1798(?)	ps.OE bf.1822; OE:1825-1834; 1834-1873	-	X
	33.	New Hartford, New Hartford Pres.(First;f.First Pres.of Whitestown to 1827;f.First Cong.of Whitestown;f.First Relg.Soc.of Whitestown;nl. 01T)	1791(CG;4 sr) r.1802(PR)	nl.	j1802; 1798/ 1802-onNS	Pres.
	34.	New London, Cong.(apply OE 1831,not received;m. 1832;*Verona)	by 1831	(see text)	-	X af.1832
We	35.	New York Mills, Salem Welsh Cong.(Tr.to Eng. Assn.1930;nl.01T;*Whitestown)	1847(3 sr) 1852(98) 1848(?)	NYW ? -1867; 1867-1916, 1919-1955	-	X 1954(70; alive 65: 1967)
	36.	New York Mills, Walcott Mem.Pres.(*Whitestown)	1830(2 sr)	-	1830-1988NS	X
	37.	North Bay, Cong.(*Vienna)	by 1854(CG)	cl.1853-1858	1857-1869NS	X
	38.	Oneida Castle, Cochran Mem.Pres.(f.a branch of #56;*Vernon)	1832(46A)	-	1846/1848-1862NS, 1861-onOS	Pres.
	39.	Oriskany, Waterbury Mem.Pres.(*Whitestown)	1831(98)	-	1833-onNS	Pres.
	40.	Oriskany Falls, Old Stone Ch.(Knox Corners;f. First Free Cong.;f.Second Cong.of Augusta to 1834;claim is as #3;Pres.:98)	1833(01,98) 1823[sic:s.01] 1797(claim)	OE:j1834; 1834-1960	-	X

NEW YORK - ONEIDA COUNTY - continued

		C	D	E	F
41.	Paris, Second Ch.of Paris,Cong.	1821	OE:1822-pb. 1823	-	1823 Merged to #43 to form #42(q.v.)
42.	Paris, Cong.UCC (Paris Hill;United Pres.Cong.; Paris Relg.Soc.;merger of #41 & #43;lt.m. 1843-1846)	1823 M(CG)	OE:1825-1834; 1834-on	1823-1825	UCC
43.	Paris, Paris Ch.(Paris Hill;Hancock Relg.Soc.; f.Second C of C of Whitestown to 1792;1820 CG r. irregular & debated in Pby.)	1791(CG;3 sr) 1795(Soc.) r.1817(PR) r.1820(CG) r.1821(PR)	OE(pb.1800)- 1817	j1818; 1814/ 1818-1823	1823 merged to #41 to form #42(q.v.)
We 44.	Paris, Welsh Cong.(l.only in 70;merged to Wesleyan Meth.& Welsh Calvinistic Meth.(nl. that denomination) to form a union ch.which evolved into Bethany Meth.(Wesleyan))	1860	NYW mnd.	-	1868 Merged, see text (s.1870:70)
We 45.	Prospect, Moriah Welsh Cong.(in Trenton;70 says merged 1896 to Eng.Cong.,we know of no such ch.;Tr.to Eng.Assn.1899;Fed.to Free Will Bapt.1937-1946 as Fed.;nl.01T)	1856(3 sr) 1853(pr.;s.01) 1860(s.01) 1864(s.01) 1857(?) r.1896(?)	NYW ? -1867; cl.1856-1858; 1867-1898, 1899-1946	-	X (1947:70)
We 46.	Prospect, <u>Ninety Six</u> Welsh Cong.(in Remsen;l.01S to 1888;nl.01T)	1841(70) 1845(65,98)	NYW ? -1867; 1867-1887	-	X (1889:65; c.1875:70)
47.	Remsen, First Pres.	by 1827	-	1826-1840/ 1842NS, 1851-1860NS	X
We 48.	Remsen, Peniel Welsh Cong.(First Welsh Cong.; Pres.(98);Tr.to Eng.Assn.1930;nl.01T)	1839(s.01, s.70) 1841(s.70) 1837(98) 1838(s.01,65, 68)	m.WP:1841- 1846; NYW ? -1867; cl.1856-1858; 1867-1944	-	X
49.	Rome, First Cong.(First Relg.Soc.;covenant of intention to org.a Ch.:1793;s.l.Pres.;s.l.r. PR 1819,but that date jPby.,not r.)	1800(CG;3 sr) 1802(Soc.) 1811(49)	OE:1812-1819	j1819; 1814/ 1818-1847	Merged to #52 to form #50(q.v.)
50.	Rome, First Pres.(f.Cong.;merger of #49 & #52)	1847 M (CG) 1846(46A) r.1852(PR)	-	1847-onNS	Pres.
We 51.	Rome, Rehoboth Welsh Cong.(*Capel Bach*,Small Ch.; nl.01T;closed 1860's-1864(70))	1851(3 sr; full:68) 1850(pr.:68, s.01) 1854(s.01)	NYW ? -1867; 1867-1927	-	X (1928:70)

NEW YORK – ONEIDA COUNTY – continued

A		B	C	D	E	F
	52.	Rome, Second Cong.Soc.	1831(CG;98)	nl.	1830-1846/ 1848NS	1847 merged to #49 to form #50(q.v.) X (nr.1878:98)
	53.	Sangerfield, Cong.(Lisbon Soc.;Sangerfield Ctr.; f.of Paris to 1795)	1797(CG;98) 1795(Soc.:44) 1794(Soc.:98) 1796(Soc.r.)	ps.OE bf.1822; OE:1825-1834; 1834-1866	-	
	54.	Sauquoit, Union Pres.(f.Cong.;Paris Union Soc.; nl.01T;*Paris;98 confuses this with Hancock Relg.Soc.:1795, X 1795:see #43 & Broome Co. #10)	1810(CG;2 sr) 1813(Soc.) r.1832(PR)	OE:j1811-1818	j1819; 1819/ 1824-onNS	Pres.
	55.	Sherrill, Plymouth Cong.(f.First Cong.to 1920; f.First Union Free to 1913(or Seneca St. Chap.,in 1886 bldg.);f.of *Vernon;Fed.to Park Meth.Epis.1939-1967 as Cooperating Chs.)	1870(pr.) r.1913(CG:99, s.01) 1914(s.01) 1916	1914-1967	-	UCC 1961-1967; Merged to form M.
	55M.	Sherrill, Plymouth Cong.(merger of #55 & Park Meth.Epis.)	1967 M	1967-2001	-	UCC 1967-2001; withdrew
	56.	Skenandoa, First Pres.of Oneida Castle & Sconondoah(*Skanando PO;s.l.Shenando;s.l. Shenendoah;now *Scononda;see also #38;in *Verona)	1819	-	j1819; 1819/ 1824-1846/ 1848NS	X
	57.	Steuben, Cong.	1801(CG;2 sr)	OE: m.1807 (not j)	m.1806-1807/ 1808	1806 merged to #60 to form #61(q.v.)
We	58.	Steuben, Ebenezer Welsh Cong.(First Welsh Cong. Soc.;*Capel Ucha*,Upper Chap.;Stone Chap.;f. First Welsh Cong.Meth.Soc.(a union ch.)to r.; 98 says union to Welsh Bapt.;nl.01T;f.Fed. 1929-1941 to unknown;Tr.to Eng.Assn.1930)	1801(CG;2 sr) 1802(70) 1800(s.98) 1804(98;incp.) r.1805(68,70)	m.WP 1846, 1855; NYW ? -1867; 1867-1941	1825-1826	X (1948:70; 1946:65)
We	59.	Steuben, *Penymynydd* Welsh Cong.(Penymymydd;Pen y mynidd(98);Pen Mount;<u>East Steuben</u> PO;Pres. (98);nl.01T;only occaisional services af. 1898)	1832(s.01,70) 1831(65)	NYW ? -1867; 1867-1893	-	X 1898(65; 1915:70)
	60.	Trenton, Oldenbarneveld Pres.(United Prot.Relg. Soc.in Trenton;l.Holland Patent;see also #27)	1795(44)	-	j1800; 1798/ 1802-1806	1806 merged to #57 to form #61(q.v.)
	61.	Trenton, Pres.(f.Cong.;f.of Oldenbarneveld to 1820;merger of #57 & #60;see also #27;f.l. Holland Patent to 1814/1818;nl.01T)	1806 M (CG) r.1816(PR:44)	nl.	1806-1877NS	X
We	62.	Trenton, Welsh Cong.of Barneveld (Trenton Hill; nl.01S 1893-1897,l.01S 1898-1899;nl.01T)	1856(68,70) 1854(01,65)	NYW ? -1867; 1867-1898, 1899-1905	-	X (1906:65; c.1900:70)

NEW YORK - ONEIDA COUNTY - continued

A	B	C	D	E	F
We 63.	Utica, Bethesda Welsh Cong.(f.Whitesboro St.; union with Bapt.1801(98);see also #17;nl. 01T;f.of *Whitestown to 1817)	1802(5 sr) 1800(s.01) 1803(?)	WP:m.1852, 1859; NYW ? -1867; cl.1856-1858; 1867-1868	-	1867(70;1871:98); Merged to #65 to form #64(q.v.)
We 64.	Utica, Bethesda Welsh Cong.(merger of #63 & #65; Tr.to Eng.Assn.1930)	1869 M(68) 1867 M(70) 1871 M(98)	1868-1963	-	UCC 1961-1963 merged to #67 to form M1.
EW 64M1.	Utica, Plymouth Bethesda Cong.(merger of #64 & #68)	1963 M	1963-1972	-	UCC 1963-1972; 1971 merged to #70 to form M2.
EW 64M2.	Utica, Plymouth Bethesda UCC (Merger of #64M1 & #70)	1971 M	1972-on	-	UCC 1972-on
We 65.	Utica, Columbia St.Welsh Cong.(Second Welsh Cong.)	1865(70,98) 1862(?)	pb.NYW ? - 1867; 1867-1868	-	1867(70;1871:98); Merged to #63 to form #64(q.v.)
66.	Utica, First Cong.	by 1843(CG)	nl.	1840/1842-1843/1845NS	X
67.	Utica, First Pres.(f.a branch of #89;f.of Whitestown to 1817;societies separate bf.ch.)	1813(98) 1804(Soc.) 1805(incp.) 1797(branch)	-	j1802; 1803/1805-onNS	Pres.
EW 68.	Utica, Plymouth Cong.	1883(01,01N)	1882-1963	-	UCC 1961-1963; Merged to #64M1.(q.v.)
69.	Utica, Second Pres.(Bleeker St.)	by 1824	-	j1824; 1819/ 1824-1840/ 1842NS	X
70.	Utica, South UCC (*New Hartford)	1920	1920-1972	-	UCC 1961-1972; 1971 merged to #64(q.v.)
71.	Utica, Third Pres.(Fayette St.)	by 1830	-	1829-1837/ 1838	X
We 72.	Utica, Welsh Indep.Ch.(l.only in 70)	1840(s.70) 1846(s.70)	NYW mnd.	-	X af.1848
73.	Vernon Center, Vernon Center Pres.(f.Cong.)	1801(CG;44) 1803(Soc.:98) r.c.1850(PR)	ps.OE bf.1811; 1839-1840, 1842-1850	j1811; 1809/ 1813-1837/ 1838, 1851-onNS	Pres.
74.	Vernon, Mount Vernon Pres. (Vernon village)	1805(2 sr)	-	j1811; nl.; 1814/1818-onNS	Pres.
75.	Verona, Cong.(First Relg.Cong.Soc.;l.as Fourth Ch.in 1824)	1803(CG;3 sr) 1806(Soc.)	OE pb.1803-1818;	j1818; 1814/ 1818-1837/ 1838	1837 merged to #77 to form #76(q.v.)

NEW YORK - ONEIDA COUNTY - continued

A		B	C	D	E	F
	76.	Verona, First Pres.(f.Cong.;merger of #75 & #77; s.l.as Second)	1837 M (CG) r.1881(PR)	cl.1853-1858	1837/1838-onNS	Pres.
	77.	Verona, Second Village Cong.(Second Cong.Soc.; s.l.First Pres.;Pby.minutes say Tr.from RCA, but nl.85)	? (Ref.) Tr.1824(CG) 1828(98) 1829(Soc.) 1830(99)	nl.	j1824; 1819/1824- 1837/1838	1837 merged to #75 to form #76(q.v.)
	78.	Vienna, First Pres.(nl.98;f.of *Bengal to 1816; f.of *Orange to 1808;f.of *Camden to 1807)	by 1820	-	j1820; 1819/ 1824-1856NS	X
	79.	Vienna, Second Ch. (P or C)	by 1828	nl.	1827-1831	X
	80.	Washington Mills, Messiah UCC (*New Hartford)	1890(01N,s.01) 1889(s.01)	1890-on	-	UCC
	81.	Waterville, First Pres.Ch.& Soc.(f.First Pres.of Sangerfield)	1823(2 sr)	-	j1823; 1819/ 1824-onNS	Pres.
We	82.	Waterville, Welsh Cong.(in Sangerfield;nl.01T)	1852(4 sr) 1851(s.01)	m.WP:1854; NYW ? -1867; cl.1856-1858; 1867-1927	-	X 1926(70; c.1910:65)
	83.	Westdale, Westdale Pres.(First Incorp.Relg.Soc. of West Camden;f.Second Cong.of West Camden; nl.01T;*Camden)	1851(CG;98) r.1854/1857 (mixed) r.1881(PR)	nl.	1851-1997NS	X
We	84.	Western, Western Hill Welsh Cong.(l.only in 70)	1845	NYW mnd.	-	X pb.soon
	85.	Westernville, First Pres.(f.l.Western)	1818(2 sr) 1817(11) 1803(44)	-	j1819; 1814/ 1818-onNS	Pres.
	86.	Westmoreland, First Cong.(f.of *Whitestown to 1792)	1792(CG;4 sr) 1791(Soc.) 1794(?) r.1821(PR) r.c.1839(CG)	OE:1800-1819; 1839-1840, cl.1853-1855; 1855-1953	j1819; 1814/ 1818-1839	X
	87.	Westmoreland, Indep.Cong.of Lowell	1820(98)	nl.	-	X 1850(98)
	88.	Whitesboro, First Cong.(*Whitestown;nl.01T)	1837	1837-1838, 1839-1840	-	X af.1851
	89.	Whitesboro, First Pres.(f.United Pres.Soc.of Whitestown & Old Fort Schuyler;United Cgn.of Whitestown;two branches in 1794 & 1797-1813; see also #67)	1794(4 sr) 1786(Soc.) 1793(Soc.r.) 1795(22)	-	j1791; 1788/ 1793-onNS	Pres.

NEW YORK - ONONDAGA COUNTY (org.1794) (067)

A	B	C	D	E	F
1.	Amber, Cong.(f.Union Relg.Soc.1824 to 1917,in Meth.Epis.Ch.1839-1914;in Otisco;Marietta PO)	1824(Soc.) r.1917(CG)	j1917; 1917-1980	-	Sch.I 1961-1962; UCC 1962-1980; NA 1979(j1980)-1996; CCCC 1997-on
2.	Amboy, Amboy Pres.(in Camillus;PO Syracuse;1845 ab.#48;Fed.to Belle Isle United Meth.(1851) c.1961-1998; merged to same 1998 as Amboy-Belle Isle United (dual))	1845(3 sr) 1844(22) r.1998 M	-	1843/1845-onNS	Pres. (dual, see text)
3.	Apulia, C of C,Cong.(in Fabius;lt.1839-1840)	1804(CG;90) 1806(01) r. ? (PR) r.1830(CG)	ML:1808-1810; 1839-1840; cl.1853-1858; 1862-1873	j1808; 1809/1811-1834/1835	X
4.	Baldwinsville, First Pres.(f.First of Lysander, (at Van Buren town line);f.First of Camillus to 1829;f.Cong.;org.under "Eastern Assn.of Pres.Ch.":39;r.PR af.1858(01T & cl.),pb. incor.)	1813(PR;3 sr) r.1828(CG: 3 sr) 1826(?) r.1836(PR:39 99) 1832(46A)	cl.1853-1858	1815/1816-onNS	Pres.
5.	Borodino, Pres.(Cong.forms;in Spafford)	1830(CG)	cl.1853-1858	1829-1867NS	X
6.	Camillus, First Pres.(f.Second to 1829)	1817(CG;4 sr) 1816(s.48) r.af.1858(PR: 01T)	cl.1853-1858	j1817; 1817-1923NS	X (1877:22)
7.	Cicero, Pres.Soc.of Cicero Corners (First;Tr.to Ref.(RCA,1837-1925(85));left Pby.1835)	by 1816(min) 1819(Soc.;90)	-	j1816; 1815/1816-1834/1835	Tr.to Ref. (see text)
8.	Collamer, First Pres.(East Syracuse PO;at Britton's Settlement;1974 merged to Meth. (1829)as Collamer United Ch.(dual);in DeWitt)	1842(39,98) 1843(48) r.1974 M	-	j1843; 1840/1841-onNS	Pres.(dual, see text)
9.	Delphi, P or C Ch.(in Pompey;left Pby.1832)	by 1831(min)	nl.	j1831; nl.	X 1832
10.	Elbridge, Cong.(f.First Cong.Soc.of Camillus to 1829;indep.in 01T,but l.by Pby.;Fed.to Bapt. (1813)1945/1947-on as Com.Fed.)	1800(CG;4 sr) 1807(?) 1822(Soc.)	ML:1804-1810; cl.1853-1858; 1887-on	j1808; 1809/1811-1887NS	UCC
11.	Fayetteville, First Pres.(Manlius Four Corners; in Manlius;in 1829 bldg.;f.Fed.to First Bapt.(1804,r.1871)1918/1927-1933,then merged 1933-on,as United Ch.(dual))	1830(39,98) 1829(99) r.1933 M	-	j1830; 1830-onNS	Pres.(dual, see text)

NEW YORK - ONONDAGA COUNTY - continued

A	B	C	D	E	F
12.	Jamesville, Pres.(f.Union Cong.Soc.;f.First of Manlius to 1835;moved Moorehouse Flats to Jamesville village 1827;48 says in ML,but nl. minutes;left Pby.first time 1837;Fed.to United Meth.1951-on as Jamesville Com.;in DeWitt)	1807(CG;3 sr) 1805(Soc.) 1795(44) r.1843(mixed) r.1870(PR) r.1885(46A)	OCC:m.1843; cl.1853-1858	1809/1811-1836/1837, 1840/1841-1842; j1843; 1843/1845-onNS	Pres.
We 13.	Jamesville, Welsh Cong.(in DeWitt;incor.l.in Oneida Co.:65;left Welsh Assn.1877)	1865	NYW ? -1867; 1867-1877, 1880-1883	-	X 1875(65)
14.	Jordan, First Pres.(in Elbridge)	1827(39) 1829(elders: 98) 1830(s.48)	-	j1831; 1829-1931NS	X
15.	LaFayette, Columbian Pres.(Columbian Soc.;First Pres.;f.First Cong.;f.Third West Hill of Pompey to 1825)	1809(CG;3 sr) 1805(Soc.) 1804(Soc.:98) r.1884(PR)	ML:1810-1810; cl.1853-1856	j1808; 1809/1811-onNS	Pres.
16.	Liverpool, First Pres.(in Salina;pb.f.Cong.if 48 dates correct)	1829(39,98) 1820/1821(48)	nl.	j1834(48); 1829-onNS	Pres.
17.	Lysander, Cong.(merger of #18 & First Prot.Ref.(RCA,1828-1878(85)))	1877 M(2 sr)	1876-1965	-	UCC 1961-1965; X
18.	Lysander, West Cong.(f.Second;s.named Pres.; Bett's Corners)	1820(CG;98)	cl.1853-1858	j1821; 1820-1877NS	Merged to #17(q.v.)
Nt	Manlius, Kirland Cong.(in 1849 union bldg.;ps. Kirkville;never org.as a Ch.)	1893(Soc.)	nl.	-	X pb.soon
19.	Manlius, Trinity Pres.(at Square;f.Second to 1832;incor.r.PR af.1858(01T & cl.))	1815(CG;2 sr) 1816(s.48) r.1817(PR:98)	cl.1853-1858	j1816; 1815/1816-1933NS	X
20.	Manlius Centre, Fourth Ch.of Manlius (P or C)	by 1822(min) r.1828	nl.	j1822; 1821-1834/1835	X
21.	Marcellus, First Pres.(f.First C of C;Eastern Relg.Soc.;f.of Nine Mile Creek;22 lt.as Cong.(1791) & Pres.(1801),but 1801 was Cong.(see ML);39:always mixed Cong.& Pres.;49: still CG in 1811)	1801(CG;6 sr) 1802(Soc.) 1803(?) 1791(s.22) r.1872(PR: 46A,01T) 1821(44)	ML:1804-1810; cl.1853-1858	j1808; 1809/1811-onNS	Pres.
22.	Marcellus, Second Pres.(f.Third to 1830;Cong. forms)	1819(CG)	cl.1853-1858	1819-1867NS	X
23.	Marietta, Cong.(in Marcellus)	1918(01)	1918-1927	-	X

NEW YORK - ONONDAGA COUNTY - continued

A	B	C	D	E	F
24.	Matthews Mills, Pres.(Cong.forms;in Manlius;f. First of Sullivan,Madison Co.,f.at Rapids (Sullivan),moved here 1831;f.Manlius & Sullivan;North Manlius PO)	1817(CG)	cl.1853-1858	1815/1816-1817, 1818-1857NS	X
25.	Onondaga, Onondaga Hill Pres.(First Pres.;West Hill;First Relg.Soc.;s.Syracuse PO;48 says in ML,but not in minutes;lt.22;left Pby. first time 1834;39:apply jCG 1835,turned down;r.1842/1843 as accommodation plan,48 treats as new ch.;nl.01T,;incor.X 1963:75H)	1806(PR) r.1834(CG) r.1842/1843 r.1887(PR)	(see text) cl.1853-1858; 1869-1880	j1807; 1803/1808-1834/1835,1840/1841-1872NS; 1887-on	Pres.
26.	Onondaga, Onondaga Valley Pres.(f.Onondaga Hollow Relg.Soc.;Second;united in a yoke to #37 1810-1822 as United of Onondaga Hollow & Salina;Syracuse PO)	1810 1809(46A; s.Soc.) 1825(s.Soc.) r.1822	-	j1810; 1809/1811-onNS	Pres.
27.	Onondaga, South Onondaga Cong.(f.Third;South Hollow;Syracuse PO;1854:in Pby.in 01T; in 1827 union bldg.)	1829(PR) r.1845(CG)	cl.1853-1858; 1868-1872	j1829; 1829-1851NS	X
28.	Orrville, Pres.(Orville;CG forms;f.Third of Manlius to 1832;in *DeWitt)	1815(CG)	cl.1853-1858	j1817; 1815/1816-1859NS	X
29.	Otisco, Otisco Pres.(f.Cong.;Washington Relg. Soc.;f.of Tully to 1806)	1803(CG;5 sr) 1801(pr.;98) 1804(Soc.) 1808(39;Ch. full org.) r.1907(PR)	ML:1806-1810; OE:j1833-1834 1834-1835, 1839-1840; cl.1853-1858	j1808; 1809/1811-1833; j1841; 1840/1841-onNS	Pres.
30.	Pompey, First Pres.(f.First Cong.,East Hill; First Pres.Soc.;Fed.to Chr.(Disc.,1834/1837) 1946-1948,then merged 1948-on,as Pompey United,dual)	1796(CG;2 sr) 1794(Soc.;31, 44,90) 1793/1803(48) r.1870(PR) r.1871(CG) r.af.1896(PR) r.1948 M	SA:1803- ?; ML:1804-1810; cl.1853-1858	j1808; 1809/1811-onNS	Pres.(dual, see text)
31.	Pompey, Pleasant Valley Cong.at <u>Oran</u> (Second, East Hollow)	by 1804(CG) 1806 1793/1812(48)	ML:1804-1810;	j1808; 1809/1811-1833	X
32.	Pompey, Second Pres.(at <u>Oran</u>)	1833	-	1833-1834/1835	X
33.	Pompey Centre, Cong.(s.Pres.;in Pompey)	by 1844(CG) r.af.1858(PR: 01T)	cl.1853-1858	j1844; 1843/1845-1907NS	X

NEW YORK - ONONDAGA COUNTY - continued

A	B	C	D	E	F
34.	Skaneateles, First Pres.(f.First C of C;First Cong.of Marcellus (Second Ch.)to 1830; Schaneateles Relg.Soc.)	1801(CG;6 sr) r.1818(PR)	ML:1807-1810	j1808; 1809/ 1811-onNS	Pres.
35.	Syracuse, Danforth United (f.Cong.;Fed.to First Chr.(Disc.,1863)1930-1969)	1884(01,01N)	1883-1969	-	UCC 1961-1969; X
36.	Syracuse, First Cong.(left Pby.1843;f.of *Salina to 1847)	1837(CG;3 sr) 1838(98)	nl.	j1842; 1840/ 1841-1843/ 1845NS	withdrew; X af.1850
37.	Syracuse, First Pres.(First Pres.Ch.Soc.;White Mtghse.;f.of *Salina to 1847;1940 merged to Fourth Pres.(1869/1870,l.75:1869-1941) as First United Pres.)	1826 1824(Soc.) r.1940 M	-	1826-onNS	Pres.
38.	Syracuse, First Ward Pres.(in 1805 bldg.;united in yoke to #26 1810-1822 as United of Onondaga Hollow & Salina,sharing elders;no elders 1822-1829(98);f.First Ch.& Cgn.of Salina to 1847[ch.name to 1852](at Salina Center);nl.01T;bec.North Pres.1955;1965 merged to Westminster Pres.(1886,l.75:1886-1965) as Westminster United Pres.)	1810(branch, PR) r.1822(CG) r.1829(PR;98) 1832(incp.) r.1965 M	nl.	j1822; 1821-onNS	Pres.
39.	Syracuse, Geddes Cong.(in Geddes;Fed.to South Geddes St.Chr.(Disc.,f.Rowland St.C of C) of Syracuse,1904)1962-1964)	1886(01,22)	1886-1964	-	UCC 1961-1964; Merged to form M.
39M.	Syracuse, Geddes UCC (in Geddes;merger of #39 & South Geddes St.Chr.(Disc.,f.Rowland St.C of C,1904)of Syracuse)	1964 M	1964-1978	-	UCC 1964-1978; X
40.	Syracuse, Good Will Cong.	1884(01N) 1885(01,22)	1883-1946	-	Merged to #43(q.v.)
41.	Syracuse, Park Central Pres.(f.Park to r.;Tr.to OS 1858)	1846(4 sr) 1855(Soc.) r.1858(98, s.26)	-	1846/1848-1858NS, 1857-onOS	Pres.
42.	Syracuse, Pilgrim Cong.	1903 1905(s.01)	1903-1987	-	Sch.I 1961-1987; X
43.	Syracuse, Plymouth Cong.	1873(22) 1853(4 sr)	cl.1853-1855; 1855-1946	-	Merged to #40 to form M.
43M.	Syracuse, Plymouth Cong.(merger of #40 & #43)	1946 M	1946-on	-	UCC
44.	Syracuse, Second Pres.(f.of *Salina to 1847)	1844	-	j1844; 1843/ 1845-1846/ 1848NS	X (by 1846)
45.	Syracuse, South Ave.Cong.	1893 1887(s.01)	1893-1919	-	X

NEW YORK - ONONDAGA COUNTY - continued

A	B	C	D	E	F
46.	Tully, Pres.(First Cong.)	1811(CG) 1804(Soc.)	nl.	j1833; 1832-1840/ 1841NS	X 1841(48; c.1830:98)
47.	Van Buren, Central Cong.Soc.of Camillus & Ionia (at Canton;f.Third of Camillus to 1829;lt.75: 1831-1832;48 shows not active 1830-1832;left Pby.1836;see also #48)	by 1825(CG; min) 1827(Soc.) r.1832(48)	nl.	j1825; 1825-1836/1837	X 1835
48.	Warner, Cong.(Union Soc.;Warner's Settlement; l.75 in Van Buren;f.a branch of #47)	1841(CG) 1831(Soc.)	nl.	j1843; 1840/ 1841-1842NS	X 1845 (ab.by #2)

NEW YORK - ONTARIO COUNTY (org.1789) (069)

A		B	C	D	E	F
	1.	Bristol, First Cong.of Bristol Valley (f.North; f.of Bristol #9;left Pby.1844(98,48);Fed.to Meth.(1806,r.1815,r.1846),& Univ.(1833,left UUA 1962) c.1960-1975,as United of Bristol Valley)	1799(CG:4 sr) 1809(?) 1779(s.98) 1835(s.01)	MC:mnd.; OA:j1800-1813; cl.1853-1855; 1855-1859, 1867-1975	j1823; 1820/ 1824-1851NS (left 1844)	UCC 1961-1975; Merged to form M.(q.v.)
	1M.	Bristol, United Ch.of Bristol,UCC (merger of #1, Meth.,& Univ.(as above))	1975 M	1975-on	-	UCC
	2.	Canadice, Cong.Soc.(f.a branch of #22 1828-1829; f.Second South of Richmond to 1829;left Pby. 1839(48,51))	1828(CG:s.48) 1829(s.48) 1832(98)	nl.	j1829; 1829-1832, 1833-1850NS	X
	3.	Canandaigua, Ch. (Bates Ch.)	1790(12)	nl.	-	X, pb.soon
	4.	Canandaigua, First Cong.(1792 mtg.to seek clergy,pb.not org.;specifically CG on Pby.l. 1828-1829,1832-1833;15 considers this a Unitar.Ch.1812-X af.1817(sv.by Unitar.leaning pastors))	1799(CG:3 sr) 1812(15)	OA:j1800-1810 1839-1840, 1849-on	j1827; 1827- 1834/1835	UCC
	5.	Centerfield, Cong.(in Canadaigua;indep.in 01T, but l.by Pby.)	1832(CG)	cl.1853-1858	j1833; 1833-1856NS	X
	6.	Chapin, Chapinville Cong.(f.Chapin Mills;in Hopewell)	by 1836(CG)	1849-1851	j1835/1836; 1834/1835- 1837/1838, 1852-1853NS	1852 Tr.to Meth.Epis.
	7.	East Bloomfield, First Cong.of Bloomfield (Indep.Cong.Soc.;f.Pres.(22);f.First of Bloomfield to 1833;f.of Bloomfield:T#10,R4; specifically CG on Pby.l.1829-1831,withdrew from Pby.first time 1826;98 says r.1873 as PR,when actually j CG)	1796(CG:4 sr) 1795(Soc.) r.1822(PR) r.1825(CG) r. ? (PR) r.1832(CG) r.1873	OA:j1800-1813; cl.1853-1858; 1873-1884, 1889-1892, 1915-on	j1822; 1820/ 1824-1832	UCC
	8.	Farmington, P or C Ch.	1817	nl.	j1817; 1817-1831	X
	9.	Geneva, First Pres.(Cong.ps.not fully org.;f.in Seneca;nl.01T;always PR:46A;1988 merged to North Pres.(f.Second (f.United Pres.(f. Associate Ref.,1824/1826,affl.AR to 1858,UPNA 1858-1874;indep.:1870;r.PR:1876)),l.75:1871-1988)as Pres.Ch.)	1794(CG;12) 1792(46A) 1798(Soc.;90) r.1800(PR) r.1988 M	nl.	j1803; 1803/1808- onNS	Pres.
Bl	10.	Geneva, Second Ch.(Colored Pres.;North Pres.;f. Cong.;f.Free Ch.,Colored;l.01T,as r.PR by 1854,but pb.already X;f.in Seneca)	1825/1826(CG: 98)	nl.	j1850; 1850-1852NS	X
	11.	Gorham, Pres.(moved Reed's Corners to Bethel (village) 1843,see #20;f.First Pres.Soc.of Bethel;lt.75:1855-1856)	1828 r.1843	-	j1827/1828; 1828-1967NS	X

NEW YORK - ONTARIO COUNTY - continued

			D	E	F
12.	Hall, Union Cong.UCC (in Seneca)	1916	1916-on	-	UCC
13.	Honeoye, Indep.(l.only by 48,pb.CG;*Richmond)	1830's(48)	nl.	-	X pb.soon
14.	Honeoye, UCC (Cong.;f.First Village;in Richmond)	1854	cl.1853-1855; 1855-1857; cl.1857-1858; 1878-on	-	UCC
15.	Hopewell, Cong.(specifically CG on Pby.l.)	by 1834(CG)	nl.	1833-1834/ 1835	X
16.	Hopewell, Pres.(lt.52;f.of Gorham to 1824;f.of Lincoln to 1807;f.of Easton to 1806)	by 1803(2 sr) 1808(90)	-	j1803; 1803/1808- 1895NS	X
17.	Naples, Cong.	by 1837	1836-1842; GC:1842-by 1848	-	X af.1842
18.	Naples, Trinity Pres.(f.First;f.Cong.;f.First Relg.Soc.Compact of Middletown to 1808;Fed.to United Meth. 1976/1989-on as Trinity Fed.)	1800(CG:2 sr) r.1815(PR)	OA:j1800-1813; ML:m.1805	j1815; 1814-onNS	Pres.
19.	Phelps, <u>Oaks Corners</u> Pres.(First;Phelps Union Relg.Soc.;see also #20)	1804(PR;2 sr) 1803(Soc.:98) r.1806(CG) 1805(?) r.1813(PR:48) 1811(PR:98)	OA:1809-1813	j1813; 1812-onNS	X; r.; Pres.
20.	Phelps, Pres.(White Ch.;Pres.of Vienna;Vienna Soc.;f.a branch of #19 1819-1831;1870 merged to First Pres.(Brick Ch.;f.of Vienna (1840 (1858:98),l.1839-1870OS) as First United Pres.of Phelps;1974 merged to Meth.as United Ch.of Phelps,dual)	1831 1820(Soc.) r.1870 M r.1974 M	-	j1831; 1831-onNS	Pres.(dual, see text)
21.	Reeds Corners, Cong.(in Gorham;divided from #10, claim as it;Tr.from Ref.(RCA,1843-1853(85)); Fed.to Bapt.(1804)1915/1919/1948-on as Fed.)	1843(Ref.) 1828(claim) Tr.1851(CG: 2 sr) 1853(85) 1857(?)	cl.1853-1858; 1861-on	-	UCC
22.	Richmond, Richmond Center Cong.(f.Pres.;f. Richmond Mills;f.of Honeoye to 1815;f.First of Pittstown to 1808;withdrew from Pby.1843, drop (48)1844;see also #2)	1801(CG) 1802(Soc.:43) r.1813(PR:48) 1810(98) r.1843(CG)	OA:j1803-1813 1848-1852; cl.1853-1858	j1813; 1812-1851NS (left 1843)	X

NEW YORK - ONTARIO COUNTY - continued

A	B	C	D	E	F
23.	Seneca, Seneca Castle Pres.(f.l.Castleton;1967 merged to Seneca Pres.(Stanley PO;1807/1808, f.Asso.Ref.,affl.AR 1807-1858,claim by UPNA 1858-1860,Tr.1858/1859,l.75:1858-1967OS) as Seneca Pres.)	1828 r.1967 M	-	j1828; 1827-onNS	Pres.
24.	Shortsville, First Pres.(in Manchester;f.Cong.at Port Gibson in Manchester;nl.01T,but picked up by cl.)	1832(CG) r.1860(PR)	cl.1855-1858	j1832/1833; 1831-1851NS; j1860; 1860-onNS	Pres.
25.	South Bristol, Pres.(f.Cong.;f.of Bristol to 1838;f.of Bristol T#8)	1796(CG:3 sr) r.bf.1848(PR: 01T,48)	OA:j1800-1813	j1816; 1815/ 1816-1870NS	X
26.	Victor, Cong.Soc.(Boughtontown;f.North of Bloomfield to 1812;f.Northeast Cong.Soc.of Bloomfield;f.of Bloomfield T#11;voted to j projected CG Assn.1816;see also #28)	1799(3 sr) 1798(2 sr)	OA:j1800-1813 GC:j1818- pb.1832	-	1832 merged to #28 to form #27(q.v.)
27.	Victor, First Pres.(f.Cong.Soc.in name to 1888; merger of #26 & #28;incor.drop 1874:75H)	1832 M(CG) r.1858(PR)	1849-1852; cl.1853-1858	1832-1850NS; j1858; 1857-onNS	Pres.
28.	Victor, Pres.(48 & 99 say majority of #26 r.PR 1827,& CG new 1828 org.)	1828 1827(99)	-	j1828; 1827-1832	Merged to #26 to form #27(q.v.)
29.	West Bloomfield, Cong.(f.of Bloomfield to 1833; f.of Bloomfield T#10R5;left Pby.1830;48 says this is Ch.in Pby.to merger,see #31)	1799(CG:3 sr) 1796(Soc.) 1794(?) r.1831(98)	OA:j1800-1813	j1813; 1812-1829	1843 merged to #31 to form #30(q.v.)
30.	West Bloomfield, Cong.(merger of #29 & #31;left Pby.1844(48);incor.l.Sch.I,was UCC)	1843 M(CG)	1848-on	1843-1850NS	UCC 1961; Sch.I late 1961-1962; UCC 1962-on
31.	West Bloomfield, Second Pres.(f.of Bloomfield to 1833;48 says this Ch.left Pby.1830,see #29)	1830(48) 1831(98)	-	j1829/1830; 1829-1843NS	1843 merged to #29 to form #30(q.v.)

NEW YORK - ORANGE COUNTY (org.1683) (071)

	B	C	D	E	F
1.	Bethlehem, Pres.(New Windsor PO;Newburgh PO;f. Salisbury Mills PO;in Cornwall;f.of *New Cornwall to 1797;pb.PR forms when sv.by MC; nl.01T;Tr.NS to OS 1858(45))	1729(PR;2 sr) 1730(90) by 1735(45) 1734/1740(53) 1726(14) by 1764(98) by 1775(22) 1785(incp.)	MC: sv.1803-1808	j1738-1743; j1769; by 1773-1774/ 1787,1794/ 1797-1854NS 1854-onOS	Pres.
2.	Blooming Grove, Cong.UCC (f.First Pres.;l.as CG by Pby.l.1829-1832;pastor expelled by Pby. 1833,Pby.tried to treat ch.as vacant,but ch. became indep.(49:r.CG),kept PR name to 1871; sv.by pastors in Amer.Chr.Conv.by 1851-1886/ 1890,l.1885(dual);nl.01T;f.of *Cornwall to 1799)	1758(PR;3 sr) 1759(49,98) c.1750(37,45) 1757(s.01) 1770(s.01) r.by 1786(CG) 1806(incp.) r.1870 1857[sic:s.01]	MC:1783-af. 1806; 1875-on	j1759; by 1773-1774/ 1787; j1810; 1812-1813; j1816; 1815-1823, 1824-1833	UCC
3.	Centerville, Pres.(South Centerville;Slate Hill PO;Middletown PO;*Wawayanda;merged to #25; separated out 1929)	1827(45) 1829(Ch.full: 38) r.1929 M	-	j1826; 1828- 1927OS; 1837-1839NS; 1929-on	Merged; r.; Pres.
4.	Chester, First Pres.(f.Cong.;plan to org.1775; land & pr.1783(45);bldg.& called pastor 1798)	1803(CG:org.) r.1813(PR) 1826(incp.)	MC:(pr.1783) 1803-1810 WAP:m.	j1810; 1810-onNS 1837-1840OS	Pres.
5.	Circleville, Pres.(Bullhack;*Wallkill)	1841(38,98)	-	j1842; 1840/ 1841-2002NS	Tr.to another denomination
6.	Cornwall, <u>Canterbury</u> Pres.(1925-1957 merged to Cornwall Pres.of Cornwall on Hudson(1855/ 1856,l.75:1855-onNS)	1827 1824(Soc.) r.1957	-	1827-1926NS, 1957-on	Merged; r.; Pres.
7.	Denton, First Pres.(New Hampton PO;*Wawaywanda)	1839(3 sr)	-	1839-onNS	Pres.
8.	Florida, First Pres.(Brookland;in 1741/1742 bldg.;if elders at start (PR),then dropped & r.CG c.1780;s.incor.l.in Montgomery Co.;jPby. af.1758:37;1878 merged to Second Pres.(1839) l.75:1837-1879OS,divided again 1879,l.75: 1879-1886,merged 1886;*Warwick)	1750(4 sr) 1748(11) 1738(46A) 1787(incp.) r.1795(PR: elders) r.1878 M r.1886 M	MC:1780-af. 1787	j1751; NSd 1751-1758; by 1773-1774/ 1787,1788/ 1793-onNS	Pres.
9.	Goshen, First Pres.	1720(5 sr) 1721(3 sr) 1715(ps.38) by 1767(22) 1784(incp.)	-	j1721-1733, j1738;NSd 1745-1758; by 1773-onOS	Pres.

NEW YORK - ORANGE COUNTY - continued

A	B	C	D	E	F
10.	Highland Falls, First Pres.(f.l.Highlands;f. Highlands West;f.l.West Point(OS);nl.01T)	by 1823(CG) 1830(PR;2 sr)	WAP: 1823-1830	1830-1840/ 1841NS, 1837-1858OS, 1857-1975NS	Merged to Meth.
11.	Howells, Cong.(f.Howell's Depot,in Wallkill; 1847/1850 moved from Gilead or Yellow Mtghse. in Mount Hope village (f.Mapestown;in Mount Hope,f.in *Calhoun 1825-1833;f.in Deerpark to 1825) to Howell's Depot;1793/1829 moved from Deerpark Four Corners(f.New Shawangunk,nr. Otisville,in Mount Hope from 1833,f.in *Calhoun 1825-1833,f.in Deerpark 1798-1825,f. in *Mamakating to 1798)to Mount Hope;f.First Cong.Ch.& Soc.of Mount Hope (r.incp.1847);f. Cong.Ch.& Soc.in Wallkill & Deerpark(r.incp. 1810);f.First Pres.of Deerpark;f.Deerpark Ch. & Cgn.;lost property in court case 1793;Fed. to #18 1827/1831-1833/1834;affl.NJ 1869-1876; lt.cl.1855-1858;see also #18)	1782(CG;3 sr) 1770(38,45) 1772/1787(53) 1785(incp.)	MC:1782-1807, WAP:m.1792; LIS:1808-1809 SNJ:1809-pb. 1828; LIS:1829-1833; 1836-1843, m.1843-1846, 1846-1982	-	UCC 1961-1982; withdrew
12.	Middletown, First Cong.(South Middletown;f. Middletown Ch.& Cgn.;f.in Wallkill;f. Shawangunk;Plains;affl.NJ 1869-1876;court battle over property 1825-1834;see also #13)	1785(CG;4 sr) 1786(incp.)	MC:1785-1820; WAP:m.1792- 1793,1818- 1819, j1820- 1824; pb.NYI: ? -1834; 1835-1843, m.1843-1847, 1846-1995	j1824; 1823-1825	UCC 1961-1995; CCCC 1978 (j1977)-on
13.	Middletown, First Pres.(f.in Wallkill;division of #12,which causes 01T l.as f.CG)	1825 1828(incp.)	-	j1825; 1825-onNS 1837-1840OS	Pres.
14.	Middletown, North Cong.(North St.)	1889(2 sr) 1880(s.01)	1889-on	-	UCC
15.	Monroe, First Pres.(f.in Seamanville;f.of Smith Clove or Clove;f.First Pres.Cgn.of Cheesecocks;f.C of C of *Southfield to 1808; f.of Cheescocks to 1801;f.of *Cornwall to 1799;nl.01T;f.of *New Cornwall to 1797)	by 1774(PR) r.1784(CG; 3 sr) 1783(11) 1788(incp.) 1801(r.incp.) r.1828(PR:98)	MC:1783-1820; WAP:j1820- 1828	by 1773-1774/ 1787; 1818-1819; j1829; 1828-onOS	Pres.
16.	Montgomery, First Pres.(pr.1830;in 1831 bldg.; 1973 ab.UMeth.(1827))	1832(38) r.1973 M	-	j1832; 1832-onNS	Pres.

NEW YORK - ORANGE COUNTY - continued

Sh 17.	Montgomery, <u>Goodwill</u> Pres.(Scotch Ch.;The Wallkill Ch.;f.of Wallkill to 1816;voted to leave Pby.1978/1979)	1729 1741(incp.) by 1759(22)	-	j1729; NSd 1745-1758; by 1773-1987OS	Tr.to Evan.Pres. 1986-on
18.	Mount Hope, First Pres.(division of #11;1834 moved Deer Park Four Corners(nr.Otisville,in Mount Hope 1833,f.in *Calhoun 1825-1833,f.in Deerpark 1798-1825,f.in *Mamakating to 1798) to Mount Hope village (in Mount Hope);Fed.to #11 1827/1831-1833/1834;1932 merged to Pres.of Otisville (in Mount Hope,f.Meth. 1848-1855,r.Pres.1855,1.75:1854-1933NS) as Mount Hope Pres.of Otisville (1.75:1933-on))	1792(98) by 1793(53)	-	j1792; 1788/ 1793-1933OS	Merged, see text
19.	Newburgh, First Cong.(1t.01N)	1889(2 sr) 1888(s.01) 1891(s.01N) 1890(s.05)	1889-1960	-	CCCC 1986-on
20.	Newburgh, First Pres.(f.a branch of #22 to 1773; 1945 merged to Calvary Pres.(1856,1.75:1856-1946OS) as Calvary Pres.(1.75:1946-on))	1773(98) 1766(14) 1784(Ch.full: 3 sr)	-	(ps.1769) by 1773-1946 OS; 1839-1840/1841NS	Merged, see text
21.	Newburgh, Second Pres.	1838(98)	-	1839-1857NS	X
22.	New Windsor, Pres.(f.West Windsor;see also #20; DUT 1767-1769;also 1.Pby.1813-1814,not natl.)	1764(14,98) 1766(3 sr) 1774(22)	-	j1766/1767; by 1773-1811, 1814-1816, 1818-1883NS	X
Gr 23.	Pine Island, St.Paul Ger.Cong.(in 1910 bldg.; 1.01K:1911/1912-1944/1948;*Warwick)	1912(01)	1912-1966	-	Sch.I 1961-1963; Sch.II 1963-1966; pb.withdrew
24.	Port Jervis, First Pres.(f.of *Deerpark)	1851(45,98)	-	1851-onNS	Pres.
25.	Ridgebury, First Pres.Cgn.(Slate Hill PO;in *Wawaywanda,f.in *Minisink to 1849;moved 1799;f.Pres.Cgn.of Drowned Lands of Goshen; elders while MC;s.Pres.name but Cong.forms; 1927 ab.#3)	1792(CG) 1787(incp.: pb.Soc.) 1805(r.incp.) r.1817(PR) r.1927 M	MC:1792-1816 WAP:m.1816	j1817; 1816-1821, 1822-onNS	Pres.
26.	Scotchtown, Pres.(Middletown PO;*Wallkill)	1796(3 sr) 1798(49) 1803(53)	-	j1798; 1798/1802-onOS	Pres.

NEW YORK - ORANGE COUNTY - continued

A	B	C	D	E	F
27.	Thompson Ridge, <u>Hopewell</u> Pres.(in Crawford;in 1778/1779 bldg.;f.in *Montgomery to 1823)	1793 1792(Soc.) 1779(90) 1778(46A) 1800(incp.)	-	1774/1787-onOS	Pres.
28.	Unionville, First Pres.(f.Soc.;f.a branch of #34;in 1825 bldg.;*Minisink)	1803(branch) r.1831(PR:98) 1832(45) 1854[sic:46A]	-	j1830; 1831-onNS 1837-1840OS	Pres.
29.	Warwick, <u>Amity</u> Pres.(Amity PO;Pine Island PO;nl. Pby.1818-1819)	1796(2 sr; Soc.:98) 1797(incp.) 1799(45) 1809(Ch.:98)	-	1798/1802-onNS 1837-1840OS	Pres.
30.	Warwick, Pres.& Dutch Ref. (Tr.to Ref.,RCA 1804-on(85);jPby.af.1758:37)	1750(4 sr) 1764(90) 1791(incp.)	-	j1751; NSd 1751-1758; by 1773-1774/ 1787,1788/ 1793-1803/ 1808	1804 Tr.to Ref. (see text)
31.	Washingtonville, First Pres.(White Ch.;*Blooming Grove)	1841(45,98) 1847(46A)	-	1840/1841-on NS	Pres.
32.	Washingtonville, Second Pres.(f.Free Cong.;Brown Ch.;*Blooming Grove)	1847 1846(s.98) 1851(incp.) pb.r.c.1856 (PR)	cl.1853-1858	1856-1893OS	X 1889
33.	Westtown, Constitutional Pres.(1838 division of #34;in *Minisink)	1842(org.) 1838	-	1837-1864NS	Merged to #34(q.v.)
34.	Westtown, First Pres.(Tr.to Ref.(RCA,1791-1805 (85)),Tr.to Pres.;see also #28;Tr.to OS 1839; 1864 merged to #33;in *Minisink)	1790(CG:3 sr) 1788(99) Tr.1791(Ref.) Tr.1803(PR) 1805(incp.) r.1864 M	MC:1790-1791	j1806; 1803/ 1805-onOS	Tr.to Ref.; Tr.; Pres.

NEW YORK - ORLEANS COUNTY (org.1824) (073)

1.	Albion, First Pres.(f.of Newport to 1826;f.in Barre;located,pb.incor.,in Gaines by 48)	1824	-	j1824/1825; 1819/1824-onNS	Pres.
2.	Barre Center, Barre Center Pres.(in Barre;f. First Cong.Soc.;f.at Benton's Corners 1824-1829;f.at Newport (now Albion) to 1824;f.of Gaines to 1818;left Pby.(first time) 1840)	1816(CG;4 sr) 1817(s.26) r.1873(PR:98) 1872(26)	1840-1842; GC:1842-1845; 1845/1846-1848, 1849-1850; cl.1853-1858	j1820; 1819-1840/1842NS; j1845; 1846/1848-onNS	Pres.
3.	Carlton, First Pres.at Kenyonville	1831(3 sr) 1832(s.48)	-	1831-1834/1835	1836 merged to #8(q.v.) (26:X 1841)
4.	Carlton, Pres.(f.First Cong.;nl.01T)	1841(CG;3 sr) r.1848(PR)	1840-1842; GC:1842-by 1848	j1849; 1848-1919NS	X (1917:22,26)
5.	Clarendon, Pres.(First Pres.Soc.in Murray;f. First Cong.Ch.:98;lt.98:s.1816(pb.Monroe Co.#11))	1820(CG;s.98) 1823(pb.PR;48) 1816(s.98)	nl.	j1823(48,51) 1819/1824-1831	Merged to #15 to form #9(q.v.)
6.	Gaines, Cong.UCC (merger of #7 & #8;1834 bldg.)	1864 M	1864-on	-	UCC
7.	Gaines, First Free Cong.Soc.	1847	1845/1846-1848, 1849-1850; cl.1853-1857; 1857-1864	-	Merged to #8 to form #6(q.v.)
8.	Gaines, First Pres.(f.First Cong.;moved 1834; 1836 ab.#3;Union Soc.1824;left Pby.1840; 1854:PR,f.CG:01T)	1821(CG;3 sr) r.1836 M r.1847/1854 (PR)	GC:m.1840,nl.	j1822; 1819/1824-1840/1842NS, 1847-1862NS	1864 merged to #7 to form #6(q.v.)
9.	Holley, First Pres.of Murray(merger of #5 & #15; at M CG forms,PR name;nl.01T,but l.cl.;98 says vote to r.PR 1836,but not done)	1831 M(CG) r.1919(PR)	cl.1853-1858	j1833; 1831-onNS	Pres.
10.	Kendall, First Pres.(f.Cong.;f.of Murray to 1837;j Pby.1844:26;nl.01T)	1833(CG) r.1844(PR)	nl.	j1834; 1833-1867NS, 1870-1872	X 1867(22,26)
11.	Knowlesville, First Pres.(f.Cong.of Ridgeway; First Relg.Soc.of Ridgeway;f.Oak Orchard; lt.75:1831-1832;nl.01T)	1817(CG;4 sr) r.1820(PR) 1821(Soc.)	nl.	j1820; 1819-1966NS	X
12.	Lyndonville, Lyndonville Pres.(f.United;f.of Yates)	1833(3 sr)	-	j1834; 1833-onNS	Pres.
13.	Medina, First Pres.(f.First Cong.;in Ridgeway; village extends into Shelby;1854:CG in 01T & cl.,pb.incor.)	1829(CG;3 sr) r.1835(PR:99)	cl.1853-1856	j1830/1831; 1831-onNS	Pres.

NEW YORK - ORLEANS COUNTY - continued

A	B	C	D	E	F
14.	Millville, Cong.(First;f.of Shelby;s.incor.l. Hillville or Melville;s.l.as if in Niagara Co.;98 says r.PR 1874,when affl.CG (ps.a schism to 1881;26 reverses form of 1820 & 1821 dates)	1820(PR) r.1821(CG)	cl.1853-1854; 1854-1855; cl.1855-1858; 1873-1909	j1821; 1819/ 1824-1837/ 1838,1839-1855NS,1856-1881NS	X (1907:26)
15.	Sandy Creek, Cong.(in Murray)	1819(CG;2 sr) 1821(48) r.1829(mixed)	nl.	j1821; 1825-1830	1831 merged to #5 to form #9(q.v.)

NEW YORK - OSWEGO COUNTY (org.1816) (075)

A	B	C	D	E	F
1.	Albion, First Pres.(same as #2 in 98;75H confuses with Orleans Co. #1)	1829(98)	-	j1830; 1829-1855NS, 1861-1863NS	X
2.	Altmar, First Cong.(f.l.Sand Banks;*Albion; replace 1834/1838 Union Soc.;see also #1)	1852(01,s.98) 1853(s.98)	1852-1914	-	X
3.	Amboy, Pres.	by 1850	-	1849-1865NS	X
4.	Black Creek, P or C Ch.(*Volney)	by 1832	nl.	1831-1850NS	X
5.	Constantia, Pres.(f.Cong.)	by 1822(CG) r.1839(PR) r.1839(CG) r.1842(PR) r.1851(39)	nl.	j1822; 1819/1824- 1846/1848NS, 1849-1948NS	Merged to part of Meth. to form M.
5M.	Constantia, Cong.(merger of #5 & part of Meth.)	1946 M	1947-on	-	UCC [Count as CC]
6.	Fulton, First Cong.(f.of Oswego Falls;f.of *Volney)	1882(3 sr)	1881-on	-	UCC
7.	Fulton, First Pres.;f.l.Oswego Falls;f.Ch.of Fulton & Granby to 1871;Pres.Soc.of Volney & Granby;Fulton f.in Volney;f.l.Granby to 1825; Ch.& Soc.merge 1832;see also #8;1997 merged to First Bapt.(1827)as First United)	1818(pb.PR) 1827(Soc.) r.1832(98) r.1997 M	-	1820-onNS	Pres.
8.	Granby, P or C (ps.lt.of #7)	by 1825	nl.	1825-1840/ 1845NS	X
9.	Hannibal, First Pres.(named Pres.at start but no elders elected;f.Cong.Soc.;Hamiltonville; f.Hammondsville;f.Hannibalville;Fed.to Hannibal Bapt.(1825) 1926-on,as Com.)	1816(mixed) r.1820(CG;39) 1822(2 sr) 1825(Soc.) r.1870(PR)	cl.1853-1858	j1817; 1815/1816- onNS	Pres.
10.	Hannibal, Second Ch.(P or C Ch.)	by 1817	nl.	1815/1816- 1820	X
11.	Hastings, Central Square Pres.(98:X 1836, property held to 1874)	1828	-	1828-1856NS	X
12.	Mexico, First Pres.Soc.(West;First Cong.Soc.; s.l.Miscico;nl.01T;98 says #13 continues First Ch.,& this org.1830)	1810(CG;2 sr) 1811(49) r.1818(PR) 1829(Soc.r.) r.1830	ps.OE bf.1818	j1818; 1814/ 1818-onNS	Pres.
13.	Mexico, Mexicoville Pres.(East;<u>Prattville</u>;98: this continues #12)	1830(CG;98) 1829(39)	cl.1853-1858	1830-1863NS	X 1859
14.	New Haven, First Cong.	1817(CG;2 sr)	cl.1853-1858; 1867-on	j1821; 1819/ 1824-1867NS	UCC

NEW YORK - OSWEGO COUNTY - continued

A	B	C	D	E	F
15.	Orwell, Union Ch.(f.First Cong.;f.Pres.;PR Soc. 1819;in Union Soc.with Meth.1844;Fed.to Meth. Epis.(1825)1922-1981;f.of *Richland to 1817)	1809(CG;98) 1819(PR Soc.) r. ? (PR) r.1858(CG)	ps.BR bf.1817; BR:1822-1823; cl.1853-1857; j1858; 1857-1981	j1823; 1819/ 1824-1863NS	Sch.I 1961-1981; X
16.	Oswego, First Cong.Soc.	1832(22) 1833(26)	nl.	-	X 1840(26)
17.	Oswego, First Pres.(1936 ab.Grace Pres.(1872,l. 75:1871-1936))	1816(4 sr) r.1936 M	-	1815/1816- 1853NS, 1853-1989OS	Merged to #18(q.v.)
18.	Oswego, UCC Cong.(f.First Cong.;f.Second Pres.of East Oswego to r.)	1837(PR;3 sr) r.1857(CG)	1856-1989	1837/1838- 1858NS	UCC 1961-1989; Merged to #17 to form M.
18M.	Oswego, Faith United Ch.(merger of #17 & #18)	1989 M	1989-on	1989-on	UCC & Pres.(dual)
19.	Palermo, Cong.(Union Ch.at Denton's Corners;f. Second of Volney to 1832;nl.01T)	1823(PR;98) r.1835(CG)	1876-1883	1819/1824- 1837/1838	X
20.	Parish, Cong.(98 says "existed about 5 yrs.", which does not fit other data;bldg.bec.Meth. 1869)	by 1837(CG) c.1841(98)	nl.	1836-1851NS	X
21.	Phoenix, First Cong.(s.l.Phenix;*Schroeppel;left Pby.1863)	1837(CG;2 sr) 1836(s.01)	cl.1853-1858; 1862-on	j1841; 1840/ 1845-1862NS	UCC
22.	Prattham, Cong.(Union Sq.PO;*Mexico)	1888(01N)	1889-1909	-	X
23.	Pulaski, First Cong.Soc.& Ch.of Richland at Pulaski(f.l.Port Ontario;f.Richland & Salmon River;org,in Pawlet,Rutland Co.,VT & immediately removed here;see also #25)	1807(CG;2 sr) 1808(s.01) 1811(Soc.;90) 1801(12)	BR:ps.bf. 1817; BR:1822-by 1824; j1840; 1839-on	j1822; 1819/ 1824-1840/ 1845NS	UCC
24.	Redfield, Cong.(f.Pres.)	1802(CG;2 sr) 1801(12) r.1872(PR) r.1923(CG;01)	cl.1853-1858; 1924-1966	1819/1824- 1877NS, 1885-1926	Sch.I 1961-1966; X
25.	Sandy Creek, Cong.(f.of Richland to 1825;f. Pres.;ps.a branch of #23 to 1825)	1817(CG;3 sr)	cl.1853-1854; 1854-1953	1825-1854NS, 1861-1862NS	X
26.	Scriba, P or C Ch.	by 1832	nl.	1831-1840/ 1845NS	X
27.	Volney, Volney UCC (First;f.Bristol Hill Cong.)	1812(CG;2 sr) 1814(90) r.1817(PR) r.1826(CG) r.1874(01N)	cl.1853-1858; 1873-on	j1820; 1819/ 1824-1873NS	UCC

NEW YORK - OSWEGO COUNTY - continued

A	B	C	D	E	F
28.	West Monroe, Pres.(f.Cong.;s.l.PR:1843)	1843(mixed;90) r.1867(CG) r.c.1890(PR)	cl.1853-1858; 1867-1881	1846/1848-1864NS, 1890-1918	X
29.	Williamstown, Cong.	1877(98)	nl.	-	X pb.soon
30.	Williamstown, Pres.(Fed.to Meth.1943-1974; 1974 merged to same as Williamstown United, dual to 1996)	1805(CG;90) r.af.1858(PR; 01T) r.1974 M	ps.OE bf.1820; cl.1853-1858	j1820; 1819/1824-1996NS	X (pb.ab. by Meth.)

NEW YORK - OTSEGO COUNTY (org.1791) (077)

A	B	C	D	E	F
1.	Burlington, C of C,Cong.(1t.1842-1843;nl.01T,but l.cl.)	1793(PR;min) 1797(pb.CG;98) r.1840	OE: ? -1808; UA 1808-1822/1829; OE:1829-1834; 1834-1844/1845, 1846-1853; cl.1853-1858	j1793;nl.	X
2.	Cherry Valley, First Pres.(in indep.Boston Pby. ps.1745-1765;DUT 1765-1775/1788;f.of *Canajoharie (Montgomery Co.)to 1791)	1741(PR;3 sr) 1740(98) r.1785(incp.)	-	(see text) j1765; by 1773-onNS	Pres.
3.	Exeter, Cong.(Exeter Ctr.;s.named Pres.;early PR in 90,but nl.Pby.)	1806(CG;98) 1809(99) 1800(l.PR:90)	OE: ? -1808; UA 1808-1822/1825; OE:1825-1833; cl.1853-1858	1833-1885NS	X
4.	Fly Creek, Pres.(f.of Fly Creek & Oak Creek;75H l.as two chs.1828-1837,each name;*Otsego)	1828(CG;98) r.af.1858(PR:01T)	cl.1853-1858	1828-1934NS	X
5.	Gilbertsville, First Pres.(f.Associated Pres. Soc.of Butternuts;f.First Cong.of Butternuts at Gilbertsville)	1797(CG;2 sr) 1787(46A) 1795/1796(90) r.1822(mixed) r.1872(PR)	ps.OE; UA:1811-1822; cl.1853-1858	j1822; 1819/1824-onNS	Pres.
6.	Hartwick, Pres.(Cong.forms;s.l.West Hartwick;f. of *Otsego to 1802)	1800(CG;98)	NAP:mnd.; OE: ? -1808; UA 1808-1822; cl.1853-1858	1822/1824-1858NS	X
7.	Laurens, Laurens Pres.(f.in Union Mtghse.(1822); Fed.to Meth.(1810) 1944-1952;1952 merged to same as Pres.)	1842(3 sr) 1844(98) r.1952 M	-	1841/1842-onNS	Pres.
8.	Maryland, Pres.	by 1831	-	1830-1858NS	X
9.	Middlefield, Pres.of Middlefield Ctr.(pb.f. Cong.;PO Cooperstown)	1805(ps.PR;90) r.1821(pb.CG;2 sr) r.af.1858(PR:01T)	cl.1853-1858	1807/1808-1814/1818, 1821/1824-1964NS	X
10.	Milford, Milford Pres.(f.First;org.as Relg.Soc., bec.Pres.Soc.at r.;nl.01T)	1803(CG;98) r.1806(PR)	nl.	j1802/1806; 1803/1805-1996NS	X

NEW YORK – OTSEGO COUNTY – continued

A		B	C	D	E	F
	11.	New Lisbon, Pres.(Cong.forms;f.First Cong.of Noblesville;f.of Lisbon to 1808;f.of *Pittsfield to 1806)	1805(CG;98) 1804(90) r.1869(01N)	SA:pb.1804-?; OE: ? -1808; UA:1808-1822; cl.1853-1858	1822/1824-1858NS, 1864-1868NS	indep.; X af.1869
	12.	Oneonta, First Pres.(f.Second Pres.Ch.of Milford 1823-1833;elders while in NAP;X 1849 & r. 1849;01T & cl.say r.PR af.1858:pb.incor.;f.of *Otego to 1830)	1823(CG) r.1849(PR)	NAP:1823- ? ; cl.1853-1858	1819/1824-onNS	Pres.
	13.	Oneonta, Pres.(99 & 46A say X & r.as Ref.(RCA) 1800 & X c.1820(nl.85);49 & 98 say X & r.PR 1800 & X bf.1823;f.of *Otego to 1830)	1786(2 sr) by 1798(22) ps.r.1800	-	nl.	X bf.1800 (see text)
	14.	Otego, Otego Pres.(f.First Cong.of Otego & vicinity;f.of *Huntsville to 1830;f.of *Unadilla to 1822;nl.01T,but pb.incor.l.as Otsego)	1805(CG;98) r.1891(PR)	pb.NAP ; 1852-1853; cl.1853-1858	1832-onNS	Pres.
	15.	Otsego, First Pres.of Cooperstown (f.Pres.& Cong.Soc.:90)	1800 1795(Soc.) 1798(Soc.;98) 1799(22)	nl.	j1795; 1794/ 1797-1834	Merged to #17 to form #16(q.v.)
	16.	Otsego, First Pres.of Cooperstown (merger of #15 & #17;01T & cl.claim a CG form,but pb.not, reference pb.to #14)	1834 M (PR)	cl.1853-1858 (see text)	1834-onNS	Pres.
	17.	Otsego, Second Pres.of Cooperstown	1833(26,98)	-	1833-1834	Merged to #15 to form #16(q.v.)
	18.	Plainfield, Cong.(nl.01T,but l.cl.;f.of *Richfield to 1799)	1793(44)	OE: ? -1808; UA:1808-1826; OE:1826-1834; 1834-1841, 1842-1853; cl.1853-1854; 1854-1855; cl.1855-1858	-	X
	19.	Plainfield, Cong.	1872(01N)	nl.	-	X pb.soon
We	20.	Plainfield, Shiloh Welsh Cong.(Plainfield Ctr.; Perry Ctr.PO;s.l."Perry,Herkimer Co.",but no such place;pb.not Perry,Wyoming Co.;Tr.to Eng.Assn.1925)	1861(4 sr)	NYW ? -1867; 1867-1941	-	X (1942:s.70; 1944:s.70)
	21.	Richfield Springs, Pres.(f.Cong.Soc.;in Richfield;f.in Monticello (village) to c.1825;apply to j OE 1826,delayed to 1828; left CG Assn.1844:s.l.r.PR(pb.incor.);1971 merged to Meth.(1872) as C of C,Uniting (dual))	1797(CG;11) 1803(3 sr) r.1868(PR) r.1971 M	OE: ? -1808; UA:1808-1826; OE:1828-1834; 1834-1843; cl.1853-1858	j1844; 1844-onNS	Pres.(dual, see text)

NEW YORK - OTSEGO COUNTY - continued

A	B	C	D	E	F
22.	Springfield, Cong.of <u>West Springfield</u>	1806	ps.NAP	-	1813 merged to #23 to form #24(q.v.)
23.	Springfield, First Pres.(f.of *Cherry Valley to 1797)	by 1791 (PR;min) 1796(ps.CG;98) by 1800(PR;49) by 1802(44)	NAP(m.44)	j1791; 1788/ 1793-1794/ 1797,1798/ 1802-1809/ 1813	1813 merged to #22 to form #24(q.v.)
24.	Springfield, First Pres.(merger of #22 & #23)	1813 M	-	1809/1813-onNS	Pres.
25.	Unadilla, First Pres.(in Harmony Soc.;f.Fed.to Bapt.1927/1938-1951)	1823	-	1819/1824-1839NS, 1840-onNS	Pres.
26.	Westford, Pres.(f.Third Cong.of Worcester to 1808)	1800(CG;98) 1820(Soc.) r.af.1879(PR;99)	ps.OE or NAP; cl.1853-1858	1831-1913NS	X
27.	Worcester, First Pres.(f.Cong.Ch.Soc.of Christ; f.Second Cong.Ch.& Soc.of Worcester 1812-1917;f.in Cherry Valley to 1797)	1792(CG;2 sr) 1803(Soc.) r.1917(PR;99)	ps.OE; NAP:j1812-1830; cl.1853-1858	j1831; 1830-onNS	Pres.

NEW YORK - PUTNAM COUNTY (org.1812) (079)

A	B	C	D	E	F
1.	Carmel, Gilead Pres.(f.Second Pres.of Carmel at Gilead;f.First Cong.of Carmel at Gilead to 1835(1803:38);1837 moved Gilead to Carmel Village;1792 moved Gregory's Par.(now in Southeast)across town line to Gilead(now in Carmel);1756 moved Tilly Foster (now in Southeast) to Gregory's Par.;in Gilead Ch.in Frederickstown 1792-1795;f.West of Southeast to 1792;f.Gregory's Par.;f.West C of C in Philips Patent;f.Western Soc.of Philips Pct.; DUT 1774(nl.1773)-1787;r.PR:1774:46A,not otherwise supported;nl.01T)	1756(CG;2 sr) 1743(14,38) 1735/1744(46A) by 1745(98) 1752(42) 1766(?) r.1792(min) r.1835(PR: elders) 1803(38)	FE(CT): 1756-1763 (1752:99); WAP:1792-1830	j1774(98,m. 49;nl.) -af.1787; j1835; 1834-onOS	Pres.
2.	Cold Spring, First Pres.of Philipstown (in 1826 union bldg.)	1828(2 sr) 1820(pr.:38)	-	1824-onOS 1837-1840/ 1841NS	Pres.
3.	Mahopac, First Pres.(Mahopac Falls PO;in Carmel; f.First of Carmel;f.Red Mills;f.Carmel Mills; f.Fourth Ch.,West Cgn.of Frederickstown to 1795;s.l.West Fredericksburg;f.a branch of Westchester Co.#35 to 1790,s.l.when a branch; DUT:s.42:1787-1793;lt.14 at Carmel & Red Mills;14 l.pastors here 1750-1754)	1790(CG;3 sr) 1761(pr.:2 s) 1750(pr.:s.14) 1784(pr.:38) 1774(s.14) r.1828(PR) 1835(38)	[MC:1785-1787]; WAP:1792-1828	[1774/1787-1788/1793] j1828/1829; 1827-onOS	Pres.
4.	Patterson, Patterson-Pawling Pres.(f.of Franklin to 1808;f.North Cgn.of Frederickstown to 1795;s.l.Fredericksburg;f.Second of Philipse Pct.;DUT 1762-1795;WAP:occaisional supplies;under suspension of Pby.1818-1823; nl.01T)	1752(CG;2 sr) 1745(s.38,49) 1730(s.38,45) 1759(99) 1775(14,98) r.1794/1795 r.1804(PR: elders)	FE(CT): 1752-1763; DUT:1762-1763 WAP:sv.1795, 1799-1800, 1802,1804-1808,1820-1823	j1763; by 1773-onOS	Pres.
Nt	Philipstown, Highlands Ch.(14 l.pr.here 1742-1743(Indep.Pby.) not otherwise identified)				
5.	Philipstown, Strict Cong.(af.1773 ab.by Cortlandt Bapt.,Westchester Co.(by 1769:10))	1751(10)	nl.	-	Tr.to Bapt.1753; (see text)
6.	Southeast, First Ch.(f.Union Soc.;Kent's Par.; f.First of Philipse Pct.;Philippi;at Doansburg;DUT 1762-1795;nl.01T;Pby.says Tr. from Fairfield East 1825,but nl.by them by 1819;1961 merged to Pres.of Brewster (in Southeast;f.of Southeast Centre to 1881;l.75: 1853-1961OS)as Brewster Pres.,l.75:1961-on)	1743(CG;3 sr) 1740(42) 1735(2 sr) 1734(99) 1730(s.38,49) r.1826(PR)	FE(CT): 1743-1763 (1734:99), j1809-1810, (ps.1825); DUT:1762-1763 WAP:sv.1811-1814	j1763; by 1773-1808; j1825; 1824-1961OS	Merged, see text

NEW YORK - QUEENS COUNTY (org.1683) (081)

A		B	C	D	E	F
Sw	1.	New York City, Queens, Corona, Bethany Swedish Cong.(f.Bethesda;f.incor.l.in Brooklyn,Kings Co.1915-1916;EC:Rgn.by 1910-1961)	1910(06) 1899 1898(s.01) 1911(s.01)	1915-1962	-	s.EC; Sch.I 1961-1962; X
Bl	2.	New York City, Queens, Corona, Cong.UCC	1916(01,21) 1917	1921-on	-	UCC
	Nt	New York City, Queens, Corona, Union Evan.(l.by Manhattan Assn.1885-1895)	1873	nl.	-	X af.1895
Bl	3.	New York City, Queens, *Elmhurst, Colored Cong. of Newtown (s.l.New Town;f.of Newtown to 1898)	by 1839	1838-1843	-	X
	4.	New York City, Queens, Elmhurst, First Pres.of Newtown (f.First Ch.of Newtown;f.of Flushing & Newtown;f.of Middelberg to 1664;f.in New Netherland to 1663;in CT 1663-1664;sett.1642 (Newtown:3 sr),1651(90),1655(s.98),1656 (s.98),1645(Flushing:90);sett.abandoned 1643-1648;nl.01T;in Par.with Jamaica 1693, Epis.took bldg.1703-1708;f.of Newtown to 1898)	1652(CG;27) 1662(org.:49) 1672(98) 1643(pr.:49) 1642(pr.:14) r.1715(PR:21) r.1724 (elders:27)	nl.	j1715;NSd 1745-1758; by 1773-onOS	Pres.
	5.	New York City, Queens, Flushing, Broadway Cong. (in 1893 bldg.)	1905(s.01) 1904	1906-1927	-	X
	6.	New York City, Queens, Flushing, First Cong. (f.of Flushing to 1898;Fed.to Ref.Prot.Dutch of Flushing (RCA,1842)1971-1974)	1851(01,98) 1852(21)	1851-1860, 1861-1974	-	UCC 1961-1974; Merged to form M.(q.v.)
bA	6M.	New York City, Queens, Flushing, Bowne St.Com. (merger of #6 & Ref.Prot.Dutch of Flushing (RCA,1842),dual;bec.predominantly Asian (mostly Taiwanese) by 1993)	1974 M	1974-on	-	UCC (dual, see text)
	7.	New York City, Queens, Forest Hills, Ch.in the Gardens, Cong.	1913(s.01) 1912(s.05)	1913-on	-	Sch.I 1961-1963; Sch.II 1963-on; NA by 1961-on
Bl	8.	New York City, Queens, Jamaica, Christ Com.	1930	1930-1938	-	X
	9.	New York City, Queens, Jamaica, First Pres.(f. First Ch.;f.of Rustdorp(Rusdorpe)to 1665; sett.1656(5 sr),1655(98);f.in New Netherland to 1663;in CT 1663-1664;nl.01T;in Par.with Newtown 1693;Grace Epis.(1702) seized bldg. 1703-1709,shared bldg.1709-1728;Closed c.1776-1783;SUF 1764-1790;always Pres.in 36;had town tax support 1672-1753,except during Epis. period;f.of Jamaica to 1898)	1661(CG;3 sr; pr.:36) 1672(3 sr; gather:36) by 1663(30, 90;pr.:27,49) 1662(46A) 1698(80) r.by 1712 (PR:49B)	nl.; sv.1760-1762	j1710/1711; NSd.1745-1758, left Pby.: 1758/1760; j1764; by 1773-onOS	Pres.

NEW YORK – QUEENS COUNTY – continued

A		B	C	D	E	F
bM	10.	New York City, Queens, Jamaica, Victoria Cong. (bec.Multi-cultural with no clear majority by 1997)	1917(01,21)	1917-on	–	UCC
Bl	11.	New York City, Queens, Queens Village, Hollis Ave.Cong.	1928	1928-on	–	UCC
	12.	New York City, Queens, Richmond Hill, Pilgrim Cong.(f.l.Brooklyn Hills;f.of *Jamaica to 1898)	1893 1903(s.01)	1894-on	–	UCC
	13.	New York City, Queens, Richmond Hill, Union Cong.(f.of *Jamaica to 1898)	1886(3 sr)	1886-on	–	Sch.I 1961-1963; UCC 1963-on
	14.	New York City, Queens, Richmond Hill, Van Wyck Ave.Cong.(f.l.Dunton;f.l.Jamaica;f.l. Brooklyn, Kings Co.PO;voted no,then yes on UCC Constit.bf.1961;f.of Jamaica to 1898)	1894(s.01,21) 1895(01N) 1893(s.01)	1895-1981	–	UCC; X
	15.	New York City, Queens, Rockaway Beach, First Cong.(Oceanus PO;f.of *Hempstead to 1898)	1886(2 sr) 1885(s.01) 1889(s.01)	1885-on	–	UCC
	16.	New York City, Queens, Woodhaven, Christ Cong.	1911(01,21)	1911-on	–	UCC
	17.	New York City, Queens, Woodhaven, First Cong. (Ozone Park PO;f.of *Jamaica to 1898)	1863(5 sr)	1862-1960	–	NA 1963(j1964)-1973; X

NEW YORK – RENSSELAER COUNTY (org.1791) (083)

A	B	C	D	E	F
1.	Brunswick, Brunswick Pres.(First;Troy PO)	1809(46A;s. Soc.) 1810(s.Soc.) 1816(Ch.,full) 1825(Soc.r.)	–	j1811; 1809/1813-onNS	Pres.
2.	Clinton Heights, Com.Cong.(f.l.East Greenbush)	1928(01)	1928-on	–	UCC
3.	East Nassau, Pres.(f.East Nassau & Brainerds; period outside Pby.sugggests CG;nl.01T)	1807(98) by 1833(elders)	nl.	1814/1818-1891NS	X
4.	Hoosick Falls, First Pres.(f.l.Hoosick)	1824(98) 1825(22,26) 1826(46A)	–	j1825; 1819/1824-onNS	Pres.
5.	Lansingburgh, First Free Pres.(bec.Second of Lansingburgh,bec.Olivet Pres.of Troy)	1835(4 sr)	–	1836-1963NS	X
6.	Lansingburgh, First Pres.(North Troy PO;f.Prot. Ref.Dutch(RCA))	1784(Ref.: 2 sr) 1774(Ref.:85) Tr.1792(PR: 5 sr) 1800(PR:85)	–	j1792; 1788/1793-onOS	Pres.
7.	Nassau, Pres.& Cong.Ch.(West Nassau;pb.f.Nassau Union;nr.Alps;nl.01T;98 says lived 30-40 yrs.;pb.not r.PR;f.of *Philipstown to 1808)	by 1805 (mixed)	nl.	j1805; 1803/1805-1886NS	X
8.	Pittstown, North Pres.(f.Pres.of Tomhannock;f. United Dutch & Pres.Soc.;f.Ref.(RCA to 1807: 85);Johnsonville PO)	1799(Ref.) Tr.1819(PR:98)	–	jby 1820; 1819/1820-1935NS	X
9.	Pittstown, South C of C (f.Cong.C of C;nl.01T)	by 1793(CG; WAP:min) 1796(12) r.1816(98) 1817(Soc.)	pb.NAP; WAP:m.1793-1796	1814/1818-1849NS	withdrew; X 1868(98)
10.	Rensselaer, First Cong.(f.l.Greenbush;f.Cong.of East Albany)	1879(3 sr) 1839[sic:s.01]	1878-2001	–	UCC 1961-2001; X
11.	Rensselaer, First Pres.of Greenbush (f.Cong.; *East Greenbush;nl.01T)	1827(PR;98) 1823(Soc.) r.1842(CG:98) r.1844(PR:98)	nl.	1827-1840/1842NS,1843/1844-onNS 1837-1841OS	Pres.

NEW YORK - RENSSELAER COUNTY - continued

A	B	C	D	E	F
12.	Sand Lake, First Pres.(f.Prot.Soc.(Cong.)to 1808;nl.01T;f.First of Greenbush to 1812; merged 1967 to Averill Park Meth.(f.Olive Chap.Meth.Epis.(1874),ab.Hoag's Corners Meth. in 1957,ab.Glass Lake Meth.in 1939) as Ch.of Covenant,United Meth.of Averill Park (*Sand Lake))	1805(CG) r.1808(PR;98, 46A)	nl.	j1809; 1809/1813-1968NS	Merged, see text
13.	Schaghticoke, <u>Hart's Falls</u> Ch.(division of #14)	1827	-	1827-1830	1830 merged to #14
14.	Schaghticoke, Pres.(Schaghticoke Point;f.Pres. Soc.;l.by Pby.bf.Ch.org.;called Pres.bf.elder chosen;sv.by Epis.1827-1830;1830 ab.#13; Fed.to Meth.Epis.(1864)1955-1960;merged to same 1960 as Pres.United)	1815(Ch.) 1803(Soc.:46A) r.1821(elders) r.1830 M r.1960 M	-	j1805; 1803/1805-1827,1830-onNS	Pres.
15.	Schodack, Pres.(Schootack)	by 1798	-	1794/1797-1798/1802	X
16.	Stephentown, Pres.(f.C of C;Garfield PO;nl.01T; Tr.Pby.1790(37);f.North division of New Lebanon (Columbia Co.);46A:1794 merger of earlier Ch.here & North of New Lebanon;Fed.to Meth.(1868)1940/1948-on as Stephentown Fed.)	1787/1788(CG) 1793(Soc.) r.1794(PR: elders)	sv.Berk.(MA) by 1789-1793	m.1790(nl.); 1794/1797-onNS	Pres.
Ar 17.	Troy, Armenian Calvary Cong.	1910(01,22)	1911-1921	-	Merged to form #26(q.v.)
18.	Troy, Bethel Pres.(f.Bethel Free;see also #19)	1832	-	1831-1840/1841NS	X
19.	Troy, Cong.Free (ps.division of #18)	1839(26)	nl.	-	X pb.soon
20.	Troy, First Cong.(in 1873 bldg.)	1900(22) 1898(s.01)	1902-1921	-	X (1919:22)
21.	Troy, First Pres.(1910 ab.#24 as First Pres.; 1971 ab.Fifth Ave.Pres.(see #23) as First United Pres.)	1791(4 sr) r.1910 M r.1971 M	-	j1792; 1788/1793-on NS	Pres.
Bl 22.	Troy, Liberty St.Pres.(f.Interdenominational to 1840)	1834(26) r.1840(4 sr) r.1882(26)	-	1840/1842-1964NS	X
23.	Troy, Second Pres.(1955 merged to Ninth Pres. (1869,l.75:1869-1955OS)as Fifth Ave.Pres.,l. 1955-1972(see #21))	1827(98) 1826(3 sr) r.1955 M	-	1827-1972OS, 1837-1840/1842NS	Merged; Merged to #21(q.v.)
24.	Troy, Second St.Pres.	1834(3 sr) 1831(22)	-	1834/1835-1911OS	1910 Merged to #21(q.v.)
Sw Nt	Troy, Swedish Evan.Mission (EC:Rgn.by 1910-1917/1921)	1897(06)	nl.	-	EC; X
25.	Troy, Third Pres.(NS faction X 1849;OS faction l.as Fourth Pres.1842-1843)	1830(3 sr) 1831(98)	-	1830-1836, 1837-1850NS; 1842-onOS	Pres.

NEW YORK - RENSSELAER COUNTY - continued

A	B	C	D	E	F
Ar 26.	Troy, United Armenian Cong.(merger of #17 & Armenian Pres.(1.75:1906-1920))	1920 M(22)	1921-on	(see text)	UCC

NEW YORK - RICHMOND COUNTY (org.1683) (085)

A		B	C	D	E	F
	1.	New York City, Staten Island, New Brighton, Cong.Ch.of Evangelists (only 1.98;f.of *Castleton to 1898)	1851(98)	nl.	-	1852 merged to form #2(q.v.)
	2.	New York City, Staten Island, New Brighton, Ch. of Redeemer, Cong.(merger of #1 & unknown; only 1.98 & entry confused;f.of *Castleton to 1898;nl.90;nl.01T)	1852 M r.1868	nl.	-	X 1874/1884
	3.	New York City, Staten Island, Oakwood Heights, Com.Cong.	1925(3 sr)	1927-1986	-	UCC 1961-1986; NA 1982-on
Sw Nt		New York City, Staten Island, Port Richmond, Swedish Evan.Zions(EC:Rgn.by 1910-1915)	1904(06)	nl.	-	EC; X
	4.	New York City, Staten Island, Prince's Bay, Cong.(f.Prince's Bay Union (Undenom.) to 1900;Ref.(RCA)1900-1904,1921-on(85);m.CG only in 85)	1899(98) r.1900(Ref.) r.1904(CG) r.1921(Ref.)	nl.	-	Tr.to Ref.(RCA)
	5.	New York City, Staten Island, Richmond, Eng. Pres.(49;98 combines this to Stony Brook,#7; f.of *Southfield to 1898)	1732(14) c.1727(27) c.1717(98)	-	j1732;Indep. Pby.1741-1745 NSd:1745-1758; by 1773-1788/ 1793	X (1776:27)
Nr	6.	New York City, Staten Island, Tottenville, Norwegian Evan.Free (f.Cong.;in Evan.Free Ch. Assn.)	1913(21) 1915(01)	1918-1958	-	Tr.to EF Ch. 1950 (1.1949)
	7.	New York City, Staten Island, *Tottenville, West Ch.of Staten Island,Pres.(Stony Brook;98 combines this to #5;f.of *Westfield to 1898)	by 1774	-	by 1773-1774/ 1787	X
Sw	8.	New York City, Staten Island, West New Brigton, Immanuel Cong.(f.of Tompkinsville;f.of *Castleton to 1898;EC:Rgn.1914-1948,full 1948-1974)	1894(01,21)	1926-1975	-	s.EC; UCC 1961-1975; X
	9.	New York City, Staten Island, Westerleigh, Immanuel Union (f.Union Cong.of Prohibition Park;f.l.West New Brighton;indep.1898-1962; f.in Counc.Com.Chs.;f.of *Castleton to 1898)	1893(21,98) 1894(01)	1894-1898; 1962-on	-	UCC 1962-on [count as UCC]

NEW YORK - ROCKLAND COUNTY (org.1798) (087)

A	B	C	D	E	F
1.	Blauvelt, Greenbush Pres.(sought to org.as Ref. (RCA,bf.1812,nl.85),turned down;l.75:with #7 1829-1841,not counted 1833-1841;*Orangetown)	1812(4 sr)	-	1811-1819, 1820-1833, 1841-onOS	Pres.
2.	Haverstraw, Central Pres.(1962 ab. #3)	1846(6 sr) r.1962 M	-	j1846; 1846-onNS	Pres.
3.	Haverstraw, First Pres.,Eng.Prot.Soc.of Haverstraw (West Haverstraw;f.of Haverstraw, Stony Point,& Clarkstown;38,45 consider 1840 a new Ch.,& OS X;had a branch at Stony Point 1844-1855(1840-1847:99);nl.01T)	1781(CG;2 sr) 1789(land,98) r.by 1817(PR) r.1840(NS:3 sr)	MC:1788-1791, 1797-1798 or later; WAP:m.1797	1788/1793-1798/1802, 1809-1842OS; j1840, 1839-1963NS	1962 Merged to #2(q.v.)
4.	Monsey, Cong.(*Ramapo)	1871(3 sr)	1871-1899	-	X
5.	New City (PO), New Hempstead Pres.(First Pres. Cgn.of Hempstead;Eng.Pres.Ch.;Kakiate;Katiate Mtghse.;indep.af.1734;pb.CG with elders when in MC;nl.01T;*Ramapo;f.of *Hampstead to 1828; f.of New Hampstead to 1797;f.of *Haverstraw to 1791)	1734(3 sr) 1754(3 sr) 1713(46A)	MC:1788-1791, 1796-1809; WAP:m.1793, 1796-1798	m.1734; by 1773-1798/1802, 1807-onOS	Pres.
6.	Nyack, Central Nyack Cong.(l.Valley Cottage PO; bec.Com.Bible;in 1876/1878 bldg.;*Clarkstown)	1901(01,s.05) 1912(s.05)	1901-1961	-	CCCC 1972-on
7.	Nyack, First Pres.(l.includes #1 1833-1841,q.v.)	1816(3 sr) 1815(38)	-	j1816, 1815-1821, 1822-1990OS	X
8.	Ramapo, Pres.at Ramapo Works (r.1867,l.75: 1867(j1868)-1997NS,X;merged 1922 to Brook Chap.Pres.of Hillburn(Black;1893,l.75:1920-1922)as Hillburn Pres.)	1810(2 sr) 1812(Soc.)	-	1810-1828 (see text)	indep.; X (45:alive to 1840,nl.; attempt r.1846,X) (r.1867,see text)
9.	Spring Valley, First Cong.(*Ramapo)	1886(01) 1896	1901-1980	-	UCC 1961-1980;Merged to form M.(q.v.)
9M.	Spring Valley, United (merger of #9 & Ref.(RCA, 1865(85;1852:99),dual;*Clarkstown)	1980 M	1980-on	-	UCC (dual, see text)
10.	Tallman, Cong.(*Ramapo)	1874(3 sr)	1875-1960	-	X
Nt	Waldberg, Pres.(Pond Ch.;Yellow Ch.;date would exclude from this l.,shown for 98 date;mixed Pres.& Dutch Ref.:98,but nl.85;*Clarkstown)	1859(38) 1830(98)	-	1859-1878OS	X 1876(38)

NEW YORK - SAINT LAWRENCE COUNTY (org.1802) (089)

1.	Brasher, Pres.(f.First Pres.& Cong.of <u>Helena</u> Village;l.Brasher:01,01T;f.l.Helena:75)	by 1829(CG;17) 1838(98) 1837(?) r.af.1858(PR; 01T)	SL:1826/1829-1834; 1834-1843, 1846-1856; cl.1856-1858	1843/1845-1861NS, 1870-1964	X 1963
2.	Brasher Falls, First Pres.(Fed.to unknown 1951-1964;*Brasher)	1844(98,99)	-	1843/1845-1964NS	X 1963
3.	Brier Hill, Young Mem.Cong.(*Morristown)	1907(s.01) 1908(s.01) 1905(s.01)	1908-1992	-	Sch.I 1961-1963; UCC 1963-1992; X
4.	Canton, First Pres.(f.Cong.;nl.01T)	1807(CG;4 sr) 1815(Soc.) r.1821(PR:98)	nl.	j1816; 1814/1818-onNS	Pres.
5.	Crarys Mill, Pres.(f.Cong.;First Calvinistic Soc.;f.of <u>South Canton</u>;*Canton)	1824 1823(Soc.) r.1901/1903	SL:1826/1829-1834; 1834-1903	1901-on	Pres.
6.	DeKalb, First Pres.(see also #46)	1817 1818(incp.)	-	j1818; 1814/1818-1921NS	X
7.	DeKalb, Village Cong.	1880(01N)	1879-1898	-	X
8.	DePeyster, First Cong.	1828 1858(Soc.)	SL:1826/1829-1834; 1834-1898, 1900-1913	-	X
9.	East Pitcairn, Cong.(f.Pres.of Pitcairn;f.of Fowler to 1836)	1829(CG;98) 1844(s.01)	SL:1826/1829-bf.1834; cl.1853-1856; 1856-1891	1849-1856NS	X
10.	Edwards, First Cong.Ch.& Soc.	1828(CG;98)	SL:1826/1829-1834; 1834-1856; cl.1856-1858	1828-1830	X
11.	Flackville, Pres. (*Lisbon)	by 1839	-	j1839; 1839-1846/1848NS	X
12.	Fullerville, Cong.(98 says bec.Pres.by 1853,but nl.75H;*Fowler)	1833(CG)	SL:1830/1834-1834; 1834-1847	(see text)	X
13.	Gouverneur, Cong.(Second Cong.)	1842 1843(s.98)	cl.1853-1858; 1859-1861	-	X
14.	Gouverneur, First Pres.(f.First Pres.or Cong.)	1817(CG;3 sr) 1820(Soc.; Ch.:46A) r.1863(PR)	cl.1853-1858	1819/1824-onNS	Pres.

NEW YORK - SAINT LAWRENCE COUNTY - continued

A	B	C	D	E	F
15.	Hammond, Hammond Pres.(First;98 confusingly says replaced by 1821 Soc.)	1827(98) c.1824(46A)	-	1827-onOS	Pres.
16.	Hermon, Cong.(f.South Hermon Pres.in name;s.l. Herman;m.BR 1840,but pb.not j;f.of *Depau to 1834)	1835(CG;98) 1828(?)	1839-1840; cl.1853-1857; 1857-1865	1837/1838-1857NS	X
17.	Hermon, Cong.(f.l.South Hermon;f.l.West Hermon)	1863(01)	1864-1898	-	X
18.	Heuvelton, First Pres.(f.First Cong.; *Oswgatchie)	1842(CG;98) r.1850(98) r.1859(PR:98)	1852-1859	1858-onOS	Pres.
19.	Heuvelton, P or C Ch.(f.l.Ogdensburg,in Oswegatchie to 1828)	by 1827	nl.	1826-1836	X
20.	Hollywood, Cong.(*Colton)	1863(01N)	1862-1870	-	X
21.	Hopkinton, First Cong.(also m.on Pby.l.as CG 1828-1830)	1808(CG;2 sr)	SL:j1825-1834; 1834-on	j1815; 1814/1818-1825	UCC
22.	Lawrenceville, Cong.Ch.& Soc.(*Lawrence)	1826(01) 1840(Soc.) r.1907	SL:1826/1829-1834; 1834-1898, 1907-1925	-	X
23.	Lisbon, First Cong.	1842(01,98) 1843(Soc.)	1842-on	-	UCC
24.	Lisbon, P or C Ch.(if org.PR,periods outside Pby.suggest CG)	1804(PR:99)	nl.	1819/1824-1829, 1832-1840/1842NS	X
25.	Louisville, Com.Cong.(f.Pres.)	by 1883(PR) r.1919(Com.; 01) 1920	1927-on	1882-1928	Sch.I
26.	Macomb, Cong.	1857	1856-1876	-	X
27.	Madrid, First Cong.UCC	1807(CG;2 sr) 1820(Soc.;98)	SL:j1825-1834, 1834-1973	1814/1818-1819/1824	UCC 1961-1973; Merged to form M.(q.v.)
27M.	Madrid, United Ch.(UCC)(merger of #27 & United Meth.(f.First Meth.Epis.of Columbia Village (1847);dual)	1973 M	1973-on	-	UCC (dual, see text)
28.	Massena, Emmanuel Cong.(f.Second;Upper Massena)	1833(s.01) 1834(98,s.01) 1844(Soc.)	SL:1830/1834-1834; 1834-on	-	UCC
29.	Massena, First Cong.(Lower Massena;Massena Ctr.; also m.on Pby.l.as CG 1829-1830)	1819(CG;2 sr) 1825(Soc.)	SL:j1825-1834; 1834-1883	(see text)	X

NEW YORK - SAINT LAWRENCE COUNTY - continued

A	B	C	D	E	F
30.	Morristown, First Cong.(f.l.Brier Hill;f.l. Chippeway St.;l.Hammond PO;incor.l.j CCCC 1967,1979(05);pb.lt.by cl.,see #31)	1852(01,s.05) 1827(3 sr) 1861(s.01)	1851-1992	-	Sch.I 1961-1992; CCCC by 1958(j1949)-1977,1979-on
31.	Morristown, First Pres.(01T & cl.say CG,pb. incor.,as in OS Pby.,pb.#30 lt.;Fed.to Morristown Meth.(1843) 1951-1967;1967 merged to Meth.to form United Meth.)	1821(CG;3 sr) 1833(Soc.)	cl.1853-1858 (see text)	1825-1968OS, 1837-1839NS	Merged; see text
32.	Norfolk, First Cong.,Upper Norfolk (see also #33;also m.on Pby.l.as CG 1829-1830)	1817(CG;2 sr) 1840(r.Soc.)	SL:j1825-1834; 1834-1936	(see text)	X
33.	Norfolk, Second Cong.,Lower Norfolk at Raymondville	1828(CG;2 sr)	SL:1826/1829-1834; 1834-1898, 1916-1925	-	X
34.	North Lawrence, Cong.(*Lawrence)	1887 1888(01N)	1888-1898, 1899-1906	-	X
35.	North Lawrence, First Cong.(*Lawrence)	1852(98) 1853(?)	1852-1877	-	X
36.	Norwood, Cong.UCC (First;f.of Raquettville,(s. Racketville);f.of Potsdam Junction;f.North Potsdam;*Potsdam)	1858(98)	1859-on	-	UCC
37.	Ogdensburg, Cong.(*Oswegatchie)	1836(98)	1835-1836	-	X
38.	Ogdensburg, First Cong.(*Oswegatchie)	1882(3 sr)	1881-on	-	UCC
39.	Ogdensburg, First Pres.(f.First Ch.& Cgn.of Christ of Oswegatchie;two factions 1825; nl.01T)	1805(CG;5 sr) r.1819(PR) 1816(46A)	nl.	j1806; 1803/1806-onOS	Pres.
40.	Ogdensburg, Stone Pres.(f.Second of Oswegatchie)	1823(46A)	-	1819/1824-onOS	Pres.
41.	Parishville, Union Cong.(f.Cong.;f.Second of Hopkinton to 1818;Fed.to Meth.Epis.(1818/1833)1891-1968 as Union Fed.)	1823(CG;2 sr) 1812(?) 1827(Soc.) r.1891	SL:1825/1827-1834; 1834-1836, 1841-1968	1827-1828	Sch.II 1961-1968; X; pb.ab.by Fed.
42.	Pierrepont, Cong.(Pres.:98)	1820	SL:1825/1828-1834; 1834-1873	-	X
43.	Potsdam, Cong.of West Potsdam	1841(s.98) 1842(s.98)	1841-1856; cl.1856-1858	-	X 1857(98)
44.	Potsdam, First Pres.(f.Cong.;from 1806 union Soc.;f.St.Paul's Soc.(1811),or Trinity Soc.(1818),bec.First Pres.Soc.(1820))	1811(CG;2 sr) 1818(r.Soc.) 1820(r.Soc.) r.1859(PR)	cl.1853-1858	j1815; 1814/1818-onNS	Pres.

NEW YORK - SAINT LAWRENCE COUNTY - continued

A		B	C	D	E	F
	45.	Rensselaer Falls, Cong.Fed.(f.of Canton Falls to 1852;Fed.to Meth.1954-2000;l.01T:1854,as in Pby.,but nl.cl.1853-1855;*Canton)	1842(CG;2 sr) 1845(s.01) 1847(Soc.)	(m.01T 1854) 1855-2001	1843/1845- 1855NS	Sch.I 1961-2001; X
	46.	Richville, First Cong.(f.First Cong.of DeKalb; f.Second of DeKalb;f.a branch of #6(PR)1827-1828;Fed.1928-1963/1965 to unknown;r.c.1964 as United,pb.ab.f.Fed.;see also #47)	1828(CG;2 sr) 1827(branch: PR) 1829(Soc.) 1840(r.Soc.) r.c.1964	SL:1826/1829-1834; 1834-on	1827-1829	Sch.I 1961-1962; UCC 1962-on
We	47.	Richville, Welsh Cong.of DeKalb (Tr.to Eng.Assn. 1931;l.1858-1859 in non-local Eng.Assn.; united to #46 1893-1896:70;no regular services af.1919:70)	1856(98) 1854(68) 1858(s.01,70) 1850(s.01) 1853(?)	cl.1856-1858; NYW ? -1867; 1858-1859, 1867-1963	-	Sch.I 1961-1963; X; (bldg.survives under 1974 Welsh Soc.)
	48.	Rossie, Oxbow Pres.(division of Jefferson Co. #26;Oxbow village in Antwerp,Jefferson Co.)	1834(2 sr)	-	1834-1840/ 1842NS; 1842-1854OS	X
	Nt	Rossie, Pres.(lt.of Jefferson Co.#26,q.v.)			1819/1824- 1826	
	49.	Russell, Cong.(f.l.Pres.(98);f.of *Hopkinton to 1807)	by 1826(CG) af.1806(98) 1856(s.01)	SL:1826/1829-1834; 1834-1870	1825-1826	X
	50.	South Colton, Cong.(*Colton)	1862(01N)	1862-1876	-	X
	51.	Stockholm, Cong.(East Stockholm)	1807(CG;2 sr)	SL:j1825-1834; 1834-1888	j1815; 1814/ 1818-1825	X
	52.	Stockholm, West Cong.(Second,at Sanfordville)	1823(98)	SL:j1825-1834; 1834-1874	-	X
	53.	Waddington, First Pres.(f.Second Cong.of Madrid to 1859)	1828(CG;98) r.1863(PR)	SL:1825/1829-1834; 1834-1840, 1841-1863	1863-onNS	Pres.
	54.	Winthrop, UCC (f.of Stockholm Depot;f.Fed.by 1919-1938 to unknown;*Stockholm)	1886(01N) 1880(s.01) 1888(?)	1886-1980	-	UCC 1961-1980; X

NEW YORK - SARATOGA COUNTY (org.1791) (091)

A	B	C	D	E	F
1.	Ballston, First Pres.of Ballston Ctr.(f.Cong.; f.of Kayderosies Patent;DUT 1770-1774/1787)	1775(CG;4 sr) by 1774(min) 1770(pr.) 1785(incp.) 1792(90) r.1787(PR:98)	nl.	ps.by 1770; by 1773-1788/ 1793,1794/ 1797-1974OS	Tr.to Asso.Ref. General Synod 1974-on
2.	Ballston Spa, Ballston Spa Pres.(First;*Milton)	1834	-	1833-onOS	Pres.
3.	Charlton, Charlton-Freehold Pres.(s.l.incor. Charlestown)	1786(3 sr) 1792(90)	-	j1791; 1788/ 1793-onOS	Pres.
4.	Corinth, First Pres.(f.in Hadley to 1818;f.of Hadley & Luzerne(Warren Co.);lt.75:1827-1830 under both town names)	1814(CG;98) r.1822(PR:98) r.1867(98)	SAP:j1814, 1814-1818	1825-1856OS, 1866-onOS	X c.1852(98); r.Pres.
5.	Edinburg, Pres.(f.Cong.;f.of *Northfield to 1808;f.at Northampton,Fulton Co.1815-1824;l. by Pby.as specifically CG 1837-1838;01T: 1854:indep.,but l.by Pby.;1931(moved: reservoir)bec.First Pres.of Batchellerville; 1959 merged to Pres.of Northville,Fulton Co. (1849,l.75:1849-1959OS) as Northville Pres., Fulton Co.(l.75:1959-on))	1808(CG;2 sr) r.1815/1824 (PR:98) r.1831(CG) r.1866(PR)	cl.1853-1858	1808-1838OS, 1839-1867NS, 1867-1960OS	1959 Merged, see text
6.	Galway, Second Pres.,East Galway (f.First Associated Pres.;nl.01T)	1804(CG;98) 1802(46A) r.af.1808(PR)	SAP:1807-1808	j1808; 1807-1940OS	Merged to Meth.
7.	Greenfield, First Cong.(s.First Pres.;l.by Pby. as specifically CG 1837-1838;lt.01T as indep. & previously Tr.to Pres.,not in Pby.then)	1790(CG;98)	CB:1790-1797; NAP:j1797-1807; SAP:1807-1818; cl.1853-1858	1819/1824-1838OS	X af.1858
8.	Malta, Cong.(f.Pres.Soc.of East Ballston;f. Ballston Cong.(1835);37 says Tr.Pby.1790,47 says jPby.1791;centered 1820/1825 at Maltaville (in Malta);f.at East Ballston (in Ballston);had two branches:at East Line (in Ballston) & nr.old cemetery in Malta to 1820/1825;divided 1843 with Cong.Ch.continuing indep.at Maltaville(in Malta;indep.in 01T),& Pres.moving to Malta (r.1845,l.75:1845-1978OS,r.2000;l.75:2000-on;Ballston Spa PO); Cong.pastor l.at Ballston PO 1843-1847)	by 1788(PR) 1793(PR Soc.) r.1798/1807 (CG) r.1820/1825 (PR) r.1834(CG) r.1840(PR) r.1843(CG)	NAP ? -1807; SAP 1807-af. 1815; m.1835(min); 1836-1843; m.1843-1847; cl.1853-1858	1774/1787-1798/1802, 1819/1824-1837	X af.1858

NEW YORK - SARATOGA COUNTY - continued

A	B	C	D	E	F
9.	Mechanicsville, First Pres.(f.Pres.Soc.of Mechanicsville & Stillwater;merger of #16 & 1839 Chap.here;had #16 as a branch 1852-1871;*Half Moon;Fed.1972 & united 1974 to Mem.Bapt.(1883) as Emmanuel United(dual))	1852 M r.1974 M	-	1852-onNS	Pres.(dual, see text)
10.	Milton, Pres.(f.Cong.;f.of *Ballston to 1792;38 confuses with ch.in Ulster Co.;01T 1.as having bec.Pres.but actually already X)	1791(CG;98)	NAP ? -1807; SAP 1807-1812	j1792; (nl.) 1794/1797-1798/1803, j1812; 1814/1818-1840/1842NS,1843/1844-1846NS, 1838-1840OS	X af.1846; (1840/1841:98)
11.	Moreau, Pres.(f.Cong.;lt.75:1825-1826;CG forms to at least 1859,lt.01T as CG in Pby.,& as r.PR earlier;in Pby.1854,but pb.CG;two branches:Reynold's Corners & at River;f.of *Northumberland to 1805)	1802(CG;2 sr)	NAP ? -1807; SAP:1807-1818; cl.1853-1858	1823-1824; j1825; 1825-1837/1838, 1840/1842-1869NS	X af.1869
12.	Providence, Pres.	by 1798	-	1794/1797-1798/1802	X
13.	Saratoga Springs, First Pres.(f.of *Saratoga to 1819;1918 ab.Second Pres.Newland Chap.(1871, 1.75:1870-1918);Fed.to #14 1973-on)	1817(Ch.) 1816(Soc.) r.1918 M	-	1814/1818-onOS	Pres.
14.	Saratoga Springs, New England Cong.(Fed.to #13 1973-on)	1865(3 sr) 1878(s.01) 1880(s.01) 1830(?) 1845(?)	1864-on	-	UCC
15.	Stillwater, First Cong.C of C(Cong.at Bemis Hgts.;Yellow Mtghse.;org.as Strict Cong.in Canaan,Litchfield Co.,CT 1752,removed here 1762;voted to j "a Pby.1815",not done,not clear if SAP or reg.Pby.implied)	1762(CG;3 sr) 1763(90) 1752(CT) r.1784(49)	WAP:m.1793-1796; NAP:pb.bf. 1800-1807; LIS:1807-1808	by 1773-1774/1787	1816 merged to #18 to form #16(q.v.)
16.	Stillwater, First Cong.Pres.Ch.& Soc.(merger of #15 & #18;two branches 1816-1817;Soc.divided 1817;continued site of #15;voted to jSAP 1817,but it X bf.Ch.received;s.considered PR when yoked to #17 1819-1833;1852 merged to #9 as a branch;r.here 1871 as Third Pres.of Stillwater)	1816 M(CG) r.1871(PR)	NAP:m.1817; SAP:m.1817	(see text) 1871-1886	1852 merged to #9 (see text) r.; X

NEW YORK - SARATOGA COUNTY - continued

A	B	C	D	E	F
17.	Stillwater, First Pres.(Schoonmaker Mem.;at site of #18;Fed.1947-1952 to Second Bapt.(1836) & Meth.(1828);1952 merged to same as United Pres.)	1818 1817(Soc.) r.1952 M	-	j1819; 1814/ 1818-onOS	Pres.
18.	Stillwater, Pres.(Tr.to Ref.as Sinthoick Ref.(RCA);Tr.to Pres.1816(99;1807:85);see also #17)	1791(PR;2 sr) 1789(85) 1794(49) Tr.1798(Ref.: 47) 1789(85) Tr.1816(PR:99) 1807(85)	-	j1791; 1788/ 1793-1798/ 1802	Tr.to Ref.; Tr.to Pres.; 1816 Merged to #15 to form #16(q.v.)
19.	Waterford, Cong.(m.only by 90,otherwise nl.)	m.1855	nl.	-	X (pb.soon)
20.	Waterford, First Pres.(united to Ref.(RCA,org. 1771) from 1799 to 1803(98);Fed.to Bapt.(1812) 1966-1981 & united 1981 as First United Ch.(dual))	by 1795 1790's(98) r.1803(98) 1804(46A) r.1981 M	-	j1795; 1794/ 1797-1798/ 1802,1803/ 1805(j1804)-onOS	Merged to Ref.; r.;Pres.(dual, see text)

NEW YORK - SCHENECTADY COUNTY (org.1809) (093)

A	B	C	D	E	F
1.	Duanesburgh, Pres.(f.Ref.(RCA to 1804(85);98: united to #3:1813)	1798(Ref.) Tr.1805(PR)	-	j1805; 1806-1830	X
2.	Princetown, <u>Currie's Bush</u> Pres.(f.Cong.:11;37: DUT:no dates;nl.01T;Tr.to Asso.Ref.;bec. Florida, Montgomery Co., Asso.Ref.in 1801; bec.Scot Bush United Pres.of Florida;affl. Asso.Ref.to 1858;UPNA 1858-1958)	1748(CG;11) 1770(pb.r.PR; 3 sr) 1771(s.49) 1761(37) Tr.1793/1798	nl.	j1771;nl.; 1774/1787-1790/1793; 1958-1972	1793(98;1798:32) Tr.to Asso.Ref. (see text) 1971 merged to #3(q.v.)
3.	Princetown, Princeton Pres.(f.<u>Currie's Bush</u>; division of & claim as #2;98:united to #1: 1813;1971 merged to #2 & Mariaville Pres. (f.Ref.(RCA)1843-1858(85;1842-1859:98), f.First Pres.of Duanesburgh to 1860,1.75: 1859-1972OS) as Christ of the Hills,Pres. in Duanesburg (Schenectady PO))	1800(98) 1770(claim) r.1971 M	-	j1805; 1806-onOS	Pres.
4.	Remsen's Bush, Pres. (location uncertain,yoked to #7;nl.47)	by 1770(14)	-	j1771;nl.; 1774/1787-1791/1793	X (1781:14)
5.	Schenectady, First Cong.(claim is as Second Ref. Dutch (RCA),which divided)	1859(01N,98) 1851(claim)	1859-1876	-	Merged to #6(q.v.)
6.	Schenectady, First Cong.(f.Evan.Cong.;f.United Peoples;merger of #5 & Free Evan.Peoples (1875,also a division of Second Ref.Dutch (RCA,1851))	1876 M(01) 1877 M(2 sr)	1876-1927	-	X
7.	Schenectady, First Pres.(dispersed during Revolutionary War)	1771(37,49) 1765(46A) 1770(14) 1760/1770(98)	-	j1771;by 1773-1806, 1808-1985OS	Tr.to PCA 1989-on
8.	Schenectady, Pilgrim Cong.(incor.1.UCC late 1961-1962,j1962)	1904(s.01) 1902(s.01)	1904-1991	-	Sch.I 1961; UCC late 1961-1991; X

NEW YORK - SCHOHARIE COUNTY (org.1795) (095)

A	B	C	D	E	F
1.	Broome, Pres.of Livingstonville (f.Cong.;nl.01T; 98 says this only CG Ch.in Co.,but not so)	1817(CG:98) r.1830(PR:98)	NAP:mnd.	1831-1912NS	X
2.	Carlisle, Pres.(claimed OS & NS:1837-1844,1852-1863;f.of *Cobleskill to 1807;nl.01T)	by 1801(PR) 1803(98)	WAP: m.1817-1818	j1801; 1798/1802-1806,1808-1863NS, 1837-1844OS, 1852-onOS	Pres.
3.	Esperance, Pres.(Old Stone;f.of Schoharie to 1846;pb.ch.l.as Schoharie in 22 1813-1843; nl.01T)	1818(CG;3 sr) 1817(pr.:46A) 1813(11,22) r.1823(PR;2 sr)	NAP 1817-af.1822; WAP:m.1818	1814/1818-on OS	Pres.
4.	Jefferson, Pres.(f.Cong.;nl.01T)	1809(CG;2 sr) r.pb.1830(PR)	NAP:m.1826	1831-1922NS	X
5.	North Blenheim, Pres.(*Blenheim)	by 1836	-	1834/1835-1855NS	X
6.	Schoharie, Schoharie Court House Cong.	by 1854	cl.1853-1858	-	X

NEW YORK - SCHUYLER COUNTY (org.1854) (097)

1.	Burdett, Burdett Pres.(in Hector:48,98)	1826(5 sr)	-	j1826; 1825-onNS	Pres.
2.	Hector, First Pres.(Northwest,Peach Orchard)	1809(5 sr) 1810(48)	-	j1810; 1809/ 1811-onNS	Pres.
3.	Mecklenburgh, Pres.(in Hector;Fed.to Meth.(1823) 1928(1943:75H)-1946)	1833(4 sr)	-	j1833/1834; 1834/1835-1946NS	X
4.	Monterey, Pres.(f.Mead's Creek or Mede's Creek; Beaver Dam PO;in Orange;f.of *Jersey to 1836)	1824	-	j1824; 1823-1936NS	X (1926:22,26)
5.	Montour Falls, First Pres.(in Montour;f.First of Havanna(h) in Catherines to 1898;Fed.to Bapt. 1916-1918)	1829(3 sr)	-	j1829; 1830-1935NS	X (1934:26)
6.	Moreland, Moreland Pres.(f.of Catlin & Dix;f. First Pres.of Catlin,(Chemung Co.);f.Cong.-Pres.Ch.,pb.gradually bec.Pres.;incor.bec.CG: 98;nl.01T;f.Watkins Glen PO;s.Beaver Dam PO; in *Dix)	1834(mixed) 1832(s.46A) r. ? (PR)	nl.	1834/1835-onNS	Pres.
Nt	Pine Grove, Pres.(l.because of 26 date,otherwise too late for listing;Watkins Glen PO;in *Tyrone)	bf.1848(26) by 1855(l.) r.1879(26)	-	j1858; 1854-1865NS, 1878-1936	X 1863(26); r.; X (1932:26)
7.	Watkins Glen, First Pres.(f.of Jefferson to 1854;f.of Irelandville;f.First of Reading;f. Second of Reading to 1824;f.of Reading & Catherines (Catherines later bec.*Catlin, then *Dix);lt.:75 both names 1818-1824; f.Watkins PO)	1818(4 sr)	-	j1819; 1818-onNS	Pres.
8.	Weston, Pres.(f.Union Ch.of Tyrone;Dundee,Yates Co.PO;f.a branch of Steuben Co.#34 1830-1831)	1832(4 sr) 1830(branch)	-	j1832; 1832-onNS	Pres.

NEW YORK - SENECA COUNTY (org.1804) (099)

		C	D	E	F
1.	Canoga, Canoga Pres.(f.Cong.;f.Second of Fayette;indep.:01T,but claim by Pby.)	1825(PR;4 sr) r.1848(CG) r.1853(PR)	cl.1853-1858	j1825; 1825-1993NS	X
2.	Fayette, First Pres.of West Fayette (at MacDougall;f.Geneva,Ontario Co.PO)	1824(48,98) 1823(3 sr)	-	j1824/1825; 1824-onNS	Pres.
3.	Junius, Junius Pres.(North Junius;f.Second to 1829;f.Cong.;s.Clyde,Wayne Co.PO;lt.52;f. Northfield)	1811(CG) r.1814(PR) 1816(?)	nl.	j1814; 1813-1825, 1826-onNS	Pres.
4.	Lodi, Lodi Pres.(C of C;First Ch.& Cgn.(Pres.)in Ovid;McNeil Ch.;attempt withdraw 1807 refused;Tr.to Ref.1808(4 sr;1805(3 sr);1809 (85)) as Ref.Dutch of Lodi(RCA);Tr.to PR 1922;1968 merged to Meth.(1837);in Ovid to 1817;f.in Covert 1817-1826)	1800(46A) 1800/1805(98) Tr.1805/1809 (Ref.) Tr.1922(PR) r.1968 M	-	j1802; to 1808;nl.; 1921-on	Tr.to Ref.; Tr.; Pres.
5.	Ovid, First Pres.(f.of Seneca,Ontario Co.to 1817;Fed.to Ovid Meth. 1955-on;m.ML 1805,not a member)	1803(4 sr) bf.1803(Soc.) r.1816(26)	(see text)	j1803; 1803/ 1808-onNS	Pres.
6.	Romulus, Pres.(l.in Varick:98,ps.#11)	1802(4 sr) 1807(Soc.)	-	j1805; 1803/ 1808-onNS	Pres.
7.	Seneca Falls, Cong.(attempt to revive 1852:98)	1834	1834-1835	-	X
8.	Seneca Falls, First Pres.(f.Red Mills;f.First Pres.of Junius to 1829;1857 ab.Pres.(by 1851, l.75:1850-1856OS)	1807(4 sr) 1805(52) r.1857 M	-	j1806(52); 1803/1808- 1825,1826- onNS	Pres.
9.	Seneca Falls, Mem.Cong.(f.First;f.Meth.)	1864(Meth.) r.1869(CG:4 sr)	1869-1971	-	UCC 1961-1971; X
10.	Tyre, Pres.(Tr.to Ref.(Makolm,Waterloo PO;RCA, 1839-on(85)))	1823(98)	-	j1834/1837; 1834/1835- 1839	Tr.to Ref. (see text)
11.	Varick, Cong.(98:ps.same as #6)	by 1854	cl.1853-1858	-	X af.1858
12.	Varick, Pres.of Romulus (of Romulus to 1830)	1796(PR)	-	nl.	X c.1800; bf.1802
13.	Waterloo, First Pres.(Trip Settlement;Lundy's Corners;f.of Junius to 1829)	1817(4 sr)	-	j1817; 1817-onNS	Pres.

NEW YORK - STEUBEN COUNTY (org.1796) (101)

A	B	C	D	E	F
1.	Addison, Addison Pres. (First)	1832	-	j1833; 1832-onNS	Pres.
2.	Arkport, First Pres.(in Hornellsville)	1852	-	1852-onNS	Pres.
3.	Bath, First Pres.(f.First C of C;f.Cong.;Bath Relg.Soc.;48:sv.by OA,but nl.minutes;98:in OA;Tr.to OS 1837;1870 merged to Constitutional Pres.(1838,l.75:1837/1838-1862NS)as First Pres.)	by 1800(47) 1808(CG) 1806(Soc.) r.1811/1812 (PR:2 sr) r.1870 M	nl. (see text)	j1800; nl.; j1811; 1809/ 1811-onOS	Pres.
4.	Cameron, Pres.(1854 merged to Pres.of Lindley (by 1842,l.75:1841-1853OS))	by 1841 (min,48) 1843(26) r.1854 M	-	j1841; 1840-1851NS, 1847-1865OS	X (1860:26; bldg.sold 1871)
5.	Campbell, Campbell Pres.(Campbellstown;f.of Hornby to 1831)	1831(4 sr) 1830(22,26)	-	j1831; 1831-1997NS	X
6.	Campbell, First Pres.Cohocton Cgn.(Soc.of Campbell & Mud Creek)	1812(Soc.)	-	nl.	X af.1814
7.	Canisteo, Canisteo Pres.(First)	1836(4 sr) r.1853 1852(Soc.)	-	nl.; 1853-onNS	X pb.soon; r.; Pres.
8.	Caton, Second Pres.of Painted Post(f.of Wormley to 1840;in Painted Post to 1839;l.Pby.:1836-1837)	1824 1832(90)	-	j1830; 1829-1836, 1837-1843/ 1844NS, 1846-1867NS	X (1854:26,98)
9.	Cohocton, First Pres.(f.First Cong.;at Liberty Corners;full PR:1869)	1809(CG;3 sr) r.1823(PR) r.1853(CG) r.1854(PR)	OA:1811-pb. 1813	j1820; 1820-onNS	Pres.
10.	Cohocton, Second Cong.	1836(CG;s.48) 1837(s.48) r.1839(PR)	1835-1839	j1839; nl.	X by 1845
11.	Corning, First Cong.UCC	1890(01,22) 1891(?)	1890-on	-	UCC
12.	Corning, First Pres.(m.ML,not a member;1811 ab. an Indep.Meth Ch.(1810);moved Knoxville (village) to Corning 1842;1849 ab.#13; officially f.First of Painted Post to 1852; nl.01T)	by 1800 (pb.PR:47) r.1804(CG:ML) 1810(Meth.) r.1811(PR)	ML:m.1804	j1800; nl.; j1812; 1809/ 1811-onNS	Pres.
13.	Corning, Second Pres.(f.claim to be First of Painted Post to 1849,split from #12;in Painted Post to 1852)	1845(4 sr) 1846(48)	-	j1846; 1843/1844-1850NS	1849 merged to #12(q.v.)

NEW YORK – STEUBEN COUNTY – continued

A	B	C	D	E	F
14.	Erwin, Erwin Ctr.P or C Ch.	by 1834	nl.	j1834; 1834/ 1835-1843/ 1844NS	X 1843
15.	Greenwood, Pres.(f.Bennett's Creek of Canisteo to 1827)	1823 r.1829	-	j1826; 1826-1862NS	X
16.	Hammondsport, First Pres.(in Urbana)	1831 1825(Soc.)	-	j1832; 1831-onNS	Pres.
17.	Hornby, Cong.(merger of #18 & Meth.;f.Beaver Dam,Schuyler Co.PO)	1897 M	1897-on	-	UCC
18.	Hornby, Pres. (Hornsby)	1831(2 sr) 1830(s.48)	-	j1832; 1831-1897	Merged to #17(q.v.)
19.	Hornell, First Pres.(Hornellsville;1967 merged to Westminster Pres.(f.Hartshorn,1889,l.75: 1889-1967) as United Pres.)	1832 r.1967 M	-	j1834; 1834/ 1835-onNS	Pres.
20.	Howard, First Pres.(period bf.jPby.suggests CG; nl.01T;incor.OS:98;Fed.to Bapt.(1826)1923 (1956:75H)-on,as Howard Union)	1815(pb.PR)	nl.	j1820; 1819-onNS	Pres.
21.	Howard, Second Pres.	1825	-	j1826; 1825-1840/1842NS	1840 merged to #29(q.v.)
22.	Jasper, Cong. (l.only 01T & cl.)	by 1854	cl.1853-1858	-	X
23.	Jasper, First Pres.(Fed.to United Meth.(1818) 1961-on,as Jasper Fed.)	1829 1827(90) 1828(Soc.)	-	j1830; 1829-onNS	Pres.
24.	Kanona, Pres.(f.l.Kennedyville;in Bath)	1831	-	j1832; 1831-1874NS	X
25.	Painted Post, First Pres.(Village;in Erwin)	1841	-	j1842; 1840-onNS	Pres.
26.	Prattsburgh, First Pres.(f.C of C;f.Cong.; Prattsburgh Relg.Soc.;f.of Pulteney to 1813; f.of Bath to 1808)	1804(CG) 1807(Soc.) r.1839(mixed) r.1868(PR)	OA:1806-1813; cl.1853-1858	j1813; 1812-onNS	Pres.
27.	Pulteney, Cong.	1835	GC:j1835; 1834-1842; GC:1842- ? (by 1848)	-	X c.1850
28.	Pulteney, First Pres.(First Pres.Union Soc.; f.Cong.;West;nl.01T)	1809(CG) r.1817(PR)	nl.	j1817; 1817-onNS	Pres.
29.	South Dansville, Pres.(in Dansville;1840 ab.#21)	by 1820 r.1840 M	-	j1820; 1819-1856NS	X
30.	Thurston, P or C Ch. (Pres.:48)	1845	nl.	j1845; 1843/ 1844-1853NS	X
31.	Troupsburgh, P or C Ch.	1833	nl.	j1833; 1833-1846NS	X

NEW YORK - STEUBEN COUNTY - continued

A	B	C	D	E	F
32.	Urbana, West Cong.(nl.01T)	by 1856	cl.1855-1858	-	X af.1858
33.	Wayland, Pres.	by 1852	-	1851-1859NS	X
34.	Wayne, Pres.(Schuyler Co.#8 was a branch 1830-1831:Wayne & Tyrone(Schuyler Co.)Soc.;f.of Fredrickstown;l.Pby.,not natl.1813-1814)	1809(48,98) 1805(26) r.1830 r.1831	-	j1814; 1814-1871NS	X 1869(26,98)
35.	Wheeler, <u>Center Wheeler</u> Pres.(98:a r.of #36)	1831 1832(Soc.)	-	j1832; 1831-1890NS	X
36.	Wheeler, Cong.(f.Pres.;see also #35)	1824/1825(PR; 48,98) r.c.1831(CG)	nl.	j1825; 1825-1834/1835	X (1833:48)
37.	Woodhull, <u>Hedgesville</u> Pres.(First;f.Cameron Mills PO;Jasper PO)	1831(4 sr) 1830(90) 1833(48)	-	j1833; 1831-onNS	Pres.

NEW YORK - SUFFOLK COUNTY (org.1683) (103)

A	B	C	D	E	F
1.	Aquebogue, Lower Aquebogue Pres.(Acquebogue; Hockabogue;Little Quoque;First Ch.of Riverhead;f.of Southold to 1792;in Union Par. with #30 by 1777,until ab.by it;see also #27; reported as indep.,c.1770 but pastor in Pby.; SUF 1747-1790(s.nl.);l.natl.,nl.Pby.1818-1819)	1728(CG;2 sr) 1731(01) 1730(09) 1725(22,26)	SUF 1747-1749	j1749; NSd 1749-1758; by 1773-1819	1817 ab.by #30(q.v.); later r.by #27(q.v.)
2.	Aquebogue, Old Steeple Com.UCC (f.Cong.of Upper Aquebogue;Acquebogue;First Strict Cong.of Riverhead;f.First Strict Cong.of Southold to 1792;ps.a r.of #3,see also #42)	1758(4 sr) 1750(s.01,09) 1749(s.01) 1754(s.01) by 1746(98) 1753(s.99)	CT Strict m.1783,1789, j1790-1795; LIS:1791-1840; pb.LIC 1840-bf.1843; 1834-1835; m.1843-1847; 1846-1848, 1853-on	-	UCC
3.	Aquebogue, Upper Aquebogue Pres.(Acquebogue;not in a Pby.-suggests CG;ps.r.by #2;*Riverhead)	1708(99) "early 1700's"(98)	nl.	nl.	X af.1746(98)
4.	Babylon, First Pres.(f.South of Huntington;in Huntington to af.1870;f.Islip & Huntington South;f.l.Islip;f.Cong.;pb.a branch of another ch.to l.Pby.;lt.Pby.:1818-1819;75H:a NS Ch.in an OS Pby.1843-1849;lt.75:1827-1832, 1851-1853;nl.01T)	1730(CG;4 sr) r.1798(PR:26)	nl.	j1797; 1794/ 1797-onOS	Pres.
5.	Bay Shore, First Cong.(f.Cong.Meth.Soc.;f.of Penetaquit to 1867;*Islip)	1852(Cong. Meth.;98) 1853 1854(s.01) r.1860(CG)	1863-on	-	UCC
6.	Bellport, Cong.(Bell Port;divided 1852 to Pres. (l.75:1852-1944OS)which took property; *Brookhaven)	1836	pb.LIA:1836-1840;pb.LIC: 1840-1846; 1843/1846-1848,1849-1872	- (see text)	1870(98) Merged to Meth.Epis.
7.	Blue Point, Cong.(*Brookhaven)	by 1867	1866-1870	-	X
8.	Bridgehampton, Bridgehampton Pres.(Pres.Soc.& Par.of Bridge Hampton;C of C;Ch.of Sag; Sagaponack Par.;branch of #50 1652(98;1670: 22,26)-1695;named Pres.by 1712;SUF 1747-1790;*Southampton)	1695(CG;6 sr) 1670(branch) 1669(46A) r.1801(PR) 1828(incp.)	SUF 1747-1749	j1749; NSd 1749-1758; by 1773-onOS 1837-1840/ 1841NS	Pres.

NEW YORK - SUFFOLK COUNTY - continued

A	B	C	D	E	F
	9. Bridgehampton, Second Pres.(f.Strict Cong.;First Evan.;New Light;10,98:bec.Pres.,but nl.as such;*Southampton)	1749(CG;2 sr) 1748(98) r.af.1791(PR)	CT Strict: m.1788; LIS:m.1791	nl.	X "early 1800's" (98); ps.by 1810
	10. Brookhaven, Old South Haven Pres.(Fire Place; Yamphank Neck;in 1740 bldg.,divided from #46; SUF 1756-1790)	1745(98) 1755(14) 1760(?)	-	j1756; NSd: 1756-1758; by 1773-1821/ 1822,1823-on OS	Pres.
	11. Calverton(PO), Baiting Hollow Cong.UCC (Third Strict Cong.of Riverhead;branch in Calverton 1882-1912;f.of *Southold to 1792)	1791(3 sr) 1792(2 SR)	LIS:1793-1840; pb.LIC 1840-1846; 1843/1846-on	-	UCC
	12. Center Moriches, Moriches Cong.(Strict Cong.of Moriches;in 1809 Moriches Union Ch.with #13; *Brookhaven)	1817(98)	LIS:1818-1840; 1834-1835; ps.:LIC: 1840-bf.1846;	-	X 1840/1846; pb.ab.by #13
	13. Center Moriches, Moriches Pres.(Pres.Ch.& Par.of Moriches;Moriches Center;in 1809 Moriches Union bldg.with #12,took full control 1849; SUF 1756-1763(left Pby.);1849 ab.#12; *Brookhaven)	1755(CG;3 sr) by 1750(98) r.1831(PR) r.1849 M	(see text)	j1756 to 1763; NSd 1756-1758; m.1765; 1831-onOS	Indep.af.1765; X by 1775; r.; Pres.
pI	14. Cold Spring, Cong.(had an Indian pastor,but ethnic identity of ch.unclear;ps.sv. Mattinecock tribe;*Huntington)	by 1793	LIS:1793-1839; 1834-1835	-	X (pb.1839/1840)
	15. Commack, Cong.(Comac;*Huntington)	1857(01)	cl.1855-1856, 1856-1883	-	X
	16. Cutchogue, Indep.Ch. (division of #18;*Southold)	1805(CG;99) 1747(26)	nl.	nl.	Reunited to #18; 1806(99); lived 25 yrs.:46A
	17. Cutchogue, Indep.Cong.C of C (*Southold)	1862(3 sr)	1863-1864, 1868-1872	-	Indep.; X 1916(22,26)
	18. Cutchogue, Pres.Ch.& Soc.(Relg.Soc.of Cutchogue; f.Christ Ch.;f.Cong.;f.Cong.-Pres.of Southold;Cuchague;SUF 1747-c.1750,1764-1766; specifically CG on Pby.l.1832-1834;m.on Pby. l.as CG 1836-1837/1838;s.considered Indian; see also #16)	1732(CG;4 sr) 1718(49) r.1786 1801(incp.) r.1838(mixed) r.1848(PR)	SUF 1747-1749; MC:1786-pb.1797	j1740 to 1747; j1749-c.1750(NSd); j1763-1766; 1829-1836; j1848; 1837/ 1838-onNS (see text)	Pres.

NEW YORK - SUFFOLK COUNTY - continued

A		B	C	D	E	F
	19.	East Hampton, First Pres.(f.Cong.C of C;Old Town Ch.;f.of Maidstone to 1662;sett.1648/1649; f.in CT 1657-1664,1673-1674;acted in CT 1664-1667 while land was in dispute;SUF 1747-1790;town manage bldg.to 1848)	1648(CG;5 sr) 1649(3 sr) 1650(49;pr.) 1651(98) r.1799(PR)	SUF 1747-1749	j1749; NSd 1749-1758; by 1773-onOS 1837-1840/ 1841NS	Pres.
	20.	Farmingville, Christ Com.(f.Farmingville-Holtsville Cong.;Farmington;*Brookhaven)	1858(01,22)	1858-1877, 1890-1899, 1901-on	-	UCC
	21.	Fire Place Neck, Cong.(*Brookhaven)	1842 1848	pb.LIC: 1842-1846; 1843/1846- 1872	-	X
Bl	22.	Greenport, Colored Cong.(*Southold)	1853 1855	1853-1862	-	X
	23.	Greenport, Cong.(s.named Old Southold,claiming to continue #52;Southold)	1848(01,98)	1851-1858, 1861-1864, 1875-1883, 1885-1895	-	X
	24.	Greenport, First Pres.(*Southold)	1832(22,26) 1835(98)	-	1832-1979NS	X
	25.	Huntington, Old First Pres.(f.Cong.;The Huntington Ch.;sett.1653/1658;ps.continues Nassau Co.#4;f.in CT 1660-1664;lt.75:1823-1824;SUF 1747-1790;nl.01T;ps.a branch at Oyster Bay,Nassau Co.:1715)	1658(CG;5 sr) 1657(98) 1676(2 sr) ps.r.1748(PR) 1747(46A)	SUF 1747-1749	j1749; NSd 1749-1758; by 1773-onOS	Pres.
In	26.	Islip, Indian Cong.(sv.Lecatoques tribe;nl.14)	1750's(26)	IM: (nl.) m.1798	-	X af.1798
	27.	Jamesport, <u>Lower Aquebogue</u> Cong.(Acquebogue; pb.a r.of #1;nl.01T;*Riverhead)	1854(01,98) 1853(incp.) r.1873	1861-1866, 1872-1973	-	UCC 1961-1973; merged to #42 to form M.
	27M.	Jamesport, First Par.Ch.(merger of #27 & #42; *Riverhead)	1973 M	1973-on	-	UCC
	28.	Laurel, <u>Franklinville</u> Pres.(f.Cong.;nl.01T; *Southold)	1831(CG;26) r.af.1834(PR)	nl.	1834-1919NS	Merged to #30(q.v.)
	29.	Manorville, <u>Brookfield</u> Pres.(f.l.Mannsville; incor.in Nassau Co.(26);*Brookhaven)	1796(3 sr)	-	m.1796; 1803/ 1806-onOS	Pres.
	30.	Mattituck, Pres.Ch.Soc.(First;Mattatana;1788 yoked to #1 & ps.inclu.with it in 1788 Southold l.75:merged 1817 to #1 as Union Par. (s.United Par.);SUF 1752-1790(s.nl.);nl.01T; 1919 ab.#28;*Southold)	1715(CG;6 sr) 1717(Ch.full) 1784(incp.) r.1790(PR) r.1817 M r.1919 M	nl. sv.1735-1740, 1772-1773	j1717/1718; to 1735; j1740; NSd: 1745-1758; by 1773-1774/ 1787,1788/ 1793-onNS	Pres.

NEW YORK - SUFFOLK COUNTY - continued

A	B	C	D	E	F
31.	Melville, Sweet Hollow Pres.(*Huntington)	1829(4 sr)	-	1829-onOS	Pres.
32.	Middle Island, Middle Island Pres.(Middletown Par.of Brookhaven;SUF 1766-bf.1773;had a branch at Yaphank 1851-1871 which bec.a ch.)	1767(5 sr) 1766(land)	-	j1766-to 1774/1787; 1798/1802-onOS	Pres.
In 33.	Montauk, Indian Cong.(sv.Montauk tribe;nl.14; *East Hampton)	1741(2 sr) 1660(Mission: 2 sr)	IM: (nl.) m.1798	IM: (nl.) 1741-1761	X
In Nt	Moriches, Indian pr.(sv.Patchogue tribe; *Brookhaven)	-	-	IM:af.1741	X
34.	Mount Sinai, Cong.(Old Mans;First Strict Cong. of Brookhaven;f.Mount Sinai & Miller Pl.;f. United Par.of Old Mans,Miller's Pl.& Rocky Pt.(from 1807);in 1720 bldg.(1740:99);had a branch at Miller Pl.(1849,l.incor.as a ch.: cl.1855-1858);had a branch at Rocky Point 1841(1850 bldg.)-?;f.in Pby.,r.as Strict Cong.1789;SUF 1760/1761-1774/1787;see also #40)	1760(PR) 1740(pr.) r.1789(CG; 4 sr)	CT Strict: 1790-1795; LIS:1792-1840; LIC:1840-1846; 1834-1835, 1843/1846-on	j1761; by 1773-1774/ 1787	UCC
35.	New Village, First Cong.of Center Reach (Lake Grove PO;Third Strict Cong.of Brookhaven;in 1812 union mtghse.)	1815(3 sr)	LIS 1816-1840; pb.LIC:1840-1846; 1834-1835, 1843/1846-1952	-	withdrew
36.	Northport, First Pres.(Freshponds,moved 1829,f. Red Hook village;f.l.Vernon Valley;SUF 1787-1790;*Huntington)	1783(22,26) 1774(pr.:26) 1794(98) 1796(?) r.1873(26)	-	j1787-1790 (nl.); 1794/ 1797-onOS	Pres.
37.	Orient, Cong.UCC (Oyster Ponds Indep.;in 1717 bldg.;SUF 1757/1764-1773;l.specifically as CG on Pby.l.;01T:1854:asso.CG;*Southold)	1735(CG;3 sr) r.1828 1840(incp.)	LIS:m.(not j) 1819; pb.LIA 1836-1840;pb.LIC 1840-1846; 1843/1846-1849; cl.1853-1858; 1861-1866, 1870-on	j1740 to 1747;j1756/ 1764(NSd 1756-1758)-1773; 1829-1832	UCC

NEW YORK - SUFFOLK COUNTY - continued

A	B	C	D	E	F
38.	Patchogue, First Cong.Ch.& Par.(Second Strict Cong.of Brookhaven;Par.of Winthrop's Patent; specifically CG on Pby.l.;in 1787 bldg.)	1793(CG) 1783(01) 1823(incp.)	LIS:1793-1840; pb.LIC 1840-1846; 1834-1835, 1843/1846-on	1831-1832	Sch.I
In 39.	Poosepatuck, Strict Indian Cong.(Poospatuc; Poose Patoch;nl.14;on Poosepatuck Indian Reservation at *Mastic;sv.Patchogue tribe)	1750(mixed) 1740(pr.)	CT Strict: m.1790,1798; LIS:m.1791; j1812-1840; pb.LIC:1840-1846; 1834-1835, 1848-1874	IM: (nl.) 1740-1754, 1764-1788	X
40.	Port Jefferson, Cong.(nl.01T;f.a branch of #34 1848-1856;*Brookhaven)	1847	1855-1861	-	X
41.	Riverhead, First Cong.	1834(01,22) 1836	pb.LIA:1836-1840;pb.LIC: 1840-1846; 1843/1846-on	-	UCC
42.	Riverhead, Sound Ave.Cong.(First Strict Cong.of Northville;Northville Chap.;f.l.Success;moved 1834;f.Fanning Ch.;Middle Dist.of Riverhead; claim to continue #2;lt.75:1835-1836;lt.cl. 1855-1858;l.specifically CG in Pby.1833-1834; m.on Pby.l.as CG 1836-1837/1838;s.incor. considered Indian)	1829(CG;2 sr) 1834(r.Soc.) 1758(claim)	cl.1853-1858; 1861-1866, 1872(j1880)-1973	1831-1836 (see text)	UCC 1961-1973; Merged to #27(q.v.)
43.	Sag Harbor, First Pres.Ch.& Cgn.(f.Cong.;Old Barn Ch.;Whaler's;King Mem.Chap.;nl.01T; *Southampton)	1766(CG;4 sr) 1767(14) 1791(?) r.1810(PR)	nl.	1794/1797-1803/1808, 1810-onOS, 1837-1840/1841NS	Pres.
44.	Sandy Hill, Cong.(f.of Canoe Place;nr.Warrenton; *Southampton)	1862 1861(s.01)	1862-1864	-	X
45.	Sayville, Cong.UCC (Layville:01N;in 1849 bldg.; *Islip)	1858(01,01N) 1848(land) 1800[sic:22]	1860-on	-	UCC
46.	Setauket, Setauket Pres.(First Ch.of Setauket in Brookhaven;First Ch.of Brookhaven;f.C of C;f. of Ashford;separated from town 1740;Pres.by 1714:49;sett.1645/1655;f.in CT 1659-1664;SUF 1750-1790)	1660(CG;2 sr) 1665(14,49) 1662(98) 1645(2 sr) ps.r.1717(PR)	nl.	j1717; NSd 1741-1758; by 1773-onOS	Pres.

NEW YORK - SUFFOLK COUNTY - continued

A	B	C	D	E	F
47.	Shelter Island, Shelter Island Pres.(f.Cong.;SUF 1766-af.1767;incomplete org.to 1808)	1738(CG;2 sr) 1742(98) r.1808 (covenant) r.1812(PR)	nl.	j1766-af. 1767; j1812; 1811-onNS	Pres.
48.	Smithtown, First Pres.(First Ch.of Smithtown at Nisseauag;f.Branch Ch.;SUF 1751-1790;nl.01T)	1677(CG;3 sr) 1675(22,26) 1671(11) pb.r.1759(PR)	nl.	j1751; NSd 1751-1758; by 1773-onOS	Pres.
49.	South Setauket, Cong.(*Brookhaven)	1876	1875-1878	-	X
50.	Southampton, First Pres.(f.C of C;sett.1640;f.in CT 1644-1664,1673-1674;indep.(pb.CG)1727-1747;f.named Pres.by 1707;SUF 1747-1790;nl.75:by 1773-1774/1787,pb.incor.;1965 ab.Bethel Pres.(Black,1917/1918,l.75:1917-1965);see also #8)	1640(CG) ps.r.1716(PR) 1717(26) pb.r.1727(CG) ps.r.af.1749 (PR) r.1965 M	SUF 1747-1749; sv. 1727-1747	j1716 to 1727;j1749; NSd 1749-1758; 1774/1787-onOS; 1837-1840/1841NS	Pres.
In 51.	Southampton, <u>Shinnecock</u> Pres.(f.Shinnecock Cong.;on Shinnecock Reservation at Southampton;f.at Canoe Place,moved across bay;misison begun 1660:31;NY Missionary Soc. 1799-1812;l.Pby.,not natl.1818-1819;1854: assod.:01T;sv.Shinnecock tribe)	by 1741 (mixed;14) 1751(01) r.1847 1850(?) r.1887(PR)	IM (nl.): m.1790,1798; LIS:m.1791; cl.1853-1858; 1860-1874, 1876-1878	IM (nl.): 1740-1751, 1764-1788; 1819-1840/1841NS, 1887-on	Pres.
52.	Southold, First Pres.(f.Indep.Cong.;f.Strict Cong.(10:1738-1748);f.First Ch.,Cong.;sett. 1640;f.in New Haven Colony 1648-1664;in CT 1664-1664,1673-1674;98 says in Pby.1748:not otherwise supported;SUF 1774/1787-1788/1790; under Half Way Covenant 1792;see also #23)	1640(CG) 1784(incp.) r.1832(PR)	nl.	1794/1797-1803/1806, 1830-onNS	Pres.
53.	Thompson's Station, Cong.(*Islip)	1864(01N)	1863-1872	-	X
54.	Wading River, Cong.(Second Sound Strict Cong.of Riverhead;f.Second Strict Cong.of Southold to 1792;22 & 99 consider a continuation of #55)	1785(3 sr) 1784(s.01) 1807(incp.)	CT Strict: m.1787; j1790-1795; LIS:1791-1840; pb.LIC 1840-1846; 1834-1835, 1843/1846-on	-	UCC
In 55.	Wading River, Indian Pres.(SUF by 1773-1774/1787;not Indian in 99;pb.sv.Setauket &/or Corchoque tribes;see also #54;*Riverhead;f.of *Southold to 1792)	1740(22,26) by 1760(98)	-	IM: (nl.) m.1757; by 1773-1774/1787	X

NEW YORK – SUFFOLK COUNTY -continued

A	B	C	D	E	F
56.	Warrenton, Warnertown Cong.(01T:1854:assod.; pb.*Southampton)	by 1854	cl.1853-1858	-	X
57.	Westhampton, Westhampton Pres.Soc.(Beaver Dam; f.West Par.of Southampton;Ketchaboneck Par.; Westhampton Beach PO;SUF 1774/1787-1790; nl.01T)	1742(CG;2 sr) 1748(22,26) by 1758(98) 1763(Par.) r.1775(PR)	nl.	1774/1787-onOS 1837-1840/1841NS	Pres.

NEW YORK – SULLIVAN COUNTY (org.1809) (105)

A	B	C	D	E	F
1.	Barryville, Cong.(affl.NJ 1869–1876;*Highland; f.of *Lumberland to 1853)	1835(s.01,98) 1836(s.01,11) 1837(s.01)	1836–1837, 1838–1843, 1846–on	–	Sch.I
2.	Cochecton, First Pres.Ch.& Cgn.(f.a branch of #3 to by 1803;f.of *Bethel to 1828;f.of *Lumberland to 1809;l.1818–1819 natl.not Pby.;nl.01T;1855 bought out Meth.as Pres.& Meth.Epis.Soc.;1945 merged to Pres.of Lake Huntington(l.75:1910–1945) as Lake Huntington Pres.(f.Lake Huntington & Cohecton,l.75:1946–on;Ch.here r.1952))	by 1803(CG) r.1812(PR:3 sr) 1839(90) r.1855 r.1952	nl.	j1812; 1811–1946OS, 1837–1840/1841NS; 1952–1980	Merged, r.; X
3.	Eldred, Cong.(Narrow Falls;Halfway Brook;f.First of <u>Lumberland</u> to 1853;affl.NJ 1869–1876;f. Fed.by 1919–1921 to unknown;see also #2; *Highland)	1799(01,98) 1787(11)	NYI:1832–1834; 1834–1843; m.1843–1846; 1846–on	–	Sch.I
4.	Forestburg, P or C Ch.	bf.1821	ps.SNJ	j1821; 1820–1840OS, 1837–1840/1841NS	X
5.	Glen Spey, Cong.(*Lumberland)	1894(01N)	1896–1909	–	X
6.	Liberty, First Pres.	1809(2 sr) 1810(2 sr)	–	j1810; 1809–onOS, 1837–1840/1841NS	Pres.
7.	Monticello, First Pres.(Monticello Pres.Soc.;f. The Ch.of Monticello to 1833;f.l.Thompson; lt.26;nl.01T)	by 1807(pb.CG min;pr.:98) r.1810(PR; 5 sr) 1827(Soc.)	nl.	1806–onOS	Pres.
8.	Neversink, P or C Ch.	by 1813	nl.	1812–1815, 1816–1817	X
9.	Rockland, First Pres.(1859 ab.#10 as First Pres.;Lew Beach PO)	1836/1837(45) r.1859 M r.1925	–	1837/1838–1859NS, 1859–1921OS, 1925–1942	X
10.	Rockland, Roscoe Pres. (f.Second Pres.;Westfield Flats;f.Fed.to #11 & Meth.(c.1800)1968–1986 as United Ch.of Roscoe)	1842(3 sr) r.1873 1879	(see text)	j1842; 1840/1842–1859NS, 1873–on	Merged to #9; r.; Pres.
11.	Roscoe, Cong.(Fed.to #10 1968–1986, & Meth. (c.1800) 1938/1939–on as United Ch.of Roscoe *Rockland)	1889(2 sr) 1891(01N)	1891–on	(see text)	UCC

NEW YORK - SULLIVAN COUNTY - continued

A	B	C	D	E	F
12.	White Lake, Bethel Pres.(f.White Lake Pres.at Bethel;f.of *Lumberland to 1809)	1810 1805(Soc.)	-	1803/1805-1812,1813-onOS, 1837-1840/1841NS	Pres.

NEW YORK - TIOGA COUNTY (org.1791) (107)

A	B	C	D	E	F
	1. Berkshire, First Cong.(f.Pres.;f.l.Central Berkshire)	1833(CG;4 sr) 1832(s.01)	cl.1853-1858; 1867-1868, 1869-1986	j1839; 1837/ 1838-1857NS	UCC 1961-1986; CCCC 1986-on
	2. Candor, Cong.(Farmington Soc.;f.Second of Spencer to 1811;incor.l.Leander(s.75);lt.75: 1822/1823-1824;48 says in ML,but not in minutes)	1808(CG;4 sr) 1810(Soc.) r.1821(PR) r.c.1851(CG)	1852-1995	j1813; 1812-1850NS	UCC 1961-1995; NA 1994-on
	3. East Owego, P or C Ch.(in Owego)	by 1838	nl.	j1838; 1837/ 1838-1840/ 1842NS,1843/ 1845-1846/ 1848NS	X 1848
	4. Newark Valley, First Cong.(f.named Pres.;f.of Newark to 1862;f.of Westville to 1824 (Western Soc.:44,48);f.of Berkshire to 1823; f.First Pres.of Tioga (Weston Soc.)to 1808(l. to 1812);f.at Brown's Settlement,moved 1832)	1803(CG;5 sr) 1798(90) 1793(s.44) 1805(Soc.) r.1869(01N)	SA:1803-1809; cl.1853-1858; j1869; 1866-on	j1811; 1809/ 1811-1866NS	UCC
	5. Nichols, First Pres.	1829(CG) 1833(48) r.1859(PR)	cl.1853-1858	j1833; 1833-onNS	Pres.
	6. Owego, First Pres.(f.First Cong.;f.C of C;f.in Tioga to 1813;1912 merged to #8 as Union Pres.Soc.)	1817(CG;2 sr) 1810(Soc.) r.1831(PR) r.1912 M	nl.	j1817; 1817-onNS	Pres.
Gr	7. Owego, Ger.Cong.(l.01K 1920-1921/1923)	1919(01) 1920(01K,64)	1920-1925	-	X (1922:64;1921/ 1923:01K)
	8. Owego, Indep.Cong.Soc.(s.claim to continue #6)	1850 1853(Soc.) 1810(claim) 1830(s.01)	1850-1912	-	Merged to #6(q.v.)
	9. Richford, First Cong.(Columbia Soc.;f.of Arlington to 1832;f.North of Berkshire to 1831)	1823(PR) 1822(Soc.) r.1827(CG) 1826(?)	m.1844/1845- 1846; cl.1853-1858; 1867-1985	j1823; 1822/ 1823-1868NS	Sch.I 1961-1985; withdrew
	10. Spencer, Christ the King Fellowship (f.First Pres.;f.First Cong.)	1815(CG) r.1866(PR:99)	1852-1865	j1816; 1815/ 1816-1852NS, 1866-onNS	Pres.
	11. Tioga, Cong.(nl.01T)	bf.1836(48)	nl.	j1844; 1843/ 1845-1857NS	X
	12. Waverly, First Pres.(f.of Factoryville;in *Barton)	1847(4 sr)	-	j1847; 1846-onNS	Pres.

NEW YORK - TIOGA COUNTY - continued

A	B	C	D	E	F
13.	West Newark, Cong.(in Newark Valley;f.Second; f.Union Ch.of Westville & Candor;lt.75:1822/ 1823-1824,both names;f.of Westville to 1825; f.of Berkshire to 1823;f.l.West Union;f.l. Western;Pres.Union Soc.bec.CG 1878)	1823(CG;5 sr) 1824(s.01) r.1853	1851-1858, 1859-on	j1824; 1822/ 1823-1852NS	UCC

NEW YORK - TOMPKINS COUNTY (org.1817) (109)

A	B	C	D	E	F
1.	Brooktondale, Caroline Valley Cong.(in Caroline; f.l.Brookton;f.l.Mott's Corners;merger of Mott's Corners Meth.& Caroline Ref.(RCA,1800-af.1804,r.1812(99,1831:85),X 1868);Fed.to Meth.(1935 merger of Slatersville Meth.& Morris Chap.Meth.)1935/1938-on as Caroline Valley Fed.)	1868(4 sr) M 1866(s.01)	1867-on	-	UCC
2.	Caroline, Cong.of Speedsville (lt.cl.1853-1858; 1854:unassod.:01T)	1819(CG)	1851-1858, 1859-1872	j1820; 1819-1839NS, 1840/1842-1852NS	X
3.	Danby, First Cong.(f.Pres.;s.Ithaca PO;f.of Spencer to 1811;Fed.to Meth.(class 1809/1811, ch.1831/1832)1954/1957-on,as Fed.;lt.cl.1853-1857:CG in Pby. & unassod.CG)	1807(CG;4 sr) 1808(s.01) 1812(48)	1853-1854; cl.1854-1858; 1867-on	j1815; 1814-1867NS	UCC
4.	Dryden, First Pres.(f.C of C,Cong.;Dryden Village;left Pby.1848(l.to 1852);had elders when not in Pby.:1848-1859)	1808(CG;4 sr) 1800/1810(48) r.1821(PR;98) 1823(Soc.)	ML:1808-1810; 1848-1851; cl.1853-1858	j1808; 1809/1811-1852NS; j1859; 1859-onNS	Pres.
5.	Enfield, P or C Ch. (Pres.:98)	1832(s.48,98) 1831(s.48)	nl.	j1832; 1831-1852NS	X
6.	Groton, First Ch.,East (f.of Division to 1818;f. East of Locke to 1817;left Pby.1831)	1805(CG;3 sr) 1802(Soc.)	ML:1806-1810; 1839-1840, 1848-1858	j1808; 1809/ 1811-1833	X (bldg. removed 1864)
7.	Groton, First Cong.UCC (Village;f.Groton Hollow Pres.)	1849(CG;2 sr) 1847(s.01)	cl.1853-1858; 1867-1966	1848-1867NS	UCC 1961-1966; Merged to form M.
7M.	Groton, Groton Com.(merger of #7,Amer.Bapt.(bf. 1806)& Meth.(1836))	1966 M	1966-on	-	UCC
8.	Groton, Groton City Cong.(in 1853 bldg.)	1896(01)	1896-on	-	UCC
9.	Groton, Groton-Lansing Cong.(f.West Groton & Lansing Pres.;Lansing f.of Genoa to 1817; Groton f.of Division to 1818,f.of Locke to 1817)	1816(CG;3 sr) 1817(s.01)	cl.1853-1858; 1867-1989	j1817; 1818-1859NS, 1865-1868NS	UCC 1961-1989; withdrew
10.	Ithaca, First Cong.(Tr.from Ref.(RCA,1830-1872: 85))	1830(Ref.) Tr.1873(CG: 01N,98) 1872(85)	1873-on	-	Sch.II 1961-1981; UCC 1981-on
11.	Ithaca, First Cong.of West Hill (Payson Ch.)	1847	cl.1853-1858	-	X af.1858
12.	Ithaca, First Pres.(f.South Second Pres.of Ulysses to 1821;see note at #13)	1804(3 sr) 1807(incp.)	-	j1805; nl.; 1809/1811-onNS	Pres.

NEW YORK - TOMPKINS COUNTY - continued

A	B	C	D	E	F
13.	Lansing, Pres.Ch.at Lansingsville(f.Second South Ch.of Genoa(Cayuga Co.)to 1817;f.in Teetertown;f.Second of Milton,Pres.of Milton to 1808;49 says only ch.in Cayuga Pby.in 1811 with PR forms,but that would make #12 & #19 CG)	1805(98) 1804(48)	-	j1806; 1803/ 1808-1839NS	1842 Merged to Cayuga Co.#7 to form Cayuga Co. #10(q.v.)
14.	Ludlowville, Pres.(in Lansing)	1817(98)	-	j1818; 1817-1924NS	X
15.	Ludlowville, Third South Ch.of Genoa(Cayuga Co.; Cong.;now in Lansing (from 1817);f.Third Ch., Second Cong.of Milton to 1808)	1805(CG)	ML:1804-1810	j1808; 1809/ 1811-1812	X 1813
16.	Newfield, First Pres.(f.First of Cayuta(Schuyler Co.)to 1822)	1817(CG;2 sr) 1820(98) r.af.1858(PR: 01T)	cl.1853-1858	j1818; 1817-1908NS	X
17.	Newfield, Second Ch.(P or C)	1834	nl.	j1834; 1834/ 1835-1837/ 1838	X
18.	Peruville, P or C Ch.(Peru;in Groton)	by 1820	nl.	j1820; 1819-1852NS	X
19.	Trumansburg, First Pres.of Ulysses (see note at #13;f.Fed.to First Bapt.(c.1815) 1964-1972)	1803(4 sr) 1813(Soc.)	-	j1803; 1803/ 1808-onNS	Pres.
20.	Varna, Pres.(in Dryden)	1842	-	j1842; 1840/ 1842-1858NS	X

NEW YORK - ULSTER COUNTY (org.1683) (111)

A	B	C	D	E	F
1.	Highland, First Pres.(f.l.(in) Lloyd to 1923;f. New Paltz Landing of New Paltz to 1845;Pres. Cgn.of New Paltz)	1792(CG;2 sr) 1785(38) r.1808(PR;98)	MC: 1792-1810; WAP:m.1792, 1809	j1810(3 sr); 1809-1832, 1833-onNS	Pres.
2.	Kingston, First Pres.of <u>Rondout</u> (withdrew NS Pby.by 1840:45)	1833(5 sr) 1834(45)	-	(apply 1833) j1834; 1834-1970OS 1838-1840/ 1841NS	X 1969(38)
3.	Kingston, Ponckhockie Union Cong.(withdrew from UCC 1970,l.incor.1970-1991;in 1870 bldg.)	1915(22)	1915-1991	-	UCC 1961-1991; NA 1971-on; CCCC (plan to j 1974, nl.)
4.	Malden, First Pres.(Saugerties PO;Malden-on-Hudson)	1833(26)	-	1834/1835-1908NS	X (1878:26)
5.	Marlboro, First Pres.(f.Marlborough Pres.Soc.of <u>New Marlborough</u>;land given agreeable to "Kirk of Scotland";bldg.by 1763(45);r.incp.1785 (98);nl.01T)	1764(7 sr) 1750(Soc.) r.1793(CG:MC) Soc.r.1795(98) r.1810(PR) Soc.r.1850(98)	MC: 1792-1810; WAP:m.1792, 1806,1809	j1766-1773; j1810, 1809-onOS; 1837-1840/ 1841NS	Pres.
6.	Milton, First Pres.(*Marlborough;often confused with Milton in Saratoga Co.)	1841(98)	-	1840/1841-onNS	Pres.
7.	Plattekill, First Pres.Cgn.of <u>Pleasant Valley West</u>	1813(26,s.98) 1814(s.98)	-	j1813; 1812-1815, 1818-1862NS	X (1863:38; 1870:49)
8.	Saugerties, First Cong.of Ulster	1853(3 sr)	1852-1963	-	Sch.I 1961-1963; NA 1962(j1963)-1995,1996-on
9.	Ulster Park, Cong.(*Esopus)	1897	1897-1909	-	X

NEW YORK - WARREN COUNTY (org.1813) (113)

1.	Bolton, Pres.(f.Cong.;org.as PR:90,but nl.Pby.)	1804(CG;90) r.by 1846(PR) 1885[sic:22]	SAP:sv. 1812-1815	j1821; 1819/1824-1846/1848NS, 1845-1860OS, 1857-1895NS	X
2.	Chestertown, Chester Pres.(Tr.to RCA 1825,& Tr. back 1828(nl.85))	by 1806 Tr.1825(Ref.) Tr.1828(PR)	-	j1806; 1803/1805-1823/1824, 1828-1918NS	Tr.to RCA; Tr.; X
3.	Glens Falls, First Pres.(f.Queensbury;f.Union Soc.of Pearl Village to 1848;united in yoke to Hudson Falls (Kingsbury,Washington Co.) 1810-1827;in 1803 bldg.)	1808 1807(Soc.)	-	j1809; 1809/1813-1826,1827-onNS	Pres.
4.	Lake George, First Pres.(f.Caldwell Pres.;1810 bldg.:Pres.,but not org.to 1830;26 & 98 say X 1848,& r.1851,l.through)	1830(26,98) r.1851	-	1814/1818-1819/1824, 1831-onOS 1837-1840/1842NS	(see text) Pres.
5.	Pottersville, Cong. (*Horicon)	1851	1863-1864	-	X
6.	Queensbury, Pres.(f.Union Ch.of East Lake George;f.Union Evan.;f.Cong.)	c.1867(CG;98) r.1877(PR)	nl.	j1877; 1877-1922	X
7.	Stony Creek, Pres.(l.only 90;nl.32)	1800(90)	-	nl.	X pb.soon
8.	Warrensburg, First Pres.(f.of Warrensburg & Athol to 1836;f.of Thurman to 1813;26 says always Pres.;01T says f.Cong.,r.by 1854;lt. 75:1831-1834)	1804(CG;2 sr) r.by 1854 (PR:01T)	nl.	j1806; 1803/1805-on NS	Pres.

NEW YORK – WASHINGTON COUNTY (org.1789) (115)

1.	Cambridge, Cong.	1883(3 sr)	1882-1912	-	X
2.	Cambridge, First United Pres.(Old White Mtghse.; 1769:both Asso.Ch.(Seceder) & Ref.Pres. (Covenanter)Ch.org.;Ref.Pres.dormant af.1779 (later ch.claimed to continue);these two denominations united 1782,as Asso.Ref.Pres.; locally these, Pres.,& Cong. 1784 elect joint trustees for Prot.Pres.Cgn.of Christ (incp. 1785);pastor of continuing Asso.Ch.called 1784,divided out 1786 to form Appendix IV.#1 (q.v.);rest seek PR or CG pastor,& l.PR;1790/ 1791 called Asso.Ref.pastor for Prot.Pres. Cgn.of Christ (it affl.Asso.Ref.1790 to 1858; bec.Village (First) United Pres.1858,l.Pres. 75:1958-1965,when merged here);remainder r. 1792 as this Ch.,specifically inclu.New Englanders;nl.01T;had branch at Whiteside Ch.,West Cambridge 1800-1831 (own Asso.Ref. Ch.1831-1835,when merged here;bldg.survives & sv.other denominations);two Chs.unite 1965 as Cambridge United Pres.)	1792 1793(Soc.) 1769(claim) r.1835 M r.1965 M	nl.	1774/1787- onOS, 1837-1840/ 1842NS	Pres.
3.	East Hebron, East Hebron Pres.(f.l.Hebron;s. Salem PO)	1790(Soc.) r.1804(Soc.)	-	j1791; 1788/ 1793-1858OS, 1861-onNS, 1837-1840/ 1842NS	Pres.
4.	Fort Ann, Pres.	1823(98)	-	j1824; 1819/ 1824-1869NS	X
5.	Fort Edward, First Pres.	1820/1824 r.1854	-	j1824; 1819/ 1824-1831, 1853-1931OS	X
6.	Granville, First Ch.of <u>Middle Granville</u> (Union Relg.Soc.;f.First Pres.of Grandville & Westfield (47);in 1770 bldg.;two factions 1822-1822;l.as Granville 1823-1828,North Granville 1828-1836)	1782(CG;2 sr) r.1825(PR) r.1825(CG) r.1831	PV:bf.1819; 1823-1836	j1791; nl.; 1798/1802- 1803/1808	1837 merged to #11 to form #8(q.v.)
7.	Granville, First Cong.(f.<u>South Granville</u> Cong.; 1854:in Pby.:01T,incor.)	1790 1789(plan) r.1824	PV: ? -1819 VT:1819-1820, 1828-1849; cl.1853-1858; NY:1876-1878, 1879-1928	-	X

NEW YORK - WASHINGTON COUNTY - continued

	8.	Granville, First Pres.of Middle Granville (Union Relg.Soc.;merger of #6 & #11;l.as North Granville 1837-1838,1840-1841,as Granville 1841-1846)	1837 M(CG;99) 1832 M(98) r.1846(PR)	VT:1837-1838, 1840-1846	1843/1845-onNS	Pres.
We	9.	Granville, Jerusalem Welsh Cong.at Jamesville (Pres.:98;Tr.to Eng.Assn.1912-1913,1919-on)	1873(s.01,65) 1871(s.01) 1875(s.01) 1865(68)	1873-on	-	Sch.I (bldg.for sale 1991)
We	10.	Granville, Middle Granville Welsh Cong.(Welsh Union Cong.Soc.)	1860(01,98) 1859(68)	NYW: ? -1867; 1867-1884	-	X (1886:65)
	11.	Granville, Pres.of Middle Granville Ch.(f.Pres. of East Granville to 1834;r.1831 by ab.part of #6)	1825(98) r.1831	-	1829-1837/ 1838	1837 Merged to #6 to form #8(q.v.)
	12.	Granville, Pres.of North Granville (Fair Vale Relg.Soc.;f.North Granville Cong.;f.l.West Granville(01,75);s.l.First Pres.(75);nl.01T)	1810(CG) r.1822(PR)	SWVC/PV: c.1810-1819; VT 1819-1821	j1823; 1819/ 1824-1914NS	X
	13.	Hampton, P or C Ch.	by 1834	nl.	1833-1834/ 1835	X
	14.	Hebron, Cong.(m.as CG on Pby.l.1829-1830)	by 1830	VT:1841-1843	-	X
	15.	Hudson Falls, First Pres.(f.l.Sandy Hill to 1909;f.of Kingsbury;f.united in yoke to Glens Falls(Queensbury),Warren Co.as United Pres.of Kingsbury & Queensbury 1810-1827;f. Fort Edward & Kingsbury;f.Cong.;Tr.Pby.1790 (37),jPby.1791(47))	by 1788 (pb.PR;min) r.1803(CG; 3 sr) r.1825(PR:46A) r.1848	nl.	1774/1787-1791/1793, 1794/1797-1826,1827-1840/1842NS, 1839-onOS	Pres.
	16.	Salem, First Pres.Cgn.(First Incp.Pres.Cgn.; Brick Ch.;specifically New England in origin; 12 confuses with Upper Salem,Westchester Co.; nl.01T;1959 ab.White Ch.,United Pres.(New Perth;1764(continues Ch.org.in Ireland 1751 & removed here 1764/1766),f.Asso.Ref.;f.Asso. Ch.,Pres.(Burgher);affl.Asso.Ch.1764-1782, Asso.Ref.1782-1858,UPNA 1858-1958,l.75:1958-1959) as First United Pres.)	1769(PR;5 sr) 1765(49) r.1793(49) r.1959 M	nl.	j1769; nl.; 1774/1787-on NS	Pres.
	17.	South Hartford, First Cong.(in 1805 bldg.;1854: 01T:in Pby.,incor.;s.l.as Fed.;in Hartford)	1810(Soc.) 1808(s.01)	SWVC:c1810-pb.c.1817; VT:1828-1849; cl.1853-1858; NY:1876-on	-	UCC

NEW YORK - WASHINGTON COUNTY - continued

18.	Union Village, Orthodox Cong.(in Greenwich;lt. 01S:1852-1855(two Assns.);lt.cl.1856-1858)	1837(01,98)	1838-1843; m.1843-1844/ 1845; 1851-1857, cl.1857-1858, 1858-1861, 1865-1880	-	X
19.	Union Village, Pres.(in Greenwich)	by 1802	-	1798/1802- 1814/1818	X
20.	Whitehall, First Cong.,East Whitehall (nl.01T)	1805(98) 1819(?)	VT:1821-1842, 1843-1858, 1859-1860	-	X af.1872(98)
21.	Whitehall, First Pres.(f.Asso.Ref.;affl.Asso. Ref.to 1815(32);in 1810 bldg.)	1808(AR;32) 1810(AR;99) r.1819(PR; 2 3r) by 1817(22)	-	1814/1818-on NS	Pres.

NEW YORK - WAYNE COUNTY (org.1823) (117)

A	B	C	D	E	F
1.	Clyde, First Pres.(f.of Galen)	1814(4 sr)	-	j1815; 1814-1971NS	Tr.to U.Meth.
2.	Huron, Pres.(f.of Port Bay to 1834;f.First of Wolcott to 1826 (moved 1826);see also #23)	1813	-	j1813; 1812-onNS	Pres.
3.	Lyons, First Pres.(f.First Pres.Ch.& Soc.of Sodus in Lyons to 1811;1800:trustees elected for future Ch.)	1809 1800 (see text)	-	j1811; 1809/ 1811-onNS	Pres.
4.	Marion, First Pres.(f.First Cong.C of C;f.of Winchester to 1826;f.of Williamson to 1825; withdrew from GC 1834,re-j soon;1967 merged to First Bapt.(1804,f.of Williamson to 1825) as United Ch.(dual))	1808(CG) 1824(Soc.) r.1830(PR) r.1832(CG) r.1891(PR) r.1967 M	OA:1809-1813; GC:1832-1834; 1834-1842; GC:1842-by 1848; cl.1853-1858; 1861-1866	j1831-1832, nl.; 1851-1852NS; j1868; 1867-onNS	Pres.(dual, see text)
5.	Newark, Park Pres.(f.First;in Arcadia;Soc. X 1825)	1825(4 sr) 1824(22,26)	-	j1825/1826; 1825-onNS	Pres.
6.	Ontario, Cong.(see also #7;nl.98)	bf.1817(CG)	nl. (ps.GC)	j1817; 1817-1831	withdrew; X af.1831
7.	Ontario, First Pres.(Ontario Ctr.Pres.;f.First Cong.;pb.r.of #6;r.CG 1842:46A,pb.incor.)	1832(CG;2 sr) 1833(22,46A) 1844(?) r.1857(PR)	GC: ? -1834 1834-1844/ 1845; cl.1853-1858; 1861-1864	1857-onNS	Pres.
8.	Ontario, Immanuel Cong.UCC (f.First;f.First Wesleyan Ch.(Wesleyan Meth.);bec.Indep. Wesleyan Meth.1888;in 1865 bldg.)	1857(Wesleyan Meth.) r.1899(CG)	1899-on	-	UCC
9.	Palmyra, East Palmyra Pres.(f.First Pres.of East Palmyra;f.Cong.Ch.of East Palmyra;moved to East Palmyra 1817;in OA bf.1807(43))	1793(CG;5 sr) 1797(90) r.1807(3 sr) r.1817(26) r.1833(PR)	MC:m.1802- ?; OA:1807-1813	j1807/1808, nl.; 1809/1811-1831,1832-onNS	Pres.
10.	Palmyra, Western Pres.Ch.& Soc.	1817(3 sr)	-	j1817; 1817-onNS	Pres.
11.	Pultneyville, P or C Ch.(Poultneyville;in Williamson)	1832(s.48) 1833(s.48)	nl.	j1832/1833; 1832-1851NS	Merged to #22(q.v.) (bf.1848:48)
12.	Red Creek, Red Creek Pres.(First;f.Second of Wolcott;s.confused with #23)	bf.1825(48) 1818(2 sr) 1827(?)	-	1826-onNS	Pres.
13.	Rose, First Pres.of Rose Valley (f.Third of Wolcott to 1826;nl.01T)	1825(PR;4 sr) r.1846(CG) r.1851(PR) 1862(Soc.)	nl.	j1825/1827; 1824-1947NS	X

NEW YORK - WAYNE COUNTY - continued

A	B	C	D	E	F
14.	Savannah, Cong.	1897	1897-on	-	Sch.I 1961; UCC late 1961-on
15.	Savannah, Pres.(f.Cong.;left Pby.(first time) 1841,drop 1840:48;ps.related to #18)	by 1836(CG) r.1864(PR:98) 1863(PR:26)	cl.1853-1858	j1834/1836; 1834/1835-1840/1842NS, 1864-1887NS	X (1893:26)
16.	Sodus, First United Pres.(f.First Union Relg. Soc.;f.Cong.;s.incor.l.Lodius)	1812(CG;3 sr) 1811(?) r.1819(PR:98) 1813(PR:48) 1823(26)	nl.	j1813; 1812-onNS	Pres.
17.	Sodus, Free Cong.	1843(2 sr)	nl.	-	X 1852
18.	South Butler, First Cong.of Butler & Savannah (s.l.Pres.;ps. related to #16;nl.01T)	1831(CG)	nl.	1860-1864NS	X (1860:26)
19.	Walworth, Cong.(f.First Pres.)	1832(CG) r.late 1830's (PR) r.c.1851(CG)	cl.1853-1858	j1832/1833; 1832-1851NS	X af.1858
20.	Walworth, Cong.of Walworth Corners (f.of Ontario to 1829)	1817	nl. (ps.GC)	-	X pb.bf. 1832(48)
21.	Wayne, First Pres.(f.Second of Rose;f.in Sodus; f.Pres.Ch.of Joy;01T:1854:indep.,but l.Pby.)	1845(CG) r.af.1858(PR; 01T)	cl.1853-1858	j1845; 1843/ 1845-1906NS	X
22.	Williamson, Williamson Pres.(f.First Pres.Cong. Soc.;pb.f.Second bf.1825;f.Cong.;1851(bf. 1848:48)ab.#11)	1816(CG;4 sr) r.1851 M r.af.1858(PR; 01T)	1835-1842; GC:1842-by 1848; cl.1853-1858	j1818; 1817-1837; 1855-onNS	Pres.
23.	Wolcott, Wolcott Pres.(First;claim is as #2;f. Second to 1826;s.confused with #12)	1818(48) 1813(claim)	-	j1818; 1818-onNS	Pres.

NEW YORK - WESTCHESTER COUNTY (org.1683) (119)

A		B	C	D	E	F
	1.	Bedford, Bedford Pres.(C of C;The Bedford Ch.; land in New Haven Colony to 1662;in CT 1662-1683,1696-1700;f.Bedford Pltn.of Stamford, Fairfield Co.CT 1681-1683,1696-1697;f.of Bedford,CT 1697-1700;in Par.with Rye 1700, threatened,but not taken over by St.Matthew Epis.(1706);sv.Indep.1728-1743(pb.CG);faction attempt r.CG 1753;SUF 1749-1763;DUT 1763-1795;nl.01T;f.l.Mount Pleasant PO)	1681(CG;6 sr; CT pltn.) 1680(12,s.49) 1699(14) 1677(pr.:s.98) 1697(CT town) ps.r.1720(PR) r.1756 1785(incp.)	Flfd.(CT): 1709-1720; FW(CT): m.1742; m.WAP: 1796-1797	j1720-bf. 1728; Indep.Pby. 1743-1746 j1746; NSd 1746-1758; by 1773-onOS (see text)	Pres.
	2.	Briarcliff Manor, Briarcliff Cong.(in *Ossining)	1896(01)	1898-on	-	UCC
	3.	Bronxville, West Center Cong.(*Eastchester)	1927(01)	1927-on	-	UCC
	4.	Chappaqua, First Cong.(*New Castle)	1911(s.01,22) 1912(s.01)	1912-on	-	UCC
	5.	Dobbs Ferry (PO), South Greenburg Pres.(Lower Greenburg;The Lower Ch.;*Greenburgh)	1825	-	j1825; 1824-onOS	Pres.
	6.	Eastchester, C of C (now in Mount Vernon; sett. 1654(90),1649(12),1664(49);land in New Netherland 1654-1664;in Par.with Westchester, Bronx Co.1693;submitted to St.Paul's Epis., Katonah (1702/1704)in 1708,attempt to revive 1717-1720 failed)	1699(CG;2 sr) 1665(4 sr; pr.:s.98) 1678(pr.:s.98) r.1717	nl.	j1718/1719- 1720	Submitted to Epis.1708; r.; X 1720
	7.	Elmsford, Pres.(f.Cong.;f.First of Greenburgh; Upper Greenburg;nl.01T;Tr.to Ref.(RCA,1850 (38,85)-on,1865:min.)	1788(CG;2 sr) 1790(85) r.1825(PR:98)	WAP: 1792-1802, 1822-1825	j1825; 1824-1865OS	Tr.to Ref., see text
	8.	Mount Vernon, Com.Ch.at the Circle (f.First Cong.)	1892(3 sr) 1902(s.01)	1892-on	-	UCC
bB	9.	Mount Vernon, Vernon Heights Cong.(bec. predominantly Black by 1975)	1896(01)	1896-on	-	UCC
Fr	10.	New Rochelle, Huguenot Pres.(f.Huguenot Ref., French Ref.;claimed by RCA to 1808(85); Majority submitted to Trinity Epis.(1709)in 1709;1974 ab.North Ave.Pres.(1890/1891,l.75: 1891-1974,as New Rochelle Pres.)	1688(Ref., 3 sr) 1689(2 sr) 1686(49) by 1692(98) r.1709 Tr.1808(85; incp.:98) Tr.1812(98) r.1974 M	-	j1812;1811- 1821,1823- 1844OS; 1839(j1839)- onNS	Pres.
Sw	11.	New Rochelle, Swedish Cong.(EC:Rgn.by 1910-1948, full 1948-on)	1897(01) 1891(06)	1902-1946	-	Tr.to EC
	Nt	North Castle (undesignated pr.here 1734-1736:14)				

NEW YORK - WESTCHESTER COUNTY - continued

A	B	C	D	E	F
12.	North Salem, Pres.of Upper Salem (Salem Center; Cong.Soc.;12 confuses with Salem,Washington Co.;pr.1747-1749NSd:14;1764 bldg.;DUT 1765-af.1783(42:nl.1773);nl.01T)	1765(CG;42) 1764(3 sr) 1779(98) 1772(pr.:98) 1747(pr.:14) 1786(Soc.) r.1832(PR)	MC:1787-1792; WAP:1792-1828	j1765-1783 (nl.1773); j1828; 1832-1898OS	X (1889:98)
13.	Ossining, First Pres.(f.Indep.Ch.;f.Associated Pres.;of <u>Sing Sing</u>;f.of <u>Mount Pleasant</u> to 1845(l.to 1819);DUT 1763-1774/1787(42 to 1791,nl.);1763 bldg.;nl.01T;l.Pby.,not natl. 1813-1814;98 says in Pby.:1811-1814;left Pby. (second time) 1820;f.at Sparta to 1803)	1763(CG;3 sr) 1768(2 sr) 1808(incp.) r.1826(PR) r.1832(?)	WAP: 1792-1810, 1820-1826	1763;by 1773-1774/1787; j1812/1814; 1814-1819; j1825/1826; 1828-onOS	Pres.
14.	Peekskill, Cong.(Indep.Pres.;merger of #15 & #17;two branches 1816-1826,then at Hill;l.by Pby.when not a member,only a member part of 1826;1831/1834 merged to Cortlandtown Ref.at Montrose (RCA,1717,r.1793-on(85;1729:98)) as a branch till 1850 when this bec.Van Nest Ref. of Peekskill (RCA,1850-1957(85,X);f.of *Cortlandt)	1816 M(CG)	WAP: 1816-1826, 1826-1830	1819-1820, 1823-1826 (j1826)	1831 merged to Ref., see text
15.	Peekskill, First Pres.(f.Peeskill or Hanover of Courtland Manor;branch of #35 to 1791;pr.from there by 1738(22)or 1742(14,98);bldg.at Hill by 1793;two branches (+ town bldg.)1799-1806; sv.RCA 1800-1806;1806 continue at town;f.of *Courtlandt)	1791(CG) 1787(Soc.) (pr.:see text)	WAP:m.1797, 1800; 1810-1814	j1815; 1814-1815	1816 merged to #17 to form #14
16.	Peekskill, First Pres.(at f.town bldg.;1920 ab. #18 as Peekskill Pres.;f.of *Cortlandt)	1826(98) r.1920 M	-	j1827; 1826-onOS	Pres.
17.	Peekskill, Indep.Pres.Soc.(Ch.on Hill;f.of *Cortlandt)	1806(CG;38) 1813(incp.)	nl.	-	1816 Merged to #15 to form #14(q.v.)
18.	Peekskill, Second Pres.(Payson Pres.;f.of *Cortlandt)	1841(2 sr)	-	1840/1841-1921NS	1920 merged to #16(q.v.)
19.	Pelham, Com.Cong.(f.Trinity Cong.of Tremont, New York City, Bronx Co.to 1923)	1886(01N,01)	1885-on	-	UCC
20.	Pelham, Cong.(f.Pelhamville;f.Bronx,Bronx Co., PO;in 1880 bldg.)	1888(01)	1888-1918	-	X
21.	Portchester, Cong.(in 1885 bldg.;*Rye)	1887(01)	1889-1915	-	X

NEW YORK - WESTCHESTER COUNTY - continued

A	B	C	D	E	F
22.	Pound Ridge, Pres.Ch.& Cgn.(Patterson Mem.Ch.; Ridgefield,Fairfield Co.CT PO;DUT 1770-1795; claimed by Pby.when sv.by WAP;nl.01T)	1770(PR;2 sr) 1769(?) 1760(Soc.; 4 sr) 1788(incp.) pb.r.1798(CG) r.1822(PR:98) 1828(r.incp.)	WAP:1794, 1798-1822	j1770; by 1773-1798/1802; 1803/1805-1806;j1822; 1821-1950OS	X 1949
23.	Rye, Rye Pres.(f.C of C;in New Netherland to 1660;in CT 1660-1683,1696-1700;in Par.with Bedford:1700;submitted to Christ Epis.(1703/1704)in 1704;two factions 1719(98);r.CG 1723/1728;new bldg.1727;38:in Pby.1728,but not in min.;bldg.destroyed 1776(X:98),but 42 says supplied by Pby.to 1789(but nl.);new bldg. 1793:indep.,sv.by Meth.1812-1829;r.1828/1829; DUT 1763-af.1771(ps.1789,but nl.);46 says in Philadelphia Pby.1728-1752,not supported elsewhere;branch at Portchester by 1830-1852; nl.01T)	1674(CG;2 sr) 1675(s.98) 1677(3 sr) 1660(CT town) 1662(31) r.1723(CG) 1728(38) r.1793(38) 1795(incp.) r.1828(PR:98) 1829(37,38)	FE(CT): 1723-1752	j1752; NSd 1752-1758 to 1771(ps. 1789); 1828-onOS	Submitted to Epis.1704; r.; X; r.; Pres.
24.	Scarsdale, Cong.(in 1904 bldg.;f.branch of #31 to 1924)	1903(22) 1904(01)	1924-on	-	UCC
25.	Somers, Union Pres.Soc.(f.Cong.;in 1799 bldg.;l. Pby.1813-1814,1830-1831 as specifically CG; m.on Pby.l.as CG 1829-1830;nl.01T;f.of *Stephentown to 1808)	1799(CG;2 sr) 1806(Soc.) 1808(incp.) r.1833(PR:98) 1832(?)	WAP: 1806-1830	1813-1814, 1830-1831; j1832; 1833-1839OS, 1839(j1839)-1880NS	X
26.	Somers, <u>West Somers</u> Cong.	by 1838	1837-1843	-	X
27.	South Salem, South Salem Pres.(Pres.Ch.& Cgn.in <u>Lower Salem</u>;Pres.Cgn.in Lewisboro;C of C in Salem;DUT 1762-1795;nl.01T)	1752(CG;8 sr) 1751(pr.) r.1763(PR) 1785(incp.)	FW(CT): 1752-1762; DUT 1762-1763	j1763;by 1773-onOS	Pres.
28.	Tuckahoe, Union Cong.(*Eastchester)	1898(01,05)	1898-1899, 1907-1960	-	CCCC by 1958 (j1960)-1988; X
bB 29.	White Plains, Chatterton Hill Cong.(f.branch of #31 to 1930;bec.predominantly Black by 1982)	1905(01,22) 1907	1930-on	-	UCC
30.	White Plains, Ch.of the Highlands,Cong.(f.branch of #31 to 1930;Greenridge in 22(see #31))	1922(01,22)	1930-on	-	UCC
31.	White Plains, Ridgeview Cong.(f.Greenridge Cong.;f.Westchester Cong.;f.White Plains Cong.;see also #24,#29,& #30)	1901(01,22)	1901-on	-	UCC

NEW YORK - WESTCHESTER COUNTY - continued

A	B	C	D	E	F
32.	White Plains, White Plains Pres.(First;tried to org.1719 but opposed by Epis.;f.of *Rye to 1721;sought CT aid 1727:49;38,46 say org.in Philadelphia Pby.1727,Tr.Pby.1733;DUT 1763-1788/1793;X af.Revolutionary War to r.; nl.01T)	1723(CG;4 sr) 1727(4 sr) 1787(incp.) r.1824(PR)	FE(CT):1742 (49,98;1723: 42)-1752	j1752(42,49) NSd1752-1758; by 1773-1788/ 1793; j1824; 1823-onOS	X; r.; Pres.
33.	Yonkers, First Pres.(1951(1958:38)ab.Immanuel Chap.Pres.(1920,l.75:1906-1918,1920-1921, 1946/1947-1951)as First Pres.;1964 ab. Westminster Pres.(1858,l.75:1857-1862NS,1862-1965OS)as First Westminster Pres.)	1852(5 sr) r.1951 M r.1964 M	-	j1852; 1851-1995NS	X
34.	Yorktown, First Pres.(Yorktown Heights;1865 ab. #35;Peekskill PO)	1806(3 sr) r.1865 M	-	j1806; 1803/ 1805-onOS	Pres.
35.	Yorktown, Indep.Ch.(f.Indep.Pres.or Cong.;in Crumpound (Cronpond,Crompond) Soc.;f.Hanover Pres.Ch.;f.Pres.Soc.of Hannover;in Hanover to 1788;in 1738 bldg,;lt.14,one pb.Putnam Co.#3 (l.in Dutchess Co.),f.a branch;see also #15; l.two Pbys.1773;SUF 1749-1763;DUT 1763-1774/ 1787;elders by 1765(49) to 1806,but session pb.not mtg.af.1786)	1730(PR;4 sr) 1738(3 sr) 1743(?) 1753(s.14) 1760(incp.) 1784(incp.:22) r.1786/1806 (CG;see text)	MC:1785-1792; WAP: 1792-1830; FE(CT): 1832-1850; cl.1853-1858	j1743; Indep. Pby.1742-1745 NSd1745-1758; by 1773-1774/ 1787; m.1785 1850-1864NS	1865 Merged to #34(q.v.)

NEW YORK - WYOMING COUNTY (org.1841) (121)

A	B	C	D	E	F
1.	Arcade, UCC Cong.(First Cong.;f.of China to 1866;f.First of Sheldon to 1818;f.South Second of Sheldon to 1811;lt.1865-1866;left Pby.1858(98))	1813(CG;4 sr)	cl.1853-1858; 1861-on	j1818; 1817-1843/1845NS (see text)	UCC
2.	Attica, First Cong.Soc.(f.First of Sheldon to 1811;nl.01T)	1807(CG;3 sr) 1809(90) 1819(Soc.)	nl.	j1823; nl. merge 1824	1824 merged to #6 to form #3(q.v.)
3.	Attica, First Pres.(f.First Cong.;Attica Village;merger of #2 & #6;nl.01T)	1824 M(CG) 1823 M(s.48) r.1835(PR)	nl.	j1823/1824; 1820/1824-onNS	Pres.
4.	Attica Center, P or C Ch.(left Pby.1837)	by 1833	nl.	j1833; 1833-1839	X
5.	Bennington, Pres.of Bennington Ctr.(f.First Cong.Soc.of East Bennington;f.Second of Sheldon to 1818;f.of Sheldon #T10R3;nl.01T; lt.75:1818-1819/1824;shown as l.01:1869,but nl.to 1870)	1814(CG;2 sr) 1822(incp.)	1870-1880	j1818; 1817-1866NS	X (c.1878:26)
6.	Bennington, Second Cong.(f.Third of Sheldon to 1818;lt.Pby.,not natl.:1818-1819/1824,in Pby. to 1823)	by 1818(CG)	nl.	j1818; 1817-1819/1824	1824(1823:48) merged to #2 to form #3(q.v.)
7.	Castile, First Pres.(withdrew from Pby.(first time)1847;r.1930 as United Com.(pb.Fed.),but still in Pby.;in WNYCCC to 1943)	1834(PR) r.1835(CG) 1825(Soc.) r.1870(PR) r.1930	cl.1853-1858; 1860-1870	j1835; 1833-1846/1848NS; j1870; 1870-1943	Merged to form M.
7M.	Castile, UCC (f.United Com.;f.in WNYCCC to 1943; merger of #7 & some of Meth.(1834) & some of First Bapt.(1817);f.in Counc.Com.Chs.)	1943 M	1943-on	-	UCC [Count as CC]
8.	Covington, Cong.	1817	nl.; ps.GC	-	1834 merged to #10 to form #9(q.v.)
9.	Covington, Cong.(merger of #8 & #10;left Pby. 1837)	1834 M(CG)	GC:1837-1842; 1842-1844/1845; cl.1853-1858	j1834; 1834/1835-1837/1838	X af.1858
10.	Covington, Pres.	1827(3 sr)	-	j1827; 1827-1834/1835	1834 merged to #8 to form #9(q.v.)
11.	Curriers, First Cong.of West Java (Curriers Corners;in Java;01T & cl.l.as Java)	1854(3 sr) 1855(Soc.)	cl.1853-1858; 1861-1970	-	UCC 1961-1970; withdrew
12.	Eagle, Cong.(98 says lives only a year or two; nl.01T)	by 1842(CG)	nl.	j1842; 1840/1842-1855NS	X

NEW YORK - WYOMING COUNTY - continued

A	B	C	D	E	F
13.	Gainesville, Cong.(merger of #14 & #16;withdrew from Pby.1847)	1835 M(CG)	cl.1853-1854; 1854-1898, 1899-1900, 1901-1903, 1904-1923	1834/1835-1846/1848NS, 1850-1852NS	X (1913:22)
14.	Gainesville, First Cong.Soc.(East;f.First Pres. of Hebe to 1816;in Pby.to merger)	1815(CG;3 sr) 1817(s.26) 1818(s.26)	nl.	j1816/1819; 1818-1831	1835 Merged to #16 to form #13(q.v.)
15.	Gainesville, <u>Rock Glen</u> Cong.	1891(01N) 1892(?)	1892-1895	-	X
16.	Gainesville, Second Cong.(West Gainesville; Gainesville Creek;in Pby.to merger;lt.75: 1831-1832)	1818(CG) 1827(?)	nl.	j1821; 1819/1824-1834/1835	1835 merged to #14 to form #13(q.v.)
17.	Genesee Falls, First Pres.(f.Portageville Cong.; f.First Cong.of Portage;f.of Portage (Livingston Co.)to 1846;f.of Nunda(Livingston Co.)to 1827;Tr.to OS 1843;nl.01T)	1827(CG;2 sr) 1829(Soc.) r.by 1843(PR) 1848(Soc.r.)	nl.	j1829; 1828-1843/1845NS, 1844-1895OS	X
18.	Java, First Cong.(in Pby.to X)	1832(CG)	nl.	j1833; 1833-1840/1842NS	X 1843
19.	Java, First Cong.of <u>Java Village</u> (incor.l.Sch.I 1970-1971,was Sch.II;claim is as #28)	1884(22) 1885(99) 1887(incp.:01) 1886(?) 1888(?) 1817(claim)	1889-1971	-	Sch.I 1961-1962; UCC 1962-1970; Sch.I 1970-1971; NA 1991(j1992)-on
20.	Johnsonburg, Fed.(Cong.;in Sheldon;merger of Johnsonburg Pres.(1860,l.75:1860-1903NS),& unknown;Fed.by 1919-1937 to unknown)	1903	1903-1937	(see text)	X
21.	North Java, First Cong.(in Java;1847 ab.Free Will Bapt.(1828);nl.01T,unless Java l.is this & not #11)	1847(3 sr) r.1874	1861-1872, 1873-1929	-	X (c.1890:26)
22.	Orangeville, Pres.(f.Cong.Soc.;f.of Attica #9 to 1816;01T:1854:PR,f.CG)	1812(CG;2 sr) r.c.1853(PR)	1848-1849, 1851-1852	j1813; 1812-1850NS, 1851-1923NS	X
23.	Perry, Brick Pres.(f.Village;26 says 1841 merged to Cong.of Perry Village,ps.a faction of #26 not merged 1831)	1835 1834(Soc.) 1841(incp.)	-	j1835; 1834/1835-1836, 1837/1838-onNS	Pres.
24.	Perry, First Cong.,Perry Ctr.(merger of #25 & #26;l.natl.only (special l.)1858-1859)	1831 M	cl.1853-1858; 1858-1859, 1861-on	-	UCC

NEW YORK - WYOMING COUNTY - continued

A	B	C	D	E	F
25.	Perry, First Pres.Ch.& Soc.(f.First Cong.;Perry Center)	1814(CG;5 sr) r.1817(PR; Soc.) 1815(s.48) 1816(s.48) 1818(?) 1825(Soc.r.)	nl.	j1816/1817; 1815/1816-1831	1831 Merged to #26 to form #24(q.v.)
26.	Perry, Second Cong.,Perry Village (Pres.:46A;see also #23)	1822(CG; see text)	nl.	j1822; 1820/ 1824-1831	1831 Merged to #25 to form #24(q.v.)
27.	Pike, Pres.(f.Pres.at East Koy;Cong.forms,Pres. name;moved 1831;1962 merged to part of Bapt. (1910 merger of First Bapt.(Calvinistic,1821, r.1827)& Freewill Bapt.(1852)) as Pike Com., dual)	1819(CG) r.1831 r.1855(PR) r.1962 M	cl.1853-1856	j1819; 1818-1836,1843/ 1845-onNS	Pres. (dual, see text)
28.	Sheldon, First Cong.(First Pres.;f.Fourth to 1818;Humphrey Hollow Ch.;f.of Sheldon #T9R3)	1818(CG) 1817(04) 1821(incp.)	cl.1853-1858; 1864-1867	j1818; 1817-1869NS	X
29.	Strykersville, Cong.(f.Second of Sheldon;Concord Soc.Cong.;Strikersville;Tr.PR to CG 1853:99)	1825(CG;3 sr) 1834(incp.) 1824(?)	1848-1852; cl.1853-1858; 1860-1898, 1899-1906	j1825; 1825-1856NS	X (c.1900:26; bldg.sold 1914)
30.	Varysburg, Pres.(in Sheldon)	by 1843	-	j1843; 1843/ 1845-1856NS	X
31.	Warsaw, Cong.	1827(48)	GC:1827-bf. 1834	-	X
32.	Warsaw, First Cong.(f."Ch.of Warsaw" to 1844; lt.01(not 01S)1852-1853;lt.:01S:1853-1855; Fed.to #33 1944-on as United)	1840	1839-1842; GC:1842-by 1848; 1848-on	(see text)	UCC
33.	Warsaw, First Pres.(f.First Cong.;Union Soc.;Tr. to OS 1841/1842;Fed.to #32 1944-on as United)	1808(CG) 1812(incp.) r.1831(PR:99) 1829(s.99) 1819(s.)	nl. (see text)	j1813; 1812-1840/1842NS, 1842-onOS	Pres.
34.	Weathersfield, P or C Ch.	by 1830	nl.	j1830-1834; nl.	X
35.	Weathersfield Springs, P or C Ch.(s.l. Wethersfield;in Weathersfield)	1832	nl.	j1832; 1834/ 1835-1850NS	X
36.	Wyoming, First Pres.(f.First Cong.of Middlebury; nl.01T;Tr.to OS 1842)	1817(CG;4 sr) 1819(Soc.) r.1822(PR: 2 sr) 1821(26)	nl.	j1822; 1819/ 1824-1840/ 1842NS, 1841-onOS	Pres.

NEW YORK - YATES COUNTY (org.1823) (123)

A	B	C	D	E	F
1.	Barrington, First Pres.Cgn.(at Warsaw:98)	1830(2 sr)	-	j1830; 1830-1840/1842NS	X 1840
2.	Benton, Bellona Mem.Pres.(First Pres.Cgn.of Benton;in Bellona (village) from 1839;1839 ab.Bellona Ref.of Benton (RCA,1817-1835:85, 1833-1839:98);lt.75:1837/1838-1839(two Pbys.);f.of Snell to 1810;see also #7)	1809 1816(incp.) r.1839 M	-	j1811; 1809/1811-onNS	Pres.
3.	Branchport, Pres.(in Jerusalem)	1832(3 sr) 1831(s.48)	-	j1832; 1832-1906NS	X (1900:26)
4.	Dresden, Pres.(First Pres.of West Dresden;f. Cong.Soc.of Torrey;f.in Benton to 1851;nl. 01T;26 says r.CG 1834,rather than PR)	1830(CG) 1833(26) r.1834(PR:98)	nl.	j1830/1831; 1830-1924NS	X (1923:26)
5.	Dundee, First Pres. (f.Dundee United Pres.; f.Second of Starkey)	1832(4 sr)	-	j1833; 1832-1851NS;j1853; 1852-onNS	Pres.
6.	Penn Yan, First Free Cong.Soc.(in Milo)	1841(3 sr)	1849-1857; cl.1857-1858	-	X (1855:46A;1858:22; bldg.sold 1857:98)
7.	Penn Yan, First Pres.(a branch of #2 1809/1821-1823;in Milo)	1823	-	j1822/1823; 1822/1823-onNS	Pres.
8.	Rock Stream, Rock Stream Pres.(f.Third of Starkey;Fed.to First Chr.of Rock Stream (1818)1923-1930)	1833(4 sr) 1832(s.48)	-	j1833; 1832-onNS	Pres.
9.	Rushville, First Cong.Ch.& Soc.(in Potter, village extends into Gorham(Ontario Co.);f.l. Gorham;Potter f.Middlesex to 1832,f.Augusta to 1808;f.First Cong.of Augusta & Gorham;lt. 52;f.Pres.,left Pby.1855;l.in Ontario Co.: 01T)	1802(CG;5 sr) r.1855	OA:1803/1804-1813; cl.1853-1854; 1854-on	j1814; 1813-1858NS	UCC
10.	Starkey, First Pres.(at Lakemont (village),f.l. Eddytown(village);f.First of Reading(Schuyler Co.)to 1824;lt.75:1864-1867;period bf.jPby. suggests CG;nl.01T)	1806(ps.CG; 26,48) r.1817(PR) 1822(s.98)	nl.	j1817; 1817-1887NS	X (1888:26)

NEW YORK - UNLOCATED CHURCHES

		C	D (999)	E	F
1.	Aurora, P or C Ch.(St.Lawrence Pby.,pb.not Erie nor Cayuga Cos.)	by 1826	-	1825-1826	X
2.	Bethany, P or C Ch.(St.Lawrence Pby.)	by 1830	nl.	1829-1830	X
3.	Bolivar, Cong.(l.only 01N,Madison or Allegany Co.)	1861	nl.	-	X pb.soon
4.	Brookham, Cong.(Brooklyn Assn.)	by 1849	1848-1849	-	X
5.	Collins, Cong.(Oneida Assn.;pb.not Erie Co.;ps. *Collinsville in *West Turin, Lewis Co.)	by 1838	1837-1838	-	X
6.	Concord, P or C Ch.(Hudson Pby.)	by 1806	nl.	1803/1805-1814	X
7.	Depo, P or C Ch.(St.Lawrence Pby.;pb.St.Lawrence Co.)	by 1831	nl.	1830-1837/1838	X
8.	Eastern Allotment, Pres.(Albany Pby.)	by 1794	-	1788/1793-1794/1797	X
9.	Glendale, Cong.(l.only 01N,ps.Westchester or Queens Cos.)	1877	nl.	-	X pb.soon
10.	Jericho, Cong.(s.l.as "L.I." which suggests Long Island,f.Queens Co.,now Nassau Co.; however in West NY Assn.,which would not agree;pb.not Chenango or Clinton Cos.;nl.01T)	by 1853	1852-1853; cl.1853-1858	-	X
In 11.	Mohawk Indian Mission (location uncertain;pb.no ch.org.)	1762	nl.	nl.	X 1765
12.	Parrottville, Cong.(Albany Assn.)	1864	1865-1870	-	X
13.	Wells River, Cong.(ps.PA or VT;nl.01T)	by 1856	cl.1855-1856	-	X
14.	Westville, Cong.(West NY Assn.,pb.not Franklin or Otsego Cos.)	by 1849	1848-1850	-	X
15.	Wick, Cong.(l.only 01N)	1882	nl.	-	X pb.soon

PENNSYLVANIA (42)

ADAMS COUNTY (org.1800) (001) [PC]

ALLEGHENY COUNTY (org.1788) (003) [PW]

A		B	C	D	E	F
	1.	Braddock, First Cong.	1888(01,01N)	1888-1918	-	X
Sk	2.	Braddock, Jones Ave.Slavonic Cong.	1896(01)	1896-1966	-	UCC; X
We	3.	Braddock, Welsh Cong.(affl.WPW;nl.65,66)	1882	1880/1881-1882	-	X
Sk	4.	Duquense, Bethlehem Cong.	1901(3 sr)	1901-1978	-	Sch.II 1961-1978; NA by 1961-1980; CCCC 1981(j1980)-1993; X
GP	5.	Etna, First Cong. (f.United Evan.;f.l.Sharpsburg Station;s.l.Pittsburgh;Tr.from Evan.Prot.; Affl.EP 1925-1935;Tr.to Eng.Assn.1935)	1849(01,04)	1925-on	-	Sch.I 1961-1972; Sch.II 1972-on; NA by 1961-on
GP	6.	Homestead, St.Mark's Evan.Prot.(Tr.from Evan. Prot.;affl.EP 1925-1936;Tr.to ALC Luth.by 1933,j1939;1981 merged to St.John Luth.(1874) as St.John Mark Luth.(ELCA))	1890(01)	1925-1936	-	Tr.to Luth. (see text)
We	7.	Homestead, Welsh Cong.(affl.Welsh OH 1901-1902; Tr.to Eng.Assn.1902;nl.65)	1885(3 sr)	1888-1925	-	X
Sw	8.	McKeesport, Elim Swedish Cong.	1904(01)	1904-1912	-	X
GP	9.	McKeesport, Evan.Cong.(f.First Ger.United Evan. Prot.;Tr.from Evan.Prot.;did not j Cong.until 1927;Affl.EP 1925-1935;Tr.to Eng.Assn.1935)	1846(01,04)	1925-1969	-	Sch.II 1961-1969; NA by 1961-on
	10.	McKeesport, First Cong.(l.04 in Pittsburgh 2003-on)	1899(01,s.04) 1895(s.04)	1898-1968	-	Sch.II 1961-1968; NA by 1961-on
Sh	11.	Pittsburgh, Allegheny City Cong.(f.of Allegheny City (to 1906);f.Scotch Cong., Mr.Tassey's;moved from Pittsburgh to Allegheny City 1836/1846;unassod,later l.)	by 1834	IUWR:1834-1835/1844 1846-1847	-	X
We	12.	Pittsburgh, Arlington Ave.Cong.(f.Welsh Cong.of Birmingham,Southside;f.of Birmingham to 1872; pb.affl.WP & affl.WPW to 1886;affl.Welsh OH 1900-1908;Tr.to Eng.Assn.1908)	1868(3 sr) 1838(83)	1867-1956	-	X
GP	13.	Pittsburgh, Birmingham Cong.(f.United Evan.;f.of Birmingham to 1872;Tr.from Evan.Prot.;Affl.EP 1925-1935;Tr.to Eng.Assn.1935)	1846(01,s.09) 1845(s.09)	1925-on	-	Sch.I 1961-1964; UCC 1964-on

PENNSYLVANIA - ALLEGHENY COUNTY - continued

A		B	C	D	E	F
GP	14.	Pittsburgh, Bloomfield Cong.(f.Baum's Evan.;Tr. from Evan.Prot.;Affl.EP 1925-1935;Tr.to Eng. Assn.1935;Fed.to Franklin Park Meth.1965-1968;1968 merged to Franklin Park Meth.(1868, ab.Denny Meth.in 1938) as Bloomfield Com. United Meth.)	1873(01) 1863	1925-1967	-	Sch.I 1961-1962; UCC 1962-1967; Merged to Meth. (see text)
GP	15.	Pittsburgh, Duquense Heights Evan.Prot.Cong.(Tr. from Evan.Prot.;Affl.EP 1925-1935;Tr.to Eng. Assn.1935)	1900	1925-1999	-	UCC 1961-1999; withdrew
We	16.	Pittsburgh, Fifth Ave.Cong.(f.First Welsh Cong.; merger of #28 & #29;affl.WP & WPW to 1886;Tr. to Eng.Assn.1901;sv.AMA 1859-1860)	1836 M 1844(incp.)	WP:m.1838, j1839-1866; 1856-1859, 1862-1928	-	X 1924(65,83)
GP	17.	Pittsburgh, Manchester Evan.(Tr.from Evan.Prot.; Affl.EP 1926-1929;Tr.to Eng.Assn.1929)	1865(01)	1926-1949	-	X
GP	18.	Pittsburgh, Mount Washington Cong.(f.Com.;f.Ger. Evan.;Tr.from Evan.Prot.;Affl.EP 1925-1935; Tr.to Eng.Assn.1935;Affl.American Bapt.1972-bf.1977)	1873(01,04)	1925-1970	-	UCC 1961-1970; NA 1977-on
	19.	Pittsburgh, New Plymouth Cong.	1909(01)	1908-1912	-	X
	20.	Pittsburgh, Plymouth Cong.(f.First Cong.of Allegeheny City to 1906;f.Plymouth of Pittsburgh to 1873;affl.WPA 1860-1886;1906 majority of Ch.merged to Trinity Meth.Epis. (1830),minority r.)	1859 1853(s.01) r.1901 r.c.1907	1860-1905, 1907-1923	-	X
EW	21.	Pittsburgh, Puritan Cong.(f.Southside)	1892(4 sr) 1894(s.01)	1892-1953	-	X (alive 1967:65)
	22.	Pittsburgh, Second Cong.of Allegheny City (to 1906)	1889	1889-1891	-	X
Sk	23.	Pittsburgh, Slavonic Cong.(f.Evan.Slavonic of Allegheny City to 1906)	1901(01)	1901-1962	-	UCC 1961-1962; Merged to #24(q.v.)
GP	24.	Pittsburgh, Smithfield Evan.Prot.Cong.(Tr.from Evan.Prot.;Affl.EP 1925-1935;Tr.to Eng.Assn. 1935)	1782(01,09) by 1783(98)	1925-1962	-	UCC 1961-1962; Merged to form M1.(q.v.)
	24M1.	Pittsburgh, Smithfield Cong.United (merger of #23 & #24;Fed.to Smithfield Meth.(1788/1796) 1968-1994 as Smithfield United)	1962 M	1962-1994	-	UCC 1962-1994; Merged to form M2.(q.v.)
	24M2.	Pittsburgh, Smithfield United (merger of #24M1. & Smithfield Meth.(1788/1796))	1994 M	1994-on	-	UCC

A		B	C	D	E	F
		PENNSYLAVNIA - ALLEGHENY COUNTY - continued				
GP	25.	Pittsburgh, Spring Hill UCC (f.Indep.United;Tr. from Evan.Prot.;did not j Cong.until 1926; Affl.EP 1925-1942;Tr.to Eng.Assn.1942)	1895 1892(s.01) 1900(01) 1800[sic:09]	1925-on	-	UCC
Sw	26.	Pittsburgh, Swedish Cong.(bec.Stoneridge Evan. Covenant;moved to <u>Allison Park</u> 1962;EC:Rgn. 1918-1947,full 1947-on)	1886(01) 1892(01N)	1892-1949	-	Tr.to EC
	27.	Pittsburgh, Trinity Cong.	1907	1907-1910	-	X
We	28.	Pittsburgh, Welsh Cong.(Strict Cong.)	1828	nl.	-	1836 Merged to #29 to form #16(q.v.)
We	29.	Pittsburgh, Welsh Pres.(f.Welsh Cong.)	1824(CG;2 sr) r.1828(PR)	nl.	1828-1831	1836 Merged to #28 to form #16(q.v.)
GP	30.	Pittsburgh, West End UCC (f.Ger.Evan.;Tr.from Evan.Prot.;Affl.EP 1925-1935;Tr.to Eng.Assn. 1935)	1864(01) 1861	1925-on	-	UCC
	31.	Sharpsburg, Cong.	1887(01N)	1886/1887-1889	-	X
GP	32.	Tarentum, First Cong.(f.Evan.;Tr.from Evan. Prot.;Affl.EP 1925-1935;Tr.to Eng.Assn.1935)	1873(01,s.04) 1853(s.04) 1856(s.04) 1854	1925-1962	-	Sch.II 1961-1962; NA by 1961-2003; X
		ARMSTRONG COUNTY	(org.1800)	(005) [PW]		
We	1.	Bradys Bend, Welsh Cong.(f.Sugar Creek;affl.WP & WPW to 1886;sv.AMA 1861-1863)	1841(65,66) 1840(01)	WP:m.1838,by 1850-1866; 1864-1893	-	X 1894(65)
		BEAVER COUNTY	(org.1800)	(007) [PW]		
GP	1.	Beaver Falls, First Cong.(f.First Ger.Evan. Prot.;Tr.from Evan.Prot.;Affl.EP 1925-1935;Tr.to Eng.Assn.1935)	1888(3 sr)	1925-1964	-	Sch.II 1961-1964; NA 1961(j1962)-on
	2.	Rochester, First Cong.	1892(3 sr)	1892-1916	-	X
		BEDFORD COUNTY	(org.1771)	(009) [PW]		
		BERKS COUNTY	(org.1752)	(011) [PSE]		
We	1.	Reading, Free Welsh Cong.(Affl.WP(m.) & WPE (unassod.)to 1874;nl.65)	1869(66)	1869-1875	-	X
		BLAIR COUNTY	(org.1846)	(013) [PW]		
We	1.	Duncansville, Welsh Cong.(affl.WP;nl.65,68; *Allegheney Twn.)	by 1863	WP:j1863- ?	-	X pb.soon

A		B	C	D	E	F
		PENNSYLVANIA - BRADFORD COUNTY	(org.1810;f.Ontario to 1812)		(015) [PNE]	
	1.	Athens, First Pres.(f.Cong.;f.of Tioga Point; thrown out of OS Pby.1837;1858 merged to Pres.(1838,l.75:1838-1858OS),as Ref.(RCA, 1858-1870);Tr.to Pres.1870)	1812(CG;2 sr) 1813/1814(12) r.1823(PR;98) r.1829(CG;98) r.1858(Ref.)M r.1871(PR:28)	LAS:j1812: 1812-1821	j1821; 1821-1838OS,j1840, 1840-1858NS, 1870(j1871)-on	Merged; Tr.; Tr. Pres.
We	2.	Carbon Run, Welsh Cong.(affl.WPE to 1874,1875-1883;nl.65;*Leroy/*Franklin Twn.line)	1874	1873-1874, 1875-1883	-	X
	3.	East Smithfield, Fed.(f.Cong.of Smithfield;org. in Poultney,Rutland Co.,VT & immediately removed here;thrown out of OS Pby.1837;affl. NY 1867-1946,dual PA 1907/1911-1930/1934;Fed. to Bapt.(1810) & Disc.(1831) 1918-on)	1801(CG;3 sr)	LAS:j1811: 1811-1821; 1867-1965	j1821; 1821-1837	Sch.II 1961-1965 NA 1964/1965 (j1965)-on
	4.	LeRaysville, Cong.of Pike Twn.(f.of Wyalusing & Pike;f.of Orwell to 1816;thrown out of OS Pby.1837;affl.NY 1853-1926,dual PA 1907/1911-1926;lt.1855-1856;m.as lt.1866,but nl.;Fed.to Meth.(1816)1922-1926)	1803(CG) 1804(98) 1889[sic:01N]	LAS:j1810: 1810-1821; 1853(j1859)-1926	j1821; 1821-1837OS, 1839-1859NS	Merged to form #5 (q.v.)
	5.	LeRaysville, Cong.Com.(merger of #4 & Meth. (1816);affl.NY 1926-1927,dual PA 1926-1927; *Pike Twn.)	1926 M	1926-1990	-	Sch.I 1961-1962; UCC 1962-1990; Merged to form M. UCC
	5M.	LeRaysville, Dille Par.of LeRaysville & Pottersville,UCC (merger of #5 & #8;*Pike Twn.)	1990 M	1990-on	-	
We	6.	Neath, Welsh Cong.(f.Bradford Co.Welsh;Pike Twn.;LeRaysville PO;s.l.Warrensburg;South Warren;apparently CG when in OS;l.as prps.PA l.1881-1882;affl.WP & WPE to 1886;affl.NY (Eng.)1874-1927,dual PA(Welsh) 1874-1897;dual PA(Eng.)1907/1911-1927)	1833(CG;2 sr) 1831/1833(66) 1832(01,s.04) 1842(s.04) 1829 1872(s.01)	WP:m.1838,by 1842-1867; 1864-1866, 1867-on	1839-1844OS, 1845-1851OS	Sch.II 1961-on; NA 1963-1988
	7.	Orwell, Pres.(f.Cong.l.75:as branch of #12 1824-1828;divided 1827(98);Fed.1968-1970, unknown)	1828(CG) 1824(branch) r.1832/1837 (PR)	nl.	j1828; 1828-1970OS	X (ps.ab. by Fed.)
	8.	Pottersville, First Cong.(f.of Orwell Twn.;Rome PO;incor.lt.in NY 1863-1864,m.1866;affl.NY 1850-1927,dual PA 1907/1911-1927;lt.1853-1859)	1851(2 sr) 1849(s.98) 1850(?)	1850-1859, 1860-1905, 1907-1990	-	Sch.I 1961-1962; UCC 1962-1990; 1990 Merged to #5 (q.v.)
	9.	Springfield, Cong.(f.of Murrayfield)	by 1814	LAS:j1814: 1814-1820	-	X 1820
	10.	Springfield, Cong.(Affl.NY;lt.1844/1845-1846;lt. in NY:cl.1855-1858)	by 1839	1839(j1844)-1859	-	X

PENNSYLVANIA - BRADFORD COUNTY - continued

A		B	C	D	E	F
	11.	Towanda, First Pres.(41 says Pby.1832 requests ch.to adopt Pres.form,but 98 says was Pres.at start)	1825(CG;2 sr) 1828(28) 1825(pr.:28) r.1832/1837 (PR)	nl.	1825-onOS	Pres.
	12.	Troy, First Pres.(f.Cong.;f.of Troy & Canton)	1822(CG;98) r.1833(PR;98)	nl.	j1822; 1821-onOS	Pres.
	13.	Warren, Pres.(f.Cong.;f.of Orwell & Warren to 1828(1827:98),see #7);Warrenham PO;41 says Pby.1832 requests ch.to adopt Pres.form,but 98 says r.Pres.1824)	1815(CG;98) r.1832/1837 (PR) 1824(PR;98)	LAS:j1817: 1817-1821	j1821; 1821-1955OS	X
	14.	Wells, <u>Coryland</u> Pres.(l.Gillett PO;f.First Pres. C of C of Wells;f.of Wells & Columbia;min.say org.with Pres.name but no elders elected,98 says r.Pres.1832,but 41 says org.as Pres.;lt. 75:1832-1833;had an OS schism l.75:1842-1853OS,which 98 says was main ch.)	1821(CG;2 sr) r.1832(PR)	LAS:1821-1821	j1821; 1821-onNS	Pres.
	15.	West Warren, First Cong.(Warren;Rome PO;f.l. Nichols,Tioga Co.,NY PO;affl.NY 1883-1927, dual PA 1907/1911-1927)	1884(01,01N) 1887(s.01) 1888(05)	1883-1896, 1898-1908, 1909-1992	-	Sch.I 1961-1962; UCC 1962-1992; CCCC 1992-on
	16.	Wyalusing, Camptown Pres.(f.First Pres.;f.Cong.; irregular Fed.to U.Meth.1972-on,as Camptown Com.)	1793(PR;2 sr) r.1809(CG;28) r.1831(PR)	LAS:j1810: 1810-1821	j1821; 1821-onOS	Pres.
	17.	Wysox, Cong.C of C (f.of Wysox & Towanda;f.Lower Wysox;had elders by 1794,but considered itself CG;no elders at 1809 r.;98 says r. Pres.1830,but Cong.status of #18 puts that in doubt)	1791(CG;2 sr) r.1809(98) 1812(?)	LAS:j1812: 1812-1821	j1821; 1821-1830	Merged to form #18(q.v.)
	18.	Wysox, Pres.(f.Old Pres.;f.Cong.;merger of #17 & Pres.(1828,jPby.1828(1829:98),l.75:1828-1830);98 says Pres.at merger,but 41 says Pby. 1832 requests ch.to adopt Pres.form;1870 united to #19)	1830 M(CG;28) r.1832/1837 (PR) r.1870 M	nl.	j1830; 1830-onOS	Pres.
	19.	Wysox, Second Pres.(ps.Cong.forms)	1839(form unclear)	nl.	1839-1870NS	1870 merged to #18(q.v.)

BUCKS COUNTY (org.1682) (017) [PSE]

BUTLER COUNTY (org.1800) (019) [PW]

A		B	C	D	E	F
GP	1.	Saxonburg, Mem.Evan.(f.Ger.Evan.Prot.;Tr.from Evan.Prot.;ps.did not formally vote to j Cong.;Affl.EP 1925-1945;Tr.to Eng.Assn.1951; Tr.to Pres.as Mem.Pres.)	1835(s.98) 1837(2 sr) 1895(01) r.1955(PR)	1925-1945, 1951-1953	1955-on	Pres.

PENNSYLVANIA - CAMBRIA COUNTY (org.1804) (021) [PW]

We	1.	Ebensburg, First Cong.(f.First Indep.Cgn.;f. Ebenezer Chap.at Beulah sett.(moved 1804); s.l.Elimburgh(*Kennedy OH*);Enosburgh;had a branch at Zoar Chap.(c.1857-bf.1897);see also #2;Affl.WP & WPW to 1886;Tr.to Eng.Assn.1891)	1797(4 sr) 1796(sett.; 2 sr)	IUWR:1834-1835/1844 WP:m.1838, j1839-1866; 1856-1859, 1864-on	-	UCC
We	2.	Ebensburg, North Cong.(pb.a branch of #1 to 1866;Affl.WP(j1867) & WPW to 1886;Tr.to Eng. Assn.1901;nl.68;pb.*Cambria Twn.)	1830	1866-1913	-	X (1912:65)
We	3.	Ebensburg, South UCC (f.Bethany;affl.WP(j1867) & WPW to 1886;Tr.to Eng.Assn.1901;nl.68: *Cambria Twn.)	1865(65) 1866(s.01) 1867(s.01)	1866-on	-	UCC
We	4.	Hastings, Welsh Cong.(mnd.:66;nl.65,68)	?	nl.	-	X
We	5.	Johnstown, First Cong.(affl.WP & WPW to 1886;Tr. to Eng.Assn.1887/1892;affl.to both Eng.& Welsh 1896-1897/1901)	1854(3 sr)	WP:j1855-1866; 1856-1859, 1864-1963	-	Sch.II 1961-1963; NA 1962(j1963)-1978; X 1979
	6.	Johnstown, First Pres.(f.Eng.Cong.)	1820(CG;66) r.1832(PR)	nl.	1832-onOS	Pres.

CAMERON COUNTY (org.1858) (023) [PW]

CARBON COUNTY (org.1845) (025) [PNE]

We	1.	Audenried, Horeb Welsh Cong.(union to Welsh Bapt.at start;l.<u>Hazle Village</u>,<u>Luzerne Co.</u>PO 1959-1971;f.l.Horsh;nr.Jeansville,Luzerne Co.;had a branch at Silver Brook,*Kline Twn., Schuylkill Co.1867-?;pb.affl.WP;Affl.WPE to 1886;Tr.to Eng.Assn.1931;*Banks Twn.)	1865(3 sr) 1868(s.01)	1864-1971	-	Sch.I 1961-1971; pb.withdrew
We	2.	Junedale, UCC (f.Coleraine Cong.;f.Welsh Indep. Cong.of Coleraine;f.l.Beaver Meadows;f.l. Meadows;66:lt.Beaver Meadows (incor.l.in Luzerne Co.)1844-1896 & Junedale 1837-on; Affl.WP & WPE to 1886;Tr.to Eng.Assn.1931; *Banks Twn.)	1837(CG;2 sr) r.1838(2 sr) r.1844(66) 1840(s.01) 1850	WP:j1841-1866; 1864-1895, 1912-2000	-	X 1843(66); r.; UCC 1961-2000; X
EW	3.	Lansford, Eng.Cong.UCC (f.Second;f.l.Summit Hill to 1874;affl.NJ (Eng.)1882-1891;affl.WPE 1871-1872,1873-1874,1881-1886;dual Eng.& Welsh 1882-1887/1891;then l.only Eng.Assn.;f. *Maunch Chunk Twn.)	1872(98) 1870(s.01) r.1881(01,65)	1871-1872, 1873-1874, 1880-on	-	UCC

A		B	C	D	E	F
		PENNSYLVANIA - CARBON COUNTY - continued				
We	4.	Lansford, First Welsh Cong.(f.l.Ashton to 1876; f.l.Summit Hill to 1874;f.Old Mines of Carbon Co.:68;lt.1865-1866;lt.65:Lansford 1850-on, Summit Hill 1851-1864;Affl.WP & WPE to 1886; Tr.to Eng.Assn.1931;Sch.II assigned,Ch.did not vote;f.*Maunch Chunk Twn.)	1850(01,s.65) 1851(66,s.65) 1848(98)	WP:m.1853-1866; 1864-1962	-	Sch.II 1961-1962; X
We	5.	Nesquehoning, Welsh Cong.	by 1856(66)	m.WP:1856	-	X pb.soon
		CENTRE COUNTY (org.1800) (027) [PC]				
		CHESTER COUNTY (org.1682) (029) [PSE]				
We	1.	Malvern, <u>Great Valley</u> Pres.(Welsh Ch.;"The *Dyffryn Maur*";Tre'rdyffryn Ch.;f.l. Tredryffryn Twn.;bec.Eng.by 1761:68;had a NSd schism:1740(31) in Charleston Twn.,which bec.own ch.)	1710(CG) bf.1710(68) r.1714(PR;46)	nl.	j1714; OSd: 1745-1758; by 1773-onOS	Pres.
We	2.	Phoenixville, Welsh Cong.Mission (mnd.66;nl.65, 68)	?	nl.	-	X
		CLARION COUNTY (org.1839) (031) [PW]				
		CLEARFIELD COUNTY (org.1804) (033) [PW]				
We	1.	Brisbin, Welsh Cong.(f.l.Houtzdale;01 says ch. changed name (pb.& location) 1884;65 & 66 l. as two chs.:Brisbin 1876-1889 & Houtzdale 1867-1891;one Ch.:01 & 98;nl.68;affl.WPW to 1886)	1876(01,s.65) 1867(s.65) r.1888(01N)	1875-1894	-	X (1889 or 1891: 65;l.by 01S to 1897/1901)
Sw	2.	DuBois, Swedish Bethany Covenant Cong.(EC:Rgn. 1928-1945,full 1945-on)	1898(01)	1905-1937	-	Tr.to EC
Sk	3.	Philipsburg(Centre Co.PO), Cuba Cong.(Slovak;pb. at Cuba Mines;*Decatur Twn.)	1889(01) 1893(01N)	1889-1900	-	X
	4.	Winburne, Cong.(*Cooper Twn.)	1893(01N)	nl.	-	X pb.soon
		CLINTON COUNTY (org.1839) (035) [PC]				
Sw	1.	Renovo, Swedish Evan.Covenant Cong.(EC:Rgn.1917-1950,full 1950-1976)	1890(01N) 1884(s.01) 1895(s.01)	1890-1953	-	Tr.to EC; X
		COLUMBIA COUNTY (org.1813) (037) [PNE]				
We	1.	Bloomsburg, Welsh Cong.(mnd.:66;nl.65,68)	?	nl.	-	X by early 1870's
We	2.	Centralia, Welsh Cong.(pb.affl.WP;Affl.WPE to 1873,1874-1875;nl.65)	1867(66)	1868-1873, 1874-1875	-	X

PENNSYLVANIA - CRAWFORD COUNTY (org.1800) (039) [PW]

A	#	B	C	D	E	F
	1.	Cambridge Springs, First Cong.C of C of Cambridge (sv.AMA 1853-1860;affl.WPA 1851/1852-1886)	1851	1852-1860, 1862-1906	-	X
	2.	Centerville, First Cong.(sv.AMA 1858-1862;affl. WPA:1841/1842-1850/1852,1859/1862-1886;*Rome Twn.)	1841 r.1859	1842-1850, 1862-1928	-	X
	3.	Conneaut, Center Pres.(f.Center Rd.Cong.,f.First Cong.;s.l.Linesville PO;sv.AMA 1853-1856; affl.WPA 1841/1842-1844/1847;l.natl.only 1844/1845-1847;affl.OH 1852/1856-1907;l.01S (OH) 1857/1859-1860)	by 1830(CG) 1833 r.1907(PR)	1842-1847, 1852-1859, 1860-1862, 1863-1907	1829-1843/ 1844NS, 1907-1944	X
	4.	Evansburg, Cong.(f.of Conneaut;boro now Conneaut Lake;affl.WPA by 1842-1844/1847;l.natl.only 1844/1845-1847;*Sadsbury Twn.)	by 1838	1842-1847	1837-1839NS	X
	5.	Guys Mills, Cong.(f.Pres.& Cong.Soc.of Randolph Twn.;mixed form till r.;affl.NY 1839-1840; affl.WPA 1840-1886)	1825(mixed; 2 sr) r.1839(CG;09)	1839-1840; j1840; 1842-1850, 1852-1859, 1862-1965	1825-1839NS 1837-1839OS	UCC 1961-1965; Merged to form M.(q.v.)
	5M.	Guys Mills, United Ch.(merger of #5 & Meth. (1822,f.Pisgah Meth.of Hickory's Corner to 1871))	1965 M (09)	1965-1982	-	UCC 1965-1982; Tr.to EF Ch. 1982-on
	6.	Meadville, Park Cong.(Park Ave.;affl.WPA 1881-1886;majority of First Pres.(1799/1801,l.75: 1798/1802-onOS)	1881(01,01N)	1880-1994	-	UCC 1961-1994; NA 1994-on
	7.	North Shenango Twn., Cong.Soc.(org.by Abel Jackson of MC)	c.1820	nl.	-	X (by 1885, pb.by 1840)
	8.	Riceville, First Cong.(affl.NY 1856-1858,1860-1863;affl.WPA 1863-1886;*Bloomfield Twn.)	1856 1858(01,98)	1856-1858, 1860-1908, 1909-1940	-	X
	9.	Richmond, Cong.(mnd.:1885 98)	?	nl.	-	pb. X
	10.	Spartansburg, Cong.(affl.WPA 1875-1886;*Sparta Twn.)	1875(3 sr)	1875-1912	-	X
Sw	11.	Titusville, Swedish Cong.(EC:Rgn.1917-1949)	1893(01,01N)	1893-1949	-	s.EC; X
	12.	Townville, Cong.of Steuben Twn.(affl.WPA 1859/1862-1882;lt.1863-1865)	1839	1862-1882	-	X
	13.	Troy, Cong.(affl.NY 1839-1840;affl.WPA 1840-1850/1852)	by 1840	1839-1840; j1840; 1843-1850	-	X

CUMBERLAND COUNTY (org.1750) (041) [PC]

A		B	C	D	E	F
		PENNSYLVANIA - DAUPHIN COUNTY	(org.1785)	(043)	[PC]	
We	1.	Harrisburg, Welsh Cong.(not fully org.:66;pb. affl.WP;nl.65,68)	by 1865	1864-1866	-	X
We	2.	Williamstown, Welsh Cong.(j Eng.Assn.1894;nl.65)	1889	1895-1908	-	X
		DELAWARE COUNTY	(org.1789)	(045)	[PSE]	
	1.	Chester, First Cong.	1916	1917-1920	-	X
	2.	Glenolden, First Cong.(affl.NJ 1903-1905)	1902(s.01) 1903(s.04) 1906(s.04) 1887(s.01) 1889(s.01)	1903-1972	-	UCC 1961-1972; NA 1972 (j1973)-on
	3.	Glenolden, First Pres.(f.First Pres.of Darby to 1910;f.Second Pres.of Darby to 1855;f.Darby Pres.to 1854;Cong.of Darby to 1842)	1840(CG) r.1842(PR)	nl.	1840/1842 (j1842)-onNS	Pres.
		ELK COUNTY	(org.1843)	(047)	[PW]	
Sw	1.	Johnsonburg, Mission Covenant (Quay;EC:Rgn.1917-1927,full 1927-1988)	1890(01N)	1890-1893	-	Tr.to EC; X
	2.	Ridgway, First Pres.(f.First Cong.;l.unassod. 1879-1880;affl.WPA 1880-1886;union to First Pres.(1875,l.75:1875-1897(X 1897),1885-1897))	1880(CG;01N) 1882(incp.) r.1907(PR)	1879-1907	(see text) 1906-on	Pres.
Sw	3.	Ridgway, Swedish Evan.Covenant Cong.(affl.WPA 1885-1886;EC:Rgn.1917-1945,full 1945-on)	1884 1886(incp.) 1892(s.01)	1883-1908, 1909-1921	-	Tr.to EC
		ERIE COUNTY	(org.1800)	(049)	[PW]	
	1.	Albion, Cong.(affl.OH 1893-1906)	1893(01N) 1896(s.01)	1893-1913	-	X
	2.	Beaver Dam, Cong.of <u>Wayne Twn.</u>(affl.NY 1838-1840;affl.WPA 1840-1850/1852,1859/1863-1867; sv.AMA 1856-1858)	by 1839	1838-1840; j1840; 1842-1850, 1863-1867	-	X
	3.	Concord, Cong.(affl.NY 1839-1840;affl.WPA 1840-1844/1847;l.natl.only 1844/1845-1847)	by 1834	IUWR:1834-1835/1844; 1839-1840; j1840; 1842-1847	-	X
	4.	Concord, Cong.	1892(01N)	1893-1896	-	X
	5.	Corry, First Cong.(affl.WPA 1875-1886)	1875(01N) 1874(CoH) 1877(s.01)	1875-1912	-	X
	6.	Springfield, Cong.(applied to j an OH Pby.1821, turned down)	c.1821	nl.	(see text)	1823 Merged to form #7(q.v.)

A		B	C	D	E	F
		PENNSYLVANIA - ERIE COUNTY - continued				
	7.	Springfield, Pres.(f.Cong.;East Springfield; merger of #6 & Pres.(1806;l.75:1813-1814, 1818-1823);Fed.to Chr.(1825)1931/1933-1982 (CC to 1961,Sch.I 1961-1982))	1823 M (CG) r.1824(PR)	GAWR m.1845	1823-1975NS	withdrew & merged to Fed. (indep.)
	8.	Sterrettania, Cong.(f.McKean Pres.;f.union to Meth.Epis.;pb.affl.WPA 1859/1862-1867;sv. AMA 1856-1861;McKean Twn.)	by 1837(PR) r.1858(CG)	1862-1867	1836-1858NS	X
		FAYETTE COUNTY	(org.1783)	(051) [PW]		
		FOREST COUNTY	(org.1848)	(053) [PW]		
		FRANKLIN COUNTY	(org.1784)	(055) [PC]		
	1.	Monterey, Hawley Mem.Cong.(f.Blue Ridge Summit PO;affl.NJ 1893-1905;*Washington Twn.)	1892(01)	1893-1922	-	X
		FULTON COUNTY	(org.1850)	(057) [PW]		
		GREENE COUNTY	(org.1796)	(059) [PW]		
		HUNTINGDON COUNTY	(org.1787)	(061) [PW]		
We	1.	Dudley, Welsh Cong.(f.l.Broad Top;f.l.Broad Gap; affl.WP to 1871;nl.65;*Carbon Twn.)	by 1860(66) 1862(01)	WP:j1860-1866; 1864-1866, 1868-1871	-	X (by 1872:68)
		INDIANA COUNTY	(org.1803)	(063) [PW]		
pW	1.	Green Twn., Bethesda Ch.,Indep.& Pres.(nr.Pine Flats;two congregations sharing same bldg., one still alive 1880(98);John Williams, Indep.pastor)	1842(98: bldg.)	1846-1847	(see text) nl.	X unknown date
We	2.	Indiana, First Welsh Cong.(affl.NJ 1870-1871; Affl.WP 1871-1874;always Eng.Assns.;nl.65)	1870(01N)	1869-1874	-	X
We	3.	Indiana, Welsh Cong.(affl.WP;nl.65)	by 1838(66)	WP: m.1838, j1840-1841	-	X af.1841
We	4.	Northpoint, Welsh Cong.(affl.WP(m.)1869-1871;nl. 65;*West Mahoning Twn.)	1869	1868-1871	-	X
		JEFFERSON COUNTY	(org.1804)	(065) [PW]		
We	1.	Horatio, Welsh Cong.(Tr.to Eng.Assn.1901;*Young Twn.)	1889(65,s.01) 1887(s.01)	1889-1913	-	X (65:1912)
We	2.	Lindsey, Welsh Cong.(in Punxsutawney;Tr.to Eng. Assn.1901;lt.66)	1891(01,65) 1892(01N)	1892-1925	-	X (65:1924)

PENNSYLVANIA - JEFFERSON COUNTY - continued

A		B	C	D	E	F
	3.	Stanton, Cong.(reported as dropped 1865,but nl.; *Rose Twn.)	bf.1865	nl.	-	X 1865
We	4.	Walston Mines, Welsh Cong.(affl.WPW to 1886;nl. 65;*Young Twn.)	1885	1885-1893	-	X

JUNIATA COUNTY (org.1831) (067) [PC]

LACKAWANNA COUNTY (org.1878) (069) [PNE]

A		B	C	D	E	F
We	1.	Carbondale, First Cong.(f.l.Olyphant PO;affl.NY 1834-1841;affl.WP & WPE to 1885;affl.WYO 1885-1886;Tr.to Eng.Assn.1885)	1831(3 sr) 1832 1835(98) 1852	NYI: ? -1834; WP:m.1838, j1840-1866; 1834-1841, 1865-1941	-	X (65:1930)
	2.	Carbondale, Second Cong.(affl.NY 1842-1846)	1834	1842-1843, m.1843-1846	-	X
We	3	Jermyn, <u>Gibsonburg</u> Cong.(Gibsonville;f.of Rushdale to 1872;Affl.WP & WPE to 1875,1882-1886)	1866(66) 1865(98) r.1869(65) 1870 r.1910(01)	WP:j1866; 1866-1867, 1871-1880/ 1881, 1882-1909, 1910-1921	-	X (65:1920)
We	4.	Moscow, <u>Spring Brook</u> Cong.(f.l.Beach;f.l.Beach Pond;f.Beech Woods;f.New Wales Village;f.of T of Covington;moved Beachwood to Spring Brook 1869:68;Yostville PO;Affl.WP & WPE to 1886; affl.NY 1865-1866(dual);lt.1870-1871;Tr.to Eng.Assn.1931)	1834(union:66) 1833(pr.:68) r.1839(CG: 3 sr) r.1865(66) 1869(01)	WP:j1842- 1866; 1865-2003	-	UCC 1961-2003; withdrew
EW	5.	Old Forge, Nebo Cong.(f.l.Rendham)	1887(3 sr)	1886-on	-	Sch.I 1961-1963; UCC 1963-on
We	6.	Olyphant, Bethel Cong.(f.Bethel Calvinistic Meth.Union,Williams Union;affl.WP & WPE to 1874,1875-1886;Tr.to Eng.Assn.1931)	1859(union: 3 sr) 1847(s.01) r.1873(CG:66)	WP:m.1859- 1866; 1866-1874, 1875-1963	-	Sch.I 1961-1963; X (alive 1967:65)
We	7.	Scranton, Dr.Jones Mem.UCC (f.Welsh Cong.of <u>Providence Notch</u>;Hyde Park PO;Affl.WP & WPE to 1886;Tr.to Eng.Assn.1931)	1855(5 sr)	WP:m.1856- 1866; 1864-1982	-	UCC; Merged to form M.(q.v.)
EW	7M.	Scranton, Concord UCC (merger of #7 & #13; divided 1983,see #13)	1982 M	1982-2003	-	UCC 1982-2003; X
We	8.	Scranton, First Welsh Cong.of <u>Hyde Park</u> (Old Welsh Cong.;affl.WP & WPE to 1886;Tr.to Eng. Assn.1931)	1857(65,s.01) 1858(66) 1856(s.01)	WP:j1857- 1866; 1864-1947	-	Merged to form M.(q.v.)

A	B	C	D	E	F
	PENNSYLVANIA - LACKAWANNA COUNTY - continued				
EW 8M.	Scranton, Trinity Cong.(merger of #8,#12,& #14)	1947 M	1947-on	-	Sch.I 1961-1962; NA by 1961-1962; UCC 1962-on
We 9.	Scranton, First Welsh Cong.of Scranton (at Slocum Hollow;nl.65)	1854(66)	1856-1859, 1864-1866	-	X (af.1858:66)
We 10.	Scranton, Hyde Park Welsh Cong.at Iron Ore Mines (affl.WP;nl.65,68)	by 1843(66)	WP: 1843-af.1844	-	X (pb.1850's:66)
11.	Scranton, Pilgrim Cong.	1912	1912-1914	-	X
EW 12.	Scranton, Plymouth Cong.(f.Eng.Cong.of Hyde Park;affl.WPE to 1885;affl.WYO 1885-1886)	1882(3 sr)	1881-1947	-	Merged to #8 & #14;see #8M.
Nt	Scranton, Providence (12:early CT sett.here)				
EW 13.	Scranton, Puritan Cong.UCC (f.Fifth;1982 merged to #7,see #7M;1983 part r.)	1889(4 sr) r.1983	1889-1982; 1983-2000	-	UCC 1961-1982; Merged; see #7M.; r.; UCC 1983-2000; withdrew
We 14.	Scranton, Tabernacle Welsh Cong.(affl.WPE to 1886;Tr.to Eng.Assn.1931)	1886(3 sr)	1885-1947	-	Merged to #8 & #12;See #8M.
We 15.	Scranton, Welsh Ch.of Providence (denom.unclear; nl.68)	1837(66)	nl.	-	X pb.soon
16.	Taylor, Feltsville Cong.	1895(01N)	1895-1908	-	X
We 17.	Taylor, First Cong.UCC (f.l.Taylorville;Minookap PO;f.Lackawanna Twn.;nl.68;1872 division led to org.of Feltsville Welsh Calvinistic Meth. 1875;affl.WP(j1871) & WPE to 1878,1879-1886; dual Eng.Assn.1895-1896;Tr.to Eng.Assn.1931)	1868(66) 1870(65) 1871(s.01) 1872(s.01)	1870-1878, 1879-on	-	UCC
18.	Vandling, Cong.	1894(01N)	1894-1900	-	X
	LANCASTER COUNTY	(org.1729)	(071) [PC]		
We 1.	Columbia, Welsh Cong.(affl.WP;union to Welsh Calvinistic Meth.:68;nl.65)	by 1863	WP:j1863-1866; 1864-1867	-	X
2.	Mount Joy, Cong.(affl.NJ 1882-1883)	1882(01N)	1881-1883	-	X
	LAWRENCE COUNTY	(org.1849)	(073) [PW]		
Sw 1.	Bessemer, Swedish Cong.(bec.First Covenant;l.EC: full by 1895-on)	1890(01N)	1890-1891	-	Tr.to EC
We 2.	New Castle, First Cong.(affl.Welsh OH 1894-1930; Tr.to Eng.Assn.1930)	1894(5 sr) 1896(s.04)	1894-1964	-	Sch.II 1961-1964; NA by 1961-1974; X
	LEBANON COUNTY	(org.1813)	(075) [PC]		

A		B	C	D	E	F
		PENNSYLVANIA - LEHIGH COUNTY	(org.1812)	(077)	[PNE]	
	1.	Allentown, First Cong.	1920(01)	1920-1941	-	X
We	2.	Catasauqua, Bethel Welsh Cong.(affl.WPE to 1886)	1882(4 sr)	1882-1916	-	X (65:1915)
We	3.	Slatington, First Bethel Cong.(65:lt.as X c.1870 & r.1886;affl.WP & WPE 1886;Tr.to Eng.Assn. 1931;98:a division of 1846 mixed Welsh Ch.)	1852(2 sr) 1858(98) 1859(01) r.1883(01) 1886(65)	WP:m.1858, j1859-1866; 1864-on	-	Sch.I 1961-1962; UCC 1962-on
		LUZERNE COUNTY	(org.1786)	(079)	[PNE]	
We	1.	Alden, Welsh Cong.(affl.WPE to 1886;*Newport Twn.)	1884(2 sr)	1884-1893	-	X (65:1894)
	2.	Ashley, Cong.(affl.unclear)	1882	1882-1883	-	X
We	3.	Drifton, Welsh Cong.(f.l.Dritton;f.l.Dutton; affl.WPE (j1872) to 1886;nl.68;*Foster/ *Hazle Twn.line)	1870(2 sr) 1850	1870-1895	-	X (65:1896)
We	4.	Duryea, <u>Lawrence</u> Cong.(also l.prps.1894-1895)	1895(2 sr)	1895-1900	-	X
EW	5.	Edwardsville, Bethesda Cong.(affl.WYO 1885-1886)	1886(3 sr)	1885-1987	-	Sch.I 1961-1987; withdrew
We	6.	Edwardsville, Dr.Edwards Mem.Cong.(f.l.<u>Kingston</u>; pb.f.Ross Hill Welsh Cong.of Plymouth Twn. (98);pb.affl.WP;affl.WPE 1871-1886;Tr.to Eng. Assn.1931)	1868(5 sr) 1872(s.04)	1867-on	-	Sch.II 1961-on; NA by 1961-1988
	7.	Exeter, Cong.	1883	1887-1891	-	X
	Nt	Exeter (12:early CT sett.here)				
We	8.	Five Points, Belmont Welsh Cong.(Bellemont;affl. WP;in Schuylkill Co.in 66 & 68;*Black Creek Twn.)	1833(3 sr)	WP:m.1843-1866; 1864-1866	-	X (65:incor.: 1846)
We	9.	Glen Lyon, *Bryn Sion* Cong.(Mt.Zion;*Newport Twn.)	1884(65) 1887(01)	1888-1919	-	X (65:1915)
	10.	Hanover, Cong.(CT town org.;Ch.org.:Cappon)	m.1775(Cappon) 1769(town)	nl.	-	X
We	11.	Jeansville, Welsh Cong.(affl.WP (j1867)& WPE to 1886;*Hazle Twn.)	1866(3 sr)	1866-1893	-	X (65:1894)
	Nt	Kingston, Cong.(CT town org.;12:some early pr. from #31;Ch.ps.not fully org. until #13)	1769(town)	nl.	-	X
	12.	Kingston, Eng.Cong.	1886(01N)	nl.	-	X pb.soon
	13.	Kingston, First Pres.(f.Cong.;f.a branch of #30; 1972 merged to Meth.as C of C,Uniting (dual))	1819(CG;98) 1818 r.1823(PR) r.1972 M	LAS:1819-1821	j1821; 1821-onOS	Pres.(dual, see text)
We	14.	Laurel Run, Welsh Cong.(affl.WP (j1871)& WPE to 1872;nl.65)	1871	1870-1872	-	X

PENNSYLVANIA - LUZERNE COUNTY - continued

A		B	C	D	E	F
	15.	Nanticoke, Bethel Eng.Cong.C of C (Affl.WYO 1886)	1887(01,01N)	1886-2003	-	UCC 1961-2003; withdrew
We	16.	Nanticoke, First Welsh Cong.(f.United Soc.of Congregationalists & Calvinistic Methodists; l.WPE(unassod.)1871-1872;Affl.WPE 1874-1886)	1872(01) 1870(98) 1874(65,66)	1871-1872, 1873-1892	-	Merged to #17 to form #18(q.v.)
We	17.	Nanticoke, Moriah Cong.(affl.WPE 1886-1886)	1885(66) 1883(65) 1884(s.01) 1886(s.01) 1888	1886-1892	-	Merged to #16 to form #18(q.v.)
We	18.	Nanticoke, Moriah Cong.(merger of #16 & #17;Tr. to Eng.Assn.1931)	1892 M	1892-1955	-	X (65:1952)
We	19.	Parson Station, Zoar First Cong.,Welsh (f. Parsons Twn.,Baltimore Patch;f.of Wilkes-Barre in 66;affl.WPE to 1886)	1871(4 sr)	1872-1901, 1902-1909	-	X (65:1908)
	Nt	Pittston, Cong.(CT town org.;ps.no Ch.)	1769(town)			
We	20.	Pittston, First Welsh Cong.(f.of Pittston Ferry; to Welsh Hill:1860(68);affl.WP & WPE to 1886; Tr.to Eng.Assn.1931)	1847(3 sr) 1846(68) 1848(s.01) 1858(s.01)	WP:m.1846-1867; 1864-1866, 1867-1947	-	X (65:1946)
We	Nt	Plymouth, Avondale Welsh Cong.(l.only by 68: mnd.;pb.same as some other;Plymouth Twn.)				
	21.	Plymouth, Cong.(Ch.:98;pr.:12;ps.not fully org.)	1769(pr.& town)	nl.	-	X 1802
	22.	Plymouth, Elm St.Cong.(f.Puritan)	1891(01,01N)	1891-1958	-	NA by 1961-1961; X
We	23.	Plymouth, First Welsh Cong.(Welsh Indep.Ch.; Affl.WP & WPE to 1886;Tr.to Eng.Assn.1931; X 1977 & incor.l.1977-1987)	1857(65) 1855(98) 1853(68) r.1864(2 sr) 1874(04)	WP:m.1856, j1863-1866; 1864-1987	-	Sch.II 1961-1987; NA 1963-1977; X 1977
EW	24.	Plymouth, Mountain Top Cong.(nl.65)	1891(01N)	1891-1897	-	X
EW	25.	Plymouth, Pilgrim Cong.(affl.WYO 1885-1886)	1886(65,s.01) 1885(3 sr) 1884(2 sr) 1881(s.04)	1885-1965	-	Sch.II 1961-1965; NA by 1961-1990; CCCC 1960 (j1961)-on
We	26.	Sugarloaf, Tomhicken Cong.(affl.WPE to 1886;nl.65)	1883(01) 1884(01N)	1883-1893	-	X
We	27.	Wanamie, Cong.(Waunamie;f.of Newport Twn.to 1871;affl.WP (j1871) & WPE to 1886;nl.68)	1867(65) 1870(66,s.01) 1868(s.01)	1870-1912	-	X
EW	28.	Warrior Run, Cong.(Peeley PO;nl.65)	1888(3 sr)	1888-1904	-	X (65:1903)
EW	29.	West Pittston, First Cong.(f.Tabernacle;pb.affl. WPE 1882-1885;affl.WYO 1885-1886)	1883(01,65)	1882-on	-	UCC

A	B	C	D	E	F
	PENNSYLVANIA - LUZERNE COUNTY - continued				
EW 30.	Wilkes-Barre, Buttonwood Cong.of Hanover Twn.	1903(65) 1909(s.01) 1908(s.01)	1910-on	-	Sch.I
31.	Wilkes-Barre, First Pres.(f.of Wilkes Barre & Kingston to 1818/1819;f.Wyoming Cong.;sett. 1762-1763,1769,1770,from 1772;see also #13)	1772(CG;2 sr) 1762(14) 1769(town;31) 1803(covenant) r.1829(PR;28)	LAS:j1810: 1810-1821	j1821; 1821-onOS	Pres.
We 32.	Wilkes-Barre, First Welsh Cong.(Hill Side;affl. WP (j1869) & WPE to 1886;Tr.to Eng.Assn.1931; in 1868 bldg.)	1869(4 sr) 1872(s.01)	1868-1959	-	X (65:1955)
We 33.	Wilkes-Barre, Miner Cong.(f.l.Miner Mills;f. Miner Plains;f.Mill Plain;f.Mill Creek;Laurel Run PO(68);ps.affl.WP;affl.WPE(f.l.unassod.) 1871-1886;Tr.to Eng.Assn.1931;*Plains Twn.)	1869(3 sr) 1868(65) 1860	1870-on	-	UCC
EW 34.	Wilkes-Barre, Puritan Cong.(f.Third;affl.WYO 1885-1886)	1885(4 sr)	1885-1970	-	Sch.II 1961-1970; NA by 1961-on
We 35.	Wilkes-Barre, Second Welsh Cong.(f.Parish St.; f.Rolling Mill Hill;affl.WPE to 1886;Tr.to Eng.Assn.1931)	1883(4 sr) 1882(66)	1883-1963	-	Sch.II 1961-1963; NA by 1961-1997; withdrew
36.	Wilkes-Barre, Tabernacle Cong.	1894(01N)	1894-1900	-	X
We 37.	Wilkes-Barre, Welsh Cong.(ps.not fully org.;m. WP;nl.65,68)	by 1842(66)	WP:m.1842	-	X
	LYCOMING COUNTY	(org.1795)	(081) [PC]		
Nt	12: says there were two Cong.Chs.here 1812,one pb.#4, other unknown)				
1.	Huntersville, Cong.(*Mill Creek Twn.)	1905	1905-1908	-	X
2.	Muncy Creek Twn., Charleston & Judea Twn.(nr.; New England sett.;pb.not fully org.)	af.1771	nl.	-	X c.1778
3.	Picture Rocks, Cong.(affl.unclear;*Wolf Twn.)	1867(01N)	1866-1867	-	X
4.	Pine Twn., Indep.Ch.(English sett.,ps.not fully org.)	1806(98)	nl.	-	X 1815/1816
5.	Williamsport, Cong.(affl.NY (unassod.)1869-1870; affl.NJ 1869-1881)	1867	1869-1881	-	X
6.	Williamsport, Cong.	1903(01)	1903-1921	-	X
	MC KEAN COUNTY	(org.1804)	(083) [PW]		
1.	Bradford, Cong.(Littleton Village;see also #2)	1839(98)	nl.	-	X pb.soon
2.	Bradford, First Cong.(Eng.Cong.;affl.NY 1853-1872;lt.1853-1854,as if in NY;claim is as #1)	1854(98) 1839(claim)	1853-1872	-	X (1871:bldg.Tr. to Bradford Mtghse.Assn.)

PENNSYLVANIA - MC KEAN COUNTY - continued

A		B	C	D	E	F
	3.	Duke Center, <u>Prentiss Vale</u> Cong.(First Cong.Soc. of Duke Center & Prentiss Vale;f.First Cong. of Otto Twn.;affl.NY 1859-1883;sv.AMA 1858-1859)	1851 1879(incp.)	1859-1883	-	X (sold: 1884/1885)
	4.	Farmer's Valley, Cong.(affl.NY 1859-1872; *Keating Twn.)	1859	1859-1872	-	X
	5.	Kane, First Cong.(1967 merged to Pres.(1874,l.75:1874-1967),as First United Ch.,Pres.(l.75:1967-on))	1887(01,01N)	1886/1887-1967	(see text)	UCC 1961-1967; Merged, see text
	6.	Lafayette, First Cong.(affl.NY 1858-1872)	1858	1858-1872	-	X
	7.	Port Allegany, Cong.(*Liberty Twn.)	1877(98)	nl.	-	X pb.soon
	8.	Sergeant, Burrows Cong.	1919	1919-1924	-	X
	9.	Smethport, Cong.(f.incor.l.Smithport)	by 1839(CG) 1851(incp.:98)	1846-1847	1837/1838-1839NS, 1846(j1847)-1870NS	X

MERCER COUNTY (org.1800) (085) [PW]

A		B	C	D	E	F
We	1.	Farrell, First Cong.(f.of South Sharon to 1914; affl.Welsh OH 1903-1920;Tr.to Eng.Assn.1920; nl.66)	1902(3 sr)	1902-1954	-	Merged to #6(q.v.)
	2.	Greenville, Cong.(f.of West Greenville;Tr.Assn. 1843:98;affl.WPA 1840/1842-1859/1862,1864-1867;lt.1864-1865,s.as West Granville)	1835 1840(98) r.1849	Ash.?-1843; 1842(j1843)-1850, 1852-1859, 1864-1867	-	X (98:1863)
	3.	Mercer, Cong.(affl.WPA 1850/1852-1886)	1847(98)	1852-1859, 1862-1886/1887	-	X
	4.	Millbrook, Cong.of Worth Twn.(pb.affl.WPA 1859/1862-1867;lt.1864-1865)	1859 1855	1862-1867	-	X
	5.	Salem, Cong.(pb.affl.WPA 1850/1852-1859/1862)	c.1850	1852-1859	-	X
We	6.	Sharon, First Welsh Cong.(affl.OH (Eng.)1870-1873;affl.Welsh OH 1873-1904;Tr.to Eng.Assn. 1904;nl.66;in 1853 bldg.(68))	1854(3 sr)	1856-1859, 1868-1954	-	Merged to #1 to form M.(q.v.)
EW	6M.	Sharon, United Cong.of Sharon at Hickory Twn. (merger of #1 & #6)	1954 M 1953(65)	1954-1971	-	Sch.II 1961-1971; NA by 1961-1971; X
We	7.	Wheatland, Welsh Cong.(Wheatland Furnace;affl. Welsh OH 1873-1874,1875-1918;nl.65)	1872(3 sr)	1871-1872, 1873-1874, 1876-1919	-	X
	8.	Wilmington, Cong.(affl.WPA 1850/1852-1867,1874-1880)	1848	1852-1859, 1862-1867, 1874-1880	-	X

A		B	C	D	E	F
		PENNSYLVANIA - MIFFLIN COUNTY	(org.1789)	(087)	[PC]	
	1.	Milroy, White Mem.UCC (f.Free Chr.;SS:1883;had a branch at Siglerville 1884-1958,see Appendix II.#1;*Armagh Twn.)	1884(2 sr) 1885(01) r.1904(01)	1904(j1903)-on	-	UCC
		MONROE COUNTY	(org.1836)	(089)	[PNE]	
		MONTGOMERY COUNTY	(org.1784)	(091)	[PSE]	
	1.	Eagleville(PO), Lower Providence Pres.(f.l. Trooper PO;f.Norriton-Lower Providence Pres. to 1961;(f.Providence;f.New Providence);f. Norriton Schesin Ch.to 1730;f.Norriton Indep. & Dutch Ref.Cgn.of People to 1705;begun at Norriton (*East Norriton Twn.)as Dutch Ref.; nl.85;had Puritan pr.by c.1685;r.as mixed Puritan & Dutch Ref.in 1698;r.1705;two branches 1730-1741,other at Lower Providence; divided 1741 or 1752,Lower Providence Ch., Lower Providence Twn.(Indep.Pby.1741-1745, NSd 1745-1758);reunited 1757/1758;two branches;1758-1961,Lower Providence bec.main worship place;divided OS & NS 1838-1843,when NS broke off to form own ch.in Jeffersonville;divided again 1961 when Norriton branch broken off to form Norriton Pres.of Fairview Village,l.75:1961-on)	1660(Ref.:14) nl. 1678(land:46) 1679(98) r.1698(mixed: 28) r.1705(46) r.1714(14) r.1730(pb.PR: 46,95) r.1735(28) r.1758 M r.1961		sv.1710;j1714 Pres. Osd:1741-1758 (see text); by 1773-onOS; 1838(j1838)-1846/1848NS	
		MONTOUR COUNTY	(org.1850)	(093)	[PC]	
We	1.	Danville, Welsh Cong.(affl.WP & WPE to 1886;in 1835 bldg.:98)	by 1835(98) 1840(66)	WP:m.1838, j1840-1866; 1856-1859, 1864-1904	-	X (65:1903)
We	2.	Frosty Valley, Welsh Cong.(f.l.Valley (Twn.); pb.affl.WP;affl.WPE 1871-1881;nl.65,68)	1840	1868-1881	-	X
		NORTHAMPTON COUNTY	(org.1752)	(095)	[PNE]	
We	1.	Bangor, Bethel Welsh Cong.(East Bangor;affl.WPE to 1886;Tr.to Eng.Assn.1931)	1872(65,66) 1873(s.01) 1870	1872-1946	-	X (65:1945)
We	2.	Chapmansville, Welsh Cong.(pb.affl.WP;l.WPE (unassod.)1871-1872;*Chapman Boro;nl.65)	by 1869	1868-1872	-	X
We	3.	Slateford, Welsh Cong.(nl.65,66,68;affl.unclear; *Upper Mount Bethel Twn.)	by 1869	1868-1871	-	X

A		B	C	D	E	F
		PENNSYLVANIA - NORTHAMPTON COUNTY - continued				
We	4.	Wind Gap, Salem Welsh Cong.(Tr.to Eng.Assn.1931; l.incor.UCC late 1961-1962;j UCC 1962)	1891(4 sr)	1891-1962	-	Sch.I 1961;UCC late 1961-1962;Merged to form M1.(q.v.)
	4M1.	Wind Gap, Trinity Salem UCC (merger of #4 & Trinity E&R (Ref.,1903))	1962 M	1962-1968	-	UCC; Merged to form M2.(q.v.)
	4M2.	Wind Gap, Hope UCC (merger of #4M1. & St.Peter's UCC of Pen Argyl (Plainfield Twn.;Ref.,1750))	1968 M	1968-on	-	UCC
		NORTHUMBERLAND COUNTY (org.1772) (097) [PC:divided]				
We	1.	Mount Carmel, First Cong.UCC (affl.WP & WPE to 1886;Tr.to Eng.Assn.1887/1892;affl.PNE 1963-on;01 says lt.1962-1963,but not so)	1870(3 sr)	1870-on	-	UCC
We	2.	Mount Carmel, Welsh Cong.(affl.WP;nl.65,68)	by 1864(66)	WP:m.1864-1866; 1865-1866	-	X
We	3.	Shamokin, Mount Zion Welsh Cong.(affl.WP & WPE to 1886;Tr.to Eng.Assn.1931)	1864(01,66) c.1860(65)	WP:j1864-1866; 1864-on	-	UCC
		PERRY COUNTY (org.1820) (099) [PC]				
		PHILADELPHIA COUNTY (org.1682) (101) [PSE]				
Ar	1.	Philadelphia, Armenian Martyrs Cong.(moved to Havertown,*Haverford Twn.,Delaware Co.1963)	1920(01)	1920-on	-	UCC
Sw	Nt	Philadelphia, Assembly of Brethren (bec.Calvary Covenant 1944;EC:Rgn.1922-1946,full 1946-1954)	1883(06)	nl.	-	EC; X
	2.	Philadelphia, Bethany Cong.(affl.NJ 1898-1905)	1898	1898-1905	-	X
	3.	Philadelphia, Central Cong.(unassod.to 1867; affl.NY 1867-1868,NJ 1869-1905)	1864(4 sr) 1863	1863-1953	-	X
	4.	Philadelphia, Chr.Congregationalist (f.Indep. Pres.;12 says this bec.#9,but all others disagree;early dating here may be confused with #14,which would mean this did not exist)	by 1800(12)	nl.	-	X af.1810
	Nt	Philadelphia, Clearview Cong.Mission (m.Philadelphia Assn. 1913)	1909	nl.	-	X af.1913
Bl	5.	Philadelphia, Com.Cong.(m.1922:20;other dates from 01 necrology)	bf.1922 1929	nl.	-	X af.1931

PENNSYLVANIA - PHILADELPHIA COUNTY - continued

A	B	C	D	E	F
6.	Philadelphia, First Cong.(bec.Clinton St.Pres. 1842(98:CG:X);1878 merged to Immanuel Pres. ((1873:1.75:1873-1878)merger of Western Pres. (1835,1.75:1835-1873NS) & Third Dutch Ref. (RCA,1837-1891(85)),Dutch Ref.withdrew 1876 by court order) as Clinton St.-Immanuel Pres. 1.75:1878-1903)	1836(CG;46) r.1842(PR;46) 1844(98) r.1878 M	nl.	1840/1842 (j1842)-1903NS	X 1902
7.	Philadelphia, First Cong.(unassod.)	1862(12) 1864(01N)	1863-1868	-	X
8.	Philadelphia, First Cong.of <u>Germantown</u> (affl.NJ 1891-1905)	1888(3 sr)	1888-1965	-	Sch.I 1961-1962; Sch.II 1962-1965; NA 1965(j1966)-1978; x 1979
9.	Philadelphia, First Indep.Ch.(org.pastor ord.by Cong.;bec.Chambers St.Pres.1873;1898(28) merged to Wylie Mem.Pres.(f.First Ref.Pres. (1790(46,1798:28)),Ref.Pres.1790-1833;Ref. Pres.(Gen.Sy.)1833-1868;Indep.1868-1885; Pres.:j1885,1.75:1885-1898)as Chambers-Wylie Pres.;see #4)	1825(CG;28) 1826(46) 1820(98) r.1873(PR) r.1898 M	nl.	j1873; 1873-2000	X
10.	Philadelphia, First Pres.(First Ch.;Old Buttonwood;division of 1692 Pres.& Bapt.Ch.; always PR:30;two factions 1736-1738;1928 ab. Calvary Pres.(1853,1.75:1853-1929NS);1949 ab. Second Pres.(Whitefield Soc.;1743;Indep.Pby. 1743-1745;NSd:1745-1748;by 1773-1949OS)	1698(CG;3 sr) 1692 r.af.1706(PR) r.1928 M r.1949 M	nl.	j1706;OSd: 1745-1758; by 1773-onNS	Pres.
11.	Philadelphia, <u>Frankford</u> Cong.	1928	1928-2001	-	UCC; X
12.	Philadelphia, <u>Frankford</u> Trinity Cong.(affl.NJ 1874-1877)	1874	1874-1877	-	X
13.	Philadelphia, Hunting Park Ave.Cong,.	1888(01N)	nl.	-	X pb.soon
14.	Philadelphia, Indep.Tabernacle (Cong.in Pby.;Tr. as Second Dutch Ref.(RCA);Tr.as Seventh Pres.;1840 ab.Assembly Pres.(1838,1.75:1838-1839OS) as Seventh Pres.;1873(28) merged to Sixth Pres.(1814(28),1.75:1814/1818-1873OS) as Tabernacle Pres.;Fed.to Tabernacle UCC (1959,E&R,1.1959-1982,UCC)1959-1982;new org. 1816:98)	1804(CG;28) r.1816(Ref.: 3 sr) 1818(85) r.1819(PR: 3 sr) 1820 (85,s.28) r.1840 M r.1873 M	nl.	1809/1813-1814/1818; 1819/1824 (j1819)-1982OS	Merged to form M.
14M.	Philadelphia, Tabernacle United (merger of #14 & Tabernacle UCC (E&R,1959))	1982 M	1982-on	1982-on	UCC & Pres. [UCC count as E&R]

PENNSYLVANIA - PHILADELPHIA COUNTY - continued

A		B	C	D	E	F
	15.	Philadelphia, <u>Kensington</u> Cong.(affl.NJ 1895-1905)	1895(01,01N)	1895-on	-	UCC
	16.	Philadelphia, Lindley Cong.	1908	1908-1910	-	X
	17.	Philadelphia, Midvale Cong.	1905(01)	1905-1915	-	X
Nr	18.	Philadelphia, Norwegian Cong.(affl.unclear)	1891(01N)	1891-1896	-	X
	19.	Philadelphia, Park Cong.(affl.NJ 1893-1905)	1893(01,01N)	1893-1977	-	UCC; X
	20.	Philadelphia, Pilgrim Cong.(affl.NJ 1897-1905;in 1870/1872 bldg.)	1897(01)	1897-on	-	UCC
	21.	Philadelphia, Plymouth Cong.(affl.NY 1867-1868, NJ 1869-1877;Tr.to Pres.as Northwestern Pres.)	1866(CG,01N) r.1878(PR)	1866-1877	1878-1883	withdrew 1883
	22.	Philadelphia, Puritan Cong.	1906	1906-1910	-	X
	23.	Philadelphia, <u>Roxborough</u> Cong.(First Cong.of)	1910(01)	1910-1917	-	X
	24.	Philadelphia, Second Cong.(unassod.to 1867;affl. NY 1867-1868)	1864(01N)	1863-1869	-	X
	25.	Philadelphia, Snyder Ave.Cong.(affl.NJ 1897-1905)	1896(01,s.05) 1895(s.05)	1896-1965	-	Sch.I 1961-1963; Sch.II 1963-1965; CCCC 1963 (j1964)-on
	26.	Philadelphia, Union Cong.	1906(01)	1906-1912	-	X
We	27.	Philadelphia, Welsh Cong.(pb.affl.WP;affl.NJ 1871-1872;affl.WPE(unassod.)1871-1874;nl. 65,68)	1867	1866-1874	-	X

PIKE COUNTY (org.1814) (103) [PNE]

A		B	C	D	E	F
	1.	Wallenpaupack, Lackaway & Bozrah Plntns.Cong. (Lackawack;CT sett.here 1774-1779,some returned 1783, and later helped org.Wayne Co. #4;ps.not fully org.;*Palmyra Twn.)	1774(12)	nl.	-	X 1779 (services end)

POTTER COUNTY (org.1804) (105) [PC]

SCHUYLKILL COUNTY (org.1811) (107) [PSE:divided]

A		B	C	D	E	F
We	1.	Ashland, Welsh Cong.(First;affl.WP & WPE to 1886;Boro crosses into Columbia Co.)	1855(2 sr) 1854 1857 1844(98)	WP:m.1860-1866; 1864-1898, 1905-1908	-	X (65:1899)
We	2.	Coaldale, First Cong.(l.Summit Hill,Carbon Co.: 68;affl.WP(j1871) & WPE to 1886;Tr.to Eng. Assn.1887/1892;affl.PNE 1963-on)	1870(s.01,65) 1871(98) 1877(s.01)	1869-on	-	UCC (65:X:1930)
EW	3.	Coaldale, Second Cong.	1892(3 sr) 1877(s.01)	1892-1920	-	X (65:1919)

PENNSYLVANIA - SCHUYLKILL COUNTY - continued

A		B	C	D	E	F
EW	4.	Fountain Springs, Christ Cong.UCC (f.Second Cong.of Ashland;l.thrice:01N;affl.NJ (Eng.) 1885-1901;affl.WPE 1885-1886;dual Eng.& Welsh 1885-1887/1892;*Butler Twn.)	1885(2 sr) 1884(2 sr)	1885-1899, 1904-on	-	UCC
We	5.	Mahanoy City, First Cong.(f.Bethel Welsh Cong.; f.l.Mahanoy;affl.WP & WPE to 1886;Tr.to Eng. Assn.1931)	1863(3 sr) 1864(s.01) 1865(s.01)	WP:m.1864, j1866-1866; 1864-on	-	UCC
We	6.	Minersville, First Cong.(affl.WP & WPE to 1886; Tr.to Eng.Assn.1897/1910;in 1834 bldg.:98)	1832(3 sr) 1833(65) 1831(s.01) 1836(98)	WP:m.1838,by 1843-1866; 1856-1859, 1864-1965	-	Sch.II 1961-1965; NA 1962-1997; ps.withdrew
We	7.	Pottsville, Welsh Cong.(pb.pastor l.at Port Carbon:1860;affl.WP & WPE to 1886;lt.1886-1887:01S)	1833(2 sr) 1831(98) 1845(s.01) 1851(65)	WP:m.1838, j1839-1866; 1857-1858, 1864-1913	-	X (65:1912)
We	8.	Saint Clair, Welsh Cong.(f.Pottsville PO;affl.WP & WPE to 1876,1877-1886;1840 bldg.:98)	1835 1845(65)	WP:m.1842-1866; 1864-1876, 1877-1888, 1897-1898	-	X (65:1889)
We	9.	Shenandoah, First Cong.(affl.WP & WPE to 1886;in union with Welsh Calvinistic Meth.to 1869; Tr.to Eng.Assn.1897/1910;Sch.II assigned,Ch. did not vote)	1866(3 sr) 1865(pr.:68)	WP:j1866; 1866-1962	-	Sch.II 1961-1962; X
We	10.	Tamaqua, Welsh Cong.(affl.WP & WPE to 1886)	1842(65) 1847(66) 1848(98) 1867	WP:m.1848-1866; 1857-1859, 1865-1888	-	X (65:1889)

SNYDER COUNTY (org.1855) (109) [PC]

SOMERSET COUNTY (org.1795) (111) [PW]

SULLIVAN COUNTY (org.1847) (113) [PNE]

SUSQUEHANNA COUNTY (org.1810) (115) [PNE]

A		B	C	D	E	F
	1.	Ararat, First Pres.(Mt. Ararat Cong.)	1813(CG;98) 1849(Soc.) r.1874(PR;98)	LAS:1815-1821	j1821; 1821-1937NS	X
	2.	Brooklyn, Pres.(f.of Hopbottom to 1825;f.of Waterford to 1823;f.Second Cong.of Bridgewater to 1814;lt.75:1823-1824)	1810(CG;2 sr) r.1823(PR:2 sr)	LAS:j1810: 1810-1821	j1821; 1821-1948NS	X
	3.	Clifford, West Cong.	1918	1919-1928	-	X

PENNSYLVANIA – SUSQUEHANNA COUNTY – continued

A		B	C	D	E	F
We	4.	DeRiseville, Welsh Cong.(f.ReRiceville;Jackson Valley PO;affl.unclear;nl.65,66;*Middletown Twn.)	by 1866	1865–1867	–	X
	5.	Dundaff, Pres.(f.mixed Cong.& Pres.;pb.bec. gradually full Pres.;*Clifford Twn.)	1825(Soc.; mixed;98) 1853(incp.)	nl.	1824–1895NS	X
We	6.	Forest City, Bethany Welsh Cong.	1889(2 sr) 1891(65) 1893(s.01)	1889–1928	–	X
	7.	Forest Lake, Cong.(f.of Middletown to 1836;f. First Cong.C of C of Rush to 1814)	1811(CG;98)	LAS:j1811(98) 1811/1812–1821	j1821; 1821–1840/ 1842NS	X (af.1837:98)
	8.	Franklin Hill, Franklin Hill Pres.(Franklin Twn.;f.of Lawsville to 1835;f.Union Cong.of Lawsville & New Milford(with a branch at New Milford)to 1826)	1813(CG;98) r.1836(PR;98)	LAS:1815–1821	j1821; 1821–onNS	Pres.
	9.	Gibson, Pres.(f.Cong.& Pres.Ch.)	1818(mixed;98) r.1833(PR;98)	LAS:1819–1821	j1821; 1821–1937NS	X
	10.	Hallstead, First United Pres.(f.of Great Bend to 1874;f.Cong.;f.of Willingboro)	1790(CG;98) 1789(Soc.) 1791/1792(?) 1798(12) r.1802(98) r.1831(PR;98) 1830(PR;28)	SA:1803–1807/1809; LAS:j1815(98) 1814–1821	j1821; 1821–onNS	Pres.
	11.	Harford, First Cong.C of C(f.of Nine Partners; f.in *Nicholson Twn.to 1808;org.by New England people with a Pres.pastor; specifically CG on Pby.l.1834/1835–1836; affl.NY 1894–1927,dual PA:1907/1911–1927))	1800(PR;98) r.1803(CG) 1794(pr.)	SA:1803–1807/1809; LAS:j1810: 1810–1821; 1886/1887–on	j1821; 1821–1876NS (w1870)	Sch.I 1961–1967; UCC 1967–on
	12.	Jackson, Cong.(North Jackson;affl.NY 1839–1859)	1838(CG;98)	1839(j1843)–1859	j1859;1859–1867NS (w1868)	withdrew;pb. X
	13.	Liberty, Pres.(f.Cong.;Franklin Forks PO)	by 1836(CG;98) pb.r.af.1870 (PR)	nl.	1836–1910NS	X (incor.1883: 98)
	14.	Montrose, First Pres.(f.First Cong.of Bridgewater to 1824;in Montrose village 1816; j Pby.1826:28)	1810(CG;2 sr) r.1823(PR;2 sr)	LAS:j1810: 1810–1821	j1821; 1821–1823, 1824–onNS	Pres.

PENNSYLVANIA - SUSQUEHANNA COUNTY - continued

A		B	C	D	E	F
	15.	New Milford, First Pres.(f.First Cong.(in name: 28)to 1912;s.l.Milford;f.branch of #8 1813-1826;affl.NY 1839-1842,1844/1846-1848,1849-1850)	1826(CG;98) 1813(28) by 1821(41) r.1869(PR;98)	1839-1842/ 1845; j1844; 1846-1848, 1849-1850	j1826; 1826-1839NS; j1849; 1850-1990NS	X
	16.	Silver Lake, Silver Lake Pres.(Brackney PO;f. C of C of Silver Lake & Choconut;met in Choconut to 1833;inactive 1837-1847(98); incor.l.in NY by 75:1868-1870)	1816(CG;98) r.1847(PR;98)	LAS:1816-1821	j1821; 1821-1840/ 1842NS; 1847-1864OS; 1868-1870NS; 1871-on	Pres.
	17.	Springville, Pres.(min.& 41 imply Pres.in 1821, but later dual l.suggests a CG period; unassod.1857-1859)	1819(98) 1821(min.) ps.r.af.1859 (PR)	LAS:1821-1821; 1857-1859	j1821; 1821-1937NS	X
	18.	Susquehanna (PO), First Cong.of Oakland (affl. NY 1903-1933;dual PA 1907/1911-1930/1933)	1900	1900-1939	-	X
We	19.	Uniondale, Bethel Tabernacle Welsh Cong. (Clifford Twn.;f.Welsh Hill;f.l.Dundaff;f.l. South Gibson PO;affl.WP & WPE to 1886;Tr.to Eng.Assn.1897/1910)	1834(CG;98) 1835(65) 1869(incp.)	WP:j1840-1867; 1864-1866, 1867-on	1835-1860NS	Sch.I

TIOGA COUNTY (org.1804) (117) [PC]

A		B	C	D	E	F
We	1.	Antrim, Welsh Cong.(affl.WPE to 1886;*Duncan Twn.)	1874(4 sr)	1878-1893	-	X (65:1894)
We	2.	Arnot, Puritan Welsh Cong.(f.Bethel;affl.WPE 1881-1885;affl.WYO 1885-1886;Tr.to Eng.Assn. 1885;had a branch at Landrus:98;65 l.c1882-1885;*Bloss Twn.)	1877(2 sr) 1875(01) r.1886(01N) 1887(98) 1888(01)	1880/1881 (j1881)- 1882,1886/ 1887-1928	-	X
We	3.	Blossburg, Mount Zion Cong.(f.First;affl.WP & WPE to 1886;Tr.to Eng.Assn.1931;65 reverses close dates on this & #4,here we show consistent to 01;Sch.II l.assigned,Ch.did not vote)	1840(2 sr) 1841(65) 1842(01) r.1870(01)	WP:m.1845-1866; 1864-1962	-	Sch.II 1961-1962; X (pb.ch.65 shows as closed 1950)
EW	4.	Blossburg, Second Cong.(affl.WYO 1885-1886;see also #3)	1886(2 sr) 1887(incp.)	1885-1919	-	X (pb.ch.65 shows as closed 1921)
We	5.	Carbondale, Welsh Cong.of Carbondale of Tioga Co.(nl.65;Twn.unknown)	1874(66)	nl.	-	X pb.soon
We	6.	Charleston, Cherry Flat Welsh Cong.(Welsh Cgn.& Soc.;Welsh Settlement;f.l.Blossburg PO;f.l. Wellsboro PO;early affl.unclear;affl.WPE to 1886;Tr.to Eng.Assn.1897/1910)	1840(3 sr) 1839(s.01) r.1860	1864-1928	-	X (65:1927)

PENNSYLVANIA - TIOGA COUNTY - continued

A		B	C	D	E	F
	7.	Elkland, First Cong.	1832(2 sr) 1830(s.98)	nl.	-	1834 merged to #9 to form #8(q.v.)
	8.	Elkland, First Pres.of Elkland & Osceola (f. First Cong.;merger of #7 & #9;bec.Parkhurst Mem.;branch at Osceola from 1870/1871;divided 1910,when Osceola set off (l.75:1910-on))	1834 M(CG) r.1835(PR:98) r.1910	nl.	1834/1835-1852NS, 1845-onOS	Pres.
	9.	Elkland, Second Cong.at Beecher's Island (merged;r.as Pres.;Nelson PO;*Nelson Twn.)	1834(CG;98) r.1844(PR;98)	nl.	1843/1845 (j1844)-onNS	1834 merged to #7 to form #8; r.; Pres.
	10.	Knoxville, First Evan.Cong.(affl.NY 1866-1888; met at bldg.of Free Ch.Soc.(1851) to 1871; 1888 ab.by First Pres.Assn.(1888,l.75:1888-1940,X)	1867(01N,98) 1870(incp.)	1866-1867, 1868-1889	(see text)	Merged (see text)
	11.	Lawrenceville, Cong.(unassod.;s.suggested that this is First Pres.(1824,incp.1840,l.75:1830-1973NS,1870 ab.Second Pres.l.75:1860-1870OS), but pastoral lists disagree;*Lawrence Twn.)	pb.1862 1826(01,99) 1831(Shaw) 1840(98)	1862-1863, 1864-1867	(see text)	X
	12.	Mansfield, First Pres.of Richmond at Mansfield (f.C of C of Mansfield;f.of Richmond & Sullivan;1844 ab. Pres.of Sullivan (j1842, l.75:1841/1842-1844))	1832(CG) r.1834(PR) r.1844 M r.1870	nl.	1832-1840NS, 1841/1842-onNS	Pres.
We	13.	Morris Run, First Welsh Cgn.(f.Blossburg PO; affl.WP & WPE to 1886;*Hamilton Twn.)	1864(3 sr) 1867(incp.)	WP:j1864-1866; 1864-1894	-	X (65:1895;l.01S to 1897)

UNION COUNTY (org.1813) (119) [PC]

VENANGO COUNTY (org.1800) (121) [PW]

WARREN COUNTY (org.1800) (123) [PW]

A		B	C	D	E	F
	1.	Akeley, Gouldtown Cong.(s.l.Ackley;affl.NY 1873-1903;*Pine Grove Twn.)	1873(01N)	1873-1905	-	X
Sw	2.	Chandler's Valley, Swedish Cong.(*Sugar Grove Twn.)	1883(01)	1903-1928	-	X
	3.	Clarendon, Cong.(affl.NY 1884-1891)	1879(01) 1880(01N)	1885-1892	-	X
	4.	Columbus, Com.Cong.	1921 1926(s.01)	1923-on	-	UCC
	5.	Columbus, Cong.(unassod.)	by 1847	1846-1847	-	X
In	6.	Corydon, Seneca Indian Cong.(affl.NY 1852-1867; incor.lt.as if in NY 1855-1857;sv.Seneca tribe;ABCFM mission;bec.*Mead Twn.1965)	1853	1852-1867	-	X

PENNSYLVANIA - WARREN COUNTY - continued

A		B	C	D	E	F
	7.	Farmington, First Cong.(Lander PO;f.East Sugar Grove;f.First Pres. to 1839;98:f.Pres.,but not 1.75;f.at Pond's Corner,moved to Farmington Center 1878/1882;affl.NY,1.01S: 1844-1925)	1830(2 sr) 1831(s.01) r.1839(98) 1838(01)	(j1839:98) 1844/1845-1914	?-1838(98)	X (1.01S to 1925)
	8.	Lottsville, Cong.(f.Sacketsburg;*Freehold Twn.; 1825 merged to Sugar Grove, Pres.(1821),1.75: 1822-1823,1824-onOS)	1816(CG)	nl.	1817(j1820)-1825	1825 merged (see text)
	9.	Pine Grove, Cong.(affl.NY 1838-1840/1841,1842-1844/1845;1.natl.only 1844/1845-1847)	by 1831(CG)	1838-1840/1841,1842-1847	1830-1839OS	X
	10.	Spring Creek, Cong.(f.Brooks Hill;f.Spring Creek Station;also 1.as prps.1881-1882;affl.WPA 1882-1886;f.Fed.to Meth.Epis.(1886)1919-1939)	1882(01,04) 1881(s.04) r.1888(01)	1882-1886/1887, 1890-1898, 1899-1939	-	Merged to form M.(q.v.)
	10M.	Spring Creek, Cong.(merger of #10 & Meth.Epis. (1886))	1939 M	1939-on	-	Sch.II 1961-on; NA by 1961-on
	11.	Spring Creek, Hills Cong.	1907(01) 1904(s.01)	1907-1916	-	X
	12.	Sugar Grove, Cong.(majority of 1821 Pres.Ch.(see #8),but lost property in court case;affl.NY 1838-1840,1858-1890,1891-1894;affl.WPA 1840-1850/1852)	1838 r.1856	1838-1840; j1840; 1842-1850, 1858-1890, 1891-1894, 1904-1924	-	X
Sw	13.	Warren, Bethlehem Swedish Covenant Cong.(1t.01N; EC:Rgn.1922-1944,full 1944-on;1870 bldg.)	1891(2 sr) 1890(s.01) 1893(s.01N)	1891-1945	-	Tr.to EC
	14.	Warren, First Pres.(pr.1819(98),Pres.name but no elders elected to 1824)	by 1810(mixed) 1822(98) r.1829(CG;98) r.1836(PR;98)	nl.	1809-1815, 1816-onOS	Pres.
	15.	West Spring Creek, Cong.(f.1.Spring Creek;affl. NY 1856-1880;affl.WPA 1847-1850/1852,1881-1886;1t.1864-1866 in NY)	1847(3 sr) 1890(s.01)	1847-1850, 1856-1862, 1863-on	-	Sch.II 1961-on; NA by 1961-1971, 1972-on

WASHINGTON COUNTY (org.1781) (125) [PW]

A		B	C	D	E	F
Sk	1.	Charleroi, Bethlehem Cong.(f.1.Stockdale)	1900(01)	1903-1989	-	UCC; X

		B	C	D	E	F
		PENNSYLVANIA – WAYNE COUNTY (org.1798) (127) [PNE]				
	1.	Bethany, Bethany Pres.(f.Cong.;f.Dyberry;l.Pby., not natl.1818-1819;1818 full org.:98;f.a branch of #4)	c.1809(CG;45) 1810(Soc.) by 1813(12) 1814(?) r.1818(PR;98) r.1956	nl.	j1819; 1819-1937NS, 1956-on	Pres.
	Nt	Cushutunk, (Cong.settlement;pb.not fully org.; *Damascus Twn.)	1757	nl.	-	X af.1778 (scattered)
Gr	2.	Hawley, Ger.Cong.(Ger.Evan.;dual Ger.Evan.Synod: 1892-1894,1895-1904;affl.NY:1862-1868;NJ: 1869-1901;bec.St.Paul Luth.(l.GCLuth.(indep.) 1906-1913,GSLuth.1914(j1915)-on(ELCA)))	1853(98) 1857(Evan.Sy) 1860(01) 1867(01N,64)	1862-1899	-	(dual,see text); Tr.to Luth.(see text) (incor.X 1900:64)
	3.	Mount Pleasant, Pres.(f.Cong.;First Middle Ch.; Pleasant Mtn.PO)	1814(CG;98) r.1831(PR)	nl.	j1825; 1824-1831, 1832-1953NS	X
	4.	Salem, Pres.(f.Cong.of Salem & Palmyra;Palmyra in Pike Co.;see also #1;see also Pike Co.#1)	1805(CG) 1808(98) r.1832(PR)	LAS:j1811: 1811-1821	j1821; 1821-1920NS	X
	5.	Sterling, Pres.(f.Cong.(unassod.);Angels PO)	by 1835(CG) 1837(98) r.1871(PR)	1846-1847	1834-1843/ 1844NS, 1848-1849NS, 1871-1942	X
		WESTMORELAND COUNTY (org.1773) (129) [PW]				
We	1.	Irwin's Station, Union Welsh Cong.(pb.affl.WP; affl.WPW 1872-1886;nl.66;*North Huntingdon Twn.)	1869 r.1873(65)	1868-1871, 1872-1888	-	X (65:1889)
	2.	Monessen, Cong.	1905	1905-1908	-	X
		WYOMING COUNTY (org.1842) (131) [PNE]				
	1.	Windham, Braintrim & Windham Pres.(Black Walnut Bottom;f.Cong.;org.as "Half Way Covenant Pres.";lt.75H:1835-1853,as if two chs.,one in each town)	1796(see text) r.c.1806(CG) r.1829(PR)	LAS:j1810: 1810-1821	j1821; 1821-1853OS	X 1854
		YORK COUNTY (org.1749) (133) [PC]				
We	1.	Delta, Slate Hill Welsh Cong.(f.l.West Bangor; affl.WP & WPE to 1875,1877-1886;Tr.to Eng. Assn.1901;affl.NJ (66)1901- ? (nl.NJ:01S); lt.1870-1871;merged to Rehoboth Welsh Calvinistic Meth.Ch.(1854),which bec.Pres., l.75:1919-1969,X;Peach Bottom Twn.)	1856(65) 1855(s.01) 1854	WP:j1858-1866; 1856-1859, 1864-1875, 1877-1916	(see text)	Merged (65:1915), (see text)

PENNSYLVANIA - UNLOCATED CHURCHES (999)

A		B	C	D	E	F
	1.	Barberton, Cong.(l.only 01N)	1882(01N)	nl.	-	X pb.soon
We	2.	Cwmburia. Welsh Cong.(Cwmburla (68);nr.Five Points (which 68 says is in Schuylkill Co., but usually shown in Luzerne Co.);affl. unclear;nl.65,66)	by 1867	1866-1867	-	X
We	3.	Garnague, Welsh Cong.(Garangus;affl.unclear;nl. 65,66)	by 1865	1864-1866	-	X
	4.	Sturmerville, Cong.(l.only 01N)	1883(01N)	nl.	-	X; pb.soon

APPENDIX I. - UNITARIAN CHURCHES

A	B	C	D	E	F
		NEW JERSEY (34)			
		MIDDLESEX COUNTY (023)			
1.	New Brunswick, Unitar.	1846(15)	U:1845-1847	-	X "early"(15)
		UNION COUNTY (039)			
1.	Feltsville, Unitar.(*New Providence Twn.)	1849(15)	U:1849-1851	-	X af.1856(15)
		NEW YORK (36)			
		ALBANY COUNTY (001)			
1.	Albany, First Unitar.Soc.(Unity Ch.;also dual to Univ.1929-c.1938)	1842(3 sr) r.1895	U:1845-1851	-	UUA
		CAYUGA COUNTY (011)			
1.	Union Springs, Unitar.(*Springport;nl.90)	1838(15)	U:nl.	-	X af.1867(15)
		DUTCHESS COUNTY (027)			
1.	Fishkill, Unitar.(Fishkill Landing;nl.90,98; 1870 Merged to Ch.of Our Father,Unitar.of Newburgh,Orange Co.(1868,UUA))	1830(15)	U:1845-1848	-	1870 merged, see text
		ERIE COUNTY (029)			
1.	Buffalo, First Unitar.Cong.,Ch.of Our Father (1953 ab.First Grace Messiah Univ.(1831:81) as Unitar.Univ.;dual to 1961)	1831(3 sr) 1833(81) r.1953 M	U:1845-1851	-	UUA
		KINGS COUNTY (047)			
1.	New York City, Brooklyn, First Unitar.Cong.Soc., Ch.of Savior (f.of Brooklyn to 1898)	1833(03) 1834(15) r.1842(15,21)	U:1845-1851	-	UUA
		MADISON COUNTY (053)			
1.	Peterborough, Liberal Chr.Soc.(Free Ch.:90; *Smithfield)	1843(15)	U:nl.	-	X af.1871(15)
		MONROE COUNTY (055)			
1.	Rochester, First Unitar.Cong.Soc.	1829(s.03,15) 1841(3 sr)	U:1845-1851	-	UUA
		NEW YORK COUNTY (061)			
1.	New York City, Manhattan, First Cong.(Ch.of Divine Unity;Unitar.Ch.of All Souls;Indep. Cgn.;also a Ministry-at-Large,f.a branch of this Ch.from 1833,org.1836,X af.1858(15))	1819(3 sr)	U:1845-1851	-	UUA
2.	New York City, Manhattan, Indep.Soc.	1843(15)	U:1845-1846	-	X af.1845(15); af.1846(l.)

APPENDIX I. - UNITARIAN CHURCHES - NEW YORK - NEW YORK COUNTY - continued

A	B	C	D	E	F
3.	New York City, Manhattan, Second Cong.Unitar. (Ch.of Messiah,Unitar.;Com.Ch.of New York)	1825(3 sr) 1827(s.03) 1826(?)	U:1845-1851	-	UUA (incor.X 1919:21)
4.	New York City, Manhattan, Third Unitar.	1846(15)	U:1847-1848	-	X "early"(15)
	ONEIDA COUNTY (065)				
1.	Barneveld, Unitar.(f.Ref.Chr.of Trenton;f.of Trenton & Holland Patent;in Trenton;merger of #2 & Chr.(1806))	1811 M	U:1845-1851	-	UUA
2.	Trenton, United Prot.Relg.Soc.	1803(3 sr) 1804(incp.)	U:nl.	-	1811 Merged to form #2(q.v.);Soc.X 1811
3.	Utica, Unitar.(nl.90;ab.Ch.of Reconciliation, Univ.(1849) in 1926 as Ch.of Reconciliation, Unitar.Univ.(f.Fed.in form))	1823 r.1926 M	U:nl.	-	UUA
4.	Vernon Center, Unitar.Cong.	1841(15,98)	U:1845-1851	-	X af.1865(15)
	ONONDAGA COUNTY (067)				
1.	Syracuse, First Unitar.Cong.Soc.,Ch.of Messiah (May Mem.)	1838(3 sr)	U:1845-1851	-	UUA
	RENSSELAER COUNTY (083)				
1.	Troy, Unitar.	1845(15,98)	U:1845-1851	-	X af.1935(15)
	SCHUYLER COUNTY (097)				
1.	Jefferson, Unitar.(now *Watkins Glen,*Dix;nl.: 15)	by 1849	U:1849-1851	-	X 1853
2.	Searsburg, Unitar.(*Hector)	1849(15)	U:1849-1851	-	X af.1851(15)
	PENNSYLVANIA (42)				
	ALLEGHENY COUNTY (003)				
1.	Pittsburgh, Unitar.(r.1890)	1820(15)	U:nl.	-	X af.1838(15)
	CRAWFORD COUNTY (039)				
1.	Meadville, Indep.Cong.Unitar.	1825(03,15)	U:1845-1851	-	UUA
	DAUPHIN COUNTY (043)				
1.	Harrisburg, Unitar.	1829(15)	U:nl.	-	X "early"(15)
	NORTHUMBERLAND COUNTY (097)				
1.	Northumberland, Unitar.Ch.& Soc.at Joseph Priestly Mem.Chap.(Cgn.1.inactive 1952/1953-1962;the X;natl.UUA maintain Chap.as pr.pl. 1962-1988;new cgn.in bldg.:Unitar.Univ.Cgn.of Susquehanna Valley,org.1992 in Chap.,1.UUA 1992-on)	1794(03,15)	U:1846-1851	-	UUA; X (see text)
	PHILADELPHIA COUNTY (101)				
1.	Philadelphia, First Unitar.	1796(03,15)	U:1845-1851	-	UUA
	UNION COUNTY (119)				
1.	Lewisburg, Unitar.	1823(15)	U:nl.	-	X "early"(15)

APPENDIX II. - CONGREGATIONAL CHRISTIAN CHURCHES

A		B	C	D	E	F
		NEW JERSEY (34)				
		BERGEN COUNTY (003)				
	1.	Emerson, Com.(f.Cong.;f.Union;f.of Etna;SS:1897)	1899 1900(24)	1934-1946	-	Tr.to IFCA
	2.	Hasbrouck Heights, Com.UCC	1899	1955-on	-	UCC
	3.	Paramus, Cong.	1950	1950-on	-	UCC
	4.	Ridgefield, Moresemere Com.	1922	1942-on	-	UCC
		ESSEX COUNTY (013)				
	1.	Cedar Grove, Com.UCC	1947	1948-on	-	UCC
	2.	Livingston, Olivet UCC (f.Star Soc.:SS:1889;Fed. to Livingston Bapt.(1851)1978-on as Fed.)	r.1935(24) 1889(24)	1935-on	-	UCC
	3.	Short Hills, Com.Cong.(*Millburn Twn.)	1953	1953-on	-	UCC
		MIDDLESEX COUNTY (023)				
Bl	1.	New Brunswick, Rescue Mission (affl.AC)	1934	1935-1940	-	X
		MORRIS COUNTY (027)				
	1.	Brookside, Com.(f.Union Chap.to 1929;*Mendham Twn.)	1894	1954-on	-	UCC
	2.	Mountain Lakes, Com.(Tr.from RCA:1913-1955)	1913	1955-on	-	UCC
		UNION COUNTY (039)				
	1.	Summit, Christ Ch.(f.First Bapt.;Tr.from & dual to American Bapt.)	1876(23,98) 1884(incp.)	1958-on	-	UCC (dual, see text)
		NEW YORK (36)				
		ALBANY COUNTY (001)				
	1.	Potter Hollow, CC (ps.a lt.or branch of CC of Preston Hollow, Schoharie Co.(1842,f.Chr.; f.l.here);*Rensselaerville)	1897	1947-1953	-	X
		BRONX COUNTY (005)				
Sp	1.	New York City, Bronx, Bronx Spanish Evan.	1941(09)	1956-1965	-	UCC;Merged to form M.
Sp	1M.	New York City, Bronx, Bronx Spanish Evan.(merger of #1 & #4)	1965 M	1965-on	-	UCC
Bl	2.	New York City, Bronx, Ebenezer CC (affl.AC)	1936	1940-1941	-	X
	3.	New York City, Bronx, Edgehill Com.	1869	1939-on	-	UCC
Sp	4.	New York City, Bronx, United Evan.of Puerto Rico (affl.PR)	1959	1959-1965	-	UCC;Merged to #1 (q.v.)
		BROOME COUNTY (007)				
Ar	1.	Binghamton, Armenian Cong.	1917	1942-1954	-	X
		CHAUTAUQUA COUNTY (013)				

Nt Sherman, Com. - See main list #29M.

APPENDIX II. - CONGREGATIONAL CHRISTIAN CHURCHES - NEW YORK - continued

A		B	C	D	E	F
		CORTLAND COUNTY (023)				
	Nt	Preble, Com. - See main list #12M.				
		ERIE COUNTY (029)				
	1.	Amherst, Com.(f.l.Snyder;l.Buffalo;dual Disc.;f. dual Counc.Com.Chs.;f.in WNYCCC)	1915(22)	1943-on	-	UCC (dual, see text)
	2.	Boston, Com.(f.in WNYCCC;dual Counc.Com.Chs. 1943-1957,still l.there 1961)	1932 1832(22)	1943-1960	-	(dual); Merged to form M.
	2M.	Boston, Faith UCC (merger of #2 & St.Paul E&R (1834.r.1857);dual(to E&R)1960-1961;lt.1961-1963)	1960 M	1960-on	-	UCC
	3.	Buffalo, Oak Grove Com.(Oak Grove Ave.;f.in WNYCCC;f.Pres.)	1915(PR) r.1917(22,81)	1943-1945	1915-1917	ps. X
Bl	4.	Buffalo, Peoples Com.(f.dual Counc.Com.Chs.;f.in WNYCCC)	1938	1943-on	-	UCC
	5.	Cheektowaga, Union Rd.Com.(l.Buffalo;f.in WNYCCC)	1926 1922(22)	1943-on	-	UCC
	6.	Eggertsville, Eggertsville UCC (l.Buffalo; *Amherst)	1945	1944-on	-	UCC
	7.	Kenmore, Ch.of the Nativity,UCC (l.Buffalo; *Tonawanda)	1947	1946-on	-	UCC
	8.	Orchard Park, Windom Com.(l.Buffalo;f.dual Counc.Com.Chs.;f.in WNYCCC)	1930	1943-1951, 1958-on	-	UCC
		GENESEE COUNTY (037)				
	1.	Pembroke, United	1935(22)	1941-1968	-	UCC 1961-1968; Merged to form M.(q.v.)
	1M.	Pembroke, Com.(merger of #1 & Disc.(either Richville Chr.(1867) or First Chr.of North Pembroke (1849));dual Disc.;Corfu PO)	1968 M	1968-on	-	UCC (dual, see text)
		LIVINGSTON COUNTY (051)				
	1.	Conesus, Com.(Pilgrim;merger of f.Fed.of Univ. (1848,l.Univ.to 1948/1950) & unknown)	1921	1945-1976	-	UCC; X
		MONROE COUNTY (055)				
	1.	Rochester, Ridgeland Com.(f.in WNYCCC; *Henrietta)	1936	1943-1953	-	ps.withdrew
	2.	Webster, UCC Cong.	1953	1953-on	-	UCC
		NASSAU COUNTY (059)				
	1.	Manhasset, Cong.(*North Hempstead)	1941	1941-on	-	UCC
	2.	New Hyde Park, Com.Cong.(f.Lakeville Estates; *Hempstead)	1941	1944-on	-	UCC
bB	3.	South Hempstead, Cong.(bec.predominantly Black by 1975;*Hempstead)	1943	1944-on	-	UCC

APPENDIX II. - CONGREGATIONAL CHRISTIAN CHURCHES - NEW YORK - continued

A	B	C	D	E	F
	NEW YORK COUNTY (061)				
	1. New York City, Manhattan, C of C in General Council (sv. military personnel)	1943	1943-1962	-	UCC;Merged to main list #12 (q.v.)
	2. New York City, Manhattan, Judson Mem.Ch.(Tr.from & dual to American Bapt.)	1892	1952-on	-	UCC (dual, see text)
ER	3. New York City, Manhattan, Martha Mem.E&R (f.St. Paul Eng.Ref.;pr.:1879;dual 1958-1961;lt. 1961-1963)	1880 1886	1958-1965	-	UCC (dual, see text); Merged to main list #12M1.(q.v.)
bB	4. New York City, Manhattan, Riverside Ch.(Tr.from & dual to American Bapt.;f.Park Ave.Bapt.to 1930;f.Fifth Ave.Bapt.to 1922;f.Norfolk St. Bapt.to 1847;bec.multi-ethnic,largest group Black by 1993)	1841	1952-on	-	UCC (dual, see text)
Bl	5. New York City, Manhattan, Second Union CC (affl. AC to 1960;moved to <u>New York City</u>, <u>Bronx</u>, <u>Bronx Co.</u> 1977)	1942	1949-on	-	Sch.I 1961-1963; UCC 1963-on
Sp	6. New York City, Manhattan, United Evan.of Puerto Rico (affl.PR)	1960	1960-1965	-	UCC; X
	ONONDAGA COUNTY (067)				
	1. Syracuse, Taunton Mem.Ch.(Tr.to UPNA 1945-1958; <u>Taunton</u> PO;*Onondaga)	1927	1937-1945	1958-on	Pres.
	OSWEGO COUNTY (075)				
	Nt Constantia, Cong. - See main list #5M.				
	QUEENS COUNTY (081)				
	1. New York City, Queens, Elmhurst, Com.	1939	1946-1954	-	Merged to form M.
	1M. New York City, Queens, Elmhurst, Com.(merger of #1 & Com.Ref.of West Forest Hills (Ref.,E&R, 1930);dual to E&R:1954-1961;lt.1961-1963)	1954 M	1954-2002	-	UCC; X
Bl	2. New York City, Queens, Jamaica, Lemuel Haynes Cong.	1938(09)	1939-on	-	UCC
Bl	3. New York City, Queens, Saint Albans, Cong.	1954	1955-on	-	UCC
	SUFFOLK COUNTY (103)				
	1. Fishers Island, Union Chap.(affl.CT;*Southold)	1893	1958-on	-	Sch.I 1961; UCC late 1961-on
	2. Huntington, Cong.	1955	1955-on	-	UCC
	TOMPKINS COUNTY (109)				
	1. McLean, Com.UCC (1951 merger of Bapt.C of C (Bapt.Ch.Soc.of Moscow,1823),Univ.(1830/1832, l.Univ.to 1944/1947,& 1948/1950-1956) & Meth. Soc.(1830);Bapt.& Univ.Fed.1933-1951;all three Fed. 1920's-1933;*Groton)	1951 M	1960-on	-	UCC

APPENDIX II. - CONGREGATIONAL CHRISTIAN CHURCHES - NEW YORK - continued

A		B	C	D	E	F
		WYOMING COUNTY (121)				
Nt		Castile, United Com. - See main list #7M.				
		PENNSYLVANIA (42)				
		ALLEGHENY COUNTY (003) [PW]				
Sk	1.	McKeesport, SS.Cyril & Methodius Slovak Cong.	1939	1939-1949	-	X
Bl	2.	Pittsburgh, St.Paul-Emmanuel People's Cong.	1932	1944-1953	-	X
		BUCKS COUNTY (017) [PSE]				
	1.	Levittown, Plymouth Cong.(*Bristol Twn.)	1955	1955-1963	-	UCC; merged to form M1.
	1M1.	Fairless Hills, Ch.of Reformation (UCC;merger of #1 & Ch.of Reformation of Fairless Hills (E&R,1954/1955);*Falls Twn.)	1963 M	1963-1972	-	UCC; Merged to form M2.
	1M2.	Fairless Hills, Ch.of Reformation (UCC;merger of #1M1. & St.Stephens UCC of Levittown (E&R, 1959,*Bristol Twn.);*Falls Twn.)	1972 M	1972-1986	-	UCC; Merged to form M3.
	1M3	Levittown, United Chr.(merger of #1M2. & First Chr.of Lower Bucks Co.(Disc.,1954);*Bristol Twn.;dual Disc.)	1986 M	1986-on	-	UCC (dual, see text)
	2.	Newportville, CC (f.Pres.;*Bristol Twn.)	1930(mission: 46) 1941(Ch.:46) r.1956(CC)	1957-1986	1929-1956	UCC 1961-1983; Sch.II 1983-1986; withdrew
		LUZERNE COUNTY (079) [PNE]				
EW	1.	Wilkes-Barre, Lynwood Com.Cong.of Hanover Twn. (Sch.I l.incor,was Sch.II)	1932	1934-on	-	Sch.I 1961-1963; Sch.II 1963-on; NA 1982-on
		MIFFLIN COUNTY (087) [PC]				
	1.	Siglerville, Cong.(f.White Mem.;Milroy PO;f.a branch of main list #1 1884-1958:*Armagh Twn.)	1884(2 sr) 1886(s.99) 1890(s.04)	1958-1988	-	Sch.II 1961-1988; NA by 1961-1998; X or withdrew
		PHILADELPHIA COUNTY (101) [PSE]				
	1.	Philadelphia, First Chr.(f.Disc.;then Indep.)	1832	1947-1975	-	UCC; X

APPENDIX III. - UNITED CHURCH OF CHRIST CONGREGATIONS

NEW JERSEY (34)

A		B	C	D	E	F
		ATLANTIC COUNTY (001)				
	1.	Margate, Com.(f.Com.Bapt.;Tr.from & dual to American Bapt.)	1929 1928(23)	1974-on	-	UCC (dual, see text)
		BERGEN COUNTY (003)				
Ko	1.	Closter, Korean Gilbott Ch.(Westwood PO;also l. as prps.1997-1998)	1995	1998-on	-	UCC
Fl	Nt	Cresskill, Asian-American Ecumenical Fellowship UCC (l.as prps.2001-on)	-	nl.	-	UCC
		BURLINGTON COUNTY (005)				
	1.	Willingboro, Holy Trinity UCC (f.of Levittown; UCC,but l.as Sch.I as not fully org.;dual 1959-1960;lt.1962-1963)	1962	1959-on	-	Sch.I 1961; UCC late 1961-on
		CAMDEN COUNTY (007)				
	1.	Cherry Hill, Pilgrim UCC (f.l.Delaware Twn.;UCC but l.as Sch.I as not fully org.;lt.1961-1963)	1961	1959-1972	-	Sch.I 1961; UCC late 1961-1972; X
		ESSEX COUNTY (013)				
Bl	1.	East Orange, Park Ave.Chr.(Tr.from & dual to Disc.)	1900	1964-on	-	UCC (dual, see text)
AI	Nt	Maplewood, Asian Indian Ch.(l.as prps.1995-1996)	-	nl.	-	UCC; withdrew
Ch	2.	Montclair, Chinese Com.of Northern NJ, Upper Montclair (later moved to <u>Parsippany</u>,Morris Co.)	1974	1974-1977	-	UCC; withdrew
		MERCER COUNTY (021)				
	1.	Princeton, Christ Cgn.(f.Calvary Bapt.;Tr.from & dual to American Bapt.)	1955 r.1966	1966-on	-	UCC (dual, see text)
AI	Nt	Princeton, New Jersey Indian Ch.at Princeton (f.l.in <u>New Brunswick</u>,Middlesex Co. to 1996; l.as prps.1995-1999;m.01S:2002)	?	nl.	-	UCC
		MIDDLESEX COUNTY (023)				
	1.	East Brunswick, Cong.(f.UCC)	1969(01) 1968(s.01)	1968-on	-	UCC
	2.	Monroe Township, Rossmoor Com.(f.l.<u>Rossmoor</u>)	1967	1967-on	-	UCC

APPENDIX III. - UNITED CHURCH OF CHRIST CONGREGATIONS - NEW JERSEY - continued

A	B	C	D	E	F
	MONMOUTH COUNTY (025)				
	1. Holmdel, Com.UCC (merger of Holmdel Ref.(Old Brick Ref.,1825,f.Neversink(Navesink);f.of Middletown to 1867;f.a branch of Freehold & Middletown Ref.(1699,other branch in *Marlborough Twn.),RCA to 1968);& Second Bapt.of Middletown at Holmdel (f.Baptistown;(1837(23);Upper Mtghse.;f.a branch of #2 (claim 1667)1688/1705-1837));f.Fed.1936-1968)	1968 M	1968-on	-	UCC
	2. Middletown, Old First Ch.(f.First Bapt.;Lower Mtghse.;sett.1665(1667:23);had two branches 1688/1705-1837,see #1;Tr.from & dual to American Bapt.)	1668(98) 1688(09,23) 1667(pr.:23) 1793(incp.)	1963-on	-	UCC (dual, see text)
	MORRIS COUNTY (027)				
	1. Madison, Ecumenical Fellowship (f.Com.Chr.of Berkeley Heights, Union Co.to 1965;Tr.from & dual to Disc.)	1961	1964-1967	-	UCC (dual, see text); X
	OCEAN COUNTY (029)				
	1. Toms River, UCC (*Dover Twn.)	1980	1980-on	-	UCC
	PASSAIC COUNTY (031)				
Sp	1. Paterson, *Unida de Cristo la Familia* (f. Hispanic;also l.as prps.1993-1999)	1999	1999-on	-	UCC
	2. Wayne, Packanack Com.(f.in Counc.Com.Chs.)	1928	1972-on	-	UCC
	SOMERSET COUNTY (035)				
Hu	1. Manville, Magyar Ref.(affl.CAL;Tr.from RCA 1915-1971)	1915	1971-on	-	UCC
	WARREN COUNTY (041)				
	1. Hackettstown, Covenant Ch.(Panther Valley Ecumenical Ministry;dual (s.l.Fed.) to Pres., Meth.,& Epis.;*Allamauchy Twn.)	1970	1971-on	1970-on	UCC & Pres.(& other dual, see text)
	NEW YORK (36)				
	ALBANY COUNTY (001)				
Bl	Nt Albany, Antioch Fellowship Chr. Center (m.2003; moved to Rensselaer,Rensselaer Co., 2004)	?	nl.	-	UCC
	BRONX COUNTY (005)				
Bl	1. New York City, Bronx, Christ UCC	1966(09)	1966-on	-	UCC
Ko	2. New York City, Bronx, Grace UCC	1999	1999-on	-	UCC
Sp	3. New York City, Bronx, Revival Chr.	1992	1992-on	-	UCC
	CAYUGA COUNTY (011)				
	Nt Union Springs, Trinity UCC - See main list #23M.				

APPENDIX III. - UNITED CHURCH OF CHRIST CONGREGATIONS - NEW YORK - continued

A		B	C	D	E	F
		KINGS COUNTY (047)				
Bl	1.	New York City, Brooklyn, Bethesda Bapt.(Tr.from & dual to Bapt.)	? r.1965	1965-on	-	UCC (dual, see text)
Ha	2.	New York City, Brooklyn, The Ch.of the Lord	1977	1982-on	-	UCC
Bl	3.	New York City, Brooklyn, Safe Haven Ministries UCC (1.01:Queens Co.:2003-on)	1995	2002-on	-	UCC
		MADISON COUNTY (053)				
	1.	Fyler, Com.(Kirkville,Onondaga Co.,PO;*Sullivan)	by 1963	1963-1984	-	UCC; withdrew
		MONROE COUNTY (055)				
	1.	Fairport, Mountain Rise UCC in Perinton (in Perinton;f.l.Rochester)	1963	1962-on	-	UCC
	2.	Rochester, Com.Chr.(f.Columbus Ave.Chr.;f.C of C (Disc.);Tr.from & dual to Disc.;moved to *Chili in 1977)	1897 r.1977	1977-on	-	UCC (dual, see text)
Bl	3.	Rochester, Ch.of the Covenant (f.in Henrietta to 1987(l.1989))	1982	1982-on	-	UCC
	4.	Rochester, House Ch.(f.dual American Bapt.)	1973 1972(pr.)	1973-1994	-	UCC (f.dual, see text); X
		NASSAU COUNTY (059)				
	1.	Long Beach, People's Ch.	1920 1921(22)	1963-on	-	UCC
	2.	Syosset, Com.(f.Union to 1929;f.Free Ch.to 1908; l.in Counc.Com.Chs.1961,ch.says not j;*Oyster Bay)	1860(99)	1962-on	-	UCC
Bl	3.	Westbury, Com.(*North Hempstead)	1966 r.1978	1978-on	-	UCC
AI	4.	Williston Park, Ch.of South India Jubilee Mem. Ch.of New York (s.Glen Oaks,Queens Co.,PO; *North Hempstead)	1996	2003-on	-	UCC
		NEW YORK COUNTY (061)				
Ch	1.	New York City, Manhattan, Chinese Com.(f. Mandarin Chr.;dual RCA 1985-on)	1969(09)	1969-on	-	UCC (dual, see text)
Sp	2.	New York City, Manhattan, *Iglesia San Romero de las Americas* (*Iglesia del Pueblo*)	2000	2003-on	-	UCC
Bl	3.	New York City, Manhattan, Ch.of the Living Hope (f.indep.)	1964 r.1999	1999-on	-	UCC
Ch	4.	New York City, Manhattan, Ch.of the Living Lord	? r.1979	1979-on	-	UCC
Bl	5.	New York City, Manhattan, Philadelphia Bapt. C of C (pb.Tr.from & dual to Bapt.)	? r.1993	1993-on	-	UCC (dual, see text)
	6.	New York City, Manhattan, Rauschenbusch Mem.(pb. incor.l.dual)	1982	1982-on	-	UCC
Bl	7.	New York City, Manhattan, Ch.of the Resurrection	1960	1963-on	-	UCC

APPENDIX III. - UNITED CHURCH OF CHRIST CONGREGATIONS - NEW YORK - continued

A		B	C	D	E	F
		ONEIDA COUNTY (065)				
	1.	McConnellsville, Com.(f.in Counc.Com.Chs.; *Annsville)	bf.1961 r.1966	1966-on	-	UCC
		ONONDAGA COUNTY (067)				
	1.	Liverpool, Bayberry UCC (l.Syracuse;*Clay)	1961	1961-on	-	UCC
	2.	Syracuse, Fairmount Com.(*Camillus)	1941	1965-on	-	UCC
		ONTARIO COUNTY (069)				
	1.	Canandaigua, Cheshire Com.(in Canandaigua)	by 1966	1966-1969	-	UCC; X
	Nt	Geneva, Covenant UCC (l.as prps.1993-1994)	-	nl.	-	UCC; X
		ORANGE COUNTY (071)				
	1.	Howells, UCC at New Vernon (*Mount Hope)	1990	1990-on	-	UCC
		QUEENS COUNTY (081)				
Sp	1.	New York City, Queens, Corona, *Iglesia Cristiana Lapalabra* (f.*Basilea*;j 1994)	1992(99) 1994(01)	1994-on	-	UCC
Tm	2.	New York City, Queens, Elmhurst, Christava Tamil Koil (in Richmond Hill;j1992)	1976(pr.) 1991(01)	1991-on	-	UCC
Sp	Nt	New York City, Queens, Elmhurst, *Iglesia Cristiana el Remarante* (m.2003)	?	nl.	-	UCC
Ko	3.	New York City, Queens, Flushing, Hahn Korean	1987	1987-on	-	UCC
	4.	New York City, Queens, Queens Village, Hollis Woods Com.(Tr.from & dual to American Bapt.)	1946	1990-on	-	UCC (dual, see text)
Fl	5.	New York City, Queens, Woodhaven, Filipino American UCC (in Richmond Hill)	1993	1993-on	-	UCC
AI	6.	New York City, Queens, Woodhaven, Malayalam Cong.	1997	1997-on	-	UCC
		RICHMOND COUNTY (085)				
Ch	1.	New York City, Staten Island, Richmond, Grace Chr.of Staten Island (dual to RCA 1990-1992)	1989(01) 1990(85) 1985(pr.)	1989-1992	-	UCC (dual, see text); Tr.to RCA
	Nt	New York City, Staten Island, Westerleigh, Immanuel Union - See main list #9.				
		SUFFOLK COUNTY (103)				
	1.	Copiague, United Chr.(ps.withdrew;*Babylon)	1980	1980-1999	-	UCC; X (see text)
	2.	Middle Island, UCC (*Brookhaven)	1982	1982-on	-	UCC
	3.	Rocky Point, UCC (*Brookhaven)	1964	1964-1980	-	UCC; X
		WESTCHESTER COUNTY (119)				
AI	1.	Bronxville, Ch.of South India Cgn.of Hudson Valley	? r.1999	1999-on	-	UCC

APPENDIX III. - UNITED CHURCH OF CHRIST CONGREGATIONS - continued

PENNSYLVANIA (42)

A		B	C	D	E	F
		ALLEGHENY COUNTY (003) [PW]				
Bl	1.	Pittsburgh, Com.of Reconciliation (l.as Multi-Ethnic with Black largest group by 1993;dual Pres.,UMeth.,American Bapt.& Disc.)	1982	1982-on	1982-on	UCC & Pres. (& other dual, see text)
	Nt	Pittsburgh, Open Arms UCC (l.as prps.2001-2002, dual Disc.)	-	nl.	-	UCC (dual, see text); X
		BEAVER COUNTY (007) [PW]				
Hu	1.	Beaver Falls, Third Ave.Hungarian Ref.(f.Third Ave.Pres.,f.Magyar Pres.,f.First Hungarian Ref.;Tr.Pres.to UCC;affl.CAL)	1907	1993-on	1910-1993	UCC
		BLAIR COUNTY (013) [PW]				
	Nt	Altoona, Faith UCC (a 2001 merger of existing UCC chs.,incor.l.as prps.UCC:2000-2001;2001 merger of First UCC (f.Christ Ref.,1863), Salem UCC (Ref.,1910) & Trinity Ref.(1888); l.full 2001-on;UCC)	-	(see text)	-	UCC
		CHESTER COUNTY (029) [PSE]				
	1.	West Chester, East Goshen UCC (East Goshen Twn.)	1971	1971-on	-	UCC
		CUMBERLAND COUNTY (041) [PC]				
	1.	Camp Hill, Chap.Hill UCC (*East Pennsboro Twn.)	1963	1962-1979	-	UCC;Merged to form M.
	1M.	Camp Hill, Chap.Hill UCC (merger of #1 & St. Matthews Ref.of Enola (1907);*East Pennsboro Twn.)	1979 M	1979-on	-	UCC
		DAUPHIN COUNTY (043) [PC]				
Bl	1.	Harrisburg, Harambee UCC (l.as prps.1993-1996)	1996	1996-on	-	UCC
		LANCASTER COUNTY (071) [PC]				
	1.	Lancaster, Disc.United Com.(f.in Millersville to 2001;also l.prps.2000-2001;dual Disc.;pb. *Manor Twn.)	2001	2001-on	-	UCC (dual, see text)
		LEHIGH COUNTY (077) [PNE]				
	1.	Macungie, Shepherd Oaks UCC (*Lower Macungie Twn.;also l.as prps.1988-1990)	1991	1991-1998	-	UCC; X
		MONTGOMERY COUNTY (091) [PSE]				
GS	1.	Lansdale, Schwenkfelder (Tr.from & dual to Schwenkfelder)	1916	1963-1986, 1992-on	-	UCC 1963-1986,1992-on;(dual,see text)
Bl	2.	Norristown, Chr.Network Outreach (also lt.as prps.2001-2002)	1987	1996-on	-	UCC
GS	3.	Norristown, Schwenkfelder (Tr.from & dual to Schwenkfelder)	1904	1965-1997	-	UCC (dual,see text); Merged to form M.

APPENDIX III. - UNITED CHURCH OF CHRIST CONGREGATIONS - PENNSYLVANIA - MONTGOMERY COUNTY - continued

A		B	C	D	E	F
	3M.	East Norriton, Olivet Schwenkfelder UCC (merger of #3 & Olivet Ref.of Norristown (1911/1915); f.l.Norristown;dual Schwenkfelder)	1997 M	1997-on	-	UCC (dual, see text)
		NORTHAMPTON COUNTY	(095)	[PNE]		
Sp	Nt	Bethlehem, First Hispanic Cong.(m.2003)	?	nl.	-	UCC
		PHILADELPHIA COUNTY	(101)	[PSE]		
Bl	1.	Philadelphia, Antioch UCC	1962	1962-1969	-	UCC; X
Sp	2.	Philadelphia, Bethel UCC	1980	1980-on	-	UCC
Bl	Nt	Philadelphia, Fellowship Tabernacle (m.2003)	?	nl.	-	UCC
GS bB	3.	Philadelphia, First Schwenkfelder (Tr.from & dual to Schwenkfelder;bec.predominantly Black by 1973)	1895(01, mission) 1898(Ch.)	1965-1970	-	UCC (dual,see text); Tr.to Schwenkfelder
AI	4.	Philadelphia, Grace Trinity UCC (lt.as prps. 2000-2003,prps.l.Newton,Bucks Co.2002-2003)	1996	1996-on	-	UCC
Bl	5.	Philadelphia, Harold O. Davis Mem.Bapt.(Tr.from & dual to Natl.Bapt.Conv.Inc.)	1974 r.1976	1976-on	-	UCC (dual, see text)
Bl	Nt	Philadelphia, Healing Streams Ministries (f. Oasis Family Worship Center;l.as prps.2003-on)	?	nl.	-	UCC
Bl	6.	Philadelphia, Wynnefield UCC	1978	1978-1994	-	UCC; X

APPENDIX IV. - CONTINUING CONGREGATIONAL CHRISTIAN CHURCHES

A	B	C	D	E	F
	NEW JERSEY (34)				
	HUNTERDON COUNTY (019)				
	1. Stockton, Sandy Ridge Com.(f.Bapt.;Tr.from Bapt.;*Delaware Twn.)	1818(23,04)	-	-	NA 1991(j1992)-1998; withdrew
	MORRIS COUNTY (027)				
	1. Randolph, Cong.	1979(04)	-	-	NA 1979-on
	OCEAN COUNTY (029)				
	1. Little Egg Harbor, Southern Ocean Chr.Com.	2002	-	-	NA 2002(j2003)-on
	SOMERSET COUNTY (035)				
	1. Warren, Pilrgim Cong.(f.l.in Short Hills, *Millburn Twn.,Essex Co.to 1995)	1992(04)	-	-	NA 1992 (j1993)-on
	NEW YORK (36)				
	ALBANY COUNTY (001)				
	1. Albany, Chr.Cong.	1985	-	-	CCCC 1986-1990; X
	2. Delmar, Normansville Com.(*Bethlehem Twn.)	1889(05)	-	-	CCCC 1963(j1964)-1981; X
	BRONX COUNTY (005)				
	1. New York City, Bronx, Bronx Household of Faith	1971(05)	-	-	CCCC 1981-on
bS	2. New York City, Bronx, South Bronx Com.(bec. predominantly Hispanic 1971/1975)	1958(05) 1957(s.05)	-	-	CCCC 1960 (j1961)-on
	CHAUTAUQUA COUNTY (013)				
	1. Fluvanna, Com.(Jamestown PO;*Ellicott)	1834(s.05) 1835(s.05) 1804(s.05)	-	-	CCCC 1961(j1959/1962)-on
	2. Jamestown, Weakland Com.(f.Allen Park Com.;Twn. uncertain)	1938(s.05) 1835[sic,s.05]	-	-	CCCC 1967/1968 (j1968)-1988; pb.withdrew
	3. Kennedy, Clarks Corners Com.(*Poland)	1956(05)	-	-	CCCC 1983-on
	CHENANGO COUNTY (017)				
	1. Afton, Hope Cong. (f.l.Vestal,Broome Co.,PO)	2000	-	-	NA 1999(j2000)-on
	ERIE COUNTY (029)				
ER	1. Buffalo, Grace Parkridge Ch. (f.Evan.,E&R,UCC)	1924	1961-1999	-	UCC 1961-1999; CCCC 2002-on
	FULTON COUNTY (035)				
	1. Johnstown, New Covenant Com.(pb.f.Second United Pres.,affl.UPNA 1858-1958,f.Asso.Pres.,affl. Asso.Ch.to 1858)	1828(05) 1825(75H) 1785(s.05)	-	1958-1969	CCCC 1985-on

APPENDIX IV. - CONTINUING CONGREGATIONAL CHRISTIAN CHURCHES - NEW YORK - continued

A	B	C	D	E	F
	HAMILTON COUNTY (041)				
1.	Speculator, North Country Bible Fellowship (f.l. Lake Pleasant;incor.nl.CCCC:2003-2004)	2000	-	-	CCCC 2002-2003, 2004-on
	HERKIMER COUNTY (043)				
1.	Herkimer, First Cong.Univ.(f.First Univ.;dual UUA & Tr.back;l.UUA full to 1980/1981,& as inactive to 1988/1990)	1881 1896(s.04) r.1965	-	-	NA (Asso.)1965-1966; NA (Full)1966(j1965)-1976;(dual,see text) Tr.to UUA; X
	KINGS COUNTY (047)				
1.	New York City, Brooklyn, All Souls Univ.(left UUA 1963;j UUA 1973;Fed.to Bethlehem Ch.(dual UCC & Disc.,l.UCC 1973-on;1973 merger of Flatbush Chr.(Disc.,1903) & Bethlehem UCC (f.Evan.,E&R,1906,l.UCC 1961-1973))as All Souls Bethlehem Ch.1995/1998-on)	1845	(see text)	-	NA (Asso.)1963-1970; Tr.to UUA
	NASSAU COUNTY (059)				
Bl 1.	Inwood, Com.Bible (f.l.Far Rockaway,in New York City,Queens Co.;f.l.Lawrence;*Hempstead)	1946(05)	-	-	CCCC 1975-on
	NEW YORK COUNTY (061)				
1.	New York City, Manhattan, Neighborhood Ch.of New York (Greenwich Village)	1972(05)	-	-	CCCC 1992-on
	NIAGARA COUNTY (063)				
1.	Lockport, Rapids Chr.Chap.	by 1970	-	-	CCCC 1969/1970 (j1970)-1973; X
	ONONDAGA COUNTY (067)				
1.	Syracuse, Trinity Fellowship (f.Orth.Pres. 1978-1979)	1978(05)	-	-	CCCC 1993-on
	SARATOGA COUNTY (091)				
1.	Malta, Saratoga Chap.(f.l.Ballston Spa)	1989	-	-	CCCC 1997-on
	SCHENECTADY COUNTY (093)				
1.	Schenectady, Christ Com.of Carman (r.of Carman Pres.,X1976;*Rotterdam)	1976(05)	-	1953-1976	CCCC 1979 (j1978)-on
2.	Scotia, East Glenville Com.(*Glenville)	1945(s.05) 1949(s.05) 1963[sic,s.05]	-	-	CCCC 1962 (j1963)-on
	STEUBEN COUNTY (101)				
1.	Canisteo, Bennett's Creek Bible	1972(05)	-	-	CCCC 1992-on
	SUFFOLK COUNTY (103)				
Nt	Copiague, Covenant Chr.Fellowship (f.Covenant Cong.to 2000;f.Calvary Chap.to 1999;m.Ref. Cong.1998-af.2001;*Babylon)	1998	-	-	Indep.

APPENDIX IV. - CONTINUING CONGREGATIONAL CHRISTIAN CHURCHES - NEW YORK - continued

A	B	C	D	E	F
	WARREN COUNTY (113)				
	1. Athol, Christ Com.(*Thurman)	?	-	-	CCCC 1965(j1966)-1972; X
	WASHINGTON COUNTY (115)				
	1. Cambridge, Associate Cgn.(f.United Pres.of Coila in Cambridge(Second);see main list #2; claim to continue 1769 Asso.Ch.;affl.Asso.Ch. 1785-1858(Bullions faction 1838-1854(non-Bullion faction existed here 1841-1863)); UPNA 1858-1958)	1786(98,99) 1785(05,35) 1769(claim)	-	1958-1978	CCCC 1987 (j1988)-on
	PENNSYLVANIA (42)				
	ALLEGHENY COUNTY (003)				
	1. Pittsburgh, Blessed Redeemer Ch.	1999	-	-	NA 2000(j2001)-on
	2. Pittsburgh, South Hills Cong.(f.l.Brentwood 1982-1983)	1962(04) 1963	-	-	NA 1962(j1963)-on
	ARMSTRONG COUNTY (005) [PW]				
ER	1. Rural Valley, St.Paul's Cgn.(f.Ref.,E&R,UCC; *Plum Creek Twn.)	1850	1961-1999	-	UCC 1961-1999; CCCC 1999-on
	BUTLER COUNTY (019) [PW]				
ER	1. Zelienople, St.Peter's Ref.(f.Indep.Evan.,Ref., E&R,UCC)	1858	1961-1998	-	UCC 1961-1998; CCCC 1999-on
	CRAWFORD COUNTY (039)				
	1. Atlantic, Atlantic Cong.(f.First Pres.;withdrew 2001 as Atlantic Com.;*East Fallowfield Twn.)	1876 1874(98) r.1965(04)	-	1874-1968	NA 1977-2001; withdrew
	ERIE COUNTY (049)				
	1. Corry, Corry Cong.	1981	-	-	NA 1981(j1982)-1982, 1984-1985; X
	2. Cranesville, Cranesville Bible (applied to j CCCC 1971, nl.)	?	-	-	CCCC (see text); withdrew
	MC KEAN COUNTY (083)				
	1. Smethport, Chr.Gospel	?	-	-	CCCC 1967/1968 (j1968)-1969/1970; withdrew 1970
	MERCER COUNTY (085) [PW]				
ER	1. Greenville (PO), Christ Com.(f.St.John's UCC;f. l.Fredonia;f.Ref.,E&R,UCC;*Delaware Twn.)	1837 1836(01)	1961-1998	-	UCC 1961-1998; CCCC 1998-on
	MONTGOMERY COUNTY (091) [PSE]				
ER	1. Stowe, St.Paul's Ch.(f.Ref.,E&R,UCC;withdrew from UCC 1995,incor.l.to 1999;*West Pottsgrove Twn.)	1920(01) 1886(05)	1961-1999	-	UCC 1961-1999; CCCC 1995-on

APPENDIX IV. - CONTINUING CONGREGATIONAL CHRISTIAN CHURCHES - PENNSYLVANIA - MONTGOMERY COUNTY - continued

A	B	C	D	E	F
ER	2. Telford, Christ Ref.of Indian Creek (f.Ref.,E&R; dual UCC;*Franconia Twn.)	1746(01,05)	1961-on	-	UCC 1961-on CCCC 1994-on
	PHILADELPHIA COUNTY (101)		[PSE]		
B1	1. Philadelphia, Covenant Com.	1974(05)	-	-	CCCC 1976(j1975)-on
ER	2. Philadelphia, St.Mark's Ch.(f.Ref.,E&R,UCC)	1876	1961-1998	-	UCC 1961-1998; CCCC 1999-on
	SCHUYLKILL COUNTY (107)		[PSE]		
ER	1. Port Clinton, St.John's Ch.(f.Ref,E&R,UCC)	1868	1961-2000	-	UCC 1961-2000; CCCC 2000-on
	WARREN COUNTY (123)				
	1. Russell, Cable Hollow Ch.(*Pine Grove Twn.)	by 1953	-	-	CCCC 1967/1968 (j1968)-1969/1970; withdrew 1970
	2. Russell, Wiltsie Com.(*Pine Grove Twn.)	1953	-	-	CCCC 1964 (j1965)-on
	3. Warren, Good News Com.	1893(s.05:pr.) 1980(05)	-	-	CCCC 1984 (j1982)-on
	WESTMORELAND COUNTY (129)				
	1. New Kensington, Redeemer Cong.	1995	-	-	CCCC 1997-on

APPENDIX V. - SCHWENKFELDER CHURCH

A		B	C	D	E	F
		PENNSYLVANIA (42)				
		BERKS COUNTY (011)				
	1.	Washington Twn., Schwenkfelder Mtghse.(Upper Dist.)	1791(bldg.)	-	-	1911 merged to form Montgomery Co. #4(q.v.)
		LEHIGH COUNTY (077)				
	1.	Lower Milford Twn., Hosensack Schwenkfelder Mtghse.(Horseneck;Upper Dist.;pr.bf.1775 was in Upper Milford Twn.)	1790(bldg.)	-	-	1911 merged to form Montgomery Co. #4(q.v.)
	2.	Lower Milford Twn., Kraussdale Schwenkfelder Mtghse.(Krassdale;Upper Dist.;1890 U.S.Census suggests this was in Milford Twn.,Bucks Co.)	1825(bldg.)	-	-	1911 merged to form Montgomery Co. #4(q.v.)
		MONTGOMERY COUNTY (091)				
	1.	Lansdale, Schwenkfelder Ch.(dual UCC 1963-1986, 1992-on)	1918(Ch.) 1916(mission)	(see text)	-	alive
	2.	Lower Salford Twn., Schwenkfelder Mtghse.(Lower/ Central Dist.;a few services af.abandoned, bldg.survived)	1869(bldg.)	-	-	abandoned c.1906
	3.	Norristown, Schwenkfelder Ch.(dual UCC 1965-1997)	1904(Ch.)	(see text)	-	Merged 1997 to form M.(q.v.)
	3M.	East Norriton Twn., Olivet Schwenkfelder United Ch.(merger of #3 & Olivet Ref.UCC (1911/ 1915);dual UCC)	1997 M	(see text)	-	alive
	4.	Palm, Schwenkfelder Ch.(merger of Berks Co.#1, Lehigh Co.#1,& #2;Upper Dist.;Upper Hanover Twn.;dual E&R 1959-1961,UCC 1961-on)	1911 M 1735(claim)	(see text)	-	alive
	5.	Towamencin Twn., Schwenkfelder Mtghse. (Towmaencin;Lower/Central Dist.)	1764(bldg.)	-	-	1951 merged to #7 to form #6(q.v.)
	6.	Worcester, Central Schwenkfelder Ch.(merger of #6 & #8;Lower/Central Dist.)	1951 M 1735(claim)	-	-	alive
	7.	Worcester Twn., Schwenkfelder Mtghse.(Lower/ Central Dist.)	1836(bldg.)	-	-	1951 merged to #6 to form #7(q.v.)
		PHILADELPHIA COUNTY (101)				
bB	1.	Philadelphia, First Schwenkfelder Ch.(j 1899; dual UCC 1965-1970;bec.predominantly Black by 1973)	1898(Ch.) 1895(mission)	(see text)	-	alive
Bl	2.	Philadelphia, Schwenkfelder Missionary Ch.	1998(Ch.)	-	-	alive

ANNOTATED BIBLIOGRAPHY

Bibliographic
Reference
Number

(01) ANNUAL STATISTICAL LISTS

This single reference number refers to the continuous annual statistics and lists of the churches. Generally we have used the national listings for this information, which usually conform to the state lists (see below).

National Publications:

The Congregational Almanac for 1846-1848
(3 volumes) (C.C.Dean (1846 volume), James French (1847 & 1848 volumes), Boston, 1845-1847)
These three volumes have reproduced a variety of state reports without consistency. The *1848 Congregational Almanac* also provides us with a list of probably unassociated churches in Pennsylvania.

American Congregational Yearbook 1854-1859
(6 volumes) (American Congregational Union, New York, 1854-1859)
[first issue called Yearbook of the American Congregational Union]
We have used these lists for statistics for the years c.1852-c.1857. During these years there are often large discrepancies with state lists when the latter are available.

Congregational Quarterly 1859-1878
(20 volumes) (American Congregational Association and American Congregational Union, Boston and New York, 1859-1878)
This magazine, beginning in 1860, devoted one issue per year to the publication of statistics, which we have used to cover the years c.1858-c.1876, nineteen years of statistics. The *Quarterly* from the start also printed information on new churches organized or received beginning with 1858.(See code 01N)

Congregational Yearbook 1879-1928
(51 volumes) (National Council of Congregational Churches, New York and Boston, 1879-1929)
We have generally followed these listings. The user of this set should be aware of two problems in dating these volumes. The *1888 Yearbook* was the first to make statistics uniform for the calendar year before the date of publication. (That volume printed the statistics ending December 31, 1887.) The earlier volumes printed variously dated reports covering c.1877-c.1885. Thus there may be a c.1886 report available from the state minutes which could fill in the continuity (See below). The other problem involves the dating of these volumes themselves. Volumes 1 to 24 bore the date of the year of their publication (1879 to 1902). Volumes 25 to 36 bore two dates, the year of publication and the year the enclosed statistics covered (1903 to 1914, statistics for 1902-1913). Volumes 37 to 51 carry the date of the covered statistics (statistics for 1914-1928). Thus, depending on the method followed, many libraries have two 1902 volumes, two 1914 volumes, or have erroneously discarded one issue. These volumes generally have statistics for c.1877-c.1885, 1887-1928. The *Quarterly* practice of separate lists for new churches organized or received was followed through the 1896 Yearbook. (See code 01N). These volumes also included a chart of building dates in the issues from 1911(statistics for 1910) through 1926, inclusive, which we have used to find congregations which may have had an earlier ecumenical or other denominational origin revealed through such a date. (Whenever we use a building date, either the original building, or the building is use during this period is implied.) These books also include a directory of independent or mission Sunday Schools related to the denomination from 1893 to 1914 (statistics for 1913) inclusive. Also summary totals of these from 1914 to 1926. We have not picked up any of this Sunday School information for this volume.

Yearbook of the Congregational (and) Christian Churches 1929-1960
(32 volumes) (General Council of the Congregational (and) Christian Churches, New York and Dayton (Ohio) 1930-1961)
We have followed these lists with statistics for 1929-1960.

ANNOTATED BIBLIOGRAPHY

Yearbook of the United Church of Christ 1962-2004
(43 volumes) (United Church of Christ, New York or Cleveland, 1962-2004)
We have followed these lists with statistics for 1961-2003.

Related national references:

CC Churches, which by their action reported as of June 15, 1961 will be counted as part of the UCC (Report of the Co-Secretaries of the United Church of Christ) (mimeo,1961). This was the first list of United Church congregations.

File of Votes of Congregational Christian Churches on the formation of the United Church of Christ 1960 ff. This file from the office of the Secretary of the United Church of Christ, formerly in New York, (now at the United Church of Christ Archives in Cleveland, OH), was used to find exact dates of congregations votes on the United Church of Christ, Schedule II., etc..

God is Still Speaking, New Congregations in the UCC Since 2002, Churches Received in the UCC, Churches in Formation, Churches in Discussion (Compiled by: Evangelism Ministry Team – for UCC General Synod 2003) Mimeographed list.

Proposed Churches:

Beginning in the *1875 Quarterly* (for c.1873) churches not yet fully organized were added in brackets. This continued through the *1922 Yearbook* (for 1922). Occasionally these churches were designated other ways, such as with an asterisk or at the end of the list without a number. On rare occasion this also happened in years other than those specified. A new listing entitled "Proposed Churches," was added to the *1989 Yearbook* (for 1988) and has appeared each year since then. We have indicated all such churches as proposed churches and note them in the column B text rather than in Column D.

Preaching Places:

It is generally not our policy to report on preaching places where there are no organized congregations. Nor was it the policy of any of the above publications to print such material.

Calendar Dating:

Statistics and reports are on a calendar year basis for all states from 1888 on.

Listings before these dates were collected either by the national *Yearbook* at various (usually designated) dates in the year, or at meetings of the various Associations. For example an 1879 Association meeting would collect data for a year which included part of 1878 and part of 1879. We have designated such a report as 1878 (since that is the year that ended in the period covered). All years before calendar dating was introduced (except for the exceptions noted below) should therefore be taken to mean "in this year or in the immediately following year."

There are the following exceptions for churches with the following affiliations: New Jersey listings marked 1878 cover only the latter part of that year, and entries from 1879 on are calendar year. Listings for the Eastern Ohio Welsh Conference marked 1873 are for only the latter part of that year, listings marked 1874 are for the calendar year, while those marked 1875 are for all of 1875 and part of 1876, and are off calendar year again until the national change. Similarly, listings for the Eastern Pennsylvania Welsh Association marked 1871 are for part of that year, while those marked 1872 cover the entire year of 1872 and part of 1873, and are off calendar year again until the national change.

The 1887 national *Yearbook* covers c.1885 reports, while the *1888 Yearbook* reports the end of the year 1887. This change left one year of data not collected by the national *Yearbook*. We have inserted calendar year data for 1886 from the 1887 minutes of New Jersey. We have inserted c.1886 data from 1887 New York minutes, and for the Congregational Association of Western Pennsylvania. (In the last cases, therefore, listings shown as 1887 only refer to the latter part of that year.) No report for the rest of the Pennsylvania data was published between the national lists for the middle of 1886 and the end of 1887. (Listings marked 1887 are for that entire year plus part of 1886).

Unusual and Missing Reports:

For churches affiliated to bodies within the General Association of New York, we have used the reports of the General Association (see 01S) for all listings from 1834 in the 1835 minutes, through and including the 1851 reports in the 1852 minutes. (See State General bodies below for missing reports.) The *Congregational Almanacs* for 1846 through 1848 all repeat the New York affiliation lists for c.1843 found in their 1844 minutes. In reporting 1852 listings and on we have used the national lists and noted discrepancies with state minutes. New Jersey listings evolve out of New York affiliations after the start of national listings. However, Pennsylvania and Welsh listings are incomplete. The *1848 Congregational Almanac* includes a list of churches in Pennsylvania, not otherwise identified. We have treated that report as one for c.1846. Some Welsh churches were affiliated to predominantly English-speaking bodies and are listed in their reports when they are so indicated. Similarly, before the beginning of the regular national lists, churches in any of the three studied states, which were affiliated to bodies in different states and reported by them, are listed. In addition to local congregations affiliating to bodies centered in other states, sometimes entire inter-church bodies have been affiliated to general bodies in other states: for example, the Congregational Association of Western Pennsylvania (founded 1840), is listed when it is part of the New York general body (1842 through and including 1849 reports), and when it was part of the Ohio and Pennsylvania general bodies (1873 reports on). However, the national listings did not always pick up listings for particular inter-church bodies when they are not part of a general body. The 1855 through 1859 Yearbooks tried to pick up churches for listings from both non-reporting inter-church bodies and unaffiliated congregations, but their listings are sporadic and not clarified. A list for the Congregational Association of Western Pennsylvania appears for c.1858, mention of the Association without church lists is noted for c.1859 and c.1860, and regular reports were picked up for c.1864 through and including c.1872. Some congregations part of Welsh bodies in Pennsylvania were listed for c.1859, and regular reports were picked up from c.1864 until they became part of a general body (although the report for c.1865 came in late and is in a separate location in the *1867 Quarterly*.) Reports for congregations part of the Welsh body in New York are implied through a pastor's list, part of the c.1866 report, and then are regularly listed from c.1867 on.

Summary Remarks:

These entries taken as a whole, are the primary source materials on which these studies are based. Unless otherwise specified, all references on listing, not listed, listed twice etc. refer to these publications.

The first date in the listing column indicates that the church first appeared in the report issued for the end of that year. The year shown as the year dropped means this is the first year end report in which the church does not appear. (The last appearance was actually in the report for one year earlier.) The number of reports a church appeared in could be easily computed by subtracting the first year from the second. Thus a church listed 1918 to 1920 appeared in two statistical reports, those for the ends of 1918 and 1919.

(01N) As stated above, in addition to the regular church lists, lists of newly organized churches were printed in the *Congregational Quarterly* in all issues, and continuing in the *Yearbook* from the first issue through the 1896 issue. These are indicated with the code 01N. (In some of my earlier volumes these entries were designated with the code ncl.01).

(01S) <u>State Publications</u>:

We have used the national lists in all cases, except as noted. Where discrepancies appear we have used the 01S code. Some churches were reported in the national publications before there was a state body in their area. The best collections of state minutes that we have found are at the Congregational Library in Boston, the Andover Harvard Library at Harvard Divinity School in Cambridge, MA, the Chicago Theological Seminary Library, and the Union Theological Seminary Library in New York. After the formation of United Church of Christ general bodies, the practice of printing annual minutes and/or directories, fell into disuse in most groups. We, therefore, have only cited pre-United Church publications below. Data from Christian or Evangelical and Reformed Inter-Church bodies was gathered for this publication primarily from national sources.

<u>General Bodies Centered in the Middle Atlantic Area:</u>

Congregational Association of Pennsylvania (Congregational Conference of Pennsylvania; Pennsylvania State Conference of Congregational Churches; Congregational Christian Conference of Pennsylvania) Organized 1886, incorporated 1908, reorganized 1931. Merged 1963. (Minutes of 1899-1900, 1908-1910, 1912, 1917, 1920-1929, 1931-1934, and 1961-1962 have not been discovered.)

General Association of Congregational Churches and Ministers of New Jersey (Congregational Association of New Jersey; Congregational Conference of New Jersey; Middle Atlantic Conference of Congregational Churches;

Middle Atlantic Congregational Christian Conference) Organized 1869, incorporated 1927/1928, reorganized 1931. Merged 1964. (Minutes of 1933 and 1935 have not been discovered.)

General Association of New York [Congregational Churches and Ministers] (Congregational Association of New York; Congregational Conference of New York; New York Congregational Christian Conference) Organized 1834, incorporated 1914. Absorbed the New York Missionary Society (begun 1870/1872) in 1926. Merged 1963. (Minutes of a Fall 1834 meeting are missing. The minutes of 1845 are printed with those of 1847, but no statistical lists were published for c.1846.)

General Bodies Centered Outside the Middle Atlantic Area, but Serving Here:

Congregational Conference of Ohio (Congregational Association of Ohio; Congregational Conference of Ohio, Ohio Conference of Congregational Christian Churches) Planned 1852, Organized 1853, incorporated 1907, reorganized 1931. Absorbed the Ohio Home Missionary Society (organized 1863, incorporated 1885) in 1907. Merged 1963. (Minutes of 1858 and 1859 have not been discovered.)

Convention of the South of Congregational Christian Churches. Organized 1950 (Black) Served in this area only 1954 to 1960. Extinct 1965. Minutes found: None.

Evangelical Protestant Conference of Congregational Churches. (Formerly Evangelical Protestant Church of North America) Organized 1911, Received by merger 1924/1925. Served in this area to 1945. Disbanded 1947. Minutes found: None.

General Conference of the Congregational Churches of Connecticut (Connecticut Conference of Congregational and Christian Churches, Connecticut Conference of the United Church of Christ) Organized 1867/1868, reorganized under the 1798 charter of the Missionary Society of Connecticut in 1879/1880. Continues. All pre-United Church minutes found. In addition, church lists were published in the 1820 through and including 1867 minutes of the General Association of Connecticut (organized 1709).

General Conference of the Congregational Churches of Massachusetts (Massachusetts Congregational Conference and Missionary Society, Massachusetts Conference of the United Church of Christ) Organized 1860, reorganized under the charter of the Massachusetts Missionary Society (begun 1799), 1927/1928. Continues. All pre-United Church minutes found. In addition church lists were published in the 1826 through 1867 minutes of the General Association of Massachusetts (Proper, organized 1802/1803), which merged to the Conference in 1868.

General Convention of Ministers (Congregational and Presbyterian) of the State of Vermont (Vermont Congregational Conference and Domestic Missionary Society, Vermont Conference of the United Church of Christ) Planned 1795. Organized 1796, incorporated 1872, reorganized 1917 by merger with the Vermont Missionary Society (organized 1807). Continues. All pre-United Church minutes found. Church lists were published from the 1820 minutes on.

United Evangelical Church of Puerto Rico. Organized 1931. Served in this area 1959 to 1965. Continues. Minutes found: None.

In addition, **non-associated churches** were sometimes listed in reports along with associated churches. From the publication of the *1860 Congregational Quarterly* on, the national annual lists published only churches reported to them by state or general bodies. In that year, one Church in New York, not reported by the state general body was also reported separately. The New York general body often listed in its reports congregations relating directly to it, and not any of its particular inter-church bodies. This was often done in order to connect to isolated churches when there were no strong bodies in a particular part of the state, or to try to form ties with churches where there were peculiar local problems. Separate lists of such churches were provided in their 1840, 1862 to 1866, and 1868 to 1879 minutes. They also recognized and reported churches served by two ministerial associations, the Manhattan Association of the 1840's, and another group with the same name (New York churches only) from 1877 to 1885. Other ministerial bodies were part of Middle Atlantic general bodies, but it appears that their churches were part of overlapping inter-church bodies.

ANNOTATED BIBLIOGRAPHY

(01K) German Listings:
The General Conference of German Congregational Churches, organized 1883, could have its various churches traced through its constituent sub-bodies in their respective state bodies. These can also be traced through its annual publication *Kirchenbote Kalender* (later *Illustrierter Kirchenbote Kalender*). This booklet, in almanac form also published regular church statistical lists. We have found the issues of 1905,1907,1911,1913-1921,1924,1926,1939-1942,1945,1949,1959,1962-1963. These would cover statistical reports for the years 1903,1905,1909,1911-1919,1922,1924,1937-1940,1943,1947,1957,1960-1961. The statistical report for 1936 is reported in 64.

(01T) "List of Congregational Churches in the State of New York"
A report in the 1854 Minutes of the General Association of New York (pp.22-27), listing not only associated Congregational churches, but also those in Presbytery under the "Plan of Union," independent Congregational churches, and churches already changed to Presbyterian forms. It was a survey put together by a committee of the New York general body and included in their minutes for 1854. They surveyed Congregational and Presbyterian clergy in various parts of the state. It is the most important attempt to list unassociated Congregational churches in the Middle Atlantic region and a primary tool for the study of the Plan of Union. The committee asked those surveyed to send in names of churches and their pastors in four categories: Associated Congregational churches; Churches with Congregational forms but connected to a Presbytery under the Plan of Union; Independent Congregational churches (not affiliated to a Congregational inter-church body or a Presbytery), and churches which had already changed their forms from Congregational to Presbyterian. These are listed by County. This is the only study from the Congregational side to try to distinguish the forms of churches within the Presbyteries (many Presbyterian historians cover up such data) and to try to list the independent churches. Without this study our overview of the Plan of Union would be very inadequate. It is a shame this study was only limited to New York, as it would have probably unearthed some other churches in the other Middle Atlantic states. The churches that still had Congregational forms, but were in Presbytery or independent in this study were then picked up and added to the associated churches in the New York lists in five issues of the *Congregational Yearbook*, from 1855 through 1859. Some information gained after the study was completed was passed on to the *Yearbook*, and we have noted it on the church lists. In our lists we have identified this study with the code 01T, and have shown non-associated independent and Presbytery churches listed with the code "cl." to indicate that they were claimed as Congregational churches in this period. Unfortunately, while a significant help, the study was not complete. The language barrier left most Welsh congregations outside of the study. Also, since a major part of the erosion of Congregational churches to Presbyterian bodies had occurred before 1854, sometimes well before that date, there were areas of the state where the general body had no members to help in putting the study together. The authors of the study are aware of this in some areas. These notes appear in the study: "Report of Cayuga county probably imperfect. Some of the Presbyterian ministers refused to furnish statistics." For Franklin county: "Returns imperfect." For Queens county (including present Nassau county): "Probably several others were originally Congregational." For Seneca county: "Report incomplete." These were, of course, areas where they knew they had problems. But in areas such as Putnam county, where the Plan of Union had wiped out Congregational churches two decades earlier, the study merely says "none reported." Also, because the study data was assembled over time by local correspondents, it is not necessarily uniform to actual conditions in its published date of 1854. There are other weaknesses as well, including a numbered summary table at the end, which does not always match the lists above it. Nonetheless, if it was not for this study, the Congregational status of many churches in the mid-nineteenth century would have been completely unknown.

Other Listings:

Early Unitarian listings come from:

(02) Unitarian Congregational Register for 1846-1851 (6 volumes) (Crosly and Nichols, Boston, 1846-1851) [The first two issues were published as the Unitarian Annual Register] Statistics are for c.1845-c.1850. We have dropped all regular Unitarian listings in 1851, although they continue thereafter.

Modern Unitarian listings come from:

(03) Unitarian Universalist Association Directory (Unitarian Universalist Association, Boston) [We have used the issues of 1965,1966,1968,1981/1982, and 2001/2002; 5 volumes published 1965,1966,1968,1982, and 2001 with statistics for c.1964,c.1965,c.1967,c.1981, and c.2000.]

(04) Congregational Christian Churches, National Association, organized 1955, began to act as a denomination 1961.

Its records are compiled jointly from these publications:

Member Churches of the National Association 9/15/61 (mimeo) This earliest list of National Association Churches is the first printed after they began to function as a denomination, and is used to indicate churches listed "by 1961."

Handbook (National Association of Congregational Christian Churches, Milwaukee) (9 volumes published as January 1962; 1963; 1964; 1965/66; 1966/67; 1967/68; 1968/69; 1970; 1971/72; published on an irregular basis (1962-1971)) These lists cover approximately one year each. Changes in listings between the 1964 and 1965/66 *Handbooks* are shown as 1964 or 1965. Changes from the 1965/1966 Handbook to the 1966/1967 *Handbook* are shown simply as 1965. Changes between the 1968/69 and 1970 *Handbooks* are shown as 1968 or 1969. Dates are always approximate because of publication irregularity. The last issue (1971/72) included statistics for the calendar year 1970, although changes in the church lists run through part of 1971. Therefore the list information may be in the year shown or in the year thereafter.

Yearbook (Congregational Christian Churches, National Association, Milwaukee or Oak Creek (WI)) (33 volumes published as 1972/73 to 1984/85, and 1986 to 2005; published 1972-2004) Statistics for 1971 to 2003, although list changes may be in the year following the statistical data.

Most National Association congregations are full member churches, which may be assumed; except that two congregations in New York state were "Associate" member churches, and are marked as such.

(05) The Conservative Congregational Christian Conference was organized in 1948. We have found no publications before the 1959 minutes. However, later issues of listings give dates when churches joined the Conference, and we have been able to reconstruct some of the earlier membership from this information. Listings are compiled from the following publications:

Minutes of the Eleventh Annual Meeting of the Conservative Congregational Christian Conference (n.p.,1959). Statistics for c.1958.

Annual Report 1966-67, The Conservative Congregational Christian Conference (mimeo) Church lists here are inserted to the listing continuity for c.1965.

Year Book (of the) Conservative Congregational Christian Conference (1960-1961; 1963-1966; 1968; 1970-2005) (43 volumes, various places, published 1961-1966, 1968, 1970-2005). Statistics for c.1959-c.1964,c.1966, c.1968,1970-2004. In the continuity of these volumes, the 1970 issue notes changes for 1967 or 1968. The 1971 issue was the first issue with calendar year reports, and notes changes 1969 or 1970.

(06) Evangelical Covenant Church lists are from Covenant Yearbook ((Swedish) Evangelical (Mission) Covenant Church, Chicago, 1896-1986) The *Yearbook* specifies full member churches and those with regional affiliation only. Also included under this number are churches in the Eastern Missionary Association (Organized 1890, records from 1911) until it became a full region of the Covenant Church. Congregations only in that group or a region of the Covenant are identified with the code "Rgn.".

Records of Inter-Church Congregational Bodies:

These various groups, including their histories and bibliographies are discussed in the section entitled "Congregational Organization in the Middle Atlantic States."

European Roots: (Arranged alphabetically)

Benedict, Philip, Christ's Churches Purely Reformed: A Social History of Calvinism, (Yale University Press, New Haven, 2002)

Bolam, C.G., Jeremy Goring, H.L. Short and Roger Thomas, The English Presbyterians From Elizabethan Puritanism to Modern Unitarianism (George Allen & Unwin Ltd., London, 1968) This is an essential book for understanding the differences between the English and Scottish Reformations.

Bremer, Francis J., *"Congregations before Congregationalism: Social and Spiritual Roots of the Cambridge Platform,"* Bulletin of the Congregational Library (Vol.49 # 3, Vol. 50 #1; pp.6-16)

Dollarhide, William, British Origins of American Colonists, 1629-1775, (Heritage Quest Genealogical Services, Bountiful (UT), 1997)

ANNOTATED BIBLIOGRAPHY

Fischer, David Hackett, Albion's Seed: Four British Folkways in America (Oxford University Press, New York, 1989) An incisive study of the differences in the cultures of colonial British America. Particularly Instructive in understanding the variations between New England Puritans and Scottish, Irish, and North English Border immigrants.

Jones, R. Tudor, Congregationalism in England 1662-1962, (Independent Press, London, 1962) This provides a parallel history for independency in England from the ejection onward.

Maclean, Fitzroy, Scotland: A Concise History (Thames and Hudson, New York, 1993)

Paul, Robert S., The Assembly of the Lord, Politics and Religion in the Westminster Assembly and the 'Grand Debate' (T. & T. Clark, Edinburgh, 1985)

Pettegree, Andrew, Alastair Duke and Gillian Lewis (Eds.), Calvinism in Europe, 1540-1620 (Cambridge University Press, Cambridge, 1994) A helpful set of articles on various topics.

Schmidt, Leigh Eric, Holy Fairs: Scottish Communions and American Revivals in the Early Modern Period, (Princeton University Press, Princeton, 1989)

Sell, Alan P. F., Saints: Visible, Orderly and Catholic, The Congregational Idea of the Church (Pickwick Publications, Allison Park (PA), 1986) A helpful theological treatment.

General Congregational, Colonial Religion, and Related Studies: (Arranged alphabetically)

Alliman, Kirk Gilbert, The Incorporation of Massachusetts Congregational Churches, 1692-1833: The Preservation of Religious Autonomy (University of Iowa, Ph.D. thesis 1970; Ann Arbor, 1971)

(07) "The Amistad Event," Special Issue of New Conversations (Vol.II., #2 & 3, Winter/Spring 1989). Includes these articles of particular note: "Northern Congregational Churches and Ministers Supported by the American Missionary Association 1846-1865," pp. 63-71; "Northern Presbyterian Churches and Ministers Supported by the American Missionary Association 1846-1865," pp.72-73; and "Northern Nonsectarian Churches (and/or Churches for Which Denominational Affiliation Was Never Identified) and Ministers Supported by the American Missionary Association, 1846-1865," p. 74.

Bartlett, S.C., Historical Sketch of the Missions of the American Board, (Arno Press, New York, 1972) A reprint of six 1876 pamphlets.

Blake, S. Leroy, The Separate or Strict Congregationalists of New England (Pilgrim Press, Boston, 1902) An exhaustive study of churches; living and extinct in New England, but with some references to this area.

Bremer, Francis J., The Puritan Experiment: New England Society from Bradford to Edwards [Revised Edition] (University Press of New England, Hanover (NH), 1995) Probably the most thorough overview.

Cappon, Lester J., Ed., Atlas of Early American History: The Revolutionary Era 1760-1790 (Newberry Library and the Institute of Early American History and Culture, Princeton University Press, 1976) Identifies all churches in New Jersey and Pennsylvania in 1775.

Dexter, Henry Martyn, The Congregationalism of the Last Three Hundred Years As Seen Through Its Literature: 2 Volumes (Burt Franklin, New York, 1970, reprint of 1880 edition)

(08) Gaustad, Edwin Scott, Historical Atlas of Religion in America (Harper and Row, New York, Revised Edition 1976)

(09) Goddard, Carolyn E., On the Trail of the UCC (United Church Press, New York, 1981) This non-exhaustive book includes several brief comments of the histories of many of the more historic churches.

ANNOTATED BIBLIOGRAPHY

(10) Goen, C.C., Revivalism and Separatism in New England, 1740-1800 (Yale University Press, New Haven (CT), 1982) [Republished by Archon Books, Hamden (CT), 1989]

Goodykoontz, Colin Brummit, Home Missions on the American Frontier (Caxton Printers, Caldwell (ID), 1939)

Hall, David D., The Faithful Shepherd,(University of North Carolina Press, Chapel Hill, 1972)

Heimert, Alan and Perry Miller, The Great Awakening (Bobbs - Merrill Co., Indianapolis, 1967)

Hovarth, David G., Editor, A Guide to the Microfilm Edition of the Papers of the American Home Missionary Society 1816-1936 (Microfilming Corporation of America, Glen Rock, NJ, 1975)

Kennedy, William S. The Plan of Union, or a History of the Presbyterian and Congregational Churches on the Western Reserve (Pentagon Steam Press, Hudson (OH), 1856)

(11) Kirkham, E.Kay, A Survey of American Church Records IV Edition (Everton Publishers, Logan (UT), 1978) This is a listings of local church records which could provide historical parameters.

Kuhns, Frederick I., "New Light on the Plan of Union," Journal of Presbyterian History Vol. 26, No.1 (March, 1948, pp.19-43)

Lucas, Paul, Valley of Discord: Church and Society Along the Connecticut River, 1636-1725 (University Press of New England, Hanover (NH), 1976)

Marsden, George M., Jonathan Edwards: A Life, (Yale University Press, New Haven, 2003)

Newman, William M. and Peter L. Halvorson, Atlas of American Religion: The Denomination Era 1776-1990 (Altamira Press, Walnut Creek (CA), 2000)

Nichols, Robert Hastings, "The Plan of Union in New York," Church History Vol.V.No.1 (March, 1936, pp.29-51)

Olmstead, Clifton E., History of Religion in the United States (Prentice-Hall Inc., Englewood Cliffs (NJ), 1960)

Paullin, Charles O., Atlas of the Historical Geography of the United States (Carnegie Institution of Washington, American Geographic Society of New York, 1932)

(12) Punchard, George, History of Congregationalism Volumes IV. & V. (Congregational Publishing Society, Boston, 1880, & 1881) [Congregationalism in America Volume I. & II.] This interesting general history takes various parts of the country and traces the early development of Congregationalism in that area.

Ross, A. Hastings, "Church and State in New England: Effects Upon American Congregationalism," Bibliotheca Sacra Vol. 49, No. 194 (April, 1892, pp.213-239)

Ross, A. Hastings, "Voluntary Societies and Congregational Churches," Bibliotheca Sacra Vol. 47 (Oct., 1890, pp.529-548)

Separate Church Papers; A set of manuscripts at the Connecticut Historical Society, Hartford, which include the minutes of the Strict Congregational Convention of Connecticut.

Silverman, Kenneth, The Life and Times of Cotton Mather (Columbia University Press, New York, 1985)

Starkey, Marion L., The Congregational Way: The Role of the Pilgrims and Their Heirs in Shaping America (Doubleday and Co., Garden City (NY), 1966)

Stiles, Ezra, A Discourse on the Christian Union, etc.. (Eden and Gill, Boston, 1761)

Sweet, William Warren, Religion on the American Frontier 1783-1850, Vol.III.: The Congregationalists (Cooper Square Publishers Inc., New York, 1964 [reprint of 1939 edition]) The best overview of Congregational mission strategy on the frontier in the period studied.

von Rohr, John, The Shaping of American Congregationalism 1620-1957 (Pilgrim Press, Cleveland, 1992)

Walker, Williston, The Creeds and Platforms of Congregationalism, (Pilgrim Press, Boston, 1960 [reprint of 1893 edition]) An essential book for understanding Congregational history.

Walker, Williston, A History of the Congregational Churches in the United States [American Church History Volume III.] (Christian Literature Co., New York, 1894)

(14) Weis, Frederick Lewis, The Colonial Churches and the Colonial Clergy of the Middle and Southern Colonies 1607-1776 (Society of the Descendants of the Colonial Clergy, Lancaster, MA, 1938) This interesting directory of all denominations is helpful, but is not as complete as the New England volume.

Weis, Frederick Lewis, The Colonial Clergy and the Colonial Churches of New England (Genealogical Publishing Company, Baltimore, 1977 [reprint of 1936 edition])

Weis, Frederick Lewis, The Colonial Clergy of the Middle Colonies (Genealogical Publishing Co., Baltimore, 1978 [reprint of 1957 edition]) These ministerial biographical collections, published later, are more complete than the church lists.

(15) Weis, Frederick Lewis, List of the Unitarian Churches and Their Ministers in the United States and Canada (Meadville Theological Seminary, typescript, n.d.(c.1960)) This helpful directory pinpoints Unitarian churches.

Woods, James, "Facts and Observations Concerning the Organization and State of the Churches in the Three Synods of Western New York and the Synod of the Western Reserve," (originally printed as a pamphlet published by G. M. Davidson at Saratoga Springs (NY), 1837), summarized in *Western Presbyterian Herald* (Volume VII, No.7, (Dec. 28, 1837); Volume VII., No.10 (Jan. 18, 1838); Volume VII., No.11 (Jan. 25, 1838); Volume VII., No.12 (Feb. 1, 1838); Volume VII., No.13 (Feb. 8,1838))

Worthley, Harold Field, An Inventory of the Particular (Congregational) Churches of Massachusetts Gathered 1620-1805 (Harvard University Press, Cambridge, 1970)

Youngs, J. William T., Jr. God's Messengers: Religious Leadership in Colonial New England 1700-1750 (Johns Hopkins University Press, Baltimore, 1976)

Zikmund, Barbara Brown,Ed., Hidden Histories of the United Church of Christ, (United Church Press, New York, 1984)

Zikmund, Barbara Brown,Ed., Hidden Histories in the United Church of Christ 2 (United Church Press, New York, 1987) These two general volumes include background information on often excluded groups.

Area Congregational Studies: (Arranged alphabetically)

(16) Austin, Jere C., Notes on Early Congregational Churches and Ministers of Suffolk County, Long Island, New York (1964 typescript, copied from A Brief *History of the Strict Congregational Convention of Long Island*, 1839)

Austin, Jere C., "The Strict Congregationalists," Long Island Forum (May, 1966, pp.90-93)

Bates, Newton W., Historical Gleanings in Western New York Congregationalism (New York Congregational Historical Society, n.p., 1906)

ANNOTATED BIBLIOGRAPHY

Beach, John T., The Middle Atlantic Conference – Historical Sketch (typescript, 1947) at Congregational Library in Boston.

"Black River Association," A history is included in the *1883 History of Lewis County, New York*

(17) A Breviary of the Doings of the St. Lawrence Consociation (n.p., after 1851)

A Brief Account of the Associated Presbyteries; and a General View of Their Sentiments Concerning Religion and Ecclesiastical Order (A Convention of Said Presbyteries, M. Croswell, Catskill (NY), 1796)

(18) Brown, William B., "The Early Congregational History of Essex County," The 1881 Yearbook of the Churches of Essex and Union Counties (A.L.Brice, Newark, 1881, pp.106-107) Despite the name of this article, it touches on other areas of the state. Not exhaustive.

(19) Brown, William B., "The Early History of Congregationalism in New Jersey and the Middle Provinces," Congregational Quarterly Vol.XIX (Oct.,1877, pp.531-545)

Chalmers, William I., The Suffolk Association of Congregational Churches and Ministers and Its Relation to Antecedent Bodies 1873-1898 (Roanoke Press, Riverhead (NY), 1898)

A Circular Letter Addressed by the Northern Associated Presbytery to the Churches in Their Connexion on the Subject of the Observances of Fasts and Thanksgivings (Passed 1824)

Constitution and By Laws of the Congregational Association of New York and Brooklyn with an Outline of Its History (C. W. Benedict, New York, 1848)

Constitution, Confession of Faith, Standing Rules and Principles of Discipline of the Association of Western Pennsylvania (Association, Randolph (PA), 1840) Includes a note on the formation of the Association.

Day, S. Mills, Outline History of the Congregational Association of Western New York (Association, Warsaw (NY), 1901)

Dill, James H., "Congregationalism in Western New York," Congregational Quarterly Vol. I. (April, 1859, pp.151-158) A review and reply to Hotchkin's book (48). Also privately printed at Rochester 1858.

Edwards, George N., A History of the Independent or Congregational Church of Charleston, S.C. (Commonly Known as Circular Church) (Pilgrim Press, Boston, 1947)

Green, Jacob "A Sketch of the Life of the Rev. Jacob Green, A.M.," (Edited by Ashbel Green), The Christian Advocate Vol. IX (Aug.-Dec.,1831, pp.408-412,465-468,522-525,578-581,633-637), Vol. X (Jan.-May,1832, pp.11-14,51-55,99-102,145-148,194-199)

Historical Brochure prepared for the 125th Anniversary of the Western Association of Congregational Christian and Community Churches of New York State, (Oct. 9, 1960; Sheridan, New York) Includes excerpts from letters of John Spencer.

Ireland, William Fleetwood, A History of the Central Association of Congregational Churches and Ministers of the State of New York (Byron and Seamans, Pulaski (NY), 1905)

Johnson, Samuel, "Black River Association, New York," Congregational Quarterly Vol. XX (Oct., 1878, pp.577-590)

Johnson, Samuel, "History of the Susquehannah Association," Congregational Quarterly, Vol.XVII (Apr.,1875, pp.296-299)

(20) Lightbourne, James H. Sr. and Richard N. Rinker, The Conference of Congregational and Christian Churches of Pennsylvania: A Brief History (mimeo,1962) A summary history with little specific church data.

Merriam, George Ernest, One Hundred Years of Congregationalism in the Empire State (New York Congregational Conference, New York City, 1933)

Mitros, David, Jacob Green and the Slavery Debate In Revolutionary Morris County New Jersey (Morris County Heritage Commission, n.p., 1993)

Moffat, T. Aird The Founders of Newark Were Congregationalists (a series of three sermons, typescript, 1916) At Congregational Library in Boston.

Molyneux, J. Chester 1958 Historical Report – One Hundred Twenty-Fifth Anniversary of the New York Congregational Christian Conference (Conference, n.p., 1958)

Nichols, Robert Hastings, "The Plan of Union in New York," Church History Vol.V, No.1 (March, 1936, pp.29-51)

Noll, Mark A., "Jacob Green's Proposal for Seminaries," Journal of Presbyterian History, Vol.58, No.3 (Fall, 1980, pp. 210-222)

Noll, Mark A., "Observations of the Reconciliation of Politics and Religion in Revolutionary New Jersey: The Case of Jacob Green," Journal of Presbyterian History, Vol. 54 (Summer, 1976, pp.217-237)

Patterson, D. Williams, "The First 'Susquehannah Association'," Congregational Quarterly, Vol.XVI (Apr.,1874, pp.285-290)

Scott, Patricia F., correspondence with the author of October 21, 2003, including copies of articles from the *Evening Sun* on various congregations in Chenango County, New York

Thompson, Joseph D., "Congregationalism in Eastern New York," Congregational Quarterly, Vol. II (Jan.,1860 pp.33-42).

A View of A Christian Church and Church Government (Associated Presbytery of Morris County, Shepard Kollock, Chatham (NJ), 1781) [Probably written by Jacob Green.]

Vosburgh, Roydon Woodward, edited versions of the records of various local congregations at the Library of Congress in Washington, DC.

Williston, Seth, The Journals of Seth Williston 1796-1800, (Broome County Historical Society, 1992)

Work Projects Administration Studies (Arranged alphabetically except for 41):

Directory of Churches in New Jersey (20 Volumes, numbered 1 to 14, and 16 to 21; one volume for each New Jersey County, except Ocean County is missing) (New Jersey Historical Records Survey, Work Projects Administration, Newark, 1940 & 1941) A interdenominational listing of living congregations.

(21) Guide to Vital Statistics in the City of New York (5 Volumes, one for each Borough: Bronx, Brooklyn, Manhattan, Queens, Richmond): Churches (Historical Records Survey, Work Projects Administration, New York, 1942) Interdenominational. Includes incomplete lists of living and extinct churches.

(22) Guide to Vital Statistics Records of Churches in New York State (Exclusive of New York City) (2 Volumes) (Historical Records Survey, Work Projects Administration, Albany, 1942) Interdenominational. Includes incomplete lists of living and extinct churches.

ANNOTATED BIBLIOGRAPHY

(23) Inventory of the Church Archives of New Jersey - Baptist Bodies (Historical Records Survey, Work projects Administration, Newark, 1938)

(24) Inventory of the Church Archives of New Jersey - Congregational Christian Churches (New Jersey Historical Records Survey, Work Projects Administration, Newark, 1941) Includes histories of all living and some extinct congregations. The compilers have followed Presbyterian historians in excluding Morris County Presbytery information from the Congregational history.

(25) Inventory of the Church Archives of New Jersey - Presbyterian (Historical Records Survey, Newark, 1940) Includes histories of all living and some extinct congregations.

(26) Inventory of the Church Archives of New York (Excluding New York City) - Presbyterian Churches (7 Volumes) Prepared by the Historical Records Survey, Work Projects Administration 1936-1941; Arranged and Indexed by Gerald W. Gillette, Presbyterian Historical Society, Philadelphia, 1965. Histories, but not exhaustive.

(27) Inventory of the Church Archives of New York City - Presbyterian Church in the U.S.A. (Historical Records Survey, New York, 1940) Histories of living and extinct churches.

Inventory of the Church Archives of New York City - Reformed Church in America (Historical Records Survey, Work Projects Administration, New York, 1939)

(28) Inventory of the Church Archives of Pennsylvania - Presbyterian Churches (25 Volumes) Prepared by the Pennsylvania Historical Records Survey of the Work Projects Administration; Arranged and Indexed by Candace W. Belfield, Presbyterian Historical Society, Philadelphia, 1971. Histories, but not exhaustive.

General Presbyterian Materials: (Arranged alphabetically)

(30) American Presbyterian Churches - 17th Century - Chronologically Listed (A document at the Presbyterian Historical Society, Philadelphia) A short dated list of churches begun before 1700.

Armstrong, Maurice A., Lefferts A. Loetscher, and Charles A. Anderson, The Presbyterian Enterprise (Westminster Press, Philadelphia, 1956)

(31) Blade, Robert E., "Pioneer Presbyterian Congregations," American Presbyterians(Journal of Presbyterian History) Vol.67, # 1 & 2 (Spring/Summer, 1989, pp.1-188). A collection of histories of the oldest living congregation in each Presbytery of the Presbyterian Church U.S.A.

Coalter, Milton J., Gilbert Tennent, Son of Thunder (Greenwood Press, New York,1986) Far more than a biography, this book adds insight to religious change in the Middle Colonies surrounding the Great Awakening.

Gillett, E.H., History of the Presbyterian Church in the U.S.A. (Presbyterian Board of Publication, Philadelphia, 1873) A general history.

(32) Glasgow, William Melancthon, Cyclopedic Manual of the United Presbyterian Church of North America, (United Presbyterian Board of Publication, Pittsburgh, 1903) An exhaustive study of this denomination and its predecessors.

(33) Green, Ashbel, Presbyterian Missions (Anson D.F.Randolph & Co., New York, 1893) Helpful in reviewing Indian work. [Commissioned in 1837].

LeBeau, Bryan F., Jonathan Dickinson and the Formative Years of American Presbyterianism (University Press of Kentucky, Lexington, 1997)

(34) Loetscher, Lefferts A., A Brief History of the Presbyterians, Fourth Edition, (The Westminster Press, Philadelphia, 1983)

Parker, Harold M. Jr., The United Synod of the South: The Southern New School Presbyterian Church (Greenwood Press, New York/Westport,CT, 1988) While particularly interested in the independent southern New School church which existed 1858 to 1864, this book attempts to show its origins in the entire New School group, particularly in the south.

(35) Scouller, James Brown, History of the United Presbyterian Church of North America, in American Church History Volume XI (Christian Literature Co., New York, 1894)

Sweet, William Warren, Religion on the American Frontier 1783-1840: Vol. II. The Presbyterians (Cooper Square Publishers, New York, 1964 [reprint of 1936 edition]) A massive documentary overview of frontier missions in the period named.

(36) Trinterud, Leonard J., The Forming of An American Tradition: A Re-examination of American Presbyterianism (Westminster Press, Philadelphia, 1949) This is a ground breaking seminal work that documents the early connections of American Congregationalism and Presbyterianism.

Area Presbyterian Studies: (Arranged alphabetically)

(37) Alexander, S.D., The Presbytery of New York 1738-1888, (Anson D.F. Randolph, New York, c.1888) Includes histories of living, and many extinct or transferred churches served by this Presbytery.

(38) (Blade, Robert E., *et al*) Hudson River Presbytery Directory 1980 (Presbytery of Hudson River, Pleasantville (NY), 1980) Summary histories of living churches.

(39) Booth, William M., History of the Syracuse Presbytery 1796-1938 (Syracuse, 1938) Histories of living and some extinct churches.

(40) Buckley, E.A., Historical Sketch of the Presbytery of Champlain, (J.W.Tuttle and Co., Plattsburgh, 1877) A well-done summary.

Chemung Presbytery Historical Notes (folder at Presbyterian Historical Society, Philadelphia, n.d.)

Comin, John and Harold F. Fredsell, History of the Presbyterian Church in Michigan (Ann Arbor Press, Ann Arbor, 1950)

(41) Corss, Charles C., Presbytery of Susquehanna (n.p.,1875)

(42) Cumming, William J., The Presbyterian Church within the Field of the Presbytery of Westchester, Synod of New York 1660-1889 (Case, Lockwood, and Brainard, Hartford, 1889) Has tried to carefully document all living and extinct congregations.

(43) Dayton, Charles H., and John Garth Coleman, A Brief History of the Presbytery of Geneva and a Tribute to Some Early Ministers (Geneva-Lyons Presbytery, Shortsville (NY), 1955) Brief treatments of some church histories.

Eaton, S.J.M., History of the Presbytery of Erie (Hurd and Houghton, New York,1868) This book treats an area needing study, but since it follows the Old School side of the Presbytery division, it is weak on early Congregational inter-connections.

Eaton, S.J.M., Supplement to the History of the Presbytery of Erie (Presbytery of Erie, Franklin (PA), 1888)

Everett, Benjamin H., The History of the Presbytery of Westchester, (Theodore Gaus' Sons, Brooklyn, 1962)

(44) Fowler, P.H., Historical Sketch of Presbyterianism Within the Bounds of the Synod of Central New York,(Curtiss and Childs, Utica, 1877) Includes brief histories of living and some extinct or withdrawn churches.

(45) Hamlin, Henry A., A History of the Presbytery of Hudson 1681-1888 (Stivers, Slauson, and Boyd, Middletown (NY), 1888) Includes histories of living churches in the wide, re-merged Presbytery.

(46) Hammonds, Kenneth A., Historical Directory of Presbyterian Churches and Presbyteries of Greater Philadelphia, 1690-1990, (Presbyterian Historical Society, Philadelphia, 1993) An excellent study of living and extinct churches. This kind of thoroughness is seldom seen, and should be an example for others.

(46A) Historical Questionnaires of the Presbyterian Churches of the Synod of New York (4 volume collection of submissions, 1932)(at Presbyterian Historical Society, Philadelphia) Apparently collected by Robert H. Nichols, this is a treasure trove. While churches are asked their organization date, pastors, and former names, they are not asked about their former organizational forms, although some offer that information. Limited to living churches with some missing. This would probably be the best place to try to knit together a list of clergy serving in the Plan of Union.

(47) "History of the Presbytery of Albany," Journal of Presbyterian History, Vol.III,#5, (March, 1906, pp.224-235).

(48) Hotchkin, James H., A History of the Purchase and Settlement of Western New York and the Rise, Progress, and Present State of the Presbyterian Church in that Section (New York, 1848) The most important book on this area, Hotchkin reviews every church up to this date. However, his Presbyterian orientation often obscures early Congregationalism. He is also reluctant to use consistent language or to make summaries.

Miller, Adam, An Historical Discourse Delivered Before the Presbytery of Lackawanna (Benjamin Smerly, Harrisburg (PA), 1873). A treatment of the Montrose Presbytery.

(49) Nichols, Robert H., and James H. Nichols, Presbyterianism in New York State (Westminster Press, Philadelphia, 1963) An important overview.

Nicholson, George, The Story of the Long Island Presbytery and Churches (Long Island Presbytery, n.p., 1956)

Osmond, J., History of the Presbytery of Luzerne, State of Pennsylvania (Presbyterian Historical Society, Wilkes-Barre (PA), 1897)

(50) Owen, John J. "Complete List of the Presbyterian Ministers in the City of New York," American Quarterly Register Vol.VIII, #4 (May, 1836, pp.321-331) Histories of living and extinct churches for New York County.

(51) Parsons, Levi, History of the Rochester Presbytery (Democrat-Chronicle Press, Rochester, 1889) Includes histories of living and extinct churches.

(51B) Pattengill, J.S., History of the Presbytery of Binghamton (Carl, Stoppard and Co., Binghamton, 1877)

(52) Porter, J. Jermain, History of the Presbytery of Geneva (Geneva (NY), 1889) Includes more data on when churches affiliated to Presbytery than on their own histories.

"Presbytery of Champlain History" included under Clinton County in the 1880 *History of Clinton and Franklin Counties.*

Shaw, Augustus C., Presbytery of Pennsylvania – Presbytery of Wellsboro (1844-1888) (typescript, 1938) (at Presbyterian Historical Society, Philadelphia)

(53) Van Doren, Isaac, History of Presbytery of Hudson (1807, manuscript at Presbyterian Historical Society, Philadelphia) Includes histories of living churches in the smaller recently divided Presbytery area.

ANNOTATED BIBLIOGRAPHY

Ethnic Studies: (Arranged randomly, so as to conform use to numbering in the New England volume)

Annual Report of the Evangelical Free Church Association, (1944, 1946-1949 (5 Volumes))

(60) DeMond, A.L., "The Negro in the Congregational Churches of America," *Louisiana Congregational Association Minutes*, 1902 pp.12-20. This short early summary gives some helpful information on specific churches.

(61) Directory of the United Church of Christ Congregations of Minority Background (United Church Board for Homeland Ministries, New York, 1980) A listing of living Hispanic, Black, American Indian, and Pacific Asian congregations. The latter group is not broken down into sub-groups.

(62) Directory of UCC Black Churches and Ministers (Black Church Development Program, New York, 1976) A list of living Black churches.

(63) Directory of United Church of Christ Congregations with Black, Hispanic, Native American, Asian or Pacific Island Members, as of January 1988, (United Church Board for Homeland Ministries, New York, 1989) The most exhaustive study ever done of living churches, it not only breaks down each Pacific Asian group, but also shows ethnic percentages within congregations.

(64) Eisenach, George J., History of the German Congregational Churches in the United States, (Pioneer Press, Yankton (SD), 1938) An exhaustive study of living and extinct German churches.

(65) Hartmann, Edward George, Americans from Wales, (Christopher Publishing House, Boston, 1967) Includes a supposedly exhaustive list of living and extinct Welsh churches.

(66) Jones, David, Memorial Volume of Welsh Congregationalists in Pennsylvania, U.S.A. (Utica (NY), 1934) This is the best book for reconstructing Pennsylvania Welsh Churches before the *Yearbook* listings begin.

(66B) Norton, H. Wilbert, *et al*, The Diamond Jubilee Story of the Evangelical Free Church of America, (Free Church Publications, Minneapolis, 1959). See particularly *"Origin and Development of the Evangelical Free Church Association,"* by Olai Urang.

(67) Norton, Margery J., American Indian Missions of the Constituent Denominations of the UCC: A Preliminary Bibliography, (United Church Board for Homeland Ministries, typescript, 1980) An excellent overview of pre-1870 Indian work, with some outlines of later work.

(67B) Odegaard, R. Arlo, With Singleness of Heart, (Free Church Press, Minneapolis, n.d., c.1971) Norwegian and Danish churches.

Strong, William E., The Story of the American Board (Pilgrim Press, Boston,1910) Some help on Indian work.

(68) Thomas, R.D., *Hanes Cymry America* [A History of the Welsh in America (Utica,1872) Translated by Phillips G. Davies] (University Press of America, Lanham (MD),1983) Mentions most known living churches, but is weak on dating.

Thomas, R.D., "Welsh Congregational Churches in the United States," (taken from *Diary of the Welsh Congregational Churches in America* for 1858), Congregational Quarterly, Vol. II. (Oct.,1860, pp.401-404)

(69) Tracy, Joseph, "History of the American Board of Commissioners for Foreign Missions," and "History of the Board of Foreign Missions of the General Assembly of the Presbyterian Church in the United States of America," in History of American Missions to the Heathen from their Commencement to the Present Time (Spooner & Howland, Worcester, 1840) A helpful delineation of the early mission groups.

(70) Williams, Jay G. III., Memory Stones: A History of Welsh-Americans in Central New York (Purple Mountain Press, Fleischmanns (NY), c.1993) The best source for churches in this most important Welsh part of the State.

Presbyterian Listing Interface:

(75) This number is used to indicate listings in Presbyterian judicatories.

General Listings: In 1774 a list of congregations was published as "A List of the Ministers and Congregations, Whether Settled or Vacant, Belonging to the Rev.Synod of New York and Philadelphia," in Aitken's General American Register, and the Gentleman's and Tradesman's Complete Annual Account Book and Calendar, etc. (Joseph Cruickshank for R.Aitken, Philadelphia, 1774) We have used the list republished in Sweet (*Presbyterians (1964/1936*, pp.12-20) Thereafter church lists were published in the Synod Minutes of 1788 and in the *Minutes of the General Assembly of the Presbyterian Church, U.S.A.* for 1794,1798,1803,1809,1814,1819,and 1825-1834 and 1836-1958. This continuity follows the Old School minutes 1838-1869. The 1948 General Assembly minutes covered the part of the year for 1947. Thereafter all reports were for full calendar years. The 1952 Minutes include two complete calendar reports from 1951 and 1952. To conform to our usage for Congregational Churches, all years of listings contained here before the General Assembly minutes of 1947, mean in that year or the year later. For example, 1946 or 1947 is shown on the listings as 1946. New School lists were published by their General Assembly in 1839,1840,1843,1846,1849-1869. There were no lists in their 1838 Minutes. These are also reports for the year before the minutes or the year of the minutes, and are shown as the earlier year. These two bodies reunited in 1870. This body then united with the United Presbyterian Church of North America in 1958 to form the United Presbyterian Church, U.S.A.. Its Minutes of 1959 to 1979 include reports for 1959 to 1979. The Presbyterian Church in the U.S. (formerly the Presbyterian Church in the Confederate States of America) broke away in 1861. There are no new lists in its 1861,1862,1864, and 1865 Minutes. Lists appear in the 1863 and 1866-1980 minutes. The 1955 Minutes include a calendar year report for 1954. The 1954 Minutes covered part of 1953. In the 1953 and earlier Minutes reports are for part of the year of the Minutes and for part of the previous year. Here we have also conformed to our policy that the year shown in a non-calendar period as the year listed or dropped means in that year or the following year.

Merged reports: These two groups published their statistics together for the three years 1980-1982 (designated as part of the 1980-1982 Minutes of the United Presbyterian Church and the 1981-1983 Minutes of the Presbyterian Church U.S.). These two groups reunited in 1983 as the Presbyterian Church, U.S.A.. The Minutes of 1983-on have the calendar year statistics for 1983-on. The last year used was the 2001 statistics.

Labeling: In showing listings for these churches: "Pres." always refers to churches in the continuity of the New York and Philadelphia Synod, General Assembly, United Presbyterian Church, U.S.A., and Presbyterian Church U.S.A.. During the period 1837 to 1870 Old School (OS) or New School (NS) are always specified. Other Presbyterian bodies are specifically identified.

Sources: Most of the data included in this book for Presbyterian listings is based on the Russell Hall cards at the Presbyterian Historical Society in Philadelphia. (See the Hall entry below.) We have adjusted Hall's records to conform to our methodology of reporting, so that Presbyterian listings will be similar to Congregational listings. Hall began with the 1825 lists, and limits himself to the national minutes. We have inserted from the minutes data from before 1825 and from the date that the cards were written to the present (much of the latter also later being inserted by staff in Philadelphia). Initially the pre-1825 data is based on those years where the national lists tried to include all congregations (noted above.) Where possible we have also used lists in Synod or Presbytery minutes to fill in the pre-1825, 1835, and New School lacunas when lists were not published nationally. In the pre-1825 era, the Synod of New York and New Jersey has particularly good reports from the 1807 minutes on. There are many reliable upstate New York Presbytery reports in the Geneva Synod records from 1813 on. Some records have come from Synod reports, while others have been found in the Presbytery records. Hall tended to show a church as continually listed when it was dropped for a short lacuna. We have corrected these when we have found them. We have also researched and corrected some other miscellaneous errors that appear in his lists.

Early Information: While not including direct church data, we have studied early Presbytery and Synod records to trace the movement of Colonial clergy. See Minutes of the Presbyterian Church in America 1706-1788 (Guy S. Klett, Editor; Presbyterian Historical Society, Philadelphia, 1976)

Hall, Russell E., Index of Congregations of the Presbyterian Churches in the United States (Written card file of churches in the Presbyterian Historical Society, Philadelphia)

(75H) In the Hall cards in Philadelphia he has sometimes also added organization dates or other information in addition to listing dates. Where that is the case we indicate by using this code.

Interdenominational and Other Denominational Studies:

(79) Denton, Emily R., Prayer and Praise: Churches in Herkimer County 1723-1981 (Herkimer County Historical Society, n.p., 1981)

(80) Disosway, Gabriel P., Earliest Churches in New York and Its Vicinity, (James G.Gregory, New York, 1865)

(81) Downer, R.E. (Publisher), Buffalo Church Directory (Buffalo Council of Churches, Buffalo (NY), 1931) Includes brief histories and dates of many living churches.

The 1881 Year Book of the Churches of Essex and Union Counties (NJ) (A.L.Brice, Newark, 1881) Interdenominational list of living congregations with some additional data.

German Genealogical Research Volume I. (German Interest Group, Western Pennsylvania Genealogical Society, Pittsburgh, 1990) Documents several churches with dates and brief histories.

(82) Greenleaf, Jonathan, A History of the Churches of All Denominations in New York (E.French, New York, 1846) Histories of living and extinct congregations, limited to New York County.

The History of American Methodism (3 Volumes) (Abingdon, New York and Nashville, 1964)

(83) Holy Pittsburgh Records (Western Pennsylvania Genealogical Society, Pittsburgh,1990)

(84) Jamison, Wallace N., Religion in New Jersey: A Brief History (D. Van Norstrand Co., Princeton, 1964)

(85) Vanden Berge, Peter N., Historical Directory of the Reformed Church in America 1628-1978 (William B. Eerdmans Publishing Co., Grand Rapids (MI), 1978) This is the second modern edition of this *Directory* (the first being published in 1966). We have used this directory because it gives detailed locations missing in some other editions. These new modern editions extend the work of Edward Tanjore Corwin, who published five directories for this denomination beginning in 1859. Corwin's work is the model that anticipates similar directories in other Presbyterian, Reformed, and Unitarian groups, and the directories of which this volume is one.

(86) Ward, F. DeW., Churches of Rochester, (Erastus Darrow, Rochester, 1871) Histories of living and some extinct churches.

(90) [See Below]

Building Study:

(95) Rose, Harold Wickliffe, The Colonial Houses of Worship in America (Hastings House, New York, 1963) Includes all pre-1776 buildings surviving, with information on their congregations.

Schwenkfelder References:

Kriebel, Howard Wiegner, The Schwenkfelders in Pennsylvania (Pennsylvania German Society, Lancaster, PA, 1904)

Meschter, W. Kyrel, Twentieth Century Schwenkfelders (Schwenkfelder Library, Pennsburg, PA, 1984)

Special References:

(97) Correspondence carried on by this author with federated and dual churches and sometimes with other churches, libraries or scholars.

ANNOTATED BIBLIOGRAPHY

(98) The present author has looked over a large number of county histories and other local history sources too numerous to list.

(99) All other references. Includes local church histories, news clippings, etc..

Local, County, and State Histories and Location sources: (Arranged alphabetically)

Locating towns and cities was done by the use of a wide range of atlases and gazetteers both modern and from the historic periods involved. Correspondence with state and local historical societies and libraries was also used for difficult locations. These are too many in number to add to this bibliography. Other sources for state and county histories and related matters came from:

Espenshade, A. Howry, Pennsylvania Place Names, (Pennsylvania State College, State College, 1925) [Republished by Genealogical Publishing Co., Baltimore, 1970]

(90) French, J.H., Gazetteer of the State of New York, (R. Pearsall Smith, Syracuse, 1860) [Republished 1980 by Heart of the Lakes Publishing, Interlaken, NY.] Includes data on early religious work or churches in each township and the number of churches of each denomination (buildings) in each township at the time of publication (based on an 1855 New York Census).

Gannett, Henry, A Geographic Dictionary of New Jersey, (Government Printing House, Washington, 1894) [Republished by Genealogical Publishing Co., Baltimore, 1978]

Halverson, F.Douglas, County Histories of the United States Giving Present Name, Date Formed, Parent County, and County Seat, (mimeo,n.d.)

Hughes, Arthur H. and Morse S. Allen, Connecticut Place Names (Connecticut Historical Society, Hartford, 1976) Tracks town and county organization.

Kane, Joseph Nathan, The American Counties, (The Scarecrow Press, New York, 1960)

Kavenagh, W. Keith, Foundations of Colonial America: A Documentary History,(Vol. II: Middle Atlantic Colonies) (Chelsea House, New York, 1983)

Kirkham, E.Kay, A Genealogical And Historical Atlas Of The United States Of America,(Keith W. Watkins & Sons, Providence,Utah, 1980)

Long, John H., Historical Atlas and Chronology of County Boundaries 1788-1980 Volume I.: Delaware, Maryland, New Jersey, Pennsylvania (G.K.Hall & Co., Boston, 1984)

Long, John H., Editor, New York Atlas of Historical County Boundaries (Simon and Schuster, New York, 1993)

Spafford, Horatio Gates, A Gazetteer of the State of New York, (B.D.Packard, Albany and Troy, 1824) [Republished 1981 by Heart of the Lakes Publishing, Interlaken, NY.]

Ten Years of Change in ... Will Be Measured by the 1970 Census, (A series of pamphlets, one for each state, named at the ... location) (U.S.Department of Commerce, Bureau of the Census, Census '70, c.1969)

Thornapple, William and William Dollarhide, Map Guide to the U.S. Federal Censuses 1790-1920, (Genealogical Publishing Co.Inc.,Baltimore, 1987)

INTRODUCTION TO THE INDEXES

Index to the Introductory Text

The index to the introductory text covers the main text including the Development of the Middle Atlantic States, Contributions Towards a History, Some Considerations about Definitions, Ethnicity, and the first part of the section on Congregational Organization (through the General Congregational Bodies ending on page 101).

The index does not include the latter sections on Congregational Organization, nor the section on Presbyterian Organization (pages 101-112). These sections are mostly directories of inter-church Congregational bodies, and Presbyterian judicatories. They are organized in chronological and similar ways to ease their use. Neither does the index cover the Introduction nor Preface.

Congregational inter-church and ministerial bodies are all listed under "Congregational." Presbyterian judicatories are listed under the name of their church of affiliation, such as "Presbyterian Church, U.S.A." Similar patterns are used for parallel inter-church bodies and judicatories with other affiliations.

Individual local congregations are given at their primary town of location, and not under their congregational name.

Italics indicate the name of a publication.

Index to Communities

This index is divided into four sections: New Jersey, New York, Pennsylvania, and a list of communities in other states.

Lists are alphabetical for local place names and minor civil divisions (in the left county), and identify the county of location where that that community may be found (in the right column). An asterisk (*) indicates that this is a minor civil division provided here for location purposes that was never used as a specific list reference for any congregation.

A numeral in parentheses following the local place name indicates that location can only be found in the appendix with that number. ("2" would indicate Appendix II. only.)

A numeral following a plus sign (+) following the local place name indicates that location can be found both in the main church list and in the appendix with that number. ("+3" would indicate the main church list and Appendix III.)

Local place names and minor civil divisions without numerical designations may be found in the main church lists.

A "see also" entry in the county column indicates that a church may be found in a different county, even if the community listed is in the county designated first. Such locations are not necessarily listed for a congregation in the actual county of location. Two counties given in the county column indicate that the community straddles a county line. Churches are shown in their actual county of location, and there are not necessarily congregations listed in all counties served by the incorporated community.

The abbreviation "Soc." indicates a society or parish name often used as a form of location.

INDEX TO INTRODUCTORY TEXT

C

D

O

P

INDEX TO INTRODUCTORY TEXT

Q

R

S

T

U

CITY OR TOWN	COUNTY
NEW JERSEY	
Allamauchy Twn. (3)	Warren
Amboy	Middlesex
Asbury Park	Monmouth
Augusta	Sussex
Baptistown (3)	Monmouth
Beemer	Sussex
Beemersville	Sussex
Berkeley Heights (3)	Union, see also Morris (3)
Berkshire Valley	Morris
Bernardsville	Somerset
Black River	Morris
Blackwell	Camden
Blackwood	Camden
Blairstown	Warren
Bloomfield	Essex
Boonton	Morris
Bottle Hill	Morris
Bound Brook	Somerset
Branchville	Sussex
Bridgewater Twn.	Somerset
Brookside (2)	Morris
Buckshire Valley	Morris
Buena Vista Twn.	Atlantic
Caldwell	Essex
Camden	Camden
Cape May	Cape May
Cedar Grove (+2)	Essex
Chatham	Morris
Chatham Village	Morris
Cherry Hill (3)	Camden
Chester	Morris
Cliffside Park	Bergen
Closter (+3)	Bergen
Clove	Sussex
Cohansey	Cumberland
Cold Spring	Cape May
Connecticut Farms	Union
Coontown	Somerset

CITY OR TOWN	COUNTY
Coytesville	Bergen
Cresskill (+3)	Bergen
Daretown	Salem
Deckertown	Sussex
Delaware Twn. (3)	Camden
Delaware Twn. (4)	Hunterdon
Dover	Morris
Dover Twn. (3)	Ocean
East Brunswick (3)	Middlesex
East Hanover	Morris
East Orange (+3)	Essex
Egg Harbor City	Atlantic
Elizabeth	Union
Elizabeth Twn.	Union
Elizabethport	Union
Elizabethtown	Union
Emerson (2)	Bergen
Englewood	Bergen
Essex Fells	Essex
Etna (2)	Bergen
Ewing	Mercer
Fairfield	Cumberland
Fairmount	Bergen
Fairton	Cumberland
Feltsville (1)	Union
Flanders	Morris
Forest Grove	Gloucester
Fort Lee	Bergen
Frankford (Twn.)	Sussex
Frankford Plains	Sussex
Franklin Dist.	Essex
Franklin Twn.	Gloucester
Franklinville	Gloucester
Freehold (+3)	Monmouth
Frehill	Monmouth
Frelinghuysen Twn.	Warren
Garfield	Bergen
Glen Ridge	Essex
Gloucester Twn.	Camden
Grantwood	Bergen
Grasselli Park	Union
Groveland	Essex

CITY OR TOWN	COUNTY
Guttenburg	Hudson
Hackensack	Bergen
Hackettstown (3)	Warren
Hamburg	Sussex
Hanover (Twn.)	Morris
Hanover Neck	Morris
Hardwick (Twn.)	Warren
Hardyston (Twn.)	Sussex
Harrington Twn.	Bergen
Hasbrouck Heights (+2)	Bergen
Haworth	Bergen
Hoboken	Hudson
Holmdel (3)	Monmouth
Hopewell	Mercer
Horseneck	Essex
Irvington	Essex, see also Union
Jefferson Twn.	Morris, see also Passaic
Jersey City	Hudson
Johnsonburg	Warren
Landis Twn.	Cumberland
Lawrenceville	Mercer
Levittown (3)	Burlington
Linden	Union
Lindenwold	Camden
Linwood	Bergen
Little Egg Harbor (4)	Ocean
Little Falls	Passaic
Little Ferry	Bergen
Livingston (+2)	Essex
Lodi	Bergen
Log Gaol	Warren
Long Branch	Monmouth
Long Pond	Passaic
Lower German Valley	Morris
Lower Twn.	Cape May
Madison (+3)	Morris
Maidenhead	Mercer
Manalpan Twn.	Monmouth
Manasquan	Monmouth

CITY OR TOWN	COUNTY
Center Moriches	Suffolk
Center Reach	Suffolk
Center Wheeler	Steuben
Centerfield	Ontario
Centerville	Allegany
Centerville	Greene
Centerville	Orange
Central Berkshire	Tioga
Central Binghamton	Broome
Central Nyack	Rockland
Central Square	Oswego
Centre Lisle	Broome
Chalmers	Niagara
Champion	Jefferson
Champlain	Clinton
Chapin	Ontario
Chapin Mills	Ontario
Chapinville	Ontario
Chappaqua	Westchester
Charleston	Livingston
Charlestown	Saratoga
Charlotte	Chautauqua
Charlotte	Monroe
Charlotte Precinct	Dutchess
Charlton	Saratoga
Chataque	Chautauqua
Chateaugay	Franklin
Chatham	Columbia
Chaumont	Jefferson
Chautauqua	Chautauqua
Chautauqua Cross Roads	Chautauqua
Chazy	Clinton
Cheektowaga (+2)	Erie
Cheesecocks	Orange
Chehocton	Delaware
Chelsea	New York
Chemung	Chemung
Chenango	Broome
Chenango Forks	Broome
Chenango Point	Broome
Cherry Creek	Chautauqua
Cherry Valley	Otsego

CITY OR TOWN	COUNTY
Chesecocks	Orange
Cheshire (3)	Ontario
Chester	Orange
Chester	Warren
Chesterfield	Essex, see also Clinton
Chestertown	Warren
Chili (+3)	Monroe
China	Wyoming
Chippeway Street	St. Lawrence
Chittenango	Madison
Chittenango Station	Madison
Churchville	Monroe
Cicero	Onondaga
Cicero Corners	Onondaga
Cilicia (Soc.)	Chenango
Cincinnatus	Cortland
Circleville	Orange
Clarence	Erie
Clarence Hollow	Erie
Clarence Union	Erie
Clarendon	Orleans, see also Genesee
Clark's Settlement	Broome
Clarks Corners (4)	Chautauqua
Clarkson	Monroe
Clarkson Corners	Monroe
Clarkstown	Rockland
Claverack	Columbia
Clay (3)	Onondaga
Clayton	Jefferson
Clayville	Oneida
Clear Creek	Cattaraugus
Clinton	Dutchess
Clinton	Oneida
Clinton Heights	Rensselaer
Clintonville	Clinton
Clove	Orange
Clyde	Wayne, see also Seneca
Clymer	Chautauqua
Clymer Hill	Chautauqua

CITY OR TOWN	COUNTY
Cobleskill	Schoharie
Cohecton	Sullivan
Cohocton	Steuben
Cohoes	Albany
Coila (4)	Washington
Colchester	Delaware
Cold Creek	Allegany
Cold Spring	Cattaraugus
Cold Spring	Putnam
Cold Spring	Suffolk
Colden	Erie
Coldwater	Monroe
Cole's Hill	Broome
Colesville	Broome
Collamer	Onondaga
Collins	Erie, see also Cattaraugus
Collins	Unlocated
Colonie	Albany
Colton	St. Lawrence
Columbia	Herkimer
Columbia	St. Lawrence
Columbia (Soc.)	Delaware
Columbia (Soc.)	Onondaga
Columbia (Soc.)	Tioga
Columbian (Soc.)	Onondaga
Columbus	Chenango
Comac	Suffolk
Commack	Suffolk
Concord	Erie
Concord	Unlocated
Concord (Soc.)	Wyoming
Concord Union (Soc.)	Herkimer
Conesus (+2)	Livingston
Conewango	Cattaraugus
Conewango Valley	Cattaraugus
Coney Island	Kings
Conklin	Broome
Constable	Franklin
Constableville	Lewis
Constantia (+2)	Oswego

CITY OR TOWN	COUNTY	CITY OR TOWN	COUNTY	CITY OR TOWN	COUNTY
Hamilton Center	Madison	Hebe	Cattaraugus	Horicon	Warren
Hamilton Union	Albany	Hebe	Wyoming	Hornby	Steuben
Hamiltonville	Oswego	Hebron	Washington	Hornell	Steuben
Hammond	St. Lawrence	Hector (+1)	Schuyler	Hornellsville	Steuben
Hammondsport	Steuben	Hedgesville	Steuben	Hornsby	Steuben
Hammondsville	Oswego	Helena	St. Lawrence	Horseheads	Chemung
Hammondville	Essex	Hempstead	Rockland	Hounsfield	Jefferson
Hampden	Delaware	Hempstead (+2,+4)	Nassau, see	Houseville	Lewis
Hampton	Washington		also Queens	Howard	Steuben
Hancock	Delaware	Henderson	Jefferson	Howell's Depot	Orange
Hancock (Soc.)	Oneida	Henrietta (+2,+3)	Monroe	Howells (+3)	Orange
Hannibal	Oswego	Herkimer (+4)	Herkimer	Hudson	Columbia
Hannibalville	Oswego	Herman	St. Lawrence	Hudson Falls	Washington,
Hannover	Westchester	Hermon	St. Lawrence		see also
Hanover	Chautauqua	Heuvelton	St. Lawrence		Warren
Hanover	Westchester	Highland	Sullivan	Hughsonville	Dutchess
Hanover (Soc.)	Oneida	Highland	Ulster	Hume	Allegany
Harford	Cortland	Highland Falls	Orange	Humphrey Hollow	Wyoming
Harlem	New York	Highlands	Orange	Hunt('s) Hollow	Livingston
Harmony	Chautauqua	Highlands	Putnam	Hunter	Greene
Harmony (Soc.)	Herkimer	Highlands West	Orange	Huntington (+2)	Suffolk
Harmony (Soc.)	Otsego	Hillburn	Rockland	Huntington South	Suffolk
Harpersfield	Delaware	Hillsdale	Columbia	Huntsville	Otsego
Harpersville	Broome	Hillville	Orleans	Huron	Wayne
Harpersville	Delaware	Hoag's Corners	Rensselaer	Independence	Allegany
Harrisburg(h)	Lewis	Hobart	Delaware	Inverness	Monroe
Harrison	Cortland	Hockabogue	Suffolk	Inwood (4)	Nassau
Harrison	Franklin	Hoffman	Essex	Ionia	Onondaga
Harrison	Jefferson	Holland	Erie	Ira	Cayuga
Harrison (Soc.)	Jefferson	Holland Patent (+1)	Oneida	Irelandville	Schuyler
Harrisville	Lewis	Holley	Orleans	Irondequoit	Monroe
Hart's Falls	Rensselaer	Hollis Woods (3)	Queens	Ironville	Essex
Hartfield	Chautauqua	Hollywood	St. Lawrence	Irving	Chautauqua,
Hartford	Livingston	Holtsville	Suffolk		see also
Hartford	Washington	Homer	Cortland		Cattaraugus
Hartland	Niagara	Honeoye	Ontario	Ischua	Cattaraugus
Hartwick	Otsego	Honeoye Falls	Monroe	Island	Erie
Hastings	Oswego	Hoosick	Rensselaer	Islip	Suffolk
Havanna(h)	Schuyler	Hoosick Falls	Rensselaer	Ithaca	Tompkins
Haven's Corners	Livingston	Hopewell	Ontario	Jamaica (+2)	Queens
Haverstraw	Rockland	Hopewell	Orange	Jamesport	Suffolk
Head of Delaware	Delaware	Hopkinton	St. Lawrence	Jamestown (+4)	Chautauqua

CITY OR TOWN	COUNTY
Jamesville	Onondaga
Jamesville	Washington
Jasper	Steuben
Java	Wyoming
Java Village	Wyoming
Jay	Essex
Jefferson	Cayuga
Jefferson	Schoharie
Jefferson (+1)	Schuyler
Jericho	Chenango
Jericho	Unlocated
Jersey	Schuyler
Jersey Settlement	Herkimer
Jerseyfield Patent	Herkimer
Jerusalem	Yates
Jerusalem Hill	Herkimer
Jewett	Greene
Jimersontown	Cattaraugus
Jimerstown	Cattaraugus
Johnsonburg	Wyoming
Johnsonville	Rensselaer
Johnstown (+4)	Fulton
Jones Settlement	Chautauqua
Jordan	Onondaga
Joy	Wayne
Junius	Seneca
Kakiate	Rockland
Kanona	Steuben
Katiate	Rockland
Katonah	Westchester
Kayderosies Patent	Saratoga
Keene	Essex
Keene Flats	Essex
Keene Plains	Essex
Keene Valley	Essex
Keeseville	Clinton & Essex
Kendall	Orleans
Kenmore (2)	Erie
Kennedy (4)	Chautauqua
Kennedyville	Steuben
Kent's (Par.)	Putnam

CITY OR TOWN	COUNTY
Kenyonville	Orleans
Ketchaboneck (Par.)	Suffolk
Kiantone	Chautauqua
Kinderhook	Columbia
King's District	Columbia
Kings Ferry	Cayuga
Kingsborough	Fulton
Kingsbury	Washington, see also Warren
Kingston	Ulster
Kirkland	Oneida
Kirkville (+3)	Onondaga, see also Madison
Kirland	Onondaga
Knowlesville	Orleans
Knox	Albany
Knox Corners	Oneida
Knoxville	Steuben
Lackawanna	Erie
LaFargeville	Jefferson
Lafayette	Onondaga
LaGrange	Dutchess
LaGrangeville	Dutchess
Lake George	Warren
Lake Grove	Suffolk
Lake Huntington	Sullivan
Lake Pleasant (4)	Hamilton
Lake View	Erie
Lakemont	Yates
Lakeport	Madison
Lakeville	Livingston
Lakeville Estates (2)	Nassau
Lakewood	Chautauqua
Lancaster	Chenango
Lancaster	Erie
Lansing	Tompkins, see also Cayuga
Lansingburgh	Rensselaer
Lansingville	Tompkins

CITY OR TOWN	COUNTY
LaSalle	Niagara
Laurel	Suffolk
Laurens	Otsego
Lawrence	St. Lawrence
Lawrence (4)	Nassau
Lawrenceville	St. Lawrence
Layville	Suffolk
Leander	Tioga
Lebanon	Madison
Lebanon (Soc.)	Columbia
Ledyard	Cayuga
Lee	Oneida
Leeville	Madison
Leicester	Livingston
Lenox	Madison
Leon	Cattaraugus
LeRay	Jefferson
LeRoy	Genesee
Lew Beach	Sullivan
Lewis	Essex
Lewis	Lewis
Lewisboro	Westchester
Lewiston	Niagara
Lewisville	Essex
Lexington	Greene
Lexington Flats	Greene
Lexington Heights	Greene
Leyden	Lewis
Leyden Hill	Lewis
Liberty	Sullivan
Liberty Corners	Steuben
Lima	Livingston
Lime (Soc.)	Genesee
Lincklaen	Chenango
Lincoln	Ontario
Lindley	Steuben
Lisbon	Otsego
Lisbon	St. Lawrence
Lisbon (Soc.)	Oneida
Lisle	Broome, see also Cortland

CITY OR TOWN	COUNTY
Litchfield	Herkimer
Litchfield (Soc.)	Chenango, see also Herkimer
Little Falls	Herkimer
Little Four Corners	Chenango
Little Nine Partners	Dutchess
Little Quoque	Suffolk
Little Valley	Cattaraugus
Littleville	Livingston
Liverpool (+3)	Onondaga
Livingstonville	Schoharie
Livonia	Livingston
Livonia Center	Livingston
Lloyd	Ulster
Locke	Cayuga, see also Tompkins
Lockport (+4)	Niagara
Lodi	Seneca
Lodi (Soc.)	Cattaraugus
Lodius	Wayne
Long Beach (3)	Nassau
Long Lake	Hamilton
Long's Corners	Genesee
Lorraine	Jefferson
Louisville	St. Lawrence
Lowell	Oneida
Lower Allegany	Cattaraugus
Lower Aquebogue	Suffolk
Lower Cattaraugus	Cattaraugus
Lower Greenburg	Westchester
Lower Massena	St. Lawrence
Lower Norfolk	St. Lawrence
Lower Salem	Westchester
Lowville	Lewis
Ludlowville	Tompkins
Lumberland	Sullivan
Lundy's Corners	Seneca
Luzerne	Warren, see also Saratoga

CITY OR TOWN	COUNTY
Lyme	Jefferson
Lyme (Soc.)	Genesee
Lyndonville	Orleans
Lyons	Wayne
Lyons Falls	Lewis
Lyonsdale	Lewis
Lysander	Onondaga
MacDougall	Seneca
Machias	Cattaraugus
Macomb	St. Lawrence
Madison	Madison
Madrid	St. Lawrence
Mahopac	Putnam
Mahopac Falls	Putnam
Maidstone	Suffolk
Maine	Broome
Makolm	Seneca
Malden	Ulster
Malden-on-Hudson	Ulster
Malone	Franklin
Malta (+4)	Saratoga
Maltaville	Saratoga
Mamakating	Sullivan, see also Orange
Manchester	Niagara
Manchester	Ontario
Manhasset (2)	Nassau
Manhattan (+1,+2,+3, +4)	New York, see also Bronx
Manhattan Island	New York
Manhattan Terrace	Kings
Manhattanville	New York
Manheim	Herkimer
Manlius	Onondaga, see also Madison
Manlius Center	Onondaga
Manlius Four Corners	Onondaga
Mannsville	Jefferson
Mannsville	Suffolk
Manny('s) Corner	Montgomery

CITY OR TOWN	COUNTY
Manorville	Suffolk
Mapestown	Orange
Maplecrest	Greene
Mapleton	Cayuga
Mapleton	Niagara
Mapleton Park	Kings
Marathon	Cortland
Marcellus	Onondaga
Marcy	Oneida
Mariaville	Schenectady
Marietta	Onondaga
Marion	Wayne
Marlboro	Ulster
Marlborough	Ulster
Marshall	Oneida
Martinsburg(h)	Lewis
Maryland	Otsego
Masonville	Delaware
Massena	St. Lawrence
Massena Center	St. Lawrence
Mastic	Suffolk
Mattatana	Suffolk
Matteawan	Dutchess
Matthews Mills	Onondaga
Mattituck	Suffolk
Mayfield	Fulton
Mayville	Chautauqua
McConnellsville (3)	Oneida
McDonough	Chenango
McGraw	Cortland
McGrawville	Cortland
McLean (2)	Tompkins
Meads Creek	Steuben, see also Schuyler
Mechanic(s)ville	Saratoga
Mecklenburgh	Schuyler
Mede's Creek	Schuyler
Medina	Orleans
Melville	Orleans
Melville	Suffolk
Mendon	Monroe

CITY OR TOWN	COUNTY
Mentz	Cayuga
Meredith	Delaware
Meridian	Cayuga
Mexico	Oswego, see also Oneida
Mexicoville	Oswego
Middelberg	Queens
Middle Granville	Washington
Middle Island (3)	Suffolk
Middlebury	Wyoming
Middlefield	Otsego
Middlefield Center	Otsego
Middleport	Niagara
Middlesex	Yates
Middletown	Delaware
Middletown	Ontario
Middletown	Orange
Midwout	Kings
Milan	Cayuga
Milford	Otsego
Miller('s) Place	Suffolk
Millerton	Dutchess
Millport	Chemung
Millville	Orleans
Milo	Yates
Milton	Cayuga & Tompkins
Milton	Saratoga
Milton	Ulster
Mina	Chautauqua
Mineville	Essex
Minisink	Orange
Miscico	Oswego
Mixville	Allegany
Mohawk Indian Mission	Unlocated
Moira	Franklin
Monroe	Orange
Monsey	Rockland
Montague	Lewis
Montauk	Suffolk
Monterey	Schuyler
Montezuma	Cayuga

CITY OR TOWN	COUNTY
Montgomery	Orange
Monticello	Otsego
Monticello	Sullivan
Montour	Schuyler
Montour Falls	Schuyler
Montrose	Westchester
Mooers	Clinton
Moorehouse Flats	Onondaga
Moravia	Cayuga
Moreau	Saratoga
Moreland	Schuyler
Moresvile	Delaware
Moriah	Essex
Moriches	Suffolk
Moriches Center	Suffolk
Morris Flats	Madison
Morrisania	Bronx
Morristown	St. Lawrence
Morrisville	Jefferson
Morrisville	Madison
Moscow	Livingston
Moscow (2)	Tompkins
Mott's Corners	Tompkins
Mount Hope (+3)	Orange
Mount Morris	Livingston
Mount Pleasant	Westchester
Mount Sinai	Suffolk
Mount Vernon	Oneida
Mount Vernon	Westchester
Mud Creek	Steuben
Mumford	Monroe
Mumfordville	Monroe
Munnsville	Madison
Murray	Orleans, see also Monroe
Nanticoke	Broome
Naples	Ontario
Napoli	Cattaraugus
Narrow Falls	Sullivan
Nassau	Rensselaer
Nassau Union	Rensselaer
Natural Bridge	Jefferson

CITY OR TOWN	COUNTY
Nelson	Madison
Nelson Flats	Madison
Neversink	Sullivan
New Berlin	Chenango
New Brighton	Richmond
New Canaan	Columbia
New Castle	Westchester
New City	Rockland
New Concord	Columbia
New Cornwall	Orange
New Durham	Greene
New Hamburg(h)	Dutchess
New Hampton	Orange
New Harlem	Fulton
New Hartford	Oneida
New Haven	Oswego
New Hempstead	Rockland
New Hudson	Allegany
New Hyde Park (2)	Nassau
New Lebanon	Columbia, see also Rensselaer
New Lisbon	Otsego
New London	Oneida
New Lots	Kings
New Marlborough	Ulster
New Paltz	Ulster
New Paltz Landing	Ulster
New Perth	Washington
New Petersburgh	Oneida
New Road	Delaware
New Rochelle	Westchester
New Scotland	Albany
New Shawangunk	Orange
New Stamford	Delaware
New Stockbridge	Madison
New Town	Suffolk
New Utrecht	Kings
New Vernon (3)	Orange
New Village	Suffolk
New Windsor	Orange

CITY OR TOWN	COUNTY
New York City (+1,+2, +3,+4)	Bronx (2,3, 4), Kings (1,3,4),New York (1,2, 3,4),Queens (2,3), Richmond (3), see also Nassau
New York Mills	Oneida
Newark	Tioga
Newark	Wayne
Newark Valley	Tioga
Newburgh (+1)	Orange, see also Dutchess (1)
Newfield	Tompkins
Newport	Herkimer
Newport	Orleans
Newry	Greene
Newstead	Erie
Newtown	Chemung
Newtown	Queens
Niagara	Niagara
Niagara City	Niagara
Niagara Falls	Niagara
Nichols	Tioga, see also Bradford, PA
Nine Mile Creek	Onondaga
Nine Partners	Dutchess
Ninety Six	Oneida
Nineveh	Broome
Nineveh	Chenango
Nisseauag	Suffolk
Noblesville	Otsego
Norfolk	St. Lawrence
Normansville (4)	Albany
North Adams	Jefferson
North Amenia	Dutchess
North Avon	Livingston
North Bangor	Franklin

CITY OR TOWN	COUNTY
North Bay	Oneida
North Bergen	Genesee
North Berkshire	Tioga
North Blenheim	Schoharie
North Burke	Franklin
North Castle	Westchester
North Chatham	Columbia
North Collins	Erie
North Dansville	Livingston
North Elba	Essex
North Evans	Erie
North Franklin	Delaware
North Granville	Washington
North Greig	Lewis
North Guilford	Chenango
North Harmony	Chautauqua
North Hempstead (+2, +3)	Nassau
North Hudson	Essex
North Java	Wyoming
North Junius	Seneca
North Lawrence	St. Lawrence
North Manlius	Onondaga
North New York	Bronx
North Norwich	Chenango
North Penfield	Monroe
North Pitcher	Chenango
North Potsdam	St. Lawrence
North Rochester	Monroe
North Salem	Westchester
North Troy	Rensselaer
North Valley	Allegany
North Walton	Delaware
Northampton	Fulton, see also Saratoga
Northampton	Genesee
Northampton	Monroe
Northeast	Dutchess
Northeast Center	Dutchess
Northfield	Delaware
Northfield	Monroe

CITY OR TOWN	COUNTY
Northfield	Richmond
Northfield	Saratoga
Northfield	Seneca
Northport	Suffolk
Northumberland	Saratoga
Northville	Cayuga
Northville	Fulton, see also Saratoga
Northville	Suffolk
Northwest	Schuyler
Nortons Mills	Monroe
Norway	Herkimer
Norwich	Chenango
Norwich (Soc.)	Chenango
Norwich (Soc.)	Herkimer
Norwich Corners	Herkimer
Norwood	St. Lawrence
Nunda	Livingston, see also Wyoming
Nyack	Rockland
Oak Creek	Otsego
Oak Grove (2)	Erie
Oak Orchard	Orleans
Oakfield	Genesee
Oakland	Livingston
Oaks Corners	Ontario
Oakwood Heights	Richmond
Oblong	Dutchess
Oceanus	Queens
Ogden	Monroe
Ogden Center	Monroe
Ogdensburg	St. Lawrence
Ohio	Herkimer
Old Fort Schuyler	Oneida
Old Mans	Suffolk
Old South Haven	Suffolk
Old Southold	Suffolk
Old Town	Cattaraugus
Oldenbarneveld	Oneida
Olean	Cattaraugus

CITY OR TOWN	COUNTY
Veddersburgh	Montgomery
Vernon (+1)	Oneida
Vernon Center (+1)	Oneida
Vernon Heights	Westchester
Vernon Valley	Suffolk
Verona	Oneida
Versailles	Cattaraugus
Vestal (4)	Broome, see also Chenango (4)
Veteran	Chemung
Victor	Ontario
Victory	Cayuga
Vienna	Oneida
Vienna	Ontario
Villenova	Chautauqua
Virgil	Cortland
Volney	Oswego
Voorheesville	Albany
Waddington	St. Lawrence
Wadhams	Essex
Wadhams Falls	Essex
Wadhams Mills	Essex
Wading River	Suffolk
Waldberg	Rockland
Wales	Erie
Wallkill	Orange
Walton	Delaware
Walworth	Wayne
Walworth Corners	Wayne
Wampsville	Madison
Wantagh	Nassau
Wappingers Creek	Dutchess
Warner	Onondaga
Warner's Settlement	Onondaga
Warnertown	Suffolk
Warren	Herkimer
Warrensburg	Warren
Warrenton	Suffolk
Warsaw	Wyoming
Warsaw	Yates
Warwick	Orange

CITY OR TOWN	COUNTY
Washington	Dutchess
Washington (Soc.)	Onondaga
Washington Heights	New York
Washington Hollow	Dutchess
Washington Mills	Oneida
Washingtonville	Orange
Wassaic	Dutchess
Waterboro(ugh)	Chautauqua
Waterford	Saratoga
Waterloo	Chautauqua
Waterloo	Seneca
Watertown	Jefferson
Watertown (Soc.)	Jefferson
Waterville	Oneida
Watervliet	Albany
Watkins	Schuyler
Watkins Glen (+1)	Schuyler
Watson	Lewis
Waverly	Cattaraugus
Waverly	Tioga
Wawayanda	Orange
Wayland	Steuben
Wayne	Steuben
Wayne	Wayne
Weakland (4)	Chautauqua
Weathersfield	Wyoming
Weathersfield Springs	Wyoming
Webster (+2)	Monroe
Weddersburgh	Montgomery
Weedsport	Cayuga
Wells River	Unlocated
Wellsburg	Chemung
Wellsville	Allegany
West Albany	Albany
West Aurora	Erie
West Bloomfield	Ontario
West Brook	Delaware
West Brunswick	Herkimer
West Cambridge	Washington
West Camden	Oneida
West Carthage	Jefferson
West Coventry	Chenango

CITY OR TOWN	COUNTY
West Delhi	Delaware
West Dresden	Yates
West Durham	Greene
West Eaton	Madison
West Falls	Erie
West Farms	Bronx
West Fayette	Seneca
West Forest Hills (2)	Queens
West Fredericksburg	Putnam
West Gainesville	Wyoming
West Galway	Fulton
West Greece	Monroe
West Groton	Tompkins
West Hartwick	Otsego
West Haverstraw	Rockland
West Hermon	St. Lawrence
West Hill	Chenango
West Hill	Onondaga
West Hill	Tompkins
West Java	Wyoming
West Lisle	Broome
West Locke	Cayuga
West Mendon	Monroe
West Monroe	Oswego
West Moriah	Essex
West Nassau	Rensselaer
West New Brighton	Richmond
West Newark	Tioga
West Otto	Cattaraugus
West Point	Essex
West Point	Orange
West Port	Essex
West Potsdam	St. Lawrence
West Pulteney	Steuben, see also Monroe
West Riga	Monroe
West Salamanca	Cattaraugus
West Seneca	Erie
West Somers	Westchester
West Sparta	Livingston
West Springfield	Otsego
West Stockbridge	Madison

CITY OR TOWN	COUNTY
West Town	Orange
West Troy	Albany
West Turin	Lewis
West Union	Tioga
West Willink	Erie
West Windsor	Orange
West Winfield	Herkimer
Westbury (3)	Nassau
Westchester	Bronx, see also Westchester
Westdale	Oneida
Westerleigh (+3)	Richmond
Westerlo	Albany
Western	Oneida
Western	Tioga
Western (Soc.)	Putnam
Western Exchange	Cayuga
Western Hill	Oneida
Westernville	Oneida
Westfield	Chautauqua
Westfield	Richmond
Westfield	Washington
Westfield (Soc.)	Dutchess
Westfield Flats	Sullivan
Westford	Otsego
Westhampton	Suffolk
Westhampton Beach	Suffolk
Westminster (Soc.)	Dutchess
Westmoreland	Oneida
Weston	Monroe
Weston	Schuyler
Weston	Tioga
Weston (Soc.)	Tioga
Westport	Essex
Westtown	Orange
Westville	Franklin
Westville	Tioga
Westville	Unlocated
Wethersfield	Wyoming
Wethersfield Springs	Wyoming
Whallonsburg(h)	Essex
Wheatfield	Niagara
Wheatland	Monroe
Wheeler	Steuben
White Lake	Sullivan
White Plains	Westchester
Whitehall	Washington
Whitelaw	Madison
Whitesboro	Oneida
Whitestown	Oneida
Whiting's Point	Broome
Whitney Point	Broome
Whitney's Point	Broome
Wick	Unlocated
Willet	Cortland
Williams Bridge	Bronx
Williamsburg	Livingston
Williamsburg(h)	Kings
Williamson	Wayne
Williamstown	Oswego
Willink	Erie, see also Niagara
Williston Park (3)	Nassau
Willsboro(ugh)	Essex
Wilmington	Essex
Wilna	Jefferson
Wilson	Niagara
Winchester	Erie
Winchester	Wayne
Windham	Greene
Windham Center	Greene
Windsor	Broome
Winfield	Herkimer
Winfield Center	Herkimer
Winthrop	St. Lawrence
Winthrop's Patent	Suffolk
Wolcott	Wayne, see also Cayuga
Woodhaven (+3)	Queens
Woodhull	Steuben
Woodville	Jefferson
Worcester	Otsego
Wormley	Steuben
Wyoming	Wyoming
Yamphank Neck	Suffolk
Yates	Orleans
Yonkers	Westchester
York	Livingston
York Center	Livingston
Yorkshire (Par.)	Broome
Yorktown	Westchester
Yorktown Heights	Westchester
Yorkville	New York
Youngstown	Niagara

PENNSYLVANIA

CITY OR TOWN	COUNTY
Ackley	Warren
Akeley	Warren
Albion	Erie
Alden	Luzerne
Allegheney (Twn.)	Blair
Allegheny City	Allegheny
Allentown	Lehigh
Allison Park	Allegheny
Altoona (3)	Blair
Angels	Wayne
Antrim	Tioga
Ararat	Susquehanna
Armagh (Twn.) (+2)	Mifflin
Arnot	Tioga
Ashland	Schuylkill & Columbia
Ashley	Luzerne
Ashton	Carbon
Athens	Bradford
Atlantic (4)	Crawford
Audenreid	Carbon
Baltimore Patch	Luzerne
Bangor	Northampton
Banks (Twn.)	Carbon
Barbertown	Unlocated
Beach	Lackawanna
Beach Pond	Lackawanna
Beachwood	Lackawanna
Beaver Dam	Erie
Beaver Falls (+3)	Beaver
Beaver Meadows	Carbon
Beech Woods	Lackawanna
Beecher's Island	Tioga
Bellemont	Luzerne (ps. Schuylkill)
Belmont	Luzerne (ps. Schuylkill)
Bessemer	Lawrence
Bethany	Wayne
Bethlehem (3)	Northampton & Lehigh
Beulah	Cambria
Birmingham	Allegheny
Black Creek (Twn.)	Luzerne
Black Walnut Bottom	Wyoming
Bloomfield	Allegheny
Bloomfield (Twn.)	Crawford
Bloomsburg	Columbia
Bloss (Twn.)	Tioga
Blossburg	Tioga
Blue Ridge Summit	Franklin
Bozrah Pltn.	Pike
Brackney	Susquehanna
Braddock	Allegheny
Bradford	McKean
Bradys Bend	Armstrong
Braintrim	Wyoming
Brentwood (4)	Allegheny
Bridgewater	Susquehanna
Brisbin	Clearfield
Bristol (Twn.) (2)	Bucks
Broad Gap	Huntingdon
Broad Top	Huntingdon
Brooklyn	Susquehanna
Brooks Hill	Warren
Burrows	McKean
Butler (Twn.)	Schuylkill
Buttonwood	Luzerne
Cambria (Twn.)	Cambria
Cambridge	Crawford
Cambridge Springs	Crawford
Camp Hill (3)	Cumberland
Camptown	Bradford
Canton	Bradford
Carbon (Twn.)	Huntington
Carbon Run	Bradford
Carbondale	Lackawanna
Carbondale	Tioga
Catasauqua	Lehigh
Centerville	Crawford
Centralia	Columbia
Chandler's Valley	Warren
Chapman	Northampton
Chapmansville	Northampton
Charleroi	Washington
Charleston	Tioga
Charleston (Twn.)	Chester
Charleston (Twn.)	Lycoming
Cherry Flat	Tioga
Chester	Delaware
Choconut	Susquehanna
Clarendon	Warren
Clifford (Twn.)	Susquehanna
Coaldale	Schuylkill
Coleraine	Carbon
Columbia	Bradford
Columbia	Lancaster
Columbus	Warren
Concord	Erie
Conneaut	Crawford
Conneaut Center	Crawford
Conneaut Lake	Crawford
Cooper (Twn.)	Clearfield
Corry (+4)	Erie
Corydon	Warren
Coryland	Bradford
Covington (Twn.)	Lackawanna
Cranesville (4)	Erie
Cuba	Centre
Cuba Mines	Clearfield
Cushutuck	Wayne
Cwmburia	Unlocated
Cwmburla	Unlocated
Damascus (Twn.)	Wayne
Danville	Montour
Darby	Delaware
Decatur (Twn.)	Clearfield
Delaware (Twn.) (4)	Mercer
Delta	York
DeRiseville	Susquehanna
Drifton	Luzerne
Dritton	Luzerne
DuBois	Clearfield

CITY OR TOWN	COUNTY
Dudley	Huntingdon
Duke Center	McKean
Duncan (Twn.)	Tioga
Duncansville	Blair
Dundaff	Susquehanna
Duquense	Allegheny
Duquense Heights	Allegheny
Duryea	Luzerne
Dutton	Huntingdon
Dyberry	Wayne
Eagleville	Montgomery
East Bangor	Northampton
East Fallowfield (Twn.) (4)	Crawford
East Goshen (Twn.) (3)	Chester
East Norriton (Twn.) (+3,+5)	Montgomery
East Pennsboro (Twn.) (3)	Cumberland
East Smithfield	Bradford
East Sprigfield	Erie
East Sugar Grove	Warren
Ebensburg	Cambria
Edwardsville	Luzerne
Elimburgh	Cambria
Elkland	Tioga
Enola (3)	Cumberland
Enosburgh	Cambria
Etna	Allegheny
Evansburg	Crawford
Exeter	Luzerne
Fairless Hills (2)	Bucks
Fairview Village	Montgomery
Falls (Twn.) (2)	Bucks
Farmers Valley	McKean
Farmington	Warren
Farmington Center	Warren
Farrell	Mercer
Feltsville	Lackawanna

CITY OR TOWN	COUNTY
Five Points	Luzerne (ps. Schuylkill), see also Unlocated
Forest City	Susquehanna
Forest Lake	Susquehanna
Foster (Twn.)	Luzerne
Fountain Springs	Schuylkill
Franconia (Twn.) (4)	Montgomery
Frankford	Philadelphia
Franklin (Twn.)	Bradford
Franklin (Twn.)	Susquehanna
Franklin Forks	Susquehanna
Franklin Hill	Susquehanna
Fredonia (4)	Mercer
Freehold (Twn.)	Warren
Frosty Valley	Montour
Garangue	Unlocated
Garangus	Unlocated
Germantown	Philadelphia
Gibson	Susquehanna
Gibsonburg	Lackawanna
Gibsonville	Lackawanna
Gillett	Bradford
Glen Lyon	Luzerne
Glenolden	Delaware
Gouldtown	Warren
Great Bend	Susquehanna
Great Valley	Chester
Green (Twn.)	Unlocated
Greenville (+4)	Mercer
Guys Mills	Crawford
Hallstead	Susquehanna
Hamilton (Twn.)	Tioga
Hanover (Twn.) (+2)	Luzerne
Harford	Susquehanna
Harrisburg (+1,+3)	Dauphin
Hastings	Cambria
Haverford (Twn.)	Delaware, see also Philadelphia

CITY OR TOWN	COUNTY
Havertown	Delaware, see also Philadelphia
Hawley	Wayne
Hazel Village	Luzerne, see also Carbon
Hazle (Twn.)	Luzerne
Hickory (Twn.)	Mercer
Hickory's Corner	Crawford
Homestead	Allegheny
Hopbottom	Susquehanna
Horatio	Jefferson
Horseneck (5)	Lehigh
Horsh	Carbon
Hosensack (5)	Lehigh
Houtzdale	Clearfield
Huntersville	Lycoming
Hyde Park	Lackawanna
Indian Creek (4)	Montgomery
Indiana	Indiana
Iron Ore Mines	Lackawanna
Irwin's Station	Westmoreland
Jackson	Susquehanna
Jackson Valley	Susquehanna
Jeansville	Luzerne, see also Carbon
Jeffersonville	Montgomery
Jermyn	Lackawanna
Johnsonburg	Elk
Johnstown	Cambria
Judea (Twn.)	Lycoming
Junedale	Carbon
Kane	McKean
Keating (Twn.)	McKean
Kensington	Philadelphia
Kingston	Luzerne
Kline (Twn.)	Schuylkill, see also Carbon
Knoxville	Tioga
Krassdale (5)	Lehigh
Krausdale (5)	Lehigh

CITY OR TOWN	COUNTY
Welsh Settlement	Tioga
West Bangor	York
West Chester (3)	Chester
West Granville	Mercer
West Greenville	Mercer
West Mahoning (Twn.)	Indiana
West Pittston	Luzerne
West Pottsgrove (Twn.) (4)	Montgomery
West Spring Creek	Warren
West Warren	Bradford
Wheatland	Mercer
Wheatland Furnace	Mercer
Wilkes-Barre (+2)	Luzerne
Williams	Lackawanna
Williamsport	Lycoming
Williamstown	Dauphin
Willingboro	Susquehanna
Wilmington	Mercer
Winburne	Clearfield
Wind Gap	Northampton
Windham	Wyoming
Wolf (Twn.)	Lycoming
Worcester (Twn.) (5)	Montgomery
Worth (Twn.)	Mercer
Wyalusing	Bradford
Wyoming	Luzerne
Wysox	Bradford
Yostville	Lackawanna
Young (Twn.)	Jefferson
Zelienople (4)	Butler

OTHER STATES

CITY OR TOWN	COUNTY
Branford, CT	New Haven, CT, see also Essex, NJ
Canaan, CT	Litchfield, CT, see also Saratoga, NY
Mansfield, CT	Tolland, CT, see also Sussex, NJ
Newfield, CT	Unlocated, CT, see also Sussex, NJ
Pawlet, VT	Rutland, VT, see also Oswego, NY
Pequot, IN	Unlocated, IN, see also Madison, NY
Poultney, VT	Rutland, VT, see also Bradford, PA
Ridgefield, CT	Fairfield, CT, see also Westchester, NY
South Kaukauna, WI	Outagamie, WI, see also Madison, NY
Stamford, CT	Fairfield, CT, see also Bronx & Westchester, NY
Statesburgh, WI	Outagamie, WI, see also Madison, NY
Stockbridge, MA	Berkshire, MA, see also Madison, NY
Stockbridge, WI	Calumet, WI, see also Madison, NY
White River, IN (nr.)	Unlocated, IN, see also Madison, NY

CITY OR TOWN	COUNTY

Library of Congress Control Number: 2005906609

ISBN-13: 978-0-962248-64-9
ISBN-10: 0-962248-64-9